The
Acto
Handb

The Actor's Handbook

Editor
JILL FENNER

General Editor
BARRY TURNER

BLOOMSBURY

The author would like to thank Clive Duncan and Jim Johnstone
for their kind assistance.

First published in 1991
This edition first published in 1998
by Bloomsbury Publishing Limited
38 Soho Square, London W1V 5DF

Publisher's note
The information in this book was correct to the best of the
Editor's and Publisher's belief at the time of going to press. While
no responsibility can be accepted for errors and omissions, the
Editor and Publisher would welcome corrections and suggestions
for items to include in future editions of this book.

A copy of the CIP entry for this book is available from the British
Library.

ISBN 0 7475 3768 2

3 5 7 9 10 8 6 4

Typeset by Palimpsest Book Production Limited, Polmont, Stirlingshire
Printed in Great Britain by Clays Ltd, St Ives plc

Contents

Foreword by Dame Judi Dench   vii

Act One, Beginners (Introductory article)   1

Training
Training for Total Theatre by Maggie Kinloch   7
Drama Schools   13
University and Further Education Courses   35
Film and Media Courses   53

Representation
The Personal Manager by Bruna Zanelli   67
The Cooperative Agency by Christopher Webber   71
Agents   75

The Workplace
Casting Directors   105
Repertory and Regional Theatres   119
Producing Theatres and Independent Managements   143
Touring Theatre Companies   155
Fringe and Alternative Theatre   195
Children's and Young People's Theatre   211
Theatre-In-Education (TIE) Companies   223
English-Language, European Theatre Companies   233
Non-Producing Theatres   237
Television   263
Radio   275
Film, Video and Independent Production Companies   287
Audiobooks   309

Organisations

Equity 315
Selected extracts from Equity Agreements 318
Organisations, Associations and Societies 329
Arts Councils and Regional Arts Associations 353

Miscellaneous

Festivals 361
Publications and Services 369
Additional Skills 373
Directors 377
Glossary 431
Index 441

Foreword

Jill Fenner's book is a most useful addition to any actor's library, but especially for those who have recently left drama school or, indeed, those potential actors who have not yet started training. The wide range of information and contacts should be a huge help to those undertaking their new journey to what we all hope will be an exciting and successful career.

Dame Judi Dench
December, 1997

Introduction
Act One, Beginners

The actor's life does not get any easier. Noël Coward's advice, 'Don't put your daughter on the stage, Mrs Worthington', is still worth noting. But if the desire to enter the profession is overwhelming, and it *needs* to be overwhelming, then this book may help to point you in the right direction.

A positive development is a relaxation of the criteria required for membership of Equity. Among the changes is the entitlement of students, on accredited courses, to become members of the union on graduating without the necessity of obtaining work. Also, a new scheme permits students taking a full-time course of one year or more to join as Student Members at the commencement of their course.

Training of the actor has developed over the years to reflect the wide diversity of work opportunities that exist for the multi-skilled actor. Maggie Kinloch's article 'Training for Total Theatre' (page 7) gives a clear picture of what the actor of the late nineties requires to survive in the marketplace. The traditional, text-based play is no longer the sole offering of today's repertory companies and the chances of finding employment in such companies are greatly enhanced if the actor possesses a range of skills.

For example, an expanding market is the use of actors in role-play situations for staff training in, for example, business, social-work departments and health authorities. For this kind of work the actor requires good improvisation skills and an ability to discuss and analyse the responses of the trainee in the improvised scenario. You may be required to play an aggressive benefit claimant or a hospital patient diagnosed as having a serious illness; several different characters may be required at any one session. A lot of the role-play companies have been established by actors and, as a result, are unlikely to advertise for new recruits. Another source of work in the business world is the use of actors at conferences to perform scenes in which trainees are interactive. Both this and the role-play work can supply a good regular income for those who break into this field and, to a certain extent, it has replaced the use of video training films which previously had been a big source of work for actors. The video market has not really picked up as successfully as the market that provides the interactive situation of performer and trainee.

What is crucial for every actor is good marketing skills. You must not be shy of selling yourself to the best of your ability. Whether applying to an agent in your search for representation or writing to a theatre director for a job, a well-presented cv and letter are your first means of contact and, as such, must put you across positively. Your letter should be to the point and not overly familiar or joky. Note some of the comments in this book from those involved in casting, particularly for stage roles. A common theme is a plea that actors familiarise themselves with the play in question and, when writing to ask for an interview, they should explain briefly to the director why they consider themselves fit for the role. A general, unfocused request to be considered for forthcoming productions is unlikely to result in an interview.

On your cv, which should be typewritten, list the work you have done, beginning with the most recent and working backwards; giving the name of the company, production, the role you played and the director. Don't worry about your cv being brief if you are just starting out; directors will understand. Give your physical characteristics, age, skills (don't exaggerate your capabilities, it could lead to embarrassing situations) and accents (highlighting your native accent).

It should go without saying that good photographs are another essential tool for persuading casting directors to consider you. But all too often, the actor falls for the lure of the 'glamour' shot. You need an honest, full-face head shot, with the eyes looking alive and connecting with the camera. It pays to go to a professional photographer who has experience of actors' portraits, even if this can prove a little expensive. Shop around; some photographers offer discounts to drama students. Most people use the 10 x 8 size although some casting directors request 7 x 5. Cheap repros of your photographs can be obtained from a number of specialists who advertise in the trade press.

Another marketing tool is an entry in *The Spotlight*, the publication to which most casting people refer (*see* Publications and Services, page 372). Agents usually insist that their clients are in it and some casting directors have been known not to consider actors who do not have an entry. It may seem a large amount of money to lay out each year but just one job gained as a result of an entry can easily cover the expense.

Having obtained an interview or audition, prepare for it as much as you can. Be ready to discuss the role you are being considered for whether it is in a play, film, commercial or television production. It makes sense to present yourself at the interview dressed appropriately, although this may not always be possible or even desirable (a friend of mine was up for the role of Hitler in *Red Dwarf*!) Punctuality for all appointments is the golden rule. Tell yourself that your interview is fifteen minutes earlier than the given time and then leave extra time for delays (particularly relevant if travelling across London). Sod's Law will ensure that the day you arrive on the dot you'll be asked to go in immediately, leaving no chance to catch your breath, and if you arrive early, they'll be running half an hour late. Never mind. Whatever the interview, there is bound to be a script or storyline to read or, in the case of commercials, forms to complete. Then try to collect yourself and relax and focus on the interview ahead.

If you don't get the job, don't despair. Rejection is a big feature of most actors' lives. Do not take it personally; quite often it is merely a question of your face not fitting the bill and rarely a comment on your abilities as an actor. It is always a good thing to meet directors and even if you're not what they are looking for this time, it could be that they'll think of you and be in touch in the future. So often, work turns up out of the blue, maybe as a result of an 'unsuccessful' interview or audition months before.

Stick with it. No one said it would be easy; determination and enthusiasm are the key.

Training

Training for Total Theatre

Maggie Kinloch

Those of us who choose to enter the world of professional theatre as performers have a responsibility to prepare ourselves for the world of work; we must train our voices, our bodies, our imaginations, our intellects, our sense of humour and our interpersonal skills.

It has been suggested that the theatre is a place we can go to 'dream in public'. Perhaps it is also a place where we can safely experience our nightmares, allowing us to explore the irrational part of ourselves in a rational way. The argument for the therapeutic role of theatre in a troubled society is a powerful one.

However, whether or not we accept the social role, we must accept the importance of our theatre and film industries to the economy of the country. Live theatre is one of the UK's biggest sources of tourist income, and the current growth in the British film industry insists that we continue to develop and train performers of the highest possible calibre.

So who are 'the performers'? What skills do they require in order to be regularly engaged in stimulating, quality work that actually matters? The difficulty one encounters here is that there used to be a clear delineation between 'the actor' and practitioners of other performance languages such as puppetry, trapeze, clowning, storytelling, dance, singing or stand-up comedy. However, several major companies now demand a fusion of these skills. Théâtre de Complicité, for example, has grown into one of the finest and most exciting companies which plays in the West End and engages in co-productions with the Royal National Theatre while continuing to tour nationally and internationally. The endorsement by the Royal National Theatre is one of the clearest signals of the wind of change which is blowing through performance in this country.

It is interesting that in 1997, a new category of award was introduced on the Edinburgh International Festival Fringe. The Total Theatre award was created in response to the growing number of companies producing work which no longer fits into the established categories of Theatre, Dance, Mime and Comedy. Total Theatre is a fast-growing form of theatre with its roots in physical work and storytelling. It utilises a more overt fusion of the skills of the performer and the skills of all other theatre artists such as designers and composers. This means, of course, that the Total Theatre performer must have a broader understanding of the work of these other practitioners.

The demand for a more rounded performer is also affected by new kinds of employer. Theme parks, interactive thrill games and heritage centres demand independent, extrovert, physical people, often with a genuine passion for active research. Independent television and video production companies demand presenting skills allied to singing, dancing and acting abilities. CD-ROM, the Internet and virtual reality games all offer employment opportunities of a very different kind.

Those performers who wish to train simply to work in 'traditional' live theatre, or in film, will find that the traditional 'acting skills' are taught in many splendid courses in the major drama schools. The conservatoire tradition of acting training is alive and well in the UK. Students of acting from all over the world still flock to the UK, and to London in particular, to seek their training.

But theatre is no longer exclusively an event that happens in theatre buildings. Theatre is happening all around us, from the 'living statues' outside art galleries, to the 'invisible theatre' of Augusto Boal's Theatre of the Oppressed; from the person dressed in the furry dolphin 'skin' outside the supermarket to the three performers doing acrobatics in the market square of any tourist town in the country. They are all professional performers, working in the world in which they live.

So just what are the country's theatre-training institutions doing to address the need to train the truly modern performer who may work in the broader field of performance? In a world where the definition of performance is constantly changing, how does education keep abreast of such change? Here are some of the most popular contemporary forms:

- Text-based theatre
- Physical theatre
- Musical theatre
- Street theatre
- Theatre-in-Education
- Site-specific performance
- Multimedia/mixed-media performance
- Puppet and object theatre
- Circus/circus theatre
- Club performance
- Performance art
- Stand-up comedy
- Mime/dance theatre
- Film
- Television

To name but a few!

In other words, the days of actor-training, specific to theatre performance in conventional theatre spaces, may well be numbered. With the virtual demise of the repertory system, the days are gone when an actor could expect to earn a living by moving from one production of a text-based play to another. The performers of the nineties must be far more multi-skilled individuals if they are to ensure their ability to work on a regular basis.

It is unlikely that any one course of training can address all the specific skills required to work in every one of the areas listed above. It is usual for performers to identify, or to grow towards, a few areas which are of particular interest to them. However, what is certain is that the time when the actor was trained to 'say the lines and not bump into the furniture' are, thankfully, behind us. The consistent disempowering of the performer, which the old tradition of training promoted, has finally begun to disappear. In its place we are beginning to see courses which promote the performers' understanding of the range of options available to them. Performers are taking charge of their own careers and creating work which stimulates them.

Of course, there are some exceptions to every rule and one could point to several well-known screen actors who rarely seem to be unemployed and appear in almost every new film being made! Equally one could argue, quite effectively, that these are indeed the exception. More typically, the young performer might be appearing in a few episodes of a television soap opera, then doing a night or two of stand-up at a comedy club, followed by a three-week run in a profit-share production of a physical interpretation of a classic text in a London pub theatre.

The gradual erosion of public subsidy for theatre has contributed also to reduced opportunities for performers to be 'employed' in live theatre. In fact, this erosion has meant that performers must be much more self-sufficient and be able to create their own work over which they have a far greater level of control.

For over two decades now, the arts funding bodies have insisted that artists consider their educational function when submitting their funding applications. How can they actively involve their local communities in their company's work? Of course, this means that we now have a generation of young professionals who benefited from that outreach work in the seventies and eighties. Possibly, their first experience of performing was in a community play led by their local professional company. They know, from first-hand experience, that theatre changed their lives.

This significant development has, I believe, led to a desire in young performers to understand their own creative process to a far greater extent, and to question it in a positive way.

In turn, this leads to more 'individual' performers, all working to their own strengths, using their own regional accents and dialects, and understanding their place in a much broader definition of 'performance'. The traditional picture of the actor who does three years at drama school and is then ready to work professionally without further development is changing. More typically we might now see, for example, the performer who has done a physical-theatre training, followed by voice development work and rounded off with a postgraduate year in a drama school; or the circus performer who has then chosen an acting training to complete his or her range of skills. These are multi-talented people with powerful performance and workshop abilities in their specialist areas.

This move has been encouraged by the growth in the number of courses being offered in institutions other than drama schools. Many very strong performance courses are now offered in universities and in broad-based arts colleges. The drama schools themselves have developed degree-level acting training and postgraduate-level performance training.

Between them, the CDS (Conference of Drama Schools) and UCAS (Universities and College Admission Service) offer more than 21 undergraduate degree courses (3 years), 11 diploma courses (3 years), 2 diploma courses (2 years), and 10 postgraduate diploma courses (1 year). These represent only the courses which are offered in Higher Education sector schools; there are many more on offer in the private sector.

I am fortunate to be a member of staff at the Central School of Speech and Drama in London. Our institution recognises, in an active sense, that diversity is the order of the day in performer training. The school proudly boasts one of the best acting degree courses in the country. The list of alumni reads like a *Who's Who* in British acting! However, alongside that course Central now offers a one-year Postgraduate Diploma in Advanced Theatre Practice. Here, performers train in collaboration with directors, writers, designers, puppeteers and dramaturgs. The notion that performers develop themselves as proactive artistic collaborators, discovering the value of the input of all theatre artists and not simply the performer, is at the very heart of this course. This recognition of diversity of training choice by a major drama school is at the forefront of the educational response to the need to train the new performer.

Opportunities for training for performers who make conscious choices about the work in which they wish to specialise are steadily increasing. The marvellous thing is that the institutions have recognised the need for choice to be available. They are responding to the demand from the individual performer and from the profession, thereby playing their role in the healthy development of the 'new' theatre in its many diverse forms.

Maggie Kinloch is Course Leader of the MA/Postgraduate Diploma in Advanced Theatre Practice at the Central School of Speech and Drama. She is also a freelance director. Between 1989 and 1994, she was Artistic Director of the Byre Theatre, St Andrews. She was Assistant Director of TAG Theatre at the Citizens' Theatre, Glasgow from 1985 to 1987. She has taught and directed many times for the Scottish Youth Theatre, and more recently for the National Youth Theatre of Great Britain.

Drama Schools

Academy Drama School
189 Whitechapel Road,
London E1 1DN
Tel: 0171 377 8735
Principal *Tim Reynolds*

Opened in 1985 with the full-time Evening Course – for many students the only possibility; working during the day to support themselves and training in the evening. Demand for the course was such that within two years the number of students had trebled to over 40. The Medallion Course is designed to help younger students (aged 17–19) to obtain a place in an adult drama school, and the Company Course is based on the repertory-company system which used to provide excellent training for actors. The school has its own theatre, the 50-seater Andrew Sketchley Theatre which operates as a club with students automatically becoming members. Receives over 1,000 applicants for courses per year. Prospectus available.

COURSES ON OFFER
Evening Course (2 years, full-time) *Entry requirements*: applicants must be over 19 years of age on entry. No particular experience is required. *Audition requirements*: two contrasting speeches, each not more than 2 minutes, from any two published plays. *Audition fee*: £25. Deadline for applications is 1 August.

Company Course (1 year, postgraduate) *Entry requirements*: by audition and interview. Applicants must be over 19 years of age and are expected to have undergone some previous training or have considerable experience. *Audition requirements*: two contrasting speeches, each not more than 3 minutes, from any two published plays. *Audition fee*: £25.

Medallion Course (1 year, foundation) *Entry requirements*: applicants must be between 17 and 21 years of age on entry. No qualifications required. *Audition requirements*: one speech, not more than 2 minutes, from any published play. *Audition fee*: £20.

Evening Course (part-time) *Entry requirements*: applicants must be over 16 years of age on entry. No previous experience is required. *Audition requirements*: one speech, not more than 2 minutes, from any published play. *Audition fee*: £20.

Evening Summer Course (2 weeks) Held in August. *Entry requirements*: applicants must be over 16 years of age on entry. No previous experience is required.

Audition Course (1 week) Held in January/February on Saturday afternoons.

'Training is vital – more so now than ever, since the Equity card is no longer a guide for employers. Choose your audition speeches with care, pick parts you could be reasonably cast in – not too old or too young or the wrong sex. (We have seen all of the above.) This is not to say you can never play a man's role if you are a woman or vice versa, but you have enough difficulties in your path without adding another at this stage. We have no objection to applicants receiving some help with their speeches but avoid anyone who says "Do it like this . . ." and then demonstrates – we want to see *your* performance, not someone else's. The same goes for performances you have seen: we want to see your interpretation, not Kenneth Branagh's. Apply for as many auditions as you can afford and remember that your audition is your chance to check out the school as well as the other way round. Try to talk to current students as well as the staff who audition you. Go and see the plays the school presents: not only will this give you an idea of the standard of their product but it will also give you something to talk about at the audition!

'Sadly, in this day and age, training is almost as much about money as talent. Grants are hard to come by and drama schools are expensive. Plan now how you are going to finance yourself. Degree courses may carry a mandatory grant but not all do, so check with the school. We continue auditioning into August because we provide a safety net for applicants who have been refused a grant and can only train by keeping on their full-time job. Many of our full-time Evening Course students have been given places at other schools but cannot afford to pay the fees. Until the government decides that it is worth spending money on training actors, it will be finance which will finally decide who trains and who does not.'

Academy of Live and Recorded Arts Ltd (ALRA)
Royal Victoria Building, Trinity Road, Wandsworth, London SW18 3SX
Tel: 0181 870 6475
Fax: 0181 875 0789
Principal *Sorrell Carson*

Founded 1979 by Sorrel Carson who wanted to create a school where 'the very best of tradition and innovation could come together'. An independent drama school offering specialist training for theatre, television, video, film and radio, ALRA's extensive premises are located in the historic Royal Victoria Building on Wandsworth Common.

COURSES ON OFFER
Acting Course (3 years; accredited by the National Council for Drama Training) Minimum age: 18. *Audition fee*: £30.

Postgraduate Course (1 year, 4 terms) *Audition fee*: £30.

Stage Management Course (1 year, 4 terms) *Audition fee*: £12.

Acting for Television and Television Presentation (Evening classes)

Standard audition pieces are not required. Candidates for the 3-year Acting Course participate for a day in a series of classes and workshops taken by senior staff, and are also interviewed by the Principal. However, those who wish to do audition pieces will have the option to do so. Auditions take place every month, the last being held in July for entry in

September of that year. The majority of students are eligible for local authority discretionary awards. There are a limited number of ALRA scholarships and bursaries. Prospectus available.

'Enjoy your audition day. Feel free to experiment. ALRA students will be there to talk to you and escort you round the building. Ask them about anything you want to know about the Academy. Always remember that you are looking for a school that will suit you and we are looking for students who will suit the school. We are both in the same boat! Don't make the mistake of accepting a place in a school if you were not happy during your audition.'

Arden School of Theatre at City College Manchester

Arden Centre, Sale Road,
Northenden, Manchester M23 0DD
Tel: 0161 957 1715
Fax: 0161 957 1715
Head of Acting Wyllie Longmore
Head of Technical Theatre Arts Dee Sidwell
Contact Barbara Howorth (Secretary)

Established in 1991 in association with the Royal Exchange Theatre Company. The school is founded on the basis of being in constant touch with the realities of the professional theatre, and the arts and entertainment industries. It aims to 'produce actors, and technical theatre practitioners, worthy to be members of their profession, able to make a living and a significant contribution to the advancement of the theatre'. Receives, on average, approximately 400 applications per year.

COURSES ON OFFER (all validated by the University of Manchester)
BA in Acting Studies (3 years, full-time) *Entry requirements*: 2 A-levels at

grade C or above or BTEC National Diploma in Performing Arts (with merits or distinctions); GNVQ (Advanced) in Performing Arts or Art and Design (with merits or distinctions); or equivalent. *Audition requirements*: 10-minute presentation of material of the candidate's choice followed by an interview at the first audition. Whole day of workshops at the second round.
BA(Hons) in Acting Studies (4 years, full-time) *Entry requirements*: as above. *Audition requirements*: as above.
BA(Hons) in Technical Theatre Arts (3 years, full-time) *Entry requirements*: as above. Candidates are required to present a portfolio and attend an interview.

'If acting is to be your life's work, then where you train is of vital importance. Not just any course will do. Find out all there is to know about a course before committing yourself to it.'

The Arts Educational Schools London*

Cone Ripman House, 14 Bath Road,
Chiswick, London W4 1LY
Tel: 0181 994 9366
Fax: 0181 994 9274
Principal Peter Fowler
Registrar Brenda Gray

COURSES ON OFFER
Drama School (3 years, full-time) *Audition requirements*: full day's audition consisting of classes in movement, voice and improvisation, and two short contrasting pieces of the candidate's own choice. *Audition fee*: £28. Comprehensive training for those seeking to pursue careers in acting. The work is Stanislavski-based, with the major emphasis being

on performance and individual development.

Musical Theatre and Dance School (3 years/1 year, full-time) *Audition requirements/fee*: as above. The course offers a flexible approach that will equip students with all-round professional abilities in dance, acting and singing.

The Schools also offer a 1-year, **Postgraduate Musical Theatre Course** of intensive training in dance, acting and singing, and a full-time **Drama Foundation Course** combining A-level options in Drama and Theatre Arts and English with practical study and work experience.

'Before applying for an audition, prospective students should think carefully about the nature of the profession they wish to enter, where (at any given time) there is high unemployment. Entry to the school is highly competitive.'

ARTTS International (Advanced Residential Theatre and Television Skillcentre)

Highfield Grange, Bubwith,
North Yorkshire YO8 7DP
Tel: 01757 288088
Fax: 01757 288253
Principal *John Sichel*
Contact *Duncan Lewis (Associate Director)*

Founded 1990. ARTTS International is a purpose-built, residential, multimedia training centre set in 4 acres of Yorkshire countryside, 17 miles south of York. Trainees work under the guidance of professional directors, writers and technicians, using broadcast-standard equipment. ARTTS

receives, on average, 3 applications per week. Prospectus available.

COURSES ON OFFER

Diploma Course in Acting, Directing or Production Operations in Television, Theatre, Film/Video and Radio (1 year – 40 weeks) All trainees cover all aspects of each discipline. *Entry requirements*: No specific academic qualifications. No audition fees. For international trainees, a good command of the English language is necessary. Deadline for applications: mid-March for April intake and mid-September for October intake.

Foundation Skills Course in Acting, Directing or Production Operations in Television, Theatre, Film/Video and Radio (10 weeks) All trainees cover all aspects of each discipline. *Entry requirements*: as above.

Summer Short Courses in Television, Theatre and Video/Film (2 weeks) All trainees cover all aspects of each discipline. *Entry requirements*: as above.

No auditions required. An interview with the company directors at the centre may be offered on the strength of the application form. Commitment, enthusiasm and willingness to cover all aspects of each discipline is essential.

'It is a central principle of all the Diploma Courses at ARTTS that practical experience is gained in all disciplines, not just the specialist subject. Thus those trainees specialising as actors can gain an invaluable understanding and some experience in the areas of production operations and directing. In this way, the actors are not only given a much fuller insight into the other major disciplines involved in theatre, television, film and radio, but may also discover another interest or aptitude that could be used or developed to advantage. It is because of this multi-skilling that 94 per cent of the graduated Diploma trainees are in regular employment in the entertainment industry.'

Birmingham School of Speech and Drama*

99 John Bright Street,
Birmingham B1 1BE
Tel: 0121 643 4376
Fax: 0121 633 0476
Principal *Professor Patricia Yardley*
Contact *Simon Woods*

Founded 1936. Offers a performance-based, vocational professional training in acting and stage management. Receives approximately 300 applications per year. Deadline for applications is late July.

COURSES ON OFFER
Diploma for Professional Theatre (3 years, full-time) *Audition requirements*: a speech from any play by Shakespeare, a contrasting speech from a modern play, a lyrical poem and a song. *Audition fee*: £22.
Diploma for Professional Theatre (1 year, full-time) *Audition requirements*: as above. *Audition fee*: as above.
Diploma for Stage Management (1 year, full-time)
'BSSD recognises that to stimulate creativity, it is necessary for the student to have the freedom to make choices. The school does not limit the student through adherence to a single style of acting, but rather seeks to provide a sound basis of skills that will allow graduates to continue to develop. Acting requires lifelong learning through every new role and experience. Drama school cannot teach you to act but rather provides the skills to allow you to learn.'

Bristol Old Vic Theatre School*

1–2 Downside Road, Clifton,
Bristol BS8 2XF
Tel: 0117 973 3535
Fax: 0117 923 9371
E-mail: enquiries@oldvic.drama.ad.uk
Principal *Christopher Denys*
Contact *Erika Neumann*

Founded in 1946 with the school being opened by Laurence Olivier. Moved to its present location in 1956. The school has a close relationship with the Bristol Old Vic Company. Student productions are staged at the Theatre Royal and New Vic Studio and there is a regular involvement of theatre personnel at the school and frequent participation of students in the Company's productions. All the acting and stage management courses are accredited by the National Council for Drama Training. The school receives between 900 and 1,000 applications for courses per year. The school made news in 1997 when it accepted two students, one of whom was blind and the other with serious sight problems, thus taking the lead in encouraging those previously considered unsuitable for a career in acting.

COURSES ON OFFER
Acting Course (3 years, full-time) *Audition requirements*: for the preliminary audition candidates must present two speeches, one classical (preferably Shakespeare) and one modern prose, the speeches together lasting no more than 4 minutes. An unaccompanied song is also required. Following the preliminary audition, candidates may be invited to attend a weekend school where they work with members of staff. *Audition fee*: £20.
Acting Course (2 years, full-time) *Audition requirements/fee*: as above.

Postgraduate Course (1 year, full-time) *Audition requirements/fee*: as above.
Stage Management and Technical Course (2 years, full-time) All candidates are interviewed in Bristol.
Design Course (1 year, full-time) All candidates must submit a portfolio of their work at their interview.
Wardrobe Course (1 year, full-time) Samples of work must be brought by applicants to their interview.

'We deliberately do *not* adhere to any one philosophy or style of teaching in acting, design or production. It is our aim to offer our students the best possible training and essentially personal preparation for a career in a profession which makes increasingly varied demands upon the individuals it employs.'

Rose Bruford College*

Lamorbey Park, Burnt Oak Lane,
Sidcup, Kent DA15 9DF
Tel: 0181 300 3024
Fax: 0181 308 0542
E-mail: admiss@bruford.ac.uk
Principal *Professor Robert Ely*
Contact *Sue McTavish (Registrar)*

Founded 1950, the college was the first to offer a degree in Acting in the UK in 1976. All courses are validated by the University of Manchester and appropriate courses are validated by the National Council for Drama Training. Receives around 4,000 applications each year.

COURSES ON OFFER
BA(Hons) Acting; Actor Musician; Musical Theatre; Directing; Stage Management; Costume Production; Lighting Design; Theatre Design; Scenic Construction and Properties; Music Technology (all 3 years, full-time) *Entry requirements*: two A-levels

or equivalent and audition/interview. *Audition requirements*: two speeches and a song. *Audition/interview fee:* £15.
MA Directing the Voice (2 years, full-time)
Also offers Distance Learning Courses: **BA(Hons) Theatre Studies; BA(Hons) Opera Studies; MA Theatre and Performance Studies; MA Dramatic Writing**, and a **One-year Foundation Course** for international students and an **International Summer School**.

Central School of Speech and Drama*

Embassy Theatre, 64 Eton Avenue,
Swiss Cottage, London NW3 3HY
Tel: 0171 722 8183
Fax: 0171 722 4132
Principal *Professor Robert S. Fowler, FRSA*
Contact *Admissions*

Founded in 1906 by Elsie Fogerty, Central is one of the leading drama schools with an illustrious list of alumni: Lord Olivier, Dame Peggy Ashcroft, Dame Judi Dench, Vanessa Redgrave, Kevin Whately, Zoe Wanamaker and Christopher Eccleston, among others. The school offers a diverse range of courses, providing training for actors, directors, writers, stage managers, theatre technicians, puppeteers and designers, drama teachers, speech therapists and voice specialists. The degree courses are validated by the Open University Validation Services and attract mandatory award status. Both the BA in Acting and the Stage Management and Technical Arts strands of the BA(Hons) Theatre Practice are accredited by the National Council for Drama Training.

COURSES ON OFFER

(The school operates a flexible admissions policy. For many courses, no formal qualifications are required and selection is based more on the perceived ability of the student to benefit from the training than on an academic record.)

BA Acting (3 years, full-time) *Audition fee*: £25. 'The "Central" philosophy subscribes to no set "method" of training, but encourages students to distil their own understanding of the working process from a wide range of vocabularies and learning opportunities. The course explores three strands of the actor's work – acting, movement and voice – seeing them not as separate subjects but as different aspects of one activity.'

BA(Hons) Drama and Education (3 years, full-time) *Entry requirements*: normally at least three GCSE passes at grade C or above, including Maths and English. Candidates will usually have specialised in arts-related subjects at post-16 level – e.g. A-level Theatre Studies. The course is suited to those who are interested in the practical applications of drama, particularly in school/college, continuing and community education.

BA(Hons) Theatre Practice: Set/ Costume/ Lighting/ Sound/ Scenic Art/ Scenic Constructions/ Prop-making/ Costume Construction/ Puppetry/ Stage Management and Technical Theatre (3 years, full-time)

Postgraduate Diploma/MA Advanced Theatre Practice – incorporating strands of: Set/ Costume/ Lighting Design/ Sound for Performance/ Directing/ Writing/ Dramaturgy/ Performance (Postgraduate Diploma: 1 year, full-time; MA: 1 year, part-time)

Postgraduate Diploma/MA in Voice Studies (Postgraduate Diploma: 1 year, full-time; MA: 1 year, part-time)

Postgraduate Diploma/MA Performance Studies (Postgraduate Diploma: 1 year, full-time; MA: 1 year, part-time)

Postgraduate Certificate in Education in Drama (PGCE) (1 year, full-time; also part-time)

Postgraduate Diploma/ MA/Postgraduate Certificate Drama and Theatre (Postgraduate Diploma: 1 year, full-time; MA: 1 year, part-time)

The school also offers courses in Art and Design at further-education and postgraduate levels, as well as a 4-year, full-time **Clinical Communication Sciences Degree** and a 1-year, full-time **Postgraduate Diploma in Drama and Movement Therapy**. Evening classes, short courses, introductory courses and summer schools are also offered. Those interested should contact the school for up-to-date information.

Cygnet Training Theatre*

Friars Gate, Exeter, Devon EX2 4AZ
Tel: 01392 277189
Artistic Director *Monica Shallis*
Administrative Director *Mary G. Evans*

Founded 1980, the company grew out of an association between Monica Shallis, Mary Evans and the Northcott Theatre Company. It is now a full-time training company, with Peter Brook as patron. As well as performing in its own studio theatre, the Cygnet Company tours to a wide range of venues with an extensive programme of modern and classical plays. As it is a theatre company and not a school, Cygnet can take only a limited number of newcomers each year; between 8 and 12 is the usual intake.

COURSES ON OFFER

Professional Acting (3 years, full-time) *Audition fee*: £22.

Professional Acting with Music (3 years, full-time) *Audition fee*: as above.
Professional Acting with Directing (3 years, full-time) *Audition fee*: as above.
Professional Acting with Stage Management (3 years, full-time) *Audition fee*: as above.

'The methods of actor training and development are influenced by Stanislavski, Michel Saint-Denis, Michael Chekhov and Peter Brook and there is interaction between the directors of Cygnet and Brook's Centre International de Créations Théâtrales in Paris.'

Drama Centre London*

176 Prince of Wales Road,
Chalk Farm, London NW5 3PT
Tel: 0171 267 1177
Fax: 0171 485 7129
E-mail: info@dcl.drama.ac.uk
Principal *Christopher Fettes*
Contact *Brenda Kaye (School Secretary)*

Founded 1962 when a group of directors and teachers – John Blatchley, Yat Malmgren and Christopher Fettes – broke away from the Central School of Speech and Drama and founded the Drama Centre London. The approach derives from 'a fusion of several major contributions to the development of European theatre in the twentieth century', including the Stanislavski Method, Rudolph Laban, whose ideas influenced the work of Michael Chekhov, forefather of the American Method, and Theatre Workshop.

COURSES ON OFFER
BA (Hons) Acting Course (3 years, full-time; accredited by the National Council for Drama Training and validated by the University of Central

Lancashire) *Entry requirements*: students are not accepted until aged 18 and there is an upper age limit of 27. *Audition requirements*: one classical speech, chosen from a selection provided by the school and one modern speech of your own choice; plus an interview by a large panel. *Audition fee*: £25. All application forms must be returned by 31 May.
Acting Diploma Course *Entry requirements*: as above.
Professional Instructors Course (2 years, full-time) *Entry requirements*: academic qualifications and previous theatrical experience are taken into account. Selection is made on the basis of a long interview. All application forms must be returned by 31 May.

Receives over 350 applications for the Acting Course each year. Students are eligible for discretionary grants. Prospectus available.

'An alarming proportion of those who seek entry to a drama school do so without ever taking time to ask themselves what they ask of a training, what their present grasp of the subject so clearly lacks, what a school can or should offer, what distinguishes one school from the next. Such answers as we are afforded seem largely grounded on unexamined assumptions. Yet good, bad or indifferent, a drama school will leave its mark on a student for a lifetime.

'Far from constituting an escape, we prefer to see art as a way of conveying information about the real world and the hazards and vicissitudes that confront ordinary people in their dealings with that world. That is why it is important not to start your training too soon . . . You need to have seen and pondered carefully what lies beyond the confines of school and home, to have achieved the adulthood necessary to the depth and complexity of professional relationships. Don't go to a school like the Drama Centre if you don't already know quite a bit about the world and about yourself.'

Drama Studio London

Grange Court, 1 Grange Road,
London W5 5QN
Tel: 0181 579 3897
Fax: 0181 566 2035
E-mail: admin@dramastl.demon.co.uk
Executive Director *Peter Layton*
Contact *Elinor Hilton*

Founded in 1966 by Peter Layton. The Studio Theatre Company presents regular productions, cast wherever possible from DSL graduates and staff.

COURSES ON OFFER

Postgraduate Acting Course (1 year, full-time) *Audition requirements*: one speech, maximum length of 2 minutes plus various group exercises. *Audition fee*: £30.

Postgraduate Directing Course (1 year, full-time) Admission is by interview with the course tutor. Candidates are asked to prepare a short scene in advance and are given actors to work with on the day.

The school also offers Summer Acting Courses for two consecutive 4-week periods.

East 15 Acting School*

Hatfields, Corbett Theatre, Rectory Lane, Loughton, Essex IG10 3RU
Tel: 0181 508 5983/8705
Fax: 0181 508 7521
E-mail: east15.acting@ukonline.co.uk
Website:
http://web.ukonline.co.uk/east15.acting
Artistic Director *Margaret Walker*

Founded in 1961 by actor and designer Margaret Walker to explore and develop the creative way of working begun by Joan Littlewood at Theatre Workshop.

COURSES ON OFFER

BA Acting (3 years, full-time; validated by the University of East London) *Audition requirements*: two classical pieces, one modern piece and a song. Auditionees must be prepared to talk about the characters and the action, to improvise, and to translate the classical texts into modern language. *Audition fee*: £25. 'Acting is action and although this course has, of necessity, an academic content, it amounts to only a part of the work . . . Movement, voice and acting are closely linked. You learn as you role-play, with expert guidance to enable you to speak, move, begin to think as your character would.'

Postgraduate Diploma in Acting (1 year, full-time) An intensive course combining the essentials of the 3-year acting course.

Faststream Acting Course (20 weeks) For mature students and professionals who wish to refocus and refresh.

Stage Management (1 year, full-time) A 'hands-on' practical course for a limited number of students.

Technical Course (3 years, full-time) Practical and theoretical training in lighting, sound, stage craftsmanship and theatre skills.

Director's Course (3 years, full-time) Designed specifically for the individual needs of those ambitious to train as directors.

Guildford School of Acting*

Millmead Terrace, Guildford,
Surrey GU2 5AT
Tel: 01483 560701
Fax: 01483 535431
E-mail: enquiries@gsa.drama.ac.uk
Website: http//gsa.drama.ac.uk
Principal *Gordon McDougall*
Contact *Mrs Katherine Mutton (Head of Administration)*

Founded 1964. The GSA's main focus is the teaching of acting but it also concentrates on the development of talent and skills in other fields, among them stage management, production, design and general drama studies. Since 1967, the Musical Theatre option of the performance course has held a unique position in the world of actor training. Receives approximately 600 applications annually. Students are eligible for discretionary grants. Prospectus available.

COURSES ON OFFER
BA (Hons) Acting Course/Diploma Acting Course (3 years, full-time; accredited by the National Council for Drama Training and validated by the University of Surrey) *Entry requirements (Degree Course)*: 5 GCSE passes, 2 A-level passes or HND, BTEC Ordinary National Diploma or Certificate, GNVQ Level 3, International Baccalaureate Diploma; *(Diploma Course)*: in some cases, academic achievement is used in addition to an audition/interview for assessing a candidate's suitability. *Audition requirements*: two speeches no longer than 2 minutes each; one from a play from before 1900 and one contemporary piece, and brief song or part of song. The candidate will also be interviewed. *Audition fee*: £15 for first audition, £15 for recall. All application forms must be returned by 31 May.

BA (Hons) Musical Theatre Course/Diploma Musical Theatre Course (3 years, full-time; accredited by the National Council for Drama Training and validated by the University of Surrey) *Entry requirements*: as above. *Audition requirements*: song from musical theatre repertoire and speech no longer than 2 minutes. The candidate will also be interviewed. *Audition fee*: as above.
Acting Course for Graduates and Mature Students (1 year, full-time) *Audition requirements*: as above.
Stage Management: Degree Course (3 years, full-time, subject to validation); **Diploma Course** (2 years, full-time) *Entry requirements*: as above. **Diploma Course for Graduates and Mature Students** (1 year, full-time) Candidates will be interviewed.

Auditions for the Acting Courses are held from November to June in Guildford, Manchester, Leeds and New York. It is advisable to apply at least 6 weeks before you hope to audition. Minimum age for candidates is 18.

'GSA is dedicated to excellence in all fields and our mission is to educate a student to the highest level of his or her ability in the most suitable dramatic field, bearing in mind that an artistic career is a continuous learning experience and a drama-school education is a vital beginning to a lifetime's development.'

Guildhall School of Music and Drama*

Barbican, London EC2Y 8DT
Tel: 0171 628 2571
Fax: 0171 256 9438
Principal *Ian Horsbrugh FGSM, FRCM, FRNCM, HonRAM, FRSAMD, HonDMus*
Contact *Drama Administrator*

Founded 1880. Administered by the Music and Drama Committee of the Corporation of London. Situated in the Barbican, in the heart of the City of London, the school offers courses which are flexible and designed to respond sympathetically to the particular strengths and enthusiasms of individual students as they progress through their course. It aims 'to offer all its students a realistic preparation for a professional career'. Receives approximately 700 applications annually. Students are eligible for discretionary grants. Prospectus available from the General Office (tel: 0171 382 7192).

COURSES ON OFFER

BA(Hons) Course in Acting (3 years, full-time; accredited by the National Council for Drama Training and validated by City University) *Entry requirements*: passes in two approved GCE A-level subjects; passes in one approved GCE A-level subject and two AS-level subjects; in some cases, academic achievement is used in addition to an audition/interview for assessing a candidate's suitability. Minimum age for applicants is 18 years. *Audition requirements*: three contrasting pieces of own choice, no longer than 3 minutes each, with at least one from Shakespeare (or other Elizabethan/Jacobean drama) and in verse, and one should be a comic piece. Candidates should also be prepared to sing a short song (unaccompanied) of their own choice. Preliminary auditions consist of a short movement warm-up and improvisation session for which no preparation is necessary, and a short workshop session using candidates' audition pieces. For those recalled, the work includes voice, movement and improvisation work, some carried out in small groups and more detailed work on audition pieces. *Audition fee*: £30.

AGSM Diploma Course in Acting (3 years, full-time; accredited by the National Council for Drama Training) *Entry requirements*: in some cases, academic achievement is used in addition to an audition/interview for assessing a candidate's suitability. Minimum age for applicants is 18 years. *Audition requirements*: as above. *Audition fee*: £30.

BA (Hons) in Stage Management and Technical Theatre (3 years, full-time; accredited by the National Council for Drama Training and validated by City University) *Entry requirements*: passes in two approved GCE A-level subjects; passes in one approved GCE A-level subject and two AS-level subjects. Minimum age for applicants is 18 years. All candidates are interviewed.

Italia Conti Academy of Theatre Arts

Italia Conti House, 23 Goswell Road, London EC1M 7AJ
Tel: 0171 608 0044/8
Fax: 0171 253 1430
Principal *A. M. Sheward*

Founded in 1922 by Italia Conti, an actress with a reputation for her work with young people.

COURSES ON OFFER

Theatre Arts School A co-ed specialist school for 10- to 16-year-olds. In addition to the National Curriculum students receive a full performer's training in all aspects of dance, acting and singing. *Audition requirements*: two contrasting short speeches of approximately 1 minute each; one song; three dance pieces, e.g. tap, modern and ballet. All candidates will be interviewed. *Audition fee*: £25.

Student Performing Arts Courses (accredited by the Council for Dance,

Education and Training, CDET) – for students aged over 16 years. *Audition requirements*: two contrasting short speeches of approximately 2 minutes each; one song; three dance pieces, e.g. tap, modern and ballet. All candidates will be interviewed. *Audition fee*: as above.

BA (Hons) Acting (validated by Middlesex University – *see under* University and Further Education Courses, page 45).

Also offers part-time and summer-school courses. Brochure available.

Desmond Jones School of Mime and Physical Theatre

St Luke's Church Hall, 450a Uxbridge Road, London W12
Administration: 20 Thornton Avenue, London W4 1QG
Tel: 0181 747 3537
Fax: 0181 747 3537
Contact *Desmond Jones, Principal (at the Administration address above)*

Founded 1979. Longest-established school of mime and physical theatre in the UK still in operation. Teaches all aspects of mime and physical theatre, aiming to keep abreast of, and ahead of, the demands of an increasingly physical modern theatre.

COURSES ON OFFER

Foundation Course (1 term – 3 months; three per year: January, April and September)
Advanced Course (4 terms – January to December)
Also operates half-day, morning or afternoon sessions.

Acceptance is by interview for those living in London or by cv from those living outside London or abroad. A £10 administration fee is charged. Students

are accepted between the ages of 18 and 35, though older students are occasionally accepted. In the main, they will be beginners, mostly actors and actresses but also painters, sculptors, puppeteers and people with some mime experience who want to extend their technique.

'The technique is based on that of Etienne Decroux, the originator of modern mime. Through it the students will learn a sense of style and precision indispensable to the modern mime. They will be made aware of the body and how to use it, and of the infinite subtlety that the body is capable of.

'The acting techniques draw on a variety of sources that have influenced modern theatre, from Jacques Lecoq to Keith Johnstone. It is not the intention of the school to produce carbon-copy performers, but to give the students a language of the body that they can use as they wish, whether it be for pure mime, clowning, the speaking theatre, or for daily life.'

LAMDA (London Academy of Music and Dramatic Art)*

Tower House, 226 Cromwell Road, London SW5 0SR
Tel: 0171 373 9883
Fax: 0171 370 4739
Principal *Peter James*

Founded in 1861, LAMDA is the oldest drama school in the English-speaking world. The school has chosen not to join with a university to obtain degree status for its courses, as it believes this would involve compromising the purely vocational character of LAMDA's courses. Around 30 students each year are admitted for the 3-year Acting Course.

COURSES ON OFFER

Acting Course (3 years, full-time) *Audition requirements*: two speeches, one Shakespeare and one modern. *Audition fee*: £20. The aim of the course is to 'encourage and develop talents already innate in each individual' rather than 'deconstruct the individual in order to rebuild a LAMDA product'.

Postgraduate Diploma Courses – **Musical Director and Répétiteur**; **Designers**; **Directors**; **Carpentry**; **Movement Instruction** (1 year, full-time) Admission by interview.

Classical Acting Course (1 year, full-time) *Audition requirements*: one Shakespeare and one classical speech plus one other speech (currently under review; check for details) *Audition fee*: as above. Students on this course have some experience of stage work, though not necessarily professional. 'The emphasis throughout is upon process and development rather than the polished finished performance.'

Stage Management Technical Theatre Course (2 years, full-time) Admission by interview. *Interview fee*: £15.

Also offers a 1-year foundation course and a 4-week Shakespeare workshop.

The London Academy of Performing Arts

Saint Matthew's Church, Saint Petersburgh Place, London W2 4LA
Tel: 0171 727 0220
Fax: 0171 727 0330
Principal *Cecilia Hocking*

Founded 1981. The policy of the London Academy of Performing Arts is to 'concentrate on the basic studies of voice and movement to develop the individual strengths of each student, to stimulate the imagination and to free the creative instincts. The overall aim is to lay the foundations for a secure technique which will enable the performer to adapt to all forms of theatrical encounter.' Students number 30–40 at any one time, of which up to 35% are American or Canadian and 5% from other countries. Auditions are held throughout the year in London, and in New York in February. Applications must be received by June for the following September. Prospectus available.

COURSES ON OFFER

Postgraduate Classical Acting Course (1 year, full-time) *Audition requirements*: two speeches of your own choice, one classical and one modern, of no longer than 2 minutes' duration, and an interview. Minimum age for entry is 21. *Audition fee*: £25 (London), £50 (New York.

Postgraduate Musical Repertory Company (1 year, full-time) *Audition requirements*: two contrasting speeches of your own choice, one modern and one classical, of no longer than 2 minutes' duration and a song from a musical or an operetta. Minimum age for entry is 20. *Audition fee*: £25 (London), £50 (New York).

Classical Acting Semester (12 weeks – September to December) A full résumé of previous experience and a letter of recommendation is required from applicants. *Audition requirements*: as for 1-year Postgraduate course.

Postgraduate Directing Course (1 year, full-time) Candidates will be interviewed by the Principal. Minimum age for entry is 21. *Interview fee*: £10.

Summer Shakespearean Acting Course (4 weeks, full-time, from mid-July)

'A Summer School is an ideal way for those without a year to spare to experience drama school.'
The Shakespearean Acting Course is designed to give students a solid grounding in this particular form of acting. All levels of ability take part, from beginners to working actors.
Entry requirements – Age 16 upwards. Past acting experience expected. No auditions. Two letters of recommendation required.

London and International School of Acting

Paddington Arts Centre, 32 Woodfield Road, London W9 2BE
Tel: 0171 727 2342
Fax: 0171 221 7210
Principal *Brian Lidstone*
Contact *The Secretary*

Founded 1983. 'The London and International School of Acting welcomes enquiries from aspiring actors prepared to work their way to the top.'

COURSES ON OFFER
Career Launching Course (3 years, full-time) *Audition requirements*: a speech of your own choice and an unaccompanied song. Applicants may be invited to demonstrate their skill in improvisation. *Audition fee*: £20.
Diploma Course (2 years, full-time) *Audition requirements*: as above. *Audition fee*: £20.
Postgraduate Course (1 year, full-time) *Audition requirements*: as above. *Audition fee*: £20.
Also holds Intensive Acting Courses of 3 or 6 months' duration. Auditions for all courses are held throughout the year and the minimum age for applicants is 18.

Manchester Metropolitan University, School of Television and Theatre*

– *see* University and Further Education Courses, page 44

Morley Theatre School at Morley College

61 Westminster Bridge Road, London SE1 7HT
Tel: 0171 928 8501
Fax: 0171 928 4074
Contact *Brian Croucher, Principal (c/o Dance and Drama Department)*

Founded 1939. Morley Theatre School offers an intensive part-time evening theatre course, ideal for those who need a foundation before applying to drama schools. 'Potential students need to have a good command of English, a commitment to study and to cooperate with members of their course group, and the confidence to put their all into every task.' Candidates are seen during September prior to the start of the course. No audition fees.
'Only go in for acting professionally if it is the only thing you want to do when you wake up in the morning. Otherwise, join a class for enjoyment and find a safer way of earning a living!'

Mountview Theatre School*

104 Crouch Hill, London N8 9EA
Tel: 0181 340 5885
Fax:0181 348 1727
E-mail: acting@mountview.drama.ac.uk
Principal *Paul Clements*
Contact *Anna Rowlands (Admissions Secretary)*

Founded 1945. Full-time acting and stage management courses introduced in 1969. Aims to 'provide high-quality education and training for people whose vocation is to work as professionals in the theatre, broadcast media and associated industries'. The school has a strong commitment to television training and students work in the school's television studio and on professionally supported location shoots. Radio technique is studied in the school's purpose-built studio. In addition to the courses listed below, the school offers part-time, adult foundation and young people's courses. Receives over 800 applications annually. Auditions are held throughout the year. Students must be aged 18 or over.

COURSES ON OFFER

BA (Hons) Performance – Acting and Musical Theatre Options (3 years, full-time; accredited by the National Council for Drama Training) *Audition requirements*: two modern speeches (post-1945) of your own choice and two songs of contrasting style. Applicants will also take part in movement and voice sessions. *Audition fee*: £30.

Stage Management, Technical Theatre and Design (2 years, full-time; accredited by the National Council for Drama Training) All candidates will be interviewed. *Interview fee*: £25.

Postgraduate Acting and Musical Theatre Course (1 year, full-time; accredited by the National Council for Drama Training) *Audition requirements*: as above. *Audition fee*: as above.

Postgraduate Stage Management, Technical Theatre and Design (1 year, full-time) *Interview fee*: as above.

Postgraduate Director's Course (1 year, full-time)

'Don't be afraid to shop around to make sure that the schools you apply for are the right ones for you. Talk to students, get to open days or try to arrange to visit the schools of your choice before you audition.

'Make sure the audition pieces you choose are ones with which you are totally comfortable. Auditions can be stressful so don't add pressure by being doubtful about your pieces. Remember, too, that people conducting auditions want to see good work – they're not watching for you to fail; they're watching for you to succeed.

'If you get a place, be prepared for long hours, hard work and the potential for serious and creative fun.'

New Era Academy of Drama and Music (London) Ltd

137B Streatham High Road, London SW16 1HJ
Tel: 0181 769 0384
Secretary *Bernard Price*
Contact *Mrs Jean Hutchins*

Founded 1941. Not a drama school as such, but an examining body with a wide-ranging syllabus including Speech and Drama, Solo Verse Speaking, Reading, Spoken English, Interview Technique, Public Speaking, Bible Reading, Mime, Stage Technique and English as a Second Language. Exams in these subjects can be taken at centres all over the UK in the presence of one or two of the academy's board of examiners. Adults and children are catered for and the Senior exams in Stage Technique are helpful for those wishing to take up theatre work as a career. Write for a syllabus which gives full details of exams.

The Oxford School of Drama
Sansomes Farm Studios, Woodstock,
Oxford OX20 1ER
Tel: 01993 812883
Fax: 01993 811220
Principal *George Peck MA*
Administrator *Sarah Johnson MA*

Founded in 1981 initially to run courses for university students in Oxford, with full-time courses being established in the following five years. The 3-year Acting Course is accredited by the National Council for Drama Training. 'The school accepts only a small number of students and this ensures you receive the personal attention which helps to nourish and develop your individual skills.'

COURSES ON OFFER
Acting Course (3 years, full-time) *Audition requirements*: two speeches: one Shakespeare and one contrasting modern piece, each no longer than 3 minutes in duration. *Audition fee*: £20. 'In this course there is a thorough analysis of the skills which are vital to those wanting to make a career in professional theatre.'
Acting Course (1 year, full-time) *Audition requirements*: as above. *Audition fee*: as above.

Also offers a six-month Foundation Course aimed at school leavers.

The Poor School
242 Pentonville Road, London N1 9JY
Tel: 0171 837 6030
Principal *Paul Caister*

Founded by Paul Caister in 1986 'in response to the need for a first-class training which was financially within the reach of all or almost all'. Training lasts for 2 years and operates in the evenings and at weekends until the final 2 terms when daytime work is involved. Thirty-two students are accepted each October. Auditions are held throughout the year. 'No one should be discouraged from applying solely on the grounds of age. Experience is an advantage only in so far as it may help you to a better audition.' *Audition requirements*: two dramatic speeches, each lasting no longer than 2 minutes; one from Shakespeare. *Audition fee*: £20. Also offers a Summer Course lasting 3 weeks and short evening courses and a 1-year Stage Management Course will be available from October 1998. Details from the address above.

Queen Margaret College*
– *see* University and Further Education Courses, page 47

Redroofs Theatre School
Littlewick Green, Maidenhead,
Berkshire SL6 3QY
Tel: 01628 822982
Fax: 01628 822461
Founder/Director *June Rose*

Founded 1947. Offers a 2-year course for students aged over 16 years. *Audition requirements*: a prepared song; two contrasting speeches, each of no more than 4 minutes' duration. All candidates will be interviewed by the Principal. *Audition fee*: £15. Part of the course is a 'rep' year during which students work with a fully professional company at the Novello Theatre in Sunninghill, near Ascot. The theatre specialises in work for children and young people. A 1-year, postgraduate course is also offered. Prospectus available.

'Redroofs has its own agency and is therefore in a position to offer representation to past and present students.'

Richmond Drama School

Parkshot Centre, Parkshot, Richmond,
Surrey TW9 2RE
Tel: 0181 940 0170 ext 325
Fax: 0181 332 6560
Director *David Whitworth*

Offers a 1-year, full-time Diploma in
Acting Course designed to provide a
comprehensive training in acting. All
students learn stage-management
skills during the course. *Audition
requirements*: two short speeches, one
by Shakespeare and the other from a
modern play. Candidates may also be
asked to sight-read. *Audition fee*: £15.

Royal Academy of Dramatic Art*

18–22 Chenies Street,
London WC1E 7EX
Tel: 0171 636 7076
Fax: 0171 323 3865
Principal *Nicholas Barter*

Founded in 1904 by Sir Herbert
Beerbohm Tree. Following an Arts
Council Lottery Board award in 1996,
the original premises in Gower Street
are being redeveloped, the GBS
Theatre updated and the Vanbrugh
Theatre and Studio 14 are to be
replaced with state-of-the-art
redesigned theatre spaces. Received
1,450 applications for the maximum of
32 places on the 3-year Acting Diploma
in 1996/7 for the 1997/8 intake.

COURSES ON OFFER

Acting Diploma (3 years, full-time)
Audition requirements: two pieces of the
candidate's choice, each no longer than
3 minutes' duration. One to be a
monologue from any play by
Shakespeare or other Elizabethan/
Jacobean playwright, the other piece
from any play which is in clear contrast

to the first. The auditions are 'lengthy
and rigorous' and the process may
span several months. Audition/
Registration fee: £27.50. The course is a
training for students who wish to earn
a living working not only in the more
traditional outlets but in the many
alternative areas of theatre, film, television and radio. During the first term,
they are introduced to Stanislavski-
based acting exercises, alongside their
vocal and physical skills classes. In the
subsequent terms they go on to explore
the application of their developing
skills in a series of in-house presentations of texts.

**Stage Management and Theatre
Production Diploma** (2 years, full-
time) Candidates are selected by interview. Up to 25 students are admitted
each September. The course embraces
all the production disciplines involved
in the mounting of professional performances, including lighting, sound,
design and scenic art, scenic construction, property making, wardrobe,
stagecraft and stage management.

MA in Text and Performance Studies
(1 year, full-time) *Entry requirements*:
usually a good honours degree,
normally in the Arts, but appropriate
experience, for example in theatre, may
be considered as an alternative.
Offered in conjunction with King's
College London, the course provides
an opportunity to explore text as a
medium for performance. Further
details from The Administrative
Assistant, School of Humanities,
King's Collége, Strand, London WC2R
2LS.

**Specialist Diploma Courses: Scenic
Art; Scenic Construction; Stage
Electrics; Property Making** (all 4 terms
of up to 13 weeks each) Candidates are
selected by interview.

Short Courses: Acting Shakespeare
(June/July); **Summer School** (July/

August); **Set Design** (July/August); **Western Classical Acting** (February/March).

Royal Scottish Academy of Music and Drama*

School of Drama, 100 Renfrew Street, Glasgow G2 3DB
Tel: 0141 332 4101
Fax: 0141 332 8901
E-mail: registry@rsamd.ac.uk
Website: http://www.rsamd.ac.uk
Principal *Philip Ledger*

Founded 1950, as the College of Dramatic Art. Took present title in 1968 and moved to purpose-built accommodation in 1987.

COURSES ON OFFER
BA Acting (3 years, full-time; accredited by the NCDT) *Entry requirements*: there is a general entry requirement for undergraduate courses although mature students and those with 'non-standard' qualifications are eligible. Work experience is taken into consideration. *Audition requirements*: for the preliminary audition, two speeches should be prepared, one (preferably in verse) by Shakespeare, the other of the candidate's choice. Each should be no more than 3 minutes in duration. *Registration fee*: £35 per course.
BA(Hons) Dramatic Studies (3 years for Ordinary degree/4 years for Honours degree) *Entry requirements*: general entry requirement for undergraduate courses – English at Higher Grade, Advanced Higher, A-level, Standard Grade or GCSE level necessary. *Audition requirements*: two contrasting speeches should be prepared, each being no more than 3 minutes in duration. Movement and voice work will be undertaken, followed by an interview. All candi-

dates participate in a short improvised drama class, followed by a written essay. *Registration fee*: as above.
BA Stage Management Studies (3 years, full-time) *Entry requirements*: there is a general entry requirement for undergraduate courses although mature students and those with 'non-standard' qualifications are eligible. Work experience is taken into consideration. All candidates are interviewed. *Registration fee*: as above.

Anna Scher Theatre Ltd

70–72 Barnsbury Road,
London N1 0ES
Tel: 0171 278 2101
Fax: 0171 833 9467
Principal *Anna Scher*
Contact *Gina Brown (General Manager)*

Founded 1968. With a membership of 1,000 and a waiting list of 3,000, to cope with demand the Anna Scher Theatre offers a 4-week summer-school acting course for children and young people during August. The Junior Group is for 6- to 11-year-olds and the Secondary Group for 12 to 18+. Sessions are led by Anna Scher and include improvisation, devised plays and drama games. Short evening courses are held twice a year in May and October for students, teachers, social workers, parents and anyone interested in the AST's Method. The large waiting list for the theatre can mean a wait of over 5 years for the 6–11 age group, 4 years for the 11–16 age group, and 18 months for 16+. Receives 10–15 applications daily, usually in person. Opportunities are available for members to work in the profession under Anna Scher Theatre Management Ltd. Famous past pupils include Pauline Quirke, Linda Robson,

Kathy Burke, Peter Hugo Daly and Charlotte Coleman.

'It's a tough profession and you have to be able to take rejection well.'

The School of the Science of Acting

67–83 Seven Sisters Road, Holloway, London N7 6BU
Tel: 0171 272 0027
Fax: 0171 272 0026
Principal *Sam Kogan*

Started running full-time courses in 1991. For those wishing to find out about the school, free seminars are held on Saturday mornings and Wednesday evenings (dates are given in a leaflet available from the school), during which the Principal explains 'the beginning of the science of acting and the main ideas behind the school'. Telephone the school and leave your name, phone number and date you wish to attend. 'If you come to a seminar we will give you the opportunity to spend a day at the school and sit in on lessons or rehearsals. This day will be free.' The school has received accreditation from the British Accreditation Council for Independent Further and Higher Education.

COURSES ON OFFER
Two-year Acting Course (full-time) *Audition requirements*: one Shakespearean speech, a fable, a piece of modern poetry or prose, a song or dance; each lasting a maximum of 2 minutes. *Audition fee*: £20.
One-year Acting Course (full-time) *Audition requirements*: as above. *Audition fee*: as above.
Two-year Acting Course (evenings) *Audition requirements*: as above. *Audition fee*: as above.

Two-year Directing Course (full-time; with optional third year) *Audition requirements*: as above. *Audition fee*: £25.
Directing Course (2 years, evenings plus third-year daytime course) *Audition requirements*: as above. *Audition fee*: £25.

Also offers short and part-time acting courses, workshops and summer school.

Barbara Speake Stage School

East Acton Lane, East Acton, London W3 7EG
Tel: 0181 743 1306
Fax: 0181 740 6542
Principal *Miss Barbara Speake, ARAD, MISTD, MIDTA*
Contact *David R. Speake BA (Hons) (Headteacher)*

Founded 1945. Independent school for children aged 4 to 16, teaching dance, drama and singing alongside a full-time academic education. An agency attached to the school provides opportunities for professional work in theatre, film and television. Famous past pupils include Phil Collins, Michelle Gayle, Brian Conley and Naomi Campbell.

Dacia Stevens Stage School

Glenavon Lodge, Lansdowne Road, South Woodford, London E18 2BE
Tel: 0181 989 0166
Principal *Dacia Stevens*

Founded 1968. Offers after-school speech, drama and stage training for children aged 5 to 16. Classes are held in the evening between 4 p.m. and 9 p.m. 'I try to give my pupils a broad outlook in life, to encourage them to work hard and enjoy all they do. Children need to be taught to speak correctly. They love to act. I teach them both.'

TAI Artists (formerly The Actors Institute)

The Glasshouse, 4 Enfield Road, London N1 5AZ
Tel: 0181 977 6130
Contact *Christine Kimberley*

Founded 1976. Offers acting workshops, short courses in all techniques, summer schools for beginners through to professional, and a 1-year postgraduate professional acting workshop. In association with the Institute for Creativity which runs 'The Mastery' and 'Samurai' workshops (*see* Additional Skills, page 374).

Webber Douglas Academy of Dramatic Art*

30 Clareville Street, London SW7 5AP
Tel: 0171 370 4154
Fax: 0171 373 5639
Principal *Raphael B. Jago*
Contact *Clare Hocter*

Founded in 1906 in Paris and 1926 in London by Amherst Webber and Walter Johnstone-Douglas. Receives over 900 applications for courses per year. Auditions are held at regular intervals between October and May, excluding December and April. Prospective students should complete an application form and return it with a small photograph.

COURSES ON OFFER

Diploma Course (3 years, full-time) A good educational background is required. *Audition requirements*: one Shakespearean speech, one modern speech and one unaccompanied song.

It is recommended that one piece should be comedy and one should involve some movement.
Audition fee: £24.

Diploma Course (2 years, full-time) A university degree or experience in the relevant field is required for this course. *Audition requirements*: as above. *Audition fee*: as above.

Postgraduate Diploma (1 year, full-time) A university degree or experience in the relevant field is required for this course. *Audition requirements*: as above. *Audition fee*: as above.

All courses are NCDT-accredited and eligible for student grants. Prospectus available. 'Our aim is to choose students who have the necessary talent, flexibility and consistency, and to develop their skills in training and performance. We also aim to help them clarify where their particular strengths lie and keep them up to date with changes in the profession.'

Also offers a Summer Course in Acting and Theatre in London for students aged from 17 to 35.

Welsh College of Music and Drama*

Castle Grounds, Cathays Park, Cardiff CF1 3ER
Tel: 01222 371440
Fax: 01222 237639
E-mail: drama.admissions@wcmd.ac.uk
Principal *Edmond Fivet*
Contact *Admissions Officer (Drama)*

Founded 1949. The college's mission statement is: 'To develop as an innovative European centre of excellence for professional training and education in the performing arts, within a sensitive, artistic and cultural environment.' For those students whose first or second language is Welsh and who wish to perform in Welsh, additional and/or alternative options and tutorials are given throughout the course.

COURSES ON OFFER

BA(Hons) Theatre Studies – Acting (3 years, full-time, accredited by the National Council for Drama Training) *Entry requirements*: 2 A-levels (or BTEC National or GNVR Advanced) and 3 GCSE passes (or non-standard qualifications for mature students). *Audition requirements*: two speeches, movement and voice warm-up and afternoon workshop.

Advanced Diploma Course in Drama – Acting (1 year, full-time, accredited by the National Council for Drama Training) *Entry requirements*: graduates or those whose previous experience is appropriate to training for professional theatre. *Audition requirements*: as above.

BA(Hons) Theatre Studies – Design (3 years, full-time) *Entry requirements*: as above. Admission by interview and portfolio.

Advanced Diploma Course in Drama – Design (1 year, full-time) *Entry requirements*: as above.

BA(Hons) Theatre Studies – Stage Management (3 years, full-time, accredited by the National Council for Drama Training) *Entry requirements*: as above. Admission is determined by interview; not all applicants are interviewed.

Advanced Diploma Course in Drama – Stage Management (1 year, full-time, accredited by the National Council for Drama Training) *Entry requirements*: as above.

The college recommends that applications for acting courses should be in before December. Audition/interview fee of £25 for all courses. The minimum age for all 3-year courses is 18; for 1-year courses, 21. A broad view is taken of applicants' potential for training and admission is not dependent solely on previous academic achievement.

'You should not consider us, in isolation, to be accurate arbiters of your talent or potential. Each drama school will be looking for something different and have their own preferences. If failure to secure a place at the first attempt discourages you from applying further afield in your present or future years, then the profession is probably not for you!

'Here, we value the ability to "inhabit" a character, generosity in working with others, expressive ability, an active interest in theatre and performing arts and life experience. We are small, innovative and able to respond to students' individual requirements and needs.

'The School of Drama's principal concern is to provide each student with a thorough training, enabling them to achieve their full potential ready for a career in the professional theatre. We work to produce an actor who uses his/her total resources as a human being in the creation and communication of a role. Training is concerned with the wholeness and uniqueness of the individual rather than simply the function which he/she is to fulfil.'

University and Further Education Courses

Barking College

Dagenham Road, Romford,
Essex RM7 0XU
Tel: 01708 766841
Fax: 01708 731067
Principal *Ted Parker*
Contact *John McDermott*

COURSES ON OFFER
BTEC National Diploma Performing Arts (2 years, full-time) *Entry requirements*: 4 passes at GCSE at grade C or better, and successful audition. Designed for those who wish to pursue a career in the performing arts, the course is concerned with the development of practical creative skills, theoretical understanding of performing arts disciplines and a range of general abilities. Allows for specialism in theatre, dance, music, arts administration and arts in society.
BTEC Higher National Certificate Performing Arts (part-time) *Entry requirements*: BTEC National Diploma or 2 GCE A levels. The course offers options in theatre, music and dance.

Also offers **GCE A-level Performing Arts** (2 years) and **GCE A-level Theatre Studies** (2 years).

Birkbeck College University of London

Centre for Extramural Studies, 26
Russell Square, London WC1B 5DQ
Tel: 0171 631 6663/6667
Fax: 0171 631 6683
E-mail: p.lazenby@cems.bbk.ac.uk
Subject Officer, Media Studies, and Drama and Theatre Studies *Penny Lazenby*

COURSES ON OFFER
Certificate/Diploma in Drama and Theatre Studies (Certificate: 2–3 years/ Diploma: 2–4 years) *Entry requirements*: none. The courses cover a wide range of plays from the beginnings in myth and ritual to the present day.

Also offers 2-term courses, including: **Approaches to Directing; Approaches to Acting; Television Drama** and short courses and weekend events. Details available from the Centre for Extramural Studies as above.

University College Bretton Hall

West Bretton, Wakefield,
West Yorkshire WF4 4LG
Tel: 01924 832017
Fax: 01924 832016
E-mail: registry@mailhost.bretton.ac.uk

Founded in 1949, Bretton Hall offers highly distinctive courses which combine theoretical study with practical creative and professional activity to a degree unusual in higher education.

COURSES ON OFFER
BA(Hons) Theatre (Acting) (3 years, full-time/5–7 years, part-time) *Entry requirements*: A-level grades of B, C; or BTEC profile of merits and distinctions in all units; non-standard applications are welcomed. Described as a programme for those who 'want to act and yet are not content just to have a director tell you what to do'. Students are encouraged to question fundamental assumptions about acting and theatre, while at the same time 'developing good actor's habits of discipline and study'. Almost all the work is practical with a concentration on the interpretative work of the actor on given scripts as well as improvisational work and how this can lead to performance.
BA(Hons) Theatre (Acting: Broadcast Media) (3 years, full-time/5–7 years, part-time) *Entry requirements*: A-level grades of B, C; or BTEC profile of merits and distinctions in all units; or experience and analytical ability. A programme which allows the student to focus upon acquiring the actor's skills appropriate to media work. The course also involves some live stage work.
BA(Hons) Theatre (Acting: Devised Performance) (3 years, full-time/5–7 years, part-time) *Entry requirements*: A-level grades of B, C; or BTEC profile of merits and distinctions in all units; or experience and analytical ability. The course encourages students to develop their potential as devisers, writers, directors and performers.

Also offer **BA(Hons) Performance Management; BA(Hons) Dance**.

University of Brighton

Mithras House, Lewes Road, Brighton,
East Sussex BN2 4AT
Tel: 01273 600900
Fax: 01273 642825
E-mail: admissions@brighton.ac.uk
Dean *Professor Bruce Brown*

COURSES ON OFFER
BA(Hons) Theatre with Visual Practice (3 years, full-time) *Entry requirements*: pre-degree course in art and design preferred; good GCSE profile; interview and portfolio. 'Involves the study of theatre and visual art practice supported by critical and historical studies.'
BA(Hons) Dance with Visual Practice (3 years, full-time) *Entry requirements*: as above. 'Offers a unique opportunity to study dance performance and choreography alongside visual practice, supported by a historical and critical programme in the visual and performing arts.'

Brunel University

Uxbridge, Middlesex UB8 3PH
Tel: 01895 274000
Fax: 01895 232806

COURSES ON OFFER
BA Modern Drama Studies (3 years, full-time) *Entry requirements*: at least 18 points at A-level, including a B in Theatre Studies; final selection is made

by audition. The degree can be studied as a single or joint honours course; Drama can be combined with English, Film and TV Studies or Music. Students study the entire spectrum of live performance, including mainstream text-based work, music theatre, popular theatre and experimental performance. Students have recently performed in Hungary and participated in festivals and conferences in Germany, Holland and Poland.

Christ Church College Canterbury

North Holmes Road, Canterbury, Kent CT1 1QU
Tel: 01227 767700
E-mail: cant.ac.uk
Principal Professor Michael Wright
Course Director Mike Radford
Contact Wendy Taylor (01227 782407)

The college, founded by the Church of England in 1962, has close links with the Cathedral, situated nearby, and surrounding city of Canterbury. Drama provision is part of the undergraduate English Degree course and is due for expansion.

COURSE ON OFFER
MA The Expressive Arts in Education (2 years, full-time) *Entry requirements*: good honours degree or equivalent professional qualifications. The course offers the opportunity to study at both practical and academic levels and consists of a first-year foundation module, 'Arts Education and Aesthetic Development', followed by a second-year module, 'Teaching the Arts'. One practical option is selected from: creative writing, visual arts, music, dance or drama.

The City Literary Institute

16 Stukeley Street, off Drury Lane, London WC2B 5LJ
Tel: 0171 430 0544
Fax: 0171 405 3347
Head of Drama Department Valerie Colgan
Contact Jennifer Hutt (Drama Administrator)

Founded in 1919 and known affectionately as 'The City Lit', courses are the cheapest in London thanks to a £4.3 million grant and educational charity status. Has a high reputation for its classes (270) in all aspects of acting, directing, stage management and lighting, set and costume, clowning, stage fighting, dance, movement and business skills as well as voice skills taught by professional actors and teachers. Prospectus available. Entry is by personal interview. Prepared speeches may be required for entry into some performance classes. There are no audition fees.

The **Drama Course** (accredited by LOCF – London Open College Federation) offers a systematic training in acting over two years. It is an intensive course requiring regular attendance at 3 classes, totalling 6 hours per week in the first year and 9 hours per week in the second. Entrants to the first year should have completed an introductory course to acting or have comparable experience; entrance to the second year is only open to those who have successfully completed the first year and are recommended by their tutors. The first year is designed to develop individual awareness and extend imagination; the second year increases technical ability and performance. Candidates are interviewed and are asked to do an audition piece of 3 minutes. 'We can only interview the first 240 people who make an appointment.'

City of Liverpool Community College
Old Swan Centre, Broadgreen Road, Liverpool L13 5SQ
Tel: 0151 252 3030

COURSES ON OFFER

Foundation Course in Performing Arts (1 or 2 years, part-time) *Entry requirements*: no formal requirements but candidates must demonstrate an interest in the area and ability to respond to direction.

BTEC First Diploma in Performing Arts (Drama) (1 year, full-time) *Entry requirements*: no formal qualifications required; candidates will take part in an audition and interview process. Open to anyone over the age of 16, the course provides training for those with little or no previous acting experience.

BTEC First Certificate in Performing Arts (Dance) (1 year, full-time) *Entry requirements*: as above. Open to anyone over the age of 16, the course provides workshop and performance experience in dance technique and dance performance at basic level.

BTEC National Diploma in Performing Arts (Drama) (1 year, full-time) *Entry requirements*: 4 GCSEs at grade C or above, or equivalent. Designed to prepare students for the professional arts world or for higher education.

BTEC National Diploma in Performing Arts (Dance) (1 year, full-time) *Entry requirements*: 4 GCSEs at grade C or above, or BTEC first or equivalent. The course develops skills through both the practical and theoretical study of dance, including ballet, contemporary and jazz dance techniques.

BTEC Higher National Diploma in Community Theatre (2 years, full-time) *Entry requirements*: 4 GCSEs at grade C or above, 1 A-level pass, or equivalent. The course prepares the performer for the realities of the job market.

City University
Department of Arts Policy and Management, Level 7, Frobisher Crescent, Barbican, London EC2Y 8HB
Tel: 0171 477 8751/3
Fax: 0171 477 8887
E-mail: artspol@city.ac.uk
Head of Department *Dr Eric Moody*
Contact *Mary Dines, Ursula Hedgley*

Established in 1973, the Department of Arts Policy and Management is unique in the British university system. It is a large and growing postgraduate department that specialises in teaching and research covering arts policy-making, arts criticism and arts and heritage management. Receives approximately 270 applications per year. Deadline for applications is the last week in March.

COURSES ON OFFER
MA in Art Criticism (1 year, full-time/ 2 years, part-time) *Entry requirements*: normally 2 or more years' work in a relevant field together with an honours degree or equivalent qualification. Good work experience may compensate for the lack of a degree. Candidates may be required to attend an interview.

MA in Arts Management (1 year, full-time or 2 years, part-time) *Entry requirements*: as above.

Postgraduate Diploma in Arts Ad-

ministration (1 year, full-time) *Entry requirements*: as above.

'Actors, like many other artists, have to consider developing a portfolio career where acting (the actor's art) is complemented by other professional activity. The tradition of actor-manager is recognised as a starting point for postgraduate training in arts management. Arts Policy and Management recruits former actors, actors who are "resting" and actors who discover they already have one of the basic skills of management – communication.'

Coventry University

Performing Arts, c/o School of Art and Design, Coventry University,
Priory Street,
Coventry CV1 5FB
Tel: 01203 418868
Fax: 01203 692374
E-mail: m.evans@coventry.ac.uk
Head of Department *Patricia Thompson*
Contact *Mark Evans*

COURSE ON OFFER
BA(Hons) in Theatre and Professional Practice (3 years, full-time) *Entry requirements*: at least 2 A-levels at grade C or above, preferably including Theatre Studies or Performing Arts; or BTEC National Diploma in Performing Arts with average of merits and 4 distinctions; or GNVQ (Advanced) in Performing Arts at merit or above; or suitable foundation/access course. *Audition requirements*: usually, one speech (published) of 2–3 minutes' duration, participation in a practical workshop and a piece of writing set prior to interview from a list of topics. The rationale of the training provided falls primarily within the small-scale touring-theatre area. Staff have strong connections with local professional theatre – some run their own theatre companies.

'Acting, like theatre, is changing. The changes are not of our making but they are not beyond our influence. To be an actor now is to enter a profession that is struggling – with low wages, with reduced employment opportunities, with widening gaps between success and failure. In such an environment it does not seem safe simply to concentrate on the preparation of yourself as an "instrument", important though the skills of the performer are. We aim to empower students with the creative, administrative and performance knowledge to develop themselves as artists in the way that best suits their creativity and the society of today as they see it.'

Dartington College of Arts

Totnes, Devon TQ9 6EJ
Tel: 01803 862224
Fax:01803 863569
E-mail: d.faulkner@dartington
Director of Theatre Studies *Roger Sell*
Contact *Margaret Eggleton (Registry)*

Dartington does not offer an acting course. The Specialist Theatre route through the undergraduate programme is committed to ensemble performance of physically based, devised theatre. There are opportunities to study and practice movement, voice, directing, scenography, choreography and dramaturgy.

COURSES ON OFFER (* Can also be combined with Arts Management)
BA(Hons) Theatre (3 years, full-time) *Entry requirements*: 5 GCSEs of which 2 are at A-level (BB, any subject) or

equivalent. Some applicants may be invited to send samples on video or audio cassette; shortlisted applicants are normally invited to visit on selection days.

BA(Hons) Theatre with Arts Management (3 years, full-time) *Entry requirements*: as above.

BA(Hons) Visual Performance (Visual Art & Performance)* (3 years, full-time) *Entry requirements*: 5 GCSEs of which 2 are at A-level (Art, grade B and one other subject) or equivalent. Some applicants may be invited to bring their portfolio.

BA(Hons) Performance Writing* (3 years, full-time) *Entry requirements*: 5 GCSEs of which 2 are at A-level (BC, any subject) or equivalent.

The courses are modular; students enrol in a subject specialism but are given opportunities to work with other disciplines during the first year. Two out of four of the modules in the second year are electives, designed to encourage investigation into new art forms and/or collaboration between the arts. The third year is when students begin to establish their own practice through individual focus.

concerned with performance in a contemporary context with much devised and "live art" work, and is best suited to applicants wishing to explore performance in all its aspects rather than wishing to seek training for the acting profession.' The Single Honours route allows students to study dance or theatre single-mindedly whereas the Joint and Combined routes allow wider-ranging study. Receives approximately 500 applications per year.

COURSES ON OFFER

Single or Joint and Combined Honours in Performing Arts (3 years, full-time) *Entry requirements*: selection, apart from academic qualifications (usually BCC at A-level or 6 distinctions at BTEC), 'is based more on an ability to deconstruct the chosen audition piece interestingly rather than on quality of acting'. *Audition requirements*: 5-minute speech, scripted or devised. Core Theatre modules include Writing for Performance; Directing; Devising; Adaptation of Novels for the Stage; Performing Shakespeare.

De Montfort University Leicester

The Gateway, Leicester LE2 9BH
Tel: 0116 250 6185
Fax: 0116 250 6188
E-mail: mwp@dmu.ac.uk
Head of Department *Professor Michael Patterson, MA, DPhil*

The Performing Arts Department incorporates Theatre, Dance and Music and offers a modular structure, allowing students to pursue their own interests while following core modules in chosen specialities. 'The course is

University of East Anglia

University Plain, Norwich,
Norfolk NR4 7TJ
Tel: 01603 592272
Fax: 01603 593009
E-mail: j.hyde@uea.ac.uk
Contact *Jon Hyde (Administrator)*

COURSES ON OFFER

BA(Hons) in Drama (3 years, full-time) *Entry requirements*: typical A-level offer is BBB/BBC; a significant involvement with drama at educational and/or amateur level is essential. *Audition requirements*: a choice from three speeches from a classic text sent to candidates plus own choice of another speech or a design portfolio. The course combines a strong practical emphasis with study of the theory, history and social significance of drama.

MA in Theatre Directing (1 year, full-time/2 years, part-time) *Entry requirements*: interview with course director. A unique course designed to combine academic study of the theory and history of directing with practical training and experimentation. Includes classes on lighting and design, visiting workshops by professional directors, the opportunity to direct small productions in the UEA Studio, and a placement at a professional theatre.

'Although clearly no course can guarantee work in the profession, many students do go on to forge careers as actors, directors, technicians, teachers of drama, etc. Those committed to performance often undertake postgraduate work at the major British drama schools and there has also been a recognisable trend towards the two-year course at the Ecole Lecoq in Paris.'

Edge Hill University College

St Helens Road, Ormskirk, Lancashire L39 4QP
Tel: 01695 575171

COURSE ON OFFER

BA(Hons) Drama (3 years, full-time; part-time option available) *Entry requirements*: 2 A-level passes (CC) or GNVQ Advanced (merit) or GNVQ Advanced (pass) plus grade C A level or equivalents. The course is available as a Major, Joint or Minor programme and is predominantly practical in content based on a modular structure. Classes are mostly workshop-based with some lectures and seminars.

University of Essex

Wivenhoe Park, Colchester,
Essex CO4 3SQ
Tel: 01206 872221
Fax: 01206 872940
E-mail: licht@essex.ac.uk
Head of Department *Jonathan Lichtenstein*

COURSES ON OFFER

MA in Contemporary Theatre Practice (1 year, full-time) *Entry requirements*: a good degree in a suitable subject plus considerable practical experience. Candidates will be given an hour-long interview.

MA in Contemporary Practice of Shakespearean Theatre (1 year, full-time) *Entry requirements*: as above.

Receives 40 applications per course with a maximum of 10 places given annually. Students experience theatre-making under the guidance of nationally and internationally renowned directors and actors.

University of Exeter

Department of Drama, Thornlea, New North Road, Exeter, Devon EX4 4JZ
Tel: 01392 264580
Fax: 01392 411949
E-mail (Secretary):
l.g.buchanan@exeter.ac.uk
Website: http://www.ex.ac.uk/drama
Head of Department *Christopher McCullough*
Contact *Lindsay Buchanan (Secretary)*

COURSES ON OFFER

BA(Hons) Drama (3 years, full-time) *Entry requirements*: all applicants must satisfy the university's general entrance requirements. 'We try to see as many applicants as possible, combining a short interview with studio sessions.'

Drama can also be studied over 3 years in combination with English and over 4 years – the third year is spent in the appropriate country – with German or Spanish. 'We do not, as drama schools might, claim to train people for the theatre as it is, but we are interested in pointing them towards a theatre that might be. While that inevitably involves some training in physical, vocal and technical skills, it also highlights the ability to communicate, initiate, participate and organise.'

MA in Theatre Practice (11 months, full-time) *Entry requirements*: a suitable first degree or comparable qualification. The Department welcomes applications from would-be researchers, particularly those with an interest in the study of performance, whether in practice or in theory.

Goldsmiths' College, University of London

New Cross, London SE14 6NW
Tel: 0171 919 7171
Fax: 0171 919 7113
E-mail: admissions@gold.ac.uk
Website: http://www.gold.ac.uk/
Warden *Professor Kenneth Gregory, PhD, DSc, FRGS*
Contact *Drama Dept: 0171 919 7414*

Goldsmiths' College is part of the University of London and was founded in 1891 for 'the promotion of the individual skill, general knowledge, health and well-being of young men and women belonging to the industrial, working and poorer classes'. It continues that tradition by facilitating access to higher education for entrants with non-standard qualifications, for mature students and for students from a range of ethnic backgrounds.

COURSES ON OFFER
BA(Hons) Drama and Theatre Arts (3 years, full-time) *Entry requirements*: A levels or various qualifications including AS levels, access courses, GNVQs and BTEC. Applicants will also be interviewed. The course offers the chance to explore the theory and practice of performance as it is produced in a range of media plus the opportunity to specialise.

BA English and Theatre Arts (3 years, full-time) *Entry requirements*: as above. The programme provides a study of literature and theatre arts and explores interdisciplinary connections between them.

MA in Theatre Arts (1 year, full-time) *Entry requirements*: normally a good first degree or being able to demonstrate an ability to undertake work at Master's level.

Also offers a **PhD in Drama** – full- or part-time course.

University of Huddersfield

Queensgate, Huddersfield,
West Yorkshire HD1 3DH
Tel: 01484 422288
E-mail: (Theatre Studies): d.k.middleton @hud.ac.uk
E-mail: (Theatre Studies with Music): s.j.nicholson@hud.ac.uk
Website: http://www.hud.ac.uk/schools/music+humanities/theatrestudies/welcome.html

COURSES ON OFFER
BA(Hons) Theatre Studies (3 years, full-time) *Entry requirements*: in addition to general entry requirements, qualifications should include at least one A-level pass, or equivalent, in Theatre Studies or English. The programme integrates studio-based

practical and theoretical methods of study. The compulsory foundation year explores performance, production and study skills through a wide range of study areas.

BA(Hons) Theatre Studies with Music (3 years, full-time) *Entry requirements*: in addition to general entry requirements, qualifications should include at least one A-level pass, or equivalent, in Theatre Studies or English. For students taking the Musicology or Composition options: A-level pass in Music; for students taking the Performance Option: grade 8 of the Associated Board of the Royal Schools of Music or equivalent. The programme enables students whose main focus is Theatre to continue studying Music through either the Musicology/Composition or Performance options for a third of their study.

A 3-year **BA(Hons) Theatre Studies and Media** course is also available.

theatregoing. All candidates are interviewed. The course gives preparation for a theatre or theatre-related career, particularly in directing, scenography, community or educational theatre, radio production, teaching and youth work, arts management and theatre journalism.

BA(Joint Hons) in Drama (3 years, full-time) *Entry requirements*: as above; offers may be made without an interview. The Joint Honours degree (particularly with Film or English or History and Theory of Art) makes a good preparation for careers in journalism, arts publishing and arts administration.

BA(Joint Hons) in Visual and Performed Arts (3 years, full-time) *Entry requirements*: as above; offers may be made without an interview. With its combination of arts studies this degree gives a good background to a career in arts management.

University of Kent at Canterbury

School of Arts and Image Study,
Eliot College,
University of Kent at Canterbury,
Canterbury, Kent CT2 7NS
Tel: 01227 764000 ext 7531
Fax: 01227 827464
E-mail: r.w.strang@ukc.ac.uk
Head of Department *Professor Christopher Baugh*
Admissions Tutor (Drama) *Ron Strang*

COURSES ON OFFER
BA(Single Hons) in Drama (4 years, full-time) *Entry requirements*: in addition to A-level achievements, an evidence of a real interest in drama and theatre is required as well as of practical involvement in theatre, and

King Alfred's University College Winchester

Winchester,
Hampshire SO22 4NR
Tel: 01962 841515
Fax: 01962 842280

COURSES ON OFFER
BA(Hons) Drama, Theatre and Television Studies (3 years, full-time) *Entry requirements*: no preferred prescribed combination of A-level or equivalent subjects as the college is interested in attracting students with a range and depth of cultural backgrounds and life experience.

BA (Combined Honours) Drama Studies (3 years, full-time) *Entry requirements*: as above.

BA(Hons) Performing Arts (3 years, full-time) *Entry requirements*: GCSE

A–C pass (or equivalent) in English Language; minimum of 2 GCE A-level passes; BTEC National Diploma/Certificate; GNVQ Advanced level with merit; or equivalent.

University of Leeds
School of English, University of Leeds, Leeds, West Yorkshire LS2 9JT
Tel: 0113 243 1751
Fax: 0113 233 4774

COURSE ON OFFER
BA (Single Honours) English Literature and Theatre Studies (3 years, full-time) *Entry requirements*: usually GCSEs and A levels or a combination of A and AS levels. Welcomes applications from mature students. Virtually all Theatre Studies seminars include practical work as a major element
MA Theatre Studies (1 year, full-time) *Entry requirements*: candidates are normally expected to have a good honours degree with a significant background in drama and theatre studies. The course offers an opportunity to study aspects of theatre in a workshop context. A strong emphasis is placed on practical work, including directing, performing, technical theatre and playwriting.

Loughborough University
Loughborough, Leicestershire LE11 3TU
Tel: 01509 263171
Fax: 01509 223905
E-mail: prospectus-enquiries@lboro.ac.uk
Website: http://info.lboro.ac.uk/home.html

COURSES ON OFFER
BA(Hons) Drama/BA(Hons) Drama with English (3 years, full-time) *Entry requirements*: typically, A levels: 22 points; BTEC is considered but preference may be given to combination of BTEC and A-level study. The course combines the theory and practice of drama. European and American theatre as well as British theatre are studied. Specialisms in technical theatre (lighting and sound), radio and television drama and playwriting may also be studied.

Manchester Metropolitan University
Faculty of Art and Design,
Department of Communication Media,
School of Television and Theatre,
Capitol Building,
School Lane,
Didsbury,
Manchester M20 6HT
Tel: 0161 247 1285
Head of Department *Amanda Wood*
Course Leader *Niamh Dowling*

The school is a member of the Conference of Drama Schools.

COURSE ON OFFER
BA(Hons) Theatre Arts (Acting) (3 years, full-time; NCDT-accredited) *Entry requirements*: normal minimum entry qualifications. *Audition requirements*: for the preliminary audition candidates must prepare three speeches, each one of no more than 2 minutes' duration. One must be by Shakespeare and in verse, one by a contemporary author and one contrasting piece. Successful candidates will be asked to attend a second audition. *Audition fee*: £20. The course is designed for students who intend to work as professional actors.

Middlesex University

White Hart Lane, London N17 8HT
Tel: 0181 362 5000
Fax: 0181 362 5649
E-mail: admissions@mdx.ac.uk

COURSES ON OFFER
BA(Hons) Acting (3 years, full-time)
Run at the Italia Conti Academy of
Theatre Arts. *Entry requirements*:
welcomes a wide variety of educational experience, including A/AS
levels; BTEC National Diploma;
GNVQs, etc. plus successful audition
and interview. An intensive professional actor's degree emphasising
practical acting skills.
**BA(Hons) Drama and Theatre Arts
(with one other subject)** (3 years, full-
time) *Entry requirements*: as above.
**BA(Hons) Drama and Technical
Theatre Arts** (3 years, full-time) *Entry
requirements*: as above.
BA(Hons) Technical Theatre Arts (3
years, full-time) *Entry requirements*: as
above.

Also offers a 3-year degree course in
Theatre Dance which is run at the
London Studio Centre; for programme
details, contact the London Studio
Centre, 42–50 York Way, London N1
9AB (tel: 0171 837 7741) and a 3-year
degree course in **Dance Performance**
which provides professional skills in
dance for small-scale and community
dance performance.

(available as Major; Type A Minor and
Elective Subject) (3 years, full-time)
Entry requirements: all applicants must
satisfy the college's standard course
entry requirements; previous qualifications in Art and Design at A level or
BTEC Diploma in Foundation Studies
in Art and Design are preferred
although not essential.
BA(Hons) Performance Studies (3
years, full-time) *Entry requirements*: all
applicants must satisfy the college's
standard course entry requirements;
applicants would normally be
expected to demonstrate evidence of
previous study or experience in the
area of dance, drama and music. One
of the key aspects of the course is its
programme of performances and
workshops designed to broaden
experience of performance from the
perspective of both the performer and
the spectator.
MA Theatre Studies (2 years, part-
time) *Entry requirements*: usually a first-
or second-class honours degree in a
related subject area. The MA Theatre
Studies course will be of particular
interest to recent graduates in Drama
and Theatre Studies, to practitioners, to
those involved in teaching Drama,
Theatre Studies or Performing Arts at
secondary or tertiary level, and to
those more generally interested in the
contexts, theories and practices of
performance.

Nene College of Higher Education, Northampton

Park Campus, Boughton Green Road,
Northampton NN2 7AL
Tel: 01604 735500
Fax: 01604 720636
E-mail: admissions@nene.ac.uk
Head of Department *George Savona*

COURSES ON OFFER
BA Combined Honours – Drama

Newark and Sherwood College

Friary Road, Newark,
Nottinghamshire NG24 1PB
Tel: 01636 680680
Fax: 01636 680681

COURSES ON OFFER
Theatre Arts Foundation (1 or 2 years,
depending on previous experience)

Entry requirements: no formal qualifications needed but an enthusiasm for the theatre is essential. 'The course is suitable for anyone who wants to have a career in the theatre or as a drama teacher. It is also appropriate for those who want to improve their theatre skills. Many former students have gone on to drama schools and are performing in professional theatre.'

Also offers **A level in Theatre Studies** and **City & Guilds Sound Recording**.

University of North London

Admissions Office,
166–220 Holloway Road,
London N7 8DB
Tel: 0171 735 3355
E-mail: admissions@unl.ac.uk

COURSES ON OFFER
BA(Hons) Performing Arts (3 years, full-time) *Entry requirements*: standard qualifications should include A levels (or equivalent) with grade C or above in one of English, Theatre Studies, Film Studies, Media Studies, Dance or Drama. Those who have completed a BTEC National Diploma or a GNVQ Advanced Diploma in Performing Arts with all Merits or Distinctions are eligible. Mature students lacking formal qualifications are welcome to apply. In addition, applicants must attend an audition consisting of a group workshop and/or a solo piece or interview. Having a strong vocational focus, the course prepares graduates for employment in any of the performing arts, in addition to careers in television, film, radio, journalism and teaching.

Also offers **BA Combined Hons. in Theatre Studies**.

University of Northumbria

Department of Visual and Performing Arts, Lipman Building,
Sandyford Road,
Newcastle upon Tyne NE1 8ST
Tel: 0191 227 3168
Fax: 0191 227 4572
Head of Department *Professor G. Roper*
Contact *Fiona MacPherson*

COURSE ON OFFER
BA(Hons) Drama (3 years, full-time) *Entry requirements*: 2 A levels (BC) or equivalent. *Audition requirements*: all candidates undertake a practical session, comprising a physical and vocal warm-up followed by a workshop led by a drama tutor, after which they will be asked to write a statement concerning the role of the arts in society. They will then lead a short exercise with the rest of the group, suitable for use in a community setting, followed by a 5-minute improvisation or role-play. The degree is designed for students who have an interest in drama in the area of community/alternative theatre and the Department has a policy of encouraging mature and other non-standard applicants. Receives, on average, 600 applications for the course.

'The would-be student should take particular notice of the specific orientation of this course. We do not offer a "traditional" actor training and specialise in the community dimensions of performance and drama facilitation.'

University of Plymouth

Drake Circus, Plymouth, Devon PL4
8AA
Tel: 01752 600600
Fax: 01752 232141
E-mail: ncrocker@plymouth.ac.uk
Website: http://www.plym.ac.uk

COURSES ON OFFER
HND Drama in the Community (2
years, full-time) *Entry requirements*: 3
GCSEs at grade C to include English,
Maths at grade D or equivalent plus
either BTEC National Diploma in
Performing Arts or related area/GCE
A level or AS level to minimum 5
points/GNVQ Level 3/successful
completion of Arts (drama or dance)
access course.
HND Dance in the Community (2
years, full-time) *Entry requirements*: as
above.

Queen Margaret College

Clerwood Terrace, Edinburgh EH12
8TS
Tel: 0131 317 3247
Fax: 0131 317 3248
Website: www.qmced.ac.uk
Head of Department *Professor Ian
Brown*
Professor of Theatre *Clive Perry*

Founded 1971. The Department of
Drama, which is part of a multi-
discipline college, was formed after the
closure of a private school called the
Edinburgh College of Speech and
Drama. The college is a member of the
Conference of Drama Schools.

COURSES ON OFFER
BA(Hons) Acting (4 years, full-time)
Entry requirements: 'motivation, talent
and experience are more important
than formal academic qualifications'.
Candidates are auditioned and inter-

viewed. 'A highly practical and
vocational course for students with the
ability and the desire to become professional actors.'
**BA(Hons) Stage Management and
Theatre Production** (4 years, full-time)
Entry requirements: as above. All candidates are interviewed. Run in conjunction with the Royal Lyceum Theatre in
Edinburgh, the course covers set design,
scenic art and construction, costume
design and wardrobe management,
lighting and sound design and operation, marketing, box-office and front-of-
house management, and all areas of
stage and production management.

University of Reading

Whiteknights, PO Box 217, Reading,
Berkshire RG6 6AH
Tel: 0118 931 8618
Fax: 0118 931 8924
E-mail: ug-prospectus@reading.ac.uk
or: schools.liaison@reading.ac.uk
Website: http/www.reading.ac.uk

COURSES ON OFFER
**BA(Hons) Theatre Arts, Education
and Deaf Culture** (3 years, full-time)
Entry requirements: standard minimum
entry requirements for applicants aged
under 21; above this age, alternative
criteria will be considered. A unique
course open to deaf, hearing and
partially hearing candidates who have
a strong interest in and aptitude for
drama and theatre. A large part of the
course concentrates on the development of the individual student's skills
as a performer while providing training in the teaching and leadership
skills necessary to work within
Theatre-in-Education and community
theatre, with special reference to the
needs of deaf children and/or adults.
BA Film and Drama – *see* Film and
Media Courses, page 60

Roehampton Institute London

Senate House, Roehampton Lane,
London SW15 5PU
Tel: 0181 392 3000
Fax: 0181 392 3131
E-mail: prospectus@roehampton.ac.uk
Website: http://www.roehampton.ac.uk

COURSE ON OFFER
BA Single Honours/BA/BSc Combined Honours Drama and Theatre Studies (3 years, full-time 4–7 years, part-time). *Entry requirements*: looks for A levels in the Arts and Humanities and Social Sciences; GNVQ (Advanced) with distinction and BTEC National Diploma with 3 distinctions in Year 2. The course combines practical and theoretical modes of study, and although the focus of study is on drama in performance, this is not a vocational degree.

Royal Holloway, University of London

Department of Drama, Theatre and Media Arts,
Egham, Surrey TW20 0EX
Tel: 01784 443922
Fax: 01784 437520

COURSES ON OFFER
BA(Hons) Drama and Theatre Studies (3 years, full-time) *Entry requirements*: a foreign language, classical or modern, at GCSE is preferred; three subjects at A level, normally including a pass in Drama and Theatre Studies or English (grade B) and a high pass in at least one other relevant subject. Special consideration is given to mature students. An integrated course, combining elements of dramatic history, theory and practice. Every student participates continually in theoretical and practical workshops, and may devote one entire term to working on a project which produces two experimental or full-scale productions.

MA Drama and Theatre Studies (10 months, full-time/22 months, part-time) *Entry requirements*: good undergraduate degree in Drama and Theatre Studies, English, a foreign language or an arts subject. Other backgrounds and qualifications may also be considered, especially in the case of mature students.

St Mary's University College

Waldegrave Road, Twickenham,
Middlesex TW1 4ST
Tel: 0181 240 4029
Fax: 0181 240 4255
Head of Drama, Media and Theatre Arts *Gerard Boynton, MA, LRAM, LGSM*

The oldest of the Catholic colleges in the United Kingdom, St Mary's was founded in 1850.

COURSES ON OFFER
BA(Hons) Drama (3 years, full-time) *Entry requirements*: usually 2 A levels or equivalent; a qualification in Theatre Studies is an advantage but not essential. As part of the third year, students are able to develop particular interests such as Avant-garde Theatre, American Drama 1920–60, or Chekhov, Stanislavski and Meyerhold.

Combined honours courses, such as **Drama and English** or **Drama and Media Arts**, are also available.

University of Salford
Salford, Greater Manchester M5 4WT
Tel: 0161 295 5000
Fax: 0161 295 5999
Website:
http://www.salford.ac.uk/homepage.html

COURSES ON OFFER
BA(Hons) Performing Arts (2 years or 3 years, full-time) *Entry requirements*: for 2-year course: HND qualification in Performing Arts or equivalent; 3-year course: 5 GCSE/GCE passes including 2 at A level or 4 GCSE/GCE passes including 3 at A level, or equivalent qualifications such as BTEC and foundation diplomas and GNVQs. Focuses on the development of creative performance skills to a professional level and covers theatre performance, TV performance and physical theatre. Modules in Television Acting, Presenting, Television Comedy and Radio Drama, Devised Theatre and Theatre Directing are some of the options available.
BA(Hons) Media and Performance (3 years, full-time) *Entry requirements*: 5 GCSE/GCE passes including 2 at A level, or 4 GCSE/GCE passes including 3 at A level, or equivalent qualifications such as BTEC and foundation diplomas and GNVQs. 'Applicants with talent but without formal entry requirements are encouraged to apply. All students must demonstrate at interview/audition a strong performance ability and interest in TV/radio production.' Equal emphasis is placed on television acting, live theatre and media work.
HND Media Performance (2 years, full-time) *Entry requirements*: 3 GCSE/GCE at grade C or higher and 1 A level, or BTEC National or foundation Diploma or Certificate in Performing Arts or Media, etc. or equivalent GNVQs. All candidates will be interviewed/auditioned. A vocational course focusing on performance training for theatre and television. Students also learn video production skills such as camerawork, scripting, directing and editing.

Trinity College Carmarthen
Carmarthen SA31 3EP
Tel: 01267 237971
Fax: 01267 230933
Head of Theatre Studies *Kevin Matherick BA, MPhil*

COURSE ON OFFER
BA Theatre Studies (3 years, full-time) *Entry requirements*: all applicants must have obtained a minimum of 2 A-level passes or an equivalent qualification in subjects relevant to the course; grade C or above in either English Language or Welsh Language at GCSE level. The course is a combination of theoretical and practical work with modules on Modern European Theatre; Playhouse and Production; Design and Production; Perspectives on Performance and Perspectives on Directing.

University College Chester
Cheyney Road, Chester CH1 4BJ
Tel: 01244 375444
Fax: 01244 373379
E-mail: b.reg@chester.ac.uk
Website: http://www.chester.ac.uk
Head of Drama, Dance and Theatre Studies *Peter Harrop*

The focus is on contemporary drama and theatre in both their 'pure' and 'applied' forms.

COURSES ON OFFER

BA(Hons) Drama and Theatre Studies – Drama Pathway (3 years, full-time) *Entry requirements*: usually grade C at A level in Theatre Studies or a merit profile at BTEC. Candidates may be called for a practical workshop.

BA(Hons) Drama and Theatre Studies – Dance Pathway (3 years, full-time) *Entry requirements*: good A-level pass in Dance or merit profile at BTEC. Candidates are usually required to demonstrate the necessary qualities to pursue the programme through attendance at a practical selection workshop. The course is concerned with current developments in dance performance as well as the broader applications of dance.

Also offers Combined Subjects degrees.

University College of Ripon and York St John
Lord Mayor's Walk,
York YO3 7EX
Tel: 01904 616850
Fax: 01904 612512

COURSES ON OFFER

BA(Hons) Drama: Performance and Communication Arts (3 years, full-time) *Entry requirements*: all applicants must satisfy the college's general course entry requirements.

BA(Hons) Dance: Performance and Communication Arts (3 years, full-time) *Entry requirements*: as above.

BA(Hons) Specialist Scheme – Film, TV, Literature and Theatre Studies – *see* Film and Media Courses, page 60

University College of St Martin
Bowerham Road, Lancaster LA1 3JD
Tel: 01524 384444
Fax: 01524 384567
E-mail: admissions@ucsm.ac.uk
Head of Department *Dr Richard McGregor*
Contact *Alison Bolton (Assistant Registrar)*

COURSES ON OFFER

BA(Hons) Performing Arts, with main option in Drama (3 years, full-time) *Entry requirements*: GCE A level (CC or CDE); BTEC (3 merits and 2 distinctions in full final-year units); GNVQ (Advance pass at merit); all subjects considered. *Audition requirements*: a short speech of approximately 3 minutes which shows the candidate's potential as a performer. The speech can be classical or modern and may include music or dance. A formal interview will follow.

BA(Joint Hons) in Drama, with main options in English, Applied Community Studies, Health Studies, History, Art, Design, Business and Management Studies, Social Ethics (3 years, full-time) *Entry/Audition requirements*: as above.

'Current drama courses within the Performing Arts degree have been developed from drama courses in the Modular Studies programme at UCSM. The philosophy of the Department is to integrate practical expertise with sound theoretical knowledge of drama and theatre. First- and second-year Performing Arts courses are taken in combination with Music and Dance. Within the Modular Studies programme Drama can be studied in conjunction with various other subjects.'

University of Ulster

Faculty of Humanities, Cromore Road,
Coleraine, Co. Londonderry BT52 1SA
Tel: 01265 44141 ext 4391
E-mail: fa.agnew@ulst.ac.uk
Faculty Administrative Officer *Felix Agnew MA, BD*

COURSE ON OFFER
BA(Hons) Theatre Studies (3 years, full-time) *Entry requirements*: typically, A level – CCC grades. Mature applicants are usually interviewed. Twenty places are available on this course which is designed to ensure an adequate grounding in experience of presentation and performance on which further analytical and professional studies may be based. 'The course stresses particular strengths which derive from its location in Irish and Ulster cultural traditions and accordingly offers study in areas where theatre and the arts serve the community and reflect its need.'

University of Wales, Aberystwyth

Department of Theatre, Film and Television Studies, 1 Laura Place, Aberyswyth, Ceredigion SY23 2AU
Tel: 01970 622828
Fax: 01970 622831
E-mail: drawww@aber.ac.uk
Head of Department *Professor Ioan M. Williams, MA BLitt Oxon, PhD Wales*
Contact *Nick Strong (Administrative Coordinator)*

One of the largest Theatre Studies departments in the UK. Receives between 600 and 700 applications annually. The BA in Theatre Studies, BA in Film and Television Studies and the MA in Theatre, Film and Television Studies are also available through the medium of Welsh. The MA in Television Studies is offered in conjunction with other Departments.

COURSES ON OFFER
BA in Theatre Studies (3 years, full-time) *Entry requirements*: BCC at A level; applications also welcomed from candidates completing BTEC, GNVQ or access course. These candidates are usually interviewed. The degree is based on a modular system giving students a wide range of choice, allowing them to put together a scheme of study which meets their individual needs.
BA in Film and Television Studies (3 years, full-time) *Entry requirements*: as above. Modular course structure, as above.
MA Theatre, Film and Television Studies (1 year, full-time) *Entry requirements*: formal qualifications may not be necessary provided the candidate can show evidence of relevant work experience. 'Designed to develop students' understanding of the process of analysis and interpretation of theatrical and film texts beyond the point which it is possible to reach within the framework of the initial degree.'
MA Theatre and the World (1 year, full-time) *Entry requirements*: as for MA above.
MA in Television Studies (1 year, full-time) *Entry requirements*: usually a good grade in the candidate's first degree, but appropriate experience is also taken into account. 'Seeks to develop a critical understanding of television and has been welcomed by the television industry in Wales.'

University of Wolverhampton

Division of Drama, SHASS,
Castle View, Dudley,
West Midlands DY1 3HR
Tel: 01902 323400
Fax: 01902 32779
Head of Department *Dr James Stredder*

COURSE ON OFFER
BA (Modular Degree and Diploma Scheme) Theatre Studies/Drama in association with a wide range of other subjects (3 years, full-time) *Entry requirements*: GCSE passes should be in English; post-16 qualifications can be in any subjects. Theatre Studies emphasises the acquisition of critical and practical theatre skills. The programme includes Theatre-in-Education and in the community and television drama, as well as providing a general study of theatrical practice and dramatic literature.

'This course is a good preparation for a wide range of careers in the arts. We send a few students on to drama schools; the course can put you in a strong position for a successful audition and a degree is clearly a good "insurance" for all potential actors.'

Film and Media
Courses

AFECT (Advancement of Film Education Charitable Trust)

Lavina Grove Studios, 16–20
Wharfdale Road, King's Cross,
London N1 9RY
Tel: 0171 837 1736
Contact *Jeremy Ross (Principal),*
4 Stanley Buildings, Pancras Road,
London NW1 2TD, tel: 0171 837 5473

Offers a 2-year, part-time 16mm-film-making course to provide practical film-making education to professional standards for those who may have neither the time, money, nor inclination to attend full-time film school. The course is roughly divided into Beginners and Intermediate stages and students must successfully complete the first part before continuing on to the second. Successive courses overlap and may start up to three times a year; enquire about starting times. A third-year, semi-independent project is being introduced. *Entry requirements*: evidence of interest ('prefer applicants who have got their hands dirty'), an ability to attend regularly and cooperate with others. The aims of the trust, whose patron is Mike Leigh, are 'to spread practical knowledge of this medium on a wider basis than hitherto, and to encourage personal and independent rather than corporate or "commercial" expression'.

The American College in London

110 Marylebone High Street,
London W1M 3DB
Tel: 0171 486 1772
Fax: 0171 935 8144

COURSES ON OFFER
BA Video Production (with options in Music Video, Commercial Video and Documentary Video) (4 years – an accelerated programme is available by which students may earn their degree more quickly). The course teaches 'the technical skills and concepts necessary to prepare students for a career in the video field'.

ARTTS International (Advanced Residential Theatre and Television Skillcentre)

– *see* Drama Schools, page 16

Barking College
Dagenham Road, Romford,
Essex RM7 0XU
Tel: 01708 766841
Fax: 01708 731067
Principal *Ted Parker*
Contact *John McDermott*

COURSES ON OFFER
BTEC National Diploma Media (2 years, full-time) *Entry requirements*: 4 GCSEs, grade C or above and a demonstrable commitment to the subject. Experience in one of the core subjects is an advantage but not essential. Mature students welcome. Designed for those seeking a career in the media industry, the course is broad-based and provides knowledge, skills and an understanding of the profession.

Access to Media (1 year, two evenings per week) *Entry requirements*: applicants should have suitable communication skills and should demonstrate a willingness to develop these further. No prior knowledge or experience of media is required. A vocational course in media, communications and new technology which prepares students for higher education.

Also offers **GCE A-level Film Studies**.

Bournemouth and Poole College of Art and Design
Wallisdown, Poole, Dorset BG12 5HH
Tel: 01202 533011
Fax: 01202 537729

One of the largest colleges in the UK specialising in art, design and media.

COURSES ON OFFER
BTEC Higher National Diploma in Film and Television Production (2 years, full-time)

Entry requirements: 4 GCSE passes at grade C or above plus 1 A level or appropriate BTEC Diploma or a GNVQ Advanced (Level 3) or satisfactory completion of a foundation course or approved commercial/industrial experience. A portfolio of work is also required. The course gives an opportunity to develop to a professional level of production. Students learn the traditional technical craft skills as well as scriptwriting, production and direction.

BTEC National Diploma in Audio-visual Production (2 years, full-time) *Entry requirements*: 4 GCSE passes at grade C or above plus 1 A level or appropriate BTEC Diploma or a GNVQ Intermediate (Level 2). A portfolio of work is also required. The course provides a foundation for those wishing to pursue a career in film and television.

BTEC Professional Development Diploma in Film Production (1 year, full-time) *Entry requirements*: a degree in a relevant subject area (upper second-class honours or above); BTEC HND (with merit or distinction grades in a minimum of five units); equivalent HE qualification from an overseas institution; substantial professional experience. A unique postgraduate intensive course in production which aims to provide students with the opportunity of making their first feature film. Nine to 15 places are available on the programme, divided between writers, directors and producers.

Brunel University
Uxbridge, Middlesex UB8 3PH
Tel: 01895 274000
Fax: 01895 232806

COURSES ON OFFER
BA Film and Television Studies (3

years, full-time; part-time option available) *Entry requirements*: preferred A-level subjects are Media Studies or Film and Television Studies or equivalent. The course, which can be taken as a single or combined honours programme, offers an opportunity to study film and television and other related media.

Central Saint Martins College of Art and Design

Southampton Row,
London WC1B 4AP
Tel: 0171 514 7015
Fax: 0171 514 7016
E-mail: shortcourse@cstm.co.uk
Website: www.csm-li.co.uk

Offers a selection of evening and Saturday courses in the following: **Making, Editing, Producing Video; Video Animation Workshop; Introduction to 16mm Film-making; Working in Low-budget Films.** All the classes are kept small, with between 10 and 20 students on most. Brochure available from the above address.

Goldsmiths' College, University of London

New Cross, London SE14 6NW
Tel: 0171 919 7171
Fax: 0171 919 7113
E-mail: admissions@gold.ac.uk
Website: http://www.gold.ac.uk/
Warden *Professor Kenneth Gregory, PhD, DSc, FRGS*
Contact *Media and Communications Dept: 0171 919 7600*

COURSES ON OFFER

BA(Hons) in Media and Communications (3 years, full-time) *Entry requirements*: A levels or various qualifications including AS levels, access

courses, GNVQs and BTEC. Candidates will be expected to demonstrate practical experience in some aspect of creative work.

MA in Television Drama (1 year, full-time) *Entry requirements*: normally a good first degree and a level of practical experience, or, as a non-graduate, relevant practical experience and able to demonstrate an ability to undertake work at Master's level. In addition to the television production component, students study the work of different playwrights and directors, examining the construction of drama narrative.

MA in Television Documentary (1 year, full-time) *Entry requirements*: as above.

MA in Radio (1 year, full-time) *Entry requirements*: normally a good first degree and a level of practical experience and able to demonstrate an ability to undertake work at Master's level.

University of Huddersfield

Queensgate, Huddersfield,
West Yorkshire HD1 3DH
Tel: 01484 478414
Fax: 01484 47828
E-mail: d.calladine@hud.ac.uk
Website: http://www.hud.ac.uk/schools/music+humanities/media/welcome.html
Contact *D. Calladine*

COURSE ON OFFER

BA(Hons) Media (3 years, full-time) *Entry requirements*: in addition to general entry requirements, an A level or equivalent in English, Communication Studies, Media Studies, Sociology or Theatre Studies would be an advantage. With options in Radio Journalism, Print Journalism and Television Production, the course provides a detailed study of the mass media. There is also the chance to develop specific skills in particular forms of media production.

King Alfred's University College Winchester

Winchester, Hampshire SO22 4NR
Tel: 01962 841515
Fax: 01962 842280

COURSES ON OFFER
BA(Hons) Media and Film Studies (3 years, full-time) *Entry requirements*: GCSE A–C pass (or equivalent) in English Language; minimum of 2 GCE A-level passes; BTEC National Diploma/Certificate; GNVQ Advanced level with merit; or equivalent. The course is distinguished by a combination of general courses in the media with a distinctive range of courses in film (including Hollywood, Third World and Black British Cinema) and broadcasting (especially television studies).

Also offers BA/BSc Combined Honours courses.

London College of Printing and Distributive Trades (LCPDT), London Institute (School of Media)

Back Hill, Clerkenwell, London EC1R 5EN
Tel: 0171 514 6500
Dean *Stuart Bartholomew*
Contact *Des McCarthy (Senior Lecturer)*

The LCPDT School of Media Studies has strong links with professional practitioners in broadcasting and media production, and it has been able to exploit its central London location.

COURSES ON OFFER
BA(Hons) Film and Video (3 years, full-time) *Entry requirements*: 2 A levels and 3 GCSEs (A–C) of which 2 must be English and Maths plus portfolio of work to demonstrate an ability to succeed in a specialist area. Theory and practice are integrated. Throughout the course students are involved in productions, with technical and practical instruction given through workshops, complemented by group tutorials.
MA Film and Video Production (1 year, full-time) *Entry requirements*: graduates with experience of film and video; portfolio of work. An advanced production-based course which seeks to encourage innovative approaches in contemporary film and video.

London Guildhall University

Communications Area, Sir John Cass School of Art, 31 Jewry Street, London EC3N 2EY
Tel: 0171 320 3001
Fax: 0171 320 3009
Head of Department *M. Hunt*
Contact *Mo Dodson (Subject Leader)*

COURSE ON OFFER
BA(Hons) Communications and Audio-visual Production Studies (3 years, full-time) *Entry requirements*: A levels (BCC); non-standard entry qualifications. The course gives students the opportunity to gain practical experience of a wide range of media skills, utilising TV, radio, photography and video, complemented by a base of theoretical studies.

London International Film School

24 Shelton Street, London WC2H 9HP
Tel: 0171 836 9642/240 0168
Fax: 0171 497 3718
E-mail: lifs@dial.pipex.com
Website:
http://www.tecc.co.uk/lifs/index.html
Principal *Martin M. Amstell*
Contact *Chrissy Bright (Librarian)*

One of the oldest film schools in the world, the present school came into being in 1975. Notable graduates include directors Bill Douglas, Mike Leigh, Frank Roddam and Les Blair, and producers Mark Forstater and Iain Smith. LIFS does not accept students to become specialists. While interest and ability may lead individuals to specialise later, students are expected to gain an all-round understanding of the process involved so that they may be better film-makers. There is an emphasis on group activity because films 'cannot be made by individuals working in isolation, only by "units" of people pooling their skills and working together as a coherent team'.

COURSE ON OFFER
Diploma Course (2 years, full-time) *Entry requirements*: no absolute educational qualifications are required. All candidates must submit a script for a short film of about 3 minutes in length, plus a written critique of a film they have seen recently. Any relevant experience is also valuable. *Application fee*: £25. The syllabus is made up of the basic principles for film-makers: scripting and planning, organisation and production, directing and acting, photography, lenses, camera, lighting and special effects, animation and titling, projection and presentation, editing, sound, music, art and design, make-up and wardrobe, film analysis and appreciation, written work and tests, plus a dissertation on a subject related to cinema.

Middlesex University

White Hart Lane,
London N17 8HT
Tel: 0181 362 5000
Fax: 0181 362 5649
E-mail: admissions@mdx.ac.uk

COURSE ON OFFER
BA(Hons) Film Studies (with one other subject) (3 years, full-time) *Entry requirements*: standard – A/AS levels, BTEC National Diploma, GNVQs. 'Cultural and social issues in film are studied alongside the practical conditions of production, distribution and reception.'

National Film and Television School

Beaconsfield Studios,
Station Road, Beaconsfield,
Buckinghamshire HP9 1LG
Tel: 01494 671234
Fax: 01494 674042
E-mail: ajones@fts.win-uk.net
Director *Henning Camre*
Contact *Central Administration*

Founded 1971. The NFTS is funded 50 per cent by the Government and 50 per cent by the industry and is world-renowned as a national centre of excellence. The school has a distinguished list of alumni, including Bill Forsyth (*Gregory's Girl, Local Hero*), Nick Park (*Wallace and Gromit*), Andrjez Sekula (*Reservoir Dogs, Pulp Fiction*), Stephen Bayly (*Richard III*), Michael Caton-Jones (*Rob Roy*). Prospectus available. The impending move to Ealing Studios will maximise the development of new digital media education and production in conjunction with the industry. The NFTS Ealing Studios will house the new Creative Media Arts and Technologies Centre (CREATEC).

COURSES ON OFFER
Animation Direction; Cinematography; Documentary Direction; Editing; Fiction Direction; Producing; Screen Design; Screen Music; Screen Sound; Screen Writing; Screen Studies. All the courses (with the exception of the 2-year Screenwriting and Screen Music courses) are 3 years, full-time. No previous degree course will give applicants automatic access but candidates need to demonstrate a knowledge of basic skills in practice and theory within their specialist areas, talent, commitment and the ability to work collaboratively. Average age of students on these courses, which are designed for people who already have some experience and/or training in their specialisation, is 25.

Nene College of Higher Education, Northampton

Park Campus, Boughton Green Road, Northampton NN2 7AL
Tel: 01604 735500
Fax: 01604 720636
E-mail: admissions@nene.ac.uk

COURSE ON OFFER
HND Media (Practice and Production) (2 years, full-time) *Entry requirements*: all applicants must satisfy the college's standard course entry requirements. The course aims to equip students with the skills and background theoretical and technical knowledge required for a career in the media.

University of North London

Admissions Office, 166–220 Holloway Road, London N7 8DB
Tel: 0171 735 3355
E-mail: admissions@unl.ac.uk

COURSE ON OFFER
BA Combined Hons. (Major, Joint, Minor) Film Studies (3 years, full-time/4 or more years, part-time/4 years if taken with a language as Major or Joint) *Entry requirements*: as well as standard entry qualifications, the subject normally demands, for A-level entry, B and C in, preferably, Film Studies and/or related subject areas. Having only a limited vocational focus, the course cannot be guaranteed to give entry into either television or film industries but it should be of particular interest to those who, having acquired practical experience of film, wish to augment this with a more academic and theoretical approach to the subject.

Northern School of Film and Television

Leeds Metropolitan University, School of Art, Architecture and Design, 2 Queen Square, Leeds, West Yorkshire LS2 8AF
Tel: 0113 283 1900
Fax: 0113 283 1901
E-mail: nsftv@lmu.ac.uk
Website: http://www.lmu.ac.uk
Head of School *Ian Macdonald*

The NSFTV, which opened in 1990, is a small postgraduate professional film school within the Faculty of Design and the Built Environment of Leeds Metropolitan University. The school focuses on drama, specialising in fiction production on film only. Sponsorship by Yorkshire Tyne Tees

Television has provided most of the school's production costs, and UK television rights in a number of graduate productions have been purchased by YTV.

COURSES ON OFFER
Postgraduate Diploma and MA in Film Production (Fiction) (1-year, full-time for Diploma, plus 1-year extension for MA) *Entry requirements*: a first degree, or substantial experience of production for those who may not have a degree or formal qualifications.

Also offers a **Postgraduate Diploma and MA in Screenwriting (Fiction)**.

Plymouth College of Art and Design

Tavistock Place, Plymouth,
Devon PL4 8AT
Tel: 01752 385959
Fax: 01752 385977
Programme Manager *Bryan Preston*

COURSE ON OFFER
Advanced Diploma in Photography, Film and Television (1 year, full-time) *Entry requirements*: candidates should normally be 20 years of age or over; BTEC HND in a related discipline or a first degree, or professional/industrial experience. Applicants with less formal qualifications are also encouraged to apply. The course gives students the opportunity to develop their chosen specialism and make the transition from student to professional practitioner. Those who successfully complete the programme are awarded Associateship of the British Institute of Professional Photography.

University of Plymouth

Drake Circus, Plymouth,
Devon PL4 8AA
Tel: 01752 600600
Fax: 01752 232141
E-mail: ncrocker@plymouth.ac.uk
Website: http://www.plym.ac.uk

COURSE ON OFFER
BA(Hons) Media Arts (3 years, full-time) *Entry requirements*: usually 3 A-level passes. In the first year, students gain a broad practical working knowledge of media practices; in year two, practical projects are undertaken with the students selecting their own subject and medium; in the final year a personal collaborative project is developed, ranging from fiction films or documentary videos to photographic portfolios or Internet projects.

Ravensbourne College of Design and Communication

School of Broadcasting, Walden Road,
Chislehurst, Kent BR7 5SN
Tel: 0181 325 8323
Fax: 0181 325 8323
E-mail: short.courses@rave.ac.uk
Website:
http/www.rave.ac.uk/shortcourses/

COURSES ON OFFER
Single Camera Production, Single Operator Recording; Basic TV Programme Operations, Advanced Multi-Camera Directing – short courses of 2–5 days. Full details of courses and fees available from the School of Broadcasting, Short Course Unit.

University of Reading
Whiteknights, PO Box 217, Reading,
Berkshire RG6 6AH
Tel: 0118 931 8618
Fax: 0118 931 8924
E-mail: ug-prospectus@reading.ac.uk
or: schools.liaison@reading.ac.uk
Website: http/www reading.ac.uk
Admissions Tutor *Brian Wolland*
(0118 931 8878)

The degree on offer is unusual as the combination of film and drama is still not widely available in universities. 'The development of cinema and television as dominating institutions has made it increasingly difficult to confine discussion of drama to theatre alone.'

COURSES ON OFFER
BA Film and Drama (3 years, full-time) *Entry requirements*: 'We are looking for students who show evidence of a real interest and enthusiasm for film, drama and television, even if they have not had the opportunity to study the subject at GCSE or A level. Some thirty films and videos are produced by students each year as part of their studies and about twenty drama productions are mounted by staff and students.'

Also offers an **MA in Film and Drama** course (1 year, full-time/2 years, part-time).

University College of Ripon and York St John
Lord Mayor's Walk, York YO3 7EX
Tel: 01904 616850
Fax: 01904 612512

COURSE ON OFFER
BA(Hons) Specialist Scheme – Film, TV, Literature and Theatre Studies (3 years, full-time) *Entry requirements*: most applicants offer A levels but other qualifications are welcome. The course offers a chance to study those subjects that are closely related and complementary.

Yorkshire Tyne Tees Television provides two bursaries to Year 1 students who are from ethnic backgrounds, currently under-represented in the broadcasting industry.

Roehampton Institute London
Senate House,
Roehampton Lane,
London SW15 5PU
Tel: 0181 392 3000
Fax: 0181 392 3131
E-mail: prospectus@roehampton.ac.uk
Website: http://www.roehampton.ac.uk

COURSE ON OFFER
BA (Single Honours)/BA/BSc (Combined Honours) Film and Television Studies (3 years, full-time 4–7 years, part-time). *Entry requirements*: minimum of 16 points at A level, including a B in Film Studies, Media Studies, English, History or another nominated subject; or equivalent qualifications. 'This programme enables you to study in depth the cultural significance of the moving image; a process that will involve research, debate, discussion, analysis and a practical engagement with the processes of production itself.'

Royal College of Art
Kensington Gore, London SW7 2EU
Tel: 0171 590 4444
Fax: 0171 590 4500
E-mail: admissions@rca.ac.uk

COURSES ON OFFER
MA/MPhil/PhD Film and Television (2 years, full-time) *Entry requirements*:

candidates should be over 21 and hold an undergraduate degree or equivalent qualification. Candidates are required to send portfolios of recent work. 'The aim of the course is to provide facilities and teaching to create the maximum opportunity for students to develop their individual talents, to nurture future leaders of the film and television industry.' Includes specialisms in Cinematography; Design for Film and Television; Direction – Film and TV Drama; Documentary – Film and TV; Editing; Production; Screenwriting; Sound Design. Successful graduates of the course include Paula Milne, Giles Foster, Thaddeus O'Sullivan and Ridley Scott.

MA(RCA) Animation (2 years, full-time) *Entry requirements*: applicants will normally be expected to have a degree in Art and Design. Approximately 11 students are selected each year. Research degrees in animation may be studied to MPhil or PhD.

NB The courses are currently under review and may be revised.

University of Salford

Salford, Greater Manchester M5 4WT
Tel: 0161 295 5000
Fax: 0161 295 5999
Website:
http://www.salford.ac.uk/homepage.html

COURSES ON OFFER
BA(Hons) Television and Radio (3 years, full-time) *Entry requirements*: all candidates are interviewed after passing a test by post and a questionnaire on the day of interview; 22 points at A level or 6 distinctions in final year of BTEC National Diploma. An enterprising course attuned to the needs of the broadcast industries and designed in consultation with major figures in those industries. The degree is modular, which enables students to choose those areas which best suit their talents and abilities.

HND Media Production (2 years, full-time) *Entry requirements*: one GCE A level in a relevant subject plus a written test before interview, or BTEC National Diploma. Mature students without the necessary entry requirements, but with prior experience, are encouraged to apply. About 70 per cent of the course is practical, involving the making of a variety of television and radio productions in the roles of producer, director, researcher, camera, sound recordist and editor.

Also offers a 1-year course for **MA Postgraduate Diploma in Television Documentary and Features**.

Surrey Institute of Art and Design

Falkner Road, Farnham,
Surrey GU9 7DS
Tel: 01252 722441
Fax: 01252 733869
E-mail: registry@surrart.ac.uk
Principal *Norman Taylor*
Contact *Sue Drury (Administrative Assistant, Registry Services)*

The Surrey Institute of Art and Design is one of Europe's largest independent colleges specialising in art, design and communication. Receives approximately 840 applications per year for the BA(Hons) Film and Video programme.

COURSES ON OFFER
BA(Hons) Film and Video (3 years, full-time/5 years, part-time) *Entry requirements*: appropriate A levels or GNVQs or equivalent qualification. Develops the students' creative and practical abilities in the production of film and video as well as an under-

standing of the social and historical context of production.

BA(Hons) Animation (3 years, full-time/5 years, part-time) *Entry requirements*: as above. Brings together the traditional techniques such as narrative, drawing and construction with aspects of new technology, interactive media and electronic imaging.

MA(Hons) Film and Video (1 year, full-time/2 years, part-time) *Entry requirements*: an honours degree in a relevant subject area or alternative qualifications.

MA(Hons) Animation (1 year, full-time/2 years, part-time) *Entry requirements*: as above.

University of Wales College, Newport

Caerleon Campus, PO Box 179, Newport NP6 1YG
Tel: 01633 432077
Fax: 01633 432037
E-mail: uic@newport.ac.uk
Website: www.newport.ac.uk
Head of Admissions *Karen Fishlock*

COURSES ON OFFER
BA(Hons) Film and Video (3 years, full-time) *Entry requirements*: A levels: 6 points; BTEC National Diploma: merits/distinctions; GNVQ Advanced: pass. Combines technical tuition with a comprehensive understanding and appreciation of film language and culture. Students can specialise in documentary natural-history film-making.

BA(Hons) Animation (3 years, full-time) *Entry requirements*: as above. The course is intended for those who want to become professional animators working in broadcasting, advertising or the independent sector of the animation industry.

MA Film (1 year, full-time) With 10 places available, this is a professional film-production course in which entry is based upon a proposed film project or script. Aims to support and develop the skills required in the production of a completed short film directed at public exhibition. Course modules include theoretical and historical study, advanced film workshops and masterclasses in directing.

University of Westminster

Harrow Campus Studios, Northwick Park, Harrow, Middlesex HA1 3TP
Tel: 0171 911 5000
Fax: 0171 911 5939
Production Tutors *Maria Hannon, Joost Hunningher, Joram Ten Brink*

The university is an active member of the Centre International de Liaison des Ecoles de Cinéma et Télévision, the National Association of Higher Education in Film and Video, the European Society for the History of Photography, and the Association of Degree Courses in Photography.

COURSES ON OFFER
BA(Hons) in Film, Photography and Digital Arts (3 years, full-time) *Entry requirements*: 5 O levels, at least 2 good A levels, 'ability' and a portfolio of scripts or VHS films, or photographs. The course offers a range of specialised and combined-option pathways, each relating to contemporary professional opportunities.

BA(Hons) in Media Studies (3 years, full-time) *Entry requirements*: as above. 'The intensive teaching of practical skills in print, radio and television is designed to provide a prelude to future professional work in the media.'

MA Film and Television Studies (2 to 5 years, part-time, evenings) *Entry requirements*: a good first degree from a British university or equivalent qualification. Mature applicants may also be admitted on the basis of non-academic knowledge or experience. 'Recognised as the leading course of its kind in the UK and probably in Europe.

'Many of the films made in the university's broadcast studios are sent to film festivals and often win prizes. The Film and Video Department welcomes photographs from actors. These are displayed for casting sessions. Please make sure contact numbers are on the back of the photographs.'

Representation

The
Personal Manager
Bruna Zanelli

Congratulations. You are now an actor. The third-year showcase is over and the audience loved you. Agents flocked around you, handing you their business cards, pressing you to join their agency.

But if this was not the case, you are still an actor and actors need agents. Of course, you could survive without an agent but the going would be ever more tough. This is the most overpopulated and frequently underpaid profession of all, and as an inexperienced actor you definitely require the services of a tried and respected agency to start you on the uphill climb to the dizzy heights to which you aspire.

First, no matter how desperate you feel, I advise you not to accept the first offer. Choosing your agent is to be possibly the most important decision you will have to make for a long time, so you want to be certain it is the right one.

An agent – client relationship is like a marriage. You have to like and trust each other because hopefully you are going to be together for a very long time (I have known several of my clients for twenty years and more) but this will not happen if you cannot talk frankly and even share a laugh. Your agent will be there to support and advise, to guide your career and nurse you along when jobs are thin on the ground. He or she will always be at the end of the telephone, but do not infringe upon their personal time, in the evenings and at weekends. Even agents have private lives. While in the office, your agent will give you 200 per cent of their time, so allow them a breather and except for emergencies, never call them at home.

What your agent is not is a worker of miracles. He or she will open the door for you but it is up to you to walk through and up the stairs. Try not to make the old mistake of blaming your agent for your failures or when things go quiet as they will from time to time. Your agent wants you to work. Needs you to work. After all, if you do not work, your agent will not eat. It is not in our interest to keep clients out of work. We want you all to work 365 days of the year and more if possible.

When approaching agents, I suggest you write a simple, straight-to-the-point letter, nothing too informal, and be certain to spell the agent's name correctly. Enclose a good 10 x 8 head shot – preferably one that resembles you and not some old 1940s movie star – together with a printed cv, enclosing a stamped addressed label.

Before meeting your prospective agent, do some research so that you know something about the agency. Be businesslike and confident. You will probably be nervous but there is no need. We are all human, honest! Try to relax and enjoy the meeting. Give a clear account of your hopes and desires. Some agencies have a contractual agreement which involves the client signing a contract binding them to the agency for a specified term. This may appear to offer security but if you happen to want to leave before that specified term, you may be asked to buy yourself out of the agreement.

Rates of commission differ widely. It is no longer the legendary 10 per cent. Some agencies charge 12 per cent, 15 per cent or even 20 per cent and if you are offered a personal management deal, the commission can be 25 per cent. Do not be afraid to ask questions if you do not fully understand any point in the conversation. No one is trying to trick you.

So you have done the rounds, met several agents and after careful thought you have made your decision. You are now set for stardom!

But what does your new agent expect from you? Speaking for myself, I demand total honesty and loyalty if we are going to work together and be successful.

Many actors, when they come to see me about representation, complain that they get all their own work and resent paying commission to their current agent who by their account does nothing for them. Let me try to explain something important: when an actor joins an agency he becomes that agency's responsibility, so all enquiries about him must come through the agency. If any contact be made direct to the actor, he should pass that information immediately to his agent who will deal with it on his behalf. Actors should never discuss fees. To haggle about money only causes embarrassment when you start work with the director/producer. Let your agent do the haggling for you. It is what we are trained to do and we are better at it than any actor, no matter what the actor may believe. Negotiating contracts is one of the reasons you pay commission. But only one. You pay also for their experience and expertise, for their time and patience and knowledge of the business you have just entered.

If, for some reason, you find yourself dissatisfied, please talk to your agent. Do not allow any problem to develop beyond the point of no return. Talk it over and more often than not the problem can be solved to your mutual satisfaction. However, if you decide it is time to move on, have the courtesy to tell your agent face to face. He will have worked to the best of his ability on your behalf and will naturally be disappointed that the fruits of his endeavours will now go to another agent but it is better for all concerned to part amicably. You may find you are unhappy in your move away and even want to return. Always leave doors open. Older, more experienced actors are frequently quoting that old chestnut: 'Changing agents is like changing deckchairs on the *Titanic*.' There is much wisdom in those nine words. Remember them.

But what if you have chosen the wrong agent? He may be a total waste of time who never sets up interviews for you and is forever complaining 'It's very quiet at the moment'. If, after a further six months, things do not improve, move on. Things are never that quiet.

Finally, if your agent decides to let you go, it will be because he has tried every avenue without success. This will not necessarily be a reflection on your potential. It can be for numerous reasons and sometimes when a career has gone stale, a change of representation can be just the kick it needs to restart it. What you must not do is take it as a personal rejection. In our business, rejection is commonplace and rarely personal. Move on to the next agent. With her different list of contacts, she may reinvent you into the new George Clooney or Helen Mirren.

What you must always do is keep the faith. Believe in yourself regardless of the knockbacks. You have chosen this profession and it can be the toughest master of all but when things go right it is sheer magic. Remember always you are a talented and gifted individual who gives boundless pleasure to audiences. Remember – you are an actor!

Good luck!

Bruna Zanelli, born in London of Italian parents, entered the business as a secretary. An agent for the past twenty years, she has represented and guided the careers of many well-known actors who regularly appear in theatre, films, television and commercials. Alongside her life as an agent, she is also a writer.

The
Cooperative Agency
Christopher Webber

The relationship between actor and agent is often more a battle than a partnership. The brutal fact is that most agents, those who are not in the charmed circle of eternal employment, are limited in what they can achieve for their clients. They conscientiously scan the trade journals and keep their contacts sweet. They tread water when it comes to the subtler strategy of managing a client's career. But, in the end, actors get most of their own work and can soon get to resent giving $12^1/_2$ per cent of their earnings (plus VAT) to a shady phantom who rarely if ever comes up with the goods. They do not like the graveyard silence as they wait for the phone to ring. Even less do they appreciate the chilling brush-offs when they finally steel themselves to call up the dead: 'Nothing out there at the moment, dear, I've never known it so slow.' Worse: 'Can't speak now, just finalising that sitcom contract for I. M. Famous, I'll ring you, darling.' Worst: 'Who are you?' No wonder the modern actor tends to float desperately from one agency marriage to the next; and after the honeymoon period he'll likely feel no better off than before.

Imagine instead a scenario in which the actor doubles as agent. Where he has the choice of which work he's put up for. Where disapproval reigns only if he doesn't phone in nearly every day. Where commission rates are lower and don't attract the dreaded VAT. Impossible? Not quite.

Actors' cooperatives emerged back in the halcyon Old Labour days of the seventies when there were grants for everything, be it loft conversion, treatment for rising damp, or even self-help agenting. The idea was simple. A group of about twenty actors would band together to act as agents for one another. If you weren't working and paying commission, you contributed by manning the office for so many days a month as necessary. Profits were ploughed back into the business, the resultant charity status and tax exemptions were good news – 10 per cent commission and no VAT reads a lot better than $12^1/_2$ per cent plus.

This is more or less how the established brand leaders, such as The Actors' Exchange or Actorum, came into the world. It's more or less how they function today, together with hosts of enthusiastic and often successful imitators. Numbers are kept manageable. As one actor leaves, another is found to fill the gap by rigorous interviews, trial days working in the office and of course talent-spotting (though auditioning would-be members is considered bad form). Not all actors are blessed with admin as well as thespian talent, so co-ops are not for everyone. Still, there's no doubt that for many, especially young actors wet from college, co-ops are a highly viable, often a preferred option. If nothing else, no actor with co-op experience is ever going to underestimate how difficult the business of agenting really is.

Co-ops are not mini-utopias, but hands-on experience of the market, and those lower commission rates are real advantages. Best of all, an actor can enjoy the self-respect of handling his own work without putting himself on the line – because of course there's always a colleague to suggest him for jobs or negotiate contracts, with the co-op's name behind them. Being in business with other professionals provides effective personal support, and sympathetic advice is always close at hand. It can give enormous satisfaction, too, to help get a job for a colleague or complete a successful pay negotiation.

This is not to suggest that Woolly Idealism Rules OK. A good co-op is as businesslike and pragmatic as any other personal management, and often far more efficient. It has to be. A handful of well-established casting directors are far from co-op friendly. Some are simply prejudiced, mistakenly believing that co-ops are only for actors who can't get a 'proper' agent. Others understandably don't like the lottery of not knowing who they'll be speaking to if they ring up for casting suggestions. The agency office has to be manned by different people every day, so it's undeniable that co-ops can't cultivate the one-to-one relations that create trust between casting director and agent. Instead they have to try hard to perfect streamlined office systems geared to clear communication (computerisation helps) and be more professional than the professionals. Progress here is slow. Some co-ops are as unreliable as some agents, and it's all too tempting for casting directors to tar the lot with the same brush.

Despite this, for most actors membership of an established co-op is at least as good a bet as the average sole agent. True, co-ops can't easily accommodate 'stars' – putting intensive time and effort into I. M. Famous's career at the expense of the other nineteen or so members is difficult to justify, and a suddenly successful co-op actor can be made to feel too demanding or egotistical. Then there are the usual drawbacks of Rule by Committee – sluggish decision-making, consensus fudges and overemphasis on the minutiae of office procedures at the expense of long-term strategy. True also, film work is particularly hard to come by when you're up against the 'packages' of stars and supporting actors that the Big Players are uniquely able to provide – but that's true for the other Second Division teams as well.

It is wrong to suggest that the cooperative agency has had its day. Co-ops have been less squeamish about facing up to the recent shift in bread-and-butter business, away from traditional theatre and towards better-paid work in the corporate video and role-play markets. Here they have a head start. If an actor has the flexibility (and energy) to be able to support himself and still devote one or two days a week to the agency office, the rewards of co-op membership will far outweigh the costs.

Christopher Webber is an actor, writer and director. He was a member of a co-op agency for seven years to September 1997 and has acted for Alan Ayckbourn at the Stephen Joseph Theatre in Scarborough and Chichester Festival Theatre. Christopher has directed many plays and operas in the UK and abroad and has written six performed plays as well as the best-selling Bluff Your Way at the Races.

Agents

An agent is a necessity in today's competitive market. A quick glance through the casting policy of many of the companies listed in this handbook will reveal that a considerable number are loath to deal with the actor directly. Whether you choose to seek representation by a personal management or go for the hands-on experience of cooperative agenting, finding an agent can prove a difficult task. Most responsible agents try to restrict their client list to actors who they think will have a reasonable chance of regular work. They may also have a limit on the number of clients in any one range of age, general physique and character type (this is particularly true of the cooperative managements). Most will want to see some evidence of ability and employment potential and, obviously, it is a help for them to see you performing. But it is a buyer's market and it can prove quite difficult to persuade agents to attend a show that you are in.

A & J Management
551 Green Lanes,
Palmers Green,
London N13 4DR
Tel: 0181 882 7716
Fax: 0181 882 5983
Contact *Jackie Michael*

Established 1986. Represents actors. Will consider demo tapes and video showreels. *Commission*: 15%

Marjorie Abel Ltd
50 Maddox Street, London W1R 9PA
Tel: 0171 499 1343
Contact *Marjorie Abel*

Established 1972. Personal management. Represents actors, including voiceover artists. Welcomes queries from actors seeking representation; prefers initial approach to be made by post. No demo tapes or video showreels. Unless well known, applicants 'should apply with a cv together with details of a production in which they can be seen – preferably a theatre production in or near London'. If the actor is well known, 'a cv will be sufficient'. *Commission*: 10% maximum

Actors Alliance
Bon Marche Building,
444 Brixton Road, London SW9 8EJ
Tel: 0171 326 0070
Fax: 0171 326 0070

Established 1976. Cooperative management. Represents actors only. Welcomes applications, in writing, from actors seeking representation. No demo tapes or video showreels. 'Actors with professional experience only considered.'

Actors Direct
Room 61, 23 New Mount Street,
Manchester M4 4DE
Tel: 0161 834 3600
Fax: 0161 953 4001

Established 1994. Cooperative management. Represents actors and voiceover artists. Welcomes queries from actors seeking representation. Send cv, photograph and letter stating why you want to join a cooperative agency. Will consider demo tapes and video showreels. 'Our members must live in or near Manchester and are all obliged to do office duty.' *Commission*: 12%

The Actors' Exchange Ltd
Unit 3/1, 11 Marshalsea Road,
London SE1 1EP
Tel: 0171 378 8441
Fax: 0171 378 8152

Established 1983. Cooperative man-

agement. Represents actors and voiceover artists. Welcomes queries from those seeking representation; approach in writing in the first instance. No unsolicited demo tapes or showreels. 'Bear in mind we are a cooperative when applying.' *Commission*: 10%

Actors File
61–71 Collier Street, London N1 9BE
Tel: 0171 278 0087
Fax: 0171 278 0364

Established 1983. Cooperative management. Represents actors only. Welcomes queries from those seeking representation; send cv, 10 × 8 photograph and covering letter expressing interest in cooperative representation. Will consider demo tapes and video showreels. 'Cooperative representation involves a great deal of commitment to the running of your career and that of every other member of the co-op (currently 22). You have to function as an actor and agent, and participate in the management of the business. We will only consider applicants after having seen their work, so the best time to contact us is when you are about to appear in a show, preferably in London, or on TV or in the cinema.'

The Actors List
Half Moon Chambers, Chapel Walks,
Manchester M2 1HN
Tel: 0161 833 1605
Fax: 0161 832 5219
Managing Director *Debra Burns*
Manager *Debbie Pine*

Established 1995. Personal management representing actors only. Welcomes queries from those seeking representation. Send up-to-date cv, recent photograph, covering letter and sae. 'Keep phone calls precise and to the point. A good time to approach agents is when you are appearing in a production so that they can see your work – but with a good period of notice. Always send an sae with your application.' No unsolicited demo tapes or video showreels. *Commission*: Theatre 10% (with a ceiling of £500 per week); TV, Film, Corporate, Radio, Voiceover, etc. 15%

Actorum

21 Foley Street, London W1P 7LH
Tel: 0171 636 6978
Fax: 0171 636 6975

Established 1976. Cooperative management representing actors. Welcomes queries from actors seeking representation; approach in writing in the first instance. Will consider demo tapes and video showreels. 'You need to be in something so that agents can see you in action. A good showreel will do.' *Commission*: Theatre and Radio 10%; Mechanical media and West End 15%

Alpha Personal Management

Berkley House, 73 Upper Richmond Road, London SW15 2SZ
Tel: 0181 870 7066
Fax: 0181 870 7077
Contact *Jonathan Evans, Angus Kennedy, Julie Neubert, John Bleasdale*

Established 1983. Cooperative management representing actors. Welcomes queries from actors seeking representation. Send letter with photograph, cv and sae. No demo tapes or video showreels. 'Make clear on cvs where jobs were done and for whom, with dates if possible. A joining fee of £175; if at the end of a six-month probation period full membership is not offered or accepted, £50 of the joining fee is returnable.' *Commission*: TV 12.5%; all other categories 10%

Jonathan Altaras Associates*

2nd Floor, 13 Shorts Gardens, London WC2H 9AT
Tel: 0171 836 8722
Fax: 0171 836 6066
Contact *Jonathan Altaras, Sue Grantley*

Established 1990. Personal management representing actors, directors and choreographers. Welcomes queries; send letter with photograph, cv and sae. No demo tapes or video showreels. *Commission*: 10%

Alvarez Management

86 Muswell Road, Muswell Hill, London N10 2BE
Tel: 0181 883 2206
Fax: 0181 444 2646
Contact *Suzanne Alvarez*

Established 1990. Personal management. Represents actors and directors. Welcomes queries by letter (with sae) and, if possible, advance news of any show in which the actor is to appear. No demo tapes or video showreels. 'Have a really good photograph that looks like you – not how you would like to look! We only see people with a view to joining if we have seen their work. Remember, it's an agent's job to "sell" you. If you are in a show please give a minimum of three weeks' warning so that we have a chance to see your work. Remember to enclose an sae so that your letter will be answered.' *Commission*: Theatre, Radio and Corporate Videos 10%; Film and TV 12.5%; Commercials 15%

ALW Associates

5 Spring Street, Paddington,
London W2 3RA
Tel: 0171 262 5506/7
Fax: 0171 402 4834
Contact *Amanda Lee-Wood, Carol
Paul*

Established 1977 as Vernon Conway
Ltd; became ALW Associates in 1997.
Personal management representing
actors only. Welcomes queries from
actors seeking representation;
approach in writing in the first
instance. No demo tapes or video
showreels. *Commission*: negotiable.

Amber Personal Management Ltd

28 St Margaret's Chambers,
5 Newton Street, Machester M1 1HN
Tel: 0161 228 0236
Fax: 0161 228 0125
Contact *Simon Bleachley*

Established 1986. Personal and cooperative management. Represents actors
only. Queries from actors seeking
representation are welcome. Send
letter, cv and photograph. No
unsolicited demo tapes or video
showreels. *Commission*: Theatre and
Radio (on wages of £300 or above per
week) 10%; (below £300 per week)
8.5%; TV, Film and Commercials 12%

ANA (Actors Network Agency)

55 Lambeth Walk, London SE11 6DX
Tel: 0171 735 0999
Fax: 0171 735 8177
Contact *Sandie Bakker
(Administrator)*

Established 1985. Cooperative management representing actors and
voiceover artists. Welcomes queries

from actors; send letter, cv, photograph
and sae. Demo tapes and video
showreels on request only. 'Photos and
cvs will be returned only if there is an
sae enclosed with your letter.'
Commission: Theatre, TV, Film,
Corporate Videos and Commercials
10%; Repeat fees for commercials 11%

Susan Angel Associates Ltd*

1st Floor, 12 D'Arblay Street,
London W1V 3FP
Tel: 0171 439 3086
Fax: 0171 437 1712
Contact *Susan Angel, Kevin Francis*

Established 1976. Personal management. Represents actors and currently
has a designer and composer on the
books. Welcomes approaches from
actors seeking representation. No
demo tapes or video showreels. Write
with sae to Kevin Francis. 'Keep letters
short; invest in a good photograph;
send an sae if you want a reply; if you
have written there is no point in
making a follow-up phone call; always
type letters – especially if your
handwriting is illegible; always write
in the first instance – do not call in or
telephone.' *Commission*: Theatre, Radio
and Voiceovers 10%; Film, TV and
Commercials 12.5%

Arena Personal Management Ltd

Panther House, 38 Mount Pleasant,
London WC1X 0AP
Tel: 0171 278 1661
Fax: 0171 278 1661

Established 1985. Cooperative management representing actors.
Welcomes queries from those seeking
representation, especially men and

women of 40+. Approach by letter enclosing cv, photograph and sae if you would like photograph to be returned. No demo tapes or video showreels. 'It is essential, when applying to the agency, that you know what being in a cooperative entails. We are interested in the reasons why you are searching for this kind of management as opposed to a commercial management.'

Artist Management Group Ltd

11–13 Broad Court, Covent Garden, London WC2B 5QN
Tel: 0171 240 5052
Fax: 0171 240 4956
Contact *Sharon Boyce, Stanley Dallas, Isabel Silverstone, Pat Hayley, Phil Dale, Nick Thomas, Jon Conway*

Personal management. Represents actors, directors, writers, variety and comedy acts and presenters. Welcomes queries regarding representation from established artists only. Approach in writing in the first instance enclosing sae. No demo tapes or video showreels. *Commission*: 10%–20%

Associated International Management*

5 Denmark Street, London WC2H 8LP
Tel: 0171 836 2001
Fax: 0171 379 0848
Contact *Danielle Webster, Caz Swinfield, Derek Webster*

Established 1984. Personal management representing actors, voiceover artists, directors and writers. Does not welcome queries from those seeking representation; considers actors by referral only. No unsolicited demo tapes or video showreels. *Commission*: 12.5%

Julian Belfrage Associates

46 Albemarle Street,
London W1X 4PP
Tel: 0171 491 4400
Fax: 0171 493 5460
Contact *Victoria Belfrage, Olivia Barker*

Established 1985. Personal management representing actors. Welcomes representation queries. 'Please write; do not turn up at the office without an appointment.' Demo tapes and video showreels on request only. *Commission*: 10%

Billboard Personal Management

The Co-op Centre, 11 Mowll Street,
London SW9 6BG
Tel: 0171 735 9956
Fax: 0171 793 0426
Contact *Ros Astengo, Will Karlsen, Peter Addis*

Established 1987. Cooperative management representing actors. Welcomes queries from those seeking representation. Approach in writing in the first instance. Will consider demo tapes and video showreels. *Commission*: Theatre 10%; Radio, TV and Film 12.5%; Commercials 15%

Richard Bucknall Management

– see **RBM**, page 97

Barry Burnett Organisation Ltd

Prince of Wales Theatre, 31 Coventry Street, London W1V 8AS
Tel: 0171 836 0202
Fax: 0171 839 0438
Contact Barry Burnett, Lindsay Granger

Established 1970. Personal management representing actors, voiceover and walk-on/supporting artists. Welcomes queries from those seeking representation; send a letter with sae. Demo tapes and video showreels only considered if accompanied by sae. *Commission*: Rep and Radio 10%; TV, Film and West End 12.5%; Commercials 15%

Basic/J. D. Agency & Panto People

3 Rushden House, Tatlow Road, Glenfield, Leicester LE3 8ND
Tel: 0116 287 9594
Fax: 0116 287 9594
Contact Johnny Dallas, John Ross, Jody Ennis

Established 1976. Personal management. Represents actors, musical theatre and pantomime artists. Welcomes queries regarding representation. Send letter with sae in the first instance. Demo tapes and video showreels considered. 'No replies without sae. Be absolutely truthful when describing your talents and looks. Nothing is more annoying than an actor turning up and looking nothing like a photograph which has been submitted. Re auditions, choose an audition piece that is suitable for the engagement you are auditioning for (a Shakespeare sonnet is useless for a panto audition). Be smart in

appearance – it may be trendy to have "grunge" looks or torn jeans but to lots of managements the actor simply looks scruffy and it follows that their work could be the same.' *Commission*: Varies according to contract – 10%–17.5% (as arranged with the actor).

Michelle Braidman Associates*

3rd Floor Suite, 10–11 Lower John Street, London W1R 3PE
Tel: 0171 437 0817
Fax: 0171 439 3600

Personal management representing actors, voiceover artists, directors and designers. Approach in writing in the first instance, enclosing a photograph, cv and sae. No demo tapes or video showreels unless requested.

Bridge Personal Management

The Tyneside Cinema,
10 Pilgrim Street,
Newcastle upon Tyne NE1 6QG
Tel: 0191 232 6110
Fax: 0191 232 6220
Contact Janet Plater

Established 1991. Both personal and cooperative management. Represents actors, voiceover artists and writers. Welcomes queries from those seeking representation. Approach in writing in the first instance, enclosing photograph, cv and sae. No demo tapes or video showreels unless requested. *Commission*: Varies according to contract.

Brunskill Management Ltd*

Suite 8A, 169 Queen's Gate,
London SW7 5HE
Tel: 0171 581 3388
Fax: 0171 589 9460
E-mail:101234.2025@compuserve.com
Director *Ms Aude Powell*

Established 1963. Personal management. Represents actors, voiceover artists and directors. Welcomes queries from those seeking representation. Approach in writing in the first instance, enclosing photograph, cv and information on current production. No demo tapes or video showreels unless requested. *Commission*: Commercials 15%; all other categories 10%

Cardiff Casting

Chapter Arts Centre, Market Road,
Canton, Cardiff CF5 1QE
Tel: 01222 233321
Fax: 01222 233380

Established 1985. Cooperative management. Represents actors and voiceover artists. Welcomes queries from those seeking representation; send cv and photograph with covering letter. Will consider demo tapes and video showreels. *Commission*: Theatre 8%; TV, Radio, Film, etc. 10%

CCM (Chancery Cooperative Management)

Panther House,
38 Mount Pleasant,
London WC1X 0AP
Tel: 0171 278 0507
Contact *Lee Moone, Julia Stallard*

Established 1993. Cooperative management representing actors. Welcomes queries from actors; approach in writing (with sae) or by telephone. Will consider demo tapes or video showreels. 'Actors must be aware of how co-ops work and their role within it. Information is available from Equity and Spotlight.' *Commission*: Theatre 10%; TV, Film and Commercials 12%

The Central Line

11 East Circus Street,
Nottingham NG1 5AF
Tel: 0115 941 2937
Fax: 0115 950 8087
Contact *Lewis Hancock, Orde Browne, Glen Kinch, Ava Hunt*

Established 1983. Cooperative management. Represents actors, voiceover artists and workshop leaders. Welcomes queries from actors based in the Midlands and the North. 'It is essential that our actors are within easy commutable distance from Nottingham and that they are genuinely committed to the cooperative structure. Send a letter stating why you want to be in a co-op and not with a personal manager. Enclose cv and photograph. We are unique in that we audition applicants on a regular basis and are always pleased to hear from actors, bearing the above in mind.' *Commission*: 10%

City Actors Management Ltd

24 Rivington Street,
London EC2A 3DU
Tel: 0171 613 2636
Fax: 0171 613 2656

Established 1981. Cooperative management representing actors only. Welcomes queries from those seeking representation; send a letter enclosing cv and photograph. No demo tapes or video showreels. *Commission*: Theatre 10%; TV 12.5%

Shane Collins Associates*
2–5 Stedham Place, Bloomsbury,
London WC1A 1HU
Tel: 0171 580 3364
Fax: 0171 580 3365
Contact *Shane Collins, Melanie Haddigan, Jorg Betts*

Personal management. Represents actors, voiceover artists and directors. Welcomes queries; send a letter enclosing photograph and cv. No demo tapes or video showreels. *Commission*: Varies according to contract.

Conway, Van Gelder Ltd*
18–21 Jermyn Street,
London SW1Y 6HP
Tel: 0171 287 0077
Fax: 0171 287 1940
Contact *Jeremy Conway, Nicola Van Gelder, John Grant*

Personal management. Represents actors. Does not welcome queries from those seeking representation. No demo tapes or video showreels. *Commission*: Commercials, Voiceovers, Public Appearances and Corporate 12.5%; all other categories 10%

Vernon Conway Ltd
– *see* **ALW Associates**, page 78

Clive Corner Associates
73 Gloucester Road, Hampton,
Middlesex TW12 2UQ
Tel: 0181 287 2726
Fax: 0181 941 2866
Contact *Clive Corner, Duncan Stratton*

Established 1987. Personal manage-

ment representing actors and writers. Welcomes queries regarding representation from 'very experienced actors only'. Approach in writing in the first instance, enclosing photograph and cv. No phone calls. No demo tapes or video showreels unless requested. *Commission*: Theatre and Radio (up to £400 per week) 12.5%; Commercials (including photographic work) 20%; all other categories 15%

Crescent Management
10 Barley Mow Passage,
London W4 4PH
Tel: 0181 994 6477
Contact *Jenny Benson, Steve Hedges*

Established 1991. Cooperative management. Represents actors and voiceover artists. Welcomes approaches by letter enclosing sae for return of photograph. Will consider demo tapes and video showreels.

Crouch Associates
9–15 Neal Street, Covent Garden,
London WC2H 9PF
Tel: 0171 379 1684
Fax: 0171 379 1991
Contact *Penny Taylor, Jeanette Scott*

Established 1957. Personal management representing actors and voiceover artists. Welcomes queries in writing from those seeking representation. Demo tapes and video showreels on request only.

Sara Crouch Management
Suite 1, Ground Floor,
1 Duchess Street, London SW14 8AW
Tel: 0171 436 4626
Fax: 0171 436 4627
Contact *Sara Crouch*

Established 1994. Personal management representing actors. Does not welcome approaches from actors seeking representation. No demo tapes or video showreels. Letters should be 'polite and chatty, not too forward or friendly. Never send showreels or voice tapes blind – always wait to be asked and send an sae if you want a reply.' *Commission*: 10%–15% according to contract.

Crowded City

1st Floor, 1–3 Stevenson Square, Manchester M1 1DN
Tel: 0161 228 2322
Fax: 0161 237 1809
E-mail: united cities@compuserve.com
Contact *Caroline Joynt, John Basham*

Established 1984. Personal management. Represents walk-on and supporting artists. Welcomes queries from those seeking representation. Approach in writing, enclosing cv and photograph. Will consider demo tapes and video showreels. *Commission*: Theatre 10%; other categories 15%

David Daly Associates

586A King's Road, London SW6 2DX
Tel: 0171 610 9560
Fax: 0171 610 9512
Contact *David Daly, Lucinda Fox, Nicola McArdle*

Established 1975. Personal management representing actors and TV directors. Welcomes queries from those seeking representation; approach in writing only. No unsolicited demo tapes or video showreels.

Larry Dalzell Associates Ltd

91 Regent Street, London W1R 7TB
Tel: 0171 287 5131
Fax: 0171 287 5161
Contact *Sarah Osborne (Assistant), Larry Dalzell (Director)*

Established 1969. Personal management. Represents actors and directors. Welcomes queries regarding representation; approach in writing in the first instance. No demo tapes or video showreels. *Commission*: 10%

Denman Casting Agency

Commerce Chambers, Elite Buildings, 33 Upper Parliament Street, Nottingham NG1 2BP
Tel: 0115 941 8421
Fax: 0115 947 3257
Contact *Jack Denman, Alison Hope (Head of Casting), Sharon Scarborough*

Established 1958. Personal management. Represents actors, voiceover and walk-on/supporting artists. Does not welcome queries from those seeking representation. Approach by letter or fax in the first instance. No demo tapes or video showreels. *Commission*: 10%–12%

Denmark Street Management

11 Packington Bridge Workspace, Packington Square, London N1 7UA
Tel: 0171 354 8555
Fax: 0171 354 8558

Established 1985. Cooperative management. Represents actors. Welcomes queries from those interested in cooperative agencies. Approach in writing with cv and photograph. 'State why you want to join a co-op.' No demo tapes or video showreels unless requested. *Commission*: Theatre

10%; Film and TV 12.5%; Commercials 15%

Ken Desmond Agency & Management
16 Clarence Road North,
South Benfleet, Essex SS7 1HW
Tel: 01268 793401
Contact *Kenneth William Ford*

Established 1973. Represents actors. Welcomes queries in writing from those seeking representation.

Direct Line Personal Management
Unit 35, The CHEL Centre,
26 Roundhay Road, Leeds,
West Yorkshire LS7 1AB
Tel: 0113 244 4991
Fax: 0113 244 4991
E-mail: daphne@franks.demon.co.uk
Contact *Daphne K. Franks*

Cooperative management. Represents actors and voiceover artists. Welcomes queries from actors seeking representation; write with cv and photograph in the first instance. No demo tapes or video showreels. *Commission*: On wages of £250 or above per week: 12.5%; £100–£250 per week: 10%; below £100 per week: 5%

Downes Agency
96 Broadway, Bexleyheath,
Kent DA6 7DE
Tel: 0181 304 0541
Fax: 0181 301 5591
Contact *Wendy Downes, Lee Downes*

Established 1987. Member of IVCA. Personal management. Represents actors, voiceover artists, presenters and hosts. Approaches from established artists only. No demo tapes or video showreels. *Commission*: TV, Radio and Theatre 10%; all other categories 20%

Bryan Drew Ltd
Quadrant House, 80–82 Regent Street, London W1R 6AU
Tel: 0171 437 2293
Fax: 0171 437 0561
Contact *Bryan Drew, Susy Wootton, Nina Parmar*

Established 1962. Personal management. Represents actors, voiceover artists, directors and writers. 'Occasionally' welcomes queries regarding representation although client list is full at present. When applying always enclose sae, cv and photograph with letter. *Commission*: basic 12.5%; Commercials 15%

Dunbar Agency
2 Manse Street, Edinburgh EH12 7TR
Tel: 0131 334 4389
Fax: 0131 316 4054 FAO Dunbar Agency
Contact *Alan Dunbar, Margaret Dunbar*

Established 1990. Personal management. Represents actors, voiceover artists, walk-on and supporting artists. Welcomes queries from those seeking representation. Approach in writing with sae in the first instance. Will consider demo tapes and video showreels. *Commission*: Theatre 7.5%; all other categories 15%

June Epstein Associates
62 Compayne Gardens,
London NW6 3RY
Tel: 0171 328 0864/372 1928
Fax: 0171 328 0684
Contact *June Epstein*

Established 1973. Personal management representing actors. Welcomes queries from actors seeking representation. Approach by letter in the first instance. Enclose sae otherwise a reply will be made only if the agency is interested. *Commission*: Commercials 15%; all other categories 10%

Kate Feast Management*
10 Primrose Hill Studios, Fitzroy Road, London NW1 8TR
Tel: 0171 586 5502
Fax: 0171 586 9817

Established 1976. Personal management. Represents actors, voiceover artists and directors. Welcomes queries from those seeking representation. Approach in writing, enclosing sae, cv and photograph. No demo tapes or video showreels. *Commission*: 10%

Sheridan Fitzgerald Management
69B Credon Road, Upton Park, London E13 9BS
Tel: 0181 471 9814
Fax: 0181 472 6829
Contact *Sheridan Fitzgerald*

Established 1987. Personal management. Represents actors, directors, voiceover artists and writers. Welcomes queries from those seeking representation. Approach by letter (not fax) enclosing adequate-size sae. No demo tapes or video showreels unless requested. 'Name theatres, TV companies, directors and producers on cv. Enclose honest photograph. Give good warning of TV or theatre appearance with "back-up" phone call on the day or during run. If, for whatever reason, representation cannot be offered, please accept with grace! Hassling and discourtesy lead to a permanent no.'

Commission: Theatre, Radio and Voiceover 10%; TV and Corporate 12.5%; Commercials and Film 15%

Focus Management Ltd
Claremont House, 22–4 Claremont Road, Surbiton, Surrey KT6 4QU
Tel: 0181 241 2446
Fax: 0181 241 2447
E-mail: ian4actors@aol.com
Contact *Ian Harvey, Mrs Ben Osborne*

Established 1982. Personal management. Represents actors (preferably with singing and instrumental skills) and voiceover artists. 'Sometimes' welcomes queries from actors seeking representation. Approach in writing with cv, photograph and sae. No demo tapes or video showreels unless requested. 'Identify your areas of specialisation. Always try to invite agent to see work but give plenty of notice.' *Commission*: Theatre and Radio 10%; all other categories 15%

Frontline Management
The Colombo Centre, 34–36 Colombo Street, London SE1 8DP
Tel: 0171 261 9466
Fax: 0171 261 9466
Contact *Brian Orrell, Miranda French*

Established 1982–3. Cooperative management representing actors only. Welcomes approaches by actors seeking representation. Send a photograph ('a good photograph, not just a home or holiday snapshot!'), cv and covering letter and details of any production in which acting work can be seen (or showcase, if a graduate). Covering letters should be well presented to give more chance of whoever reads it 'seeing you in a professional light. Not just a hand-scribbled note. Include in the letter things you have done and be enthusiastic towards what you want to do.' Will consider showreels 'if the applicant thinks that it demonstrates their acting skills'. *Commission*: TV, Film, Theatre and Voiceover 10%

Joy Galloway Management
– see **JGM**, page 89

Galloways One*
15 Lexham Mews, London W8 6JW
Tel: 0171 376 2288
Fax: 0171 376 2416
Contact *Hugh Galloway*

Established 1971. Personal management specialising in commercial and corporate videos. Represents actors and models. Welcomes queries regarding representation. 'Applicants must send in photograph, cv and sae, and showreel if available. But without an sae they will not receive a reply.' Will consider demo tapes and video showreels. 'If actors are looking for commercial representation and are already with a personal management, they must make sure, before they approach us, that the contract they have with their management permits them to do commercials with another agent. We only represent on an exclusive basis (for commercials only).' *Commission*: 18%

Kerry Gardner Management*
15 Kensington High Street,
London W8 5NP
Tel: 0171 937 4478
Fax: 0171 376 2587
Contact *Philip Knowles, Rebecca Lewis, Kerry Gardner*

Established 1983. Personal management. Represents actors, voiceover artists, directors, casting directors and voice coaches. Welcomes queries from those seeking representation. Approach in writing enclosing sae. No telephone calls.

Eric Glass Ltd
28 Berkeley Square,
London W1X 6HD
Tel: 0171 629 7162
Fax: 0171 499 6780
Contact *Janet Glass*

Established 1932. Personal management. Represents actors, voiceover artists, directors, writers, choreographers, musical directors and conductors. Welcomes queries regarding representation; approach in writing in the first instance. No unsolicited demo tapes or video showreels.

Jimmy Grafton Management
26 Tavistock Court, Tavistock Square,
London WC1R 9HE
Tel: 0171 387 1773
Fax: 0171 387 1773
Contact *Tony Boyd*

Established 1948. Personal management. Represents actors, directors, writers and light-entertainment artists. Welcomes queries from those seeking representation. Approach in writing (enclose sae). No unsolicited demo tapes or video showreels. 'Decide why you are so different from the rest of those seeking representation, or why you are so much better – or apply to agents who play the "numbers game".' *Commission*: Varies from 10% to 15%

Joan Gray Personal Management

29 Sunbury Court Island, Sunbury on Thames, Middlesex TW16 5PP
Tel: 01932 783544
Fax: 01932 783544
Contact *Joan Gray*

Established 1960. Personal management representing actors only. Not taking on any new clients. No queries regarding representation, please. No demo tapes or showreels. *Commission*: 10%

Grays Management

Panther House, 38 Mount Pleasant, London WC1X 0AP
Tel: 0171 278 1054
Fax: 0171 278 1054
Contact *Paul Rattee, Mary Elliott Nelson*

Established 1986. Cooperative management representing actors only. Welcomes queries from those seeking representation. Write with full cv and photograph plus, preferably, details of show the agency can cover. 'Make your playing age range very clear and send recent photograph. We need to see people work either on stage or video. Make clear which is available.' No unsolicited demo tapes or showreels. *Commission*: Stage 10%; Screen 15%

Sandra Griffin Management

6 Ryde Place, Richmond Road, East Twickenham TW1 2EH
Tel: 0181 891 5676
Fax: 0181 744 1812
Contact *Sandra Griffin, Howard Roberts*

Established 1989. Personal management. Represents actors, voiceover artists, directors and writers. Welcomes queries from those seeking representation. Approach in writing, enclosing cv and photograph ('sae ensures a reply'). No unsolicited demo tapes or video showreels. 'It is easier to consider potential clients if we can see their work – a properly edited showreel or a current theatre production in an easily accessible location.' *Commission*: Varies according to contract.

Sue Hammer Personal Management*

Otterbourne House, Chobham Road, Ottershaw, Surrey KT16 0QF
Tel: 01932 874111
Fax: 01932 872922
Contact *Sue Hammer, Lauverne Richins*

Established 1980. Personal management representing actors only. Does not welcome representation queries. No unsolicited demo tapes or video showreels. Recommends that those trying to find an agent should 'talk to Spotlight first'. *Commission*: Theatre and Radio 10%; TV, Film and Corporate 12.5%; Commercials 15%

Harbour & Coffey

3rd Floor, 5 Sedley Place, London W1R 1HH
Tel: 0171 499 5548
Fax: 0171 499 0884
Contact *Harry Harbour, Gillian Coffey*

Established 1969. Personal management representing actors. Welcomes queries from those seeking representation. Approach by letter in the first instance. No demo tapes or video showreels on initial contact. 'We prefer to see people working – theatre or TV – so the better time to write is when there is something to show.' *Commission*: Commercials 12.5%; all other categories 10%

Stephen Hatton Management*

1A Shepperton House,
83 Shepperton Road, London N1 3DF
Tel: 0171 359 3593
Fax: 0171 354 2189
Contact *Stephen Hatton, Patrick Hambleton, Aileen McEwan*

Personal management representing actors and designers. Welcomes queries by letter. No demo tapes or video showreels. 'Always send a cv and photograph and include an sae.'

Heavy Pencil Management

Battersea Arts Centre (BAC),
Lavender Hill, London SW11 5TF
Tel: 0171 738 9574
Fax: 0171 924 4636

Founded 1991. Cooperative management representing actors. Welcomes queries from those seeking representation; approach in writing enclosing cv and photograph with covering letter. Will consider showreels. 'When applying for membership, it is handy if you have something in which the co-op members can see you. It is also useful to know how an actors' co-op functions as being a member requires your time and commitment.'

Philippa Howell Personal Management (PHPM)

184 Bradway Road, Sheffield,
South Yorkshire S17 4QX
Tel: 0114 235 3663
Fax: 0114 235 3663
Contact *Philippa Howell*

Established 1996. Personal management. Represents actors, voiceover artists, directors and presenters. Welcomes representation queries from northern-based actors, 'especially from ethnic minorities'. Send a letter enclos-

ing cv, photograph and large sae. Will consider demo tapes and video showreels. *Commission*: Radio and Theatre 10%; TV, Corporate Events, Training Films, Voiceover 12.5%; Commercials and Film 15%

ICM Ltd (International Creative Management)

Oxford House, 76 Oxford Street,
London W1N 0AX
Tel: 0171 636 6565
Fax: 0171 323 0101
E-mail: admin@icmlondon.co.uk

Represents actors, producers, directors and writers. Welcomes queries from actors seeking representation; approach in writing in the first instance. No unsolicited demo tapes or video showreels.

Inter-City Casting

1st Floor, 1–3 Stevenson Square,
Manchester M1 1DN
Tel: 0161 237 1808
Fax: 0161 237 1809
E-mail: united cities@compuserve.com
Contact *Caroline Joynt, John Basham*

Established 1984. Personal management. Represents actors and children. Welcomes queries from those seeking representation. Approach in writing, enclosing cv and photograph. Will consider demo tapes and video showreels. *Commission*: Theatre 10%; all other categories 15%

Inspiration Management

Southbank House,
Black Prince Road,
London SE1 7SJ
Tel: 0171 587 0947
Fax: 0171 587 0947
Contact *Angela Dalton*

Established 1986. Cooperative management representing actors only. Welcomes written approaches from those seeking representation. Will consider demo tapes and video showreels. 'Be professional from the start; good photos (plenty), good cv, high commitment to the cooperative ethos.' *Commission*: Repeat fees 5%; Radio 7%; Theatre 10%; Visual and Voiceover 12%

International Creative Management
– *see* ICM Ltd, page 88

Jaclyn Agency
Thackeray House, Hempnall, Norwich, Norfolk NR15 2LP
Tel: 01508 499241
Fax: 01508 499077
Contact *Marilyn Sandiford (Proprietor), Imogen Reynolds (Casting Assistant), Sylvia Weal (Records Officer)*

Established 1952. Personal management. Represents actors, voiceover artists, walk-on and supporting artists, models, promotions personnel. Does not welcome queries regarding representation in general; only artistes with professional experience residing in East Anglia are considered. Telephone in the first instance. 'Give factual details; who you are, where you had your training/experience, where you live. Do you drive/have transport? Are your photographs up to date? Are you fully available?' *Commission*: 12%

J.D. Agency
– *see* Basic, page 80

Jeffrey & White Management*
9–15 Neal Street, London WC2H 9PU
Tel: 0171 240 7000
Fax: 0171 240 0007
Contact *Judith Jeffrey, Jeremy White*

Established 1986. Personal management representing actors only. Welcomes queries regarding representation; approach in writing with cv in the first instance. Demo tapes and video showreels on request only. *Commission*: Theatre, TV and Film 10%; Commercials 12%

JGM (Joy Galloway Management)
15 Lexham Mews, London W8 6JW
Tel: 0171 376 2414
Fax: 0171 376 2416
Contact *Hugh Galloway, Judy Franklin*

Established 1971. Pesonal management. Represents actors, voiceover artists and directors. Welcomes queries from those seeking representation. 'All interested applicants must send in a photograph, cv and sae otherwise we cannot guarantee a response.' Will consider demo tapes and video showreels but only if sent with a stamped addressed envelope/jiffy bag. *Commission*: Theatre, Film and TV 10%; Commercials and Corporates 18%

JLM
– *see* Janet Lynn Malone, page 92

Chuck Julian Associates*
Suite 51, 26 Charing Cross Road, London WC2H 0DH
Tel: 0171 437 4248
Fax: 0171 240 1296
Contact *Chuck Julian, Sue Yager, Anita Alraun*

Established 1984. Personal management. Represents actors. Welcomes queries from those seeking representation. Approach in writing with sae in the first instance. Will consider demo tapes and video showreels (with sae). *Commission*: Radio and Theatre (below £250 per week) 10%; Film and Theatre (on wages of £250 or above per week) 12.5%; Commercials 15%

Adrian King Associates
33 Marlborough Mansions,
Cannon Hill, London NW6 1JS
Tel: 0171 435 4600/4700
Fax: 0171 435 4100
Contact *Adrian King, Janice Tildsley*

Established 1989. Personal management. Represents actors only. Welcomes queries from those seeking representation but only if it is possible to view their work. Approach in writing with sae in the first instance. Will consider demo tapes and video showreels. *Commission*: Theatre and TV 10%; Commercials and Film 15%

Michael Ladkin Personal Management
Suite 1, Ground Floor, 1 Duchess Street, London W1N 3DE
Tel: 0171 436 4626
Fax: 0171 436 4627
Contact *Michael Ladkin, Lindsey Downs*

Personal management. Represents actors, directors, designers, presenters and producers. Welcomes queries regarding representation. Approach in writing with cv and photograph in the first instance. Will consider demo tapes and video showreels. *Commission*: 10%–15%

Langford Associates
17 Westfields Avenue,
London SW13 0AT
Tel: 0181 878 7148
Fax: 0181 878 7078
Contact *Barry Langford*

Established 1988. Personal management representing actors only. Queries regarding representation must always be by mail with recent photograph, and sae if return required. 'Never by phone and never, ever by fax!' No unsolicited demo tapes or video showreels. 'Only invite agents to see you perform if the production you are in is well staged, entertaining and shows you in a good light. Only use clear, relevant photographs which are a true likeness.' *Commission*: 10%–15%, according to contract.

Tessa Le Bars Management*
54 Birchwood Road, Petts Wood,
Kent BR5 1NZ
Tel: 01689 837084
Fax: 01689 837084

Established 1983. Personal management. Represents actors and writers. Does not welcome queries from those seeking representation. No demo tapes or video showreels.

L'Epine Smith & Carney Associates*
Suite 61–63 Kent House, 87 Regent Street, London W1R 7HF
Tel: 0171 434 4143
Fax: 0171 434 4173
Contact *Jessica Carney, Jean Comley*

Founded in the early fifties. Represents actors, a few directors and writers, directors of photography (film and TV), and editors. Welcomes 'selective'

enquiries from those seeking representation. 'Only send in details if you are
in a show I can cover. If you want
details returned you must send an sae.
I only have time to respond if I am
interested. No unsolicited showreels.
Commission: Commercials 15%; general
10%

Links Management
34–68 Colombo Street,
London SE1 8DP
Tel: 0171 928 0806
Fax: 0171 928 0806

Established 1983. Cooperative management representing actors.
Welcomes queries from actors seeking
representation. Approach in writing in
the first instance, enclosing cv and
photograph. Will consider demo tapes
and video showreels. 'As a co-op we
expect people to have knowledge of
how the business operates.'
Commission: Theatre 7.5%; TV and Film
10%

Lip Service Casting Ltd
4 Kingly Street, London W1R 5LF
Tel: 0171 734 3393
Fax: 0171 734 3373
E-mail: bookings@lipservice.co.uk
or: castings@lipservice.co.uk
Contact *Susan MacTavish, Hilary Oliver*

Established 1987. Member of the
Association of Voice Agents (AVA).
Represents voiceover artists only. Does
not welcome approaches from actors
seeking representation. *Commission*:
15%

Pat Lovett Agency
– see **PLA Scotland**, page 96

LWA
18 Elliott Square, London NW3 3SU
Tel: 0171 586 5867
Fax: 0171 586 1583
Contact *Jill Williams, Eileen Williams*

Established 1965. Personal management representing actors and voiceover artists. Welcomes queries from
those seeking representation; send
photograph (postcard-size acceptable)
and covering letter, and sae if you want
details returned. No unsolicited demo
tapes or video showreels. *Commission*:
Theatre and Radio 10%; TV and Film
12.5%

Dennis Lyne Agency*
108 Leonard Street,
London WC2A 4RH
Tel: 0171 739 6200
Contact *Dennis Lyne*

Personal management. Represents
actors, voiceover artists, directors,
designers and lighting cameramen.
Welcomes queries from those seeking
representation – by post only. No
unsolicited demo tapes or video
showreels.

MacFarlane Chard Associates*
7–8 Little Turnstile,
London WC1V 7DX
Tel: 0171 404 2332
Fax: 0171 404 7456
E-mail: mcauk@aol.com
Contact *Peter MacFarlane, Phillip Chard*

Established 1994. Personal management. Represents actors, voiceover
artists, directors, designers, writers,
producers, casting directors and
presenters. Welcomes queries regarding representation. Approach in

writing, enclosing photograph and cv. Will consider demo tapes and video showreels. 'Always send an sae with any correspondence.'

McIntosh Rae Management*

Thornton House, Thornton Road, Wimbledon, London SW19 4NG
Tel: 0181 944 6688
Fax: 0181 944 6624
Contact *Sheila McIntosh, Joyce Rae*

Established 1993. Personal management representing actors. Welcomes queries from those seeking representation. Approach by letter with sae for return of photograph and details. No unsolicited demo tapes or video showreels. 'We do not like being faxed by actors and we are not particularly keen on being "cold-called" by telephone. Keep cv to one page and if expecting a reply, enclose sae. Remember it is always best to have been seen working so if you have a job this is the best time to approach agents for representation. Listen to colleagues and use the advisory service offered by Spotlight or other professional bodies.' *Commission*: Varies according to contract.

Bill McLean Personal Management

23B Deodar Road, Putney, London SW15 2NP
Tel: 0181 789 8191
Contact *Bill McLean*

Established 1972. Personal management. Represents actors, directors and writers. Welcomes queries from those seeking representation. Approach in writing in the first instance. No unsolicited demo tapes or video showreels. *Commission*: 10%–15%

Magnet Personal Management

Unit 743, The Big Peg, 120 Vyse Street, Birmingham B18 6NF
Tel: 0121 628 7788
Fax: 0121 628 7788

Established 1985. Cooperative management representing actors. Welcomes applications from actors based in the Midlands. Approach in writing, enclosing cv and photograph. Will consider demo tapes and video showreels but prefers to see an actor working 'live'. 'Please be aware that Magnet is a co-op agency and our members need to be based in the Midlands. We need to see applicants working before they can become members. We do not represent walk-ons.' *Commission*: Maximum 10% (less on Theatre and Radio).

Magnolia Management

136 Hicks Avenue, Greenford, Middlesex UB6 8HB
Tel: 0181 578 2899
Fax: 0181 575 0369
Contact *Jennifer Jaffrey*

Personal management, representing actors. Approach in writing with cv and photograph. No unsolicited demo tapes or video showreels. Performance notices welcome.

Janet Lynn Malone (JLM)*

242 Acton Lane, Chiswick, London W4 5DL
Tel: 0181 747 8223
Fax: 0181 747 8286
Contact *Janet Malone, Sharon Henry*

Established 1978. Personal management. Represents actors, voiceover artists, directors and writers. Welcomes queries from those seeking representation. Approach in writing with cv. Will consider demo tapes and video showreels. *Commission*: Theatre 7.5%; TV and Film 15%

Malone & Knight Associates
26 Wellesley Road, Chiswick,
London W4 4BN
Tel: 0181 994 1619
Fax: 0181 994 2992
Contact *Malcolm Knight, Jayne Knight*

Established 1994. Personal management representing actors. Welcomes queries by post with cv and photograph. 'All enquiries replied to.' Will consider demo tapes and video showreels. *Commission*: Varies according to contract.

Marmont Management Ltd*
Langham House, 308 Regent Street,
London W1R 5AL
Tel: 0171 637 3183
Fax: 0171 323 4798
E-mail: www.marmont.demon.co.uk
Contact *Patricia Marmont, Rose Streatfeild, Penny Wesson, Sophie Gibson*

Established 1983. Personal management representing actors, directors and designers. Does not welcome queries from those seeking representation. *Commission*: Commercials 12.5%; all other categories 10%

Ronnie Marshall Agency
66 Ollerton Road, London N11 2LA
Tel: 0181 368 4958
Contact *Ronnie Marshall*

Established 1971. Personal management. Represents actors and voiceover artists. Welcomes queries from those seeking representation. Approach in writing in the first instance with 'a

businesslike letter plus recent photograph and cv'. No demo tapes or video showreels. *Commission*: 15%

Scott Marshall Personal Management*
44 Perryn Road, London W3 7NA
Tel: 0181 749 7692
Fax: 0181 740 7342
Contact *Scott Marshall, Denise Marshall, Harriet Evans, Sally Goodliffe*

Established 1972. Personal management. Represents actors, voiceover artists and directors. Welcomes queries regarding representation; approach in writing in the first instance. No unsolicited demo tapes or video showreels.

Montagu Associates
The Basement, 4 Duke Street,
London W1M 5AA
Tel: 0171 224 3585
Fax: 0171 224 3537
Contact *Beverley Montagu, Mark Lewis*

Established 1987. Personal management representing actors. Welcomes queries from those seeking representation; approach in writing in the first instance. No demo tapes or video showreels. *Commission*: Theatre 10%; all other categories 15%

Morgan & Goodman
Mezzanine, Quadrant House, 80–82 Regent Street, London W1R 5PA
Tel: 0171 437 1383
Fax: 0171 437 5293
Contact *Lyndall Goodman, Tanya Greep*

Personal management. Represents actors only. Does not welcome queries regarding representation. No demo tapes or video showreels. *Commission*: Commercials 15%; all other categories 10%

William Morris Agency (UK) Ltd*

31–32 Soho Square, London W1V 6HA
Tel: 0171 434 2191
Fax: 0171 437 0238
E-mail: padler@wma.com

Established 1965 (London), 1898 (USA). Personal management. Represents actors, voiceover artists, directors, designers and writers. Welcomes queries from those seeking representation. Approach in writing with photograph. No demo tapes or video showreels. *Commission*: 10%

Elaine Murphy Associates

310 Aberdeen House, 22–24 Highbury Grove, London N5 2EA
Tel: 0171 704 9913
Fax: 0171 704 8039
Contact *Elaine Murphy*

Established 1990. Personal management representing actors and voiceover artists. Does not welcome queries regarding representation but will consider demo tapes and video showreels.

Nemesis Agency Ltd

41 South King Street,
Manchester M2 6DE
Tel: 0161 832 8737
Fax: 0161 832 1613
Contact *Philip Wolstenholme, Katrina Brennan*

Established 1993. Personal management. Represents actors, walk-on and supporting artists. Welcomes queries from those seeking representation. Approach by telephone call in the first instance. Will consider demo tapes and video showreels. *Commission*: TV 10%; Commercials and Video 15%; Photographic 25%

Northern Lights Actors Management*

Dean Clough, Halifax,
West Yorkshire HX3 5AX
Tel: 01422 382203
Fax: 01422 360355
Contact *Angela Forrest, Maureen Magee*

Established 1997. Personal management. Represents actors, voiceover artists and directors. Welcomes queries regarding representation from northern-based actors only. Approach in writing, enclosing cv. No telephone calls. No unsolicited demo tapes or video showreels. *Commission*: Theatre 10%; all other categories 15%

North One Actors Management

The Print House, 18 Ashwin Street, London E8 3DI
Tel: 0171 254 9093
Fax: 0171 249 9989
Contact *David Hudson*

Established 1987. Cooperative management representing actors. Welcomes queries from those seeking representation. Send letter, cv and b/w photograph (10 x 8) and sae if return of details required. Will consider demo tapes and video showreels. 'It is advisable to be in a production in which we can see your work or have a forthcoming film or television programme when applying.

Administration and telephone skills are an advantage. We particularly welcome applications from non-European performers.' *Commission*: Theatre 10%; TV, Film, Corporate, Commercials 15%

1984 Personal Management Ltd

54 Peartree Street,
London EC1V 3SB
Tel: 0171 251 8046
Fax: 0171 250 0933
Contact *Susan McGoun, Robin Browne*

Established 1984. Cooperative management representing actors. Welcomes queries regarding representation. Send letter with photograph, cv and sae. No unsolicited demo tapes or video showreels. 'Only registered graduates and full and provisional Equity members need apply.' *Commission*: 10%

Nyland Management

2 Abney Road, Heaton Chapel,
Stockport,
Cheshire SK4 4QW
Tel: 0161 442 2224
Fax: 0161 432 5406
Contact *Patrick Nyland*

Established 1989. Personal management representing actors only. Welcomes queries; approach in writing, enclosing photograph, cv and sae. 'Never send anything that can't be replaced, i.e. photograph or video. Always send an sae if details are required to be returned as agents will not stand the cost of returning mail. It's time-consuming and expensive.' No demo tapes or video showreels. *Commission*: Theatre, Radio and Corporate 10%; TV 15%; Commercials 20%

Otto Personal Management Ltd

Workstation, 15 Paternoster Row,
Sheffield S1 2BX
Tel: 0114 275 2592
Fax: 0114 275 0550
E-mail: otto8@aol.com

Established 1986. Cooperative management. Represents actors and voiceover artists. Welcomes queries from those seeking representation 'Prospective applicants should be based within reasonable daily travelling distance of our office.' Send letter with 10 × 8 photograph and cv. Will consider demo tapes and video showreels. 'Applicants will only be offered an interview/membership if at least three members have seen and approved their work.' *Commission*: Theatre and Radio 8%; Training Videos and Role-play 10%; TV and Film 12%

Pan Artists Agency

1 Hollins Grove, Sale,
Cheshire M33 6RE
Tel: 0161 969 7419
Fax: 0161 973 9724
Contact *Dorothy Hall, Wendy Simpson*

Established 1975. Personal management representing actors, walk-on and supporting artists. Welcomes queries from those seeking representation; approach in writing with cv and photograph in the first instance. No demo tapes or video showreels. *Commission*: 12%

Park Personal Management Ltd

Unit 2.11, 11 Marshalsea Road,
London SW1 1EP
Tel: 0171 357 0024
Fax: 0171 357 0047
Contact *Christopher Preston, Tom Minnikin, Wendy Baxter*

Established 1986. Cooperative management representing actors and voice-over artists. Welcomes queries regarding representation. Send a cv and photograph with a covering letter. No unsolicited demo tapes or video showreels. *Commission*: 7.5%–12.5%

Frances Phillips (Agency & Artists Management)*

89 Robeson Way, Borehamwood,
Hertfordshire WD6 5RY
Tel: 0181 236 0766
Fax: 0181 236 0766
Contact *Derek Phillips, Frances Phillips*

Established 1987. Personal management. Represents actors, voiceover artists, directors and writers. Welcomes queries from those seeking representation. Approach in writing with sae for reply. No demo tapes or video showreels.

Piccadilly Management

Unit 123, 23 New Mount Street,
Manchester M4 4DE
Tel: 0161 953 4057
Fax: 0161 953 4001
Contact *Tim Lambert, Anthony Collier*

Established 1986. Cooperative management. Represents actors, voiceover artists, directors and choreographers. Welcomes queries from those seeking representation. Send cv, photograph and covering letter. Will consider demo tapes and video showreels. 'Piccadilly Management operates an Equal Opportunities policy and welcomes applications from all nationalities, irrespective of age, sex, religion or physical ability. We currently represent actors, directors and choreographers and now seek to recruit people with dance and musical skills, those with extensive cvs and very young actors. All other applications will be viewed on their own merit. If we wish to take an application further, we always cover a live performance or study a showreel prior to offering an interview.' *Commission*: 5%–15%

PLA Scotland (Pat Lovett Agency)

Picardy House, 4 Picardy Place,
Edinburgh EH1 3JT
Tel: 0131 478 7878
Fax: 0131 557 5565
Contact *Pat Lovett, Christine Dinwoodie, Dolina Logan*

Established 1981. Personal management. Represents actors, voiceover artists and walk-ons. Welcomes queries regarding representation. Approach in writing with recent photograph and cv. No unsolicited demo tapes or video showreels. 'Don't telephone before writing. Enclose an sae and allow a reasonable time for a response. If inviting agents/employers to a performance, give good notice (at least 2 weeks).' *Commission*: Theatre 6%; Walk-ons 10%; Audio 11%; Film and TV 12%

RBM (Richard Bucknall Management)*

3rd Floor, 18 Broadwick Street,
London W1V 1FG
Tel: 0171 287 5010
Fax: 0171 287 5020
Contact Richard Bucknall, Catherine Pound

Established 1991. Personal management representing comedians and writers. Welcomes representation queries from these two categories only; approach in writing in the first instance, enclosing brief, typed cv, photograph and demo tape.

Joan Reddin

Hazel Cottage, Wheeler End,
Common Lane End, Buckinghamshire
HP14 3NL
Tel: 01494 882729
Fax: 01494 521727
Contact Joan Reddin

Established 1955. Personal management representing actors only. Does not welcome queries regarding representation apart from established actors. Approach in writing in the first instance. No demo tapes or video showreels.

Rhubarb/Rhubarb Personal Management

6 Langley Street, London WC2H 9JA
Tel: 0171–836 1336 (Rhubarb)/836 0883 (Rhubarb Personal Management)
Fax: 0171 836 0444
E-mail: www.rhubarb.co.uk
Contact Ben Romer Lee (Rhubarb)/Joanna Aitken (RPM)

Established 1988. Personal management representing actors and voiceover artists. Welcomes queries from actors (not voiceover artists) seeking representation. Send letter with cv and photograph. 'Package well and simply; keep it short and to the point.' No demo tapes or video showreels. *Commission*: Voiceover 15%; varies according to contract for actors.

Stella Richards Management

42 Hazlebury Road,
London SW6 2ND
Tel: 0171 736 7786
Fax: 0171 731 5082
Contact Stella Richards, Paul McGurk

Established 1979. Personal management. Represents star-name actors and presenters, directors and designers. Does not particularly welcome queries regarding representation. 'Do not "mass-produce" the letter that accompanies your cv; always include an sae if you want an answer or return of material.' *Commission*: 10%

Rigal Management

109 Albert Bridge Road,
London SW11 4PF
Tel: 0171 228 8689
Fax: 0171 738 1742
Contact Hans Baernhoft, Muriel Rigal

Established 1986. Personal management representing actors only. Welcomes queries from those seeking representation; approach in writing in the first instance. No demo tapes or video showreels. *Commission*: 10%–15%

Rogues & Vagabonds Management Ltd

321 Essex Road, London N1 3PS
Tel: 0171 226 5885
Fax: 0171 226 0440
Contact *Porlyin Rhoden*

Established 1987. Cooperative management representing actors. Welcomes queries from those seeking representation. Send letter, enclosing cv and photograph. 'If you are in a show, write in and follow this up with a phone call.' Will consider demo tapes and video showreels ('which will be returned').

Rossmore Personal Management

Rossmore Road, London NW1 6NJ
Tel: 0171 258 1953
Fax: 0171 723 1040
Contact *Sylvia Young*

Established 1989. Personal management representing actors. Welcomes queries regarding representation; approach in writing in the first instance. 'Send practical, informative letter – nothing joky or quirky.' Will consider demo tapes and video showreels. *Commission*: 15%

Saraband Associates

265 Liverpool Road, Islington, London N1 1LX
Tel: 0171 609 5313
Fax: 0171 609 2370
Contact *Sara Randall, Bryn Newton, Christina Beyer*

Established 1972. Personal management. Represents actors only. No unsolicited approaches from those seeking representation. Will consider

demo tapes and video showreels. Write in the first instance. *Commission*: 12.5%

SCA Management

23 Goswell Road,
London EC1M 7AJ
Tel: 0171 336 6122/608 0044
Fax: 0171 253 1430
Contact *Gaynor Sheward*

Established 1976. Personal management. Represents actors, dancers and singers between the age range of 18–35 years. Welcomes queries from those seeking representation; approach in writing, enclosing cv and photograph. Will consider demo tapes and video showreels. *Commission*: 15%–20%

Tim Scott Personal Management

5 Cloisters Business Centre,
8 Battersea Park Road,
London SW8 4BG
Tel: 0171 978 1352
Fax: 0171 498 2942
Contact *Tim Scott, Fflur Holtby*

Established 1988. Personal management representing actors only. Does not welcome queries regarding representation. 'Only contact agents when you are in a show as we always see people's work before taking them on.'

Screenlite the Agency

Studio No. 61, Shepperton Studios,
Shepperton, Middlesex TW17 0QD
Tel: 01932 566977
Fax: 01932 566977

Established 1982. Represents walk-on and supporting artists only. Welcomes queries from those seeking representation in these categories. *Commission*: 11%

James Sharkey Associates*

21 Golden Square, London W1R 3PA
Tel: 0171 434 3801
Fax: 0171 494 1547
Contact *James Sharkey, Gavin Barker*

Established 1983. Personal management representing actors and voiceover artists. Welcomes queries regarding representation. Approach by letter only, enclosing cv and photograph. Will consider demo tapes and video showreels. *Commission*: 10%

Vincent Shaw Associates

20 Jay Mews, London SW7 2EP
Tel: 0171 581 8215
Fax: 0171 225 1079
E-mail: vincentshaw@clara.net
Contact *Vincent Shaw, Anna McCorquodale*

Established 1950. Personal management. Represents actors, voiceover artists, directors, designers, writers, stage and company managers and technicians. Welcomes queries from those seeking representation. Approach in writing with up-to-date photograph or *Spotlight* number and full cv. 'Find out the person to write to – a quick phone call will do this. Don't, therefore, write "Dear Sir/Madam" or, indeed, "Dear Vincent". As most casting directors want *Spotlight* numbers before seeing cvs, inclusion in *Spotlight* is vital. I can only consider actors I can see working or who have a showreel.' *Commission*: Theatre 10%; all other categories 15%

Robert Smith Agency

5 Vyvyan Road, Clifton,
Bristol BS8 3AD
Tel: 0117 973 8265
Fax: 0117 970 6956
Contact *Robert Smith, Patricia Smith*

Established 1985. Personal management. Represents actors, voiceover artists, walk-on and supporting artists and children. Welcomes queries regarding representation; approach in writing in the first instance ('No callers. Good, current pictures are imperative!') Will consider demo tapes and video showreels. *Commission*: Theatre 10%; all other categories 15%

Speak Limited

46 Old Compton Street,
London W1V 5PB
Tel: 0171 287 4646
Fax: 0171 287 5283
Contact *Abigail Wells-Hardy, Graeme Legg*

Established 1992. Personal management. Represents voiceover artists, DJs, presenters, foreign voiceover artists and disabled actors. No queries regarding representation 'unless well known'. No demo tapes or video showreels. *Commission*: 15%

Helen Stafford Management

14 Park Avenue, Bush Hill Park,
Enfield, Middlesex EN1 2HP
Tel: 0181 360 6329
Fax: 0181 482 0371
E-mail: castnet@avnet.co.uk
Contact *Helen Stafford*

Established 1992. Personal management representing actors only. Does not welcome queries from those seeking representation. No demo tapes or video showreels. *Commission*: Theatre 10%;

TV, Film, Radio, Voiceover, Commercials 15%

Stage Centre Management
41 North Road (Omnibus Business Centre), London N7 9DP
Tel: 0171 607 0872
Fax: 0171 609 0213
Contact *Alison Allan*

Established 1982. Cooperative management representing actors only. Welcomes queries regarding representation; approach in writing or by telephone. No unsolicited demo tapes or video showreels. 'Make sure cvs are well set out. Think about the reasons why you would like to join a co-op. Know where your immediate casting lies and where you'd like to see your career going. Also, remember you will be representing other actors – make every effort to do this unselfishly.' *Commission*: 10%

Talking Heads – The Voice Agency
Eastgate House,
16–19 Eastcastle Street,
London WIN 7PA
Tel: 0171 636 7755
Fax: 0171 636 5757
E-mail:106700.3414@compuserve.com
Contact *John Sachs, Anthony Blackburn, Jennifer Taylor*

Cooperative agency representing voiceover artists only. Welcomes queries regarding representation; applications 'by post only with sae if you want submission returned'. Will consider demo tapes ('*professional showreels only*'). *Commission*: 15%

Target Casting Ltd
Rhodes House, 112 St Leonardsgate, Lancaster LA1 1NN
Tel: 01524 67354
Fax: 01524 848812
E-mail: target@actorsuk.demon.co.uk
Contact *Jane Hollowood (Coordinator), Will Tacey (Chairperson)*

Cooperative management representing actors. Welcomes queries from actors seeking representation. Send letter, enclosing cv and recent photograph plus details of any current or future theatre/television production where your work can be seen. Will consider demo tapes and video showreels (enclose sae for return). 'Please be aware that we are a co-op with all the responsibilities that that entails. We are always happy to explain the essential differences between co-ops and personal management.' *Commission*: Theatre 7%; Radio, Voiceovers and Promotions 10%; TV, Film and Commercials 12%

Brian Taylor – Nina Quick Associates*
12 Abingdon Road, Kensington High Street, London W8 6AF
Tel: 0171 937 2116/7
Fax: 0171 937 2117
Contact *Brian Taylor, Nina Quick, Peter Yon, Mavis Everitt*

Established 1980. Personal management representing actors only. Welcomes queries from those seeking representation; approach in writing in the first instance, enclosing photograph and cv. Will consider demo tapes and video showreels. *Commission*: Theatre, Film, TV and Radio 10%; Commercials 15%

Jim Thompson
1 Northdown Road, Belmont,
Surrey SM2 6DY
Tel: 0181 770 2511/2
Fax: 0181 643 6687
Contact *Jim Thompson, Jenny
Donnison*

Established 1967. Personal management. Represents actors, voiceover artists, directors, writers; also children (represented by Jenny Donnison). Welcomes queries regarding representation; approach in writing in the first instance. Will consider demo tapes and video showreels. *Commission*: Commercials 15%; all other categories 12.5%

Roxane Vacca Management*
73 Beak Street, London W1R 3LF
Tel: 0171 734 8085
Fax: 0171 734 8086

Established 1991. Personal management representing actors only. Welcomes written queries regarding representation. No demo tapes or video showreels. *Commission*: 10%

The Voice Box
PO Box 82, Altrincham,
Cheshire WA16 0QD
Tel: 0161 928 3222
Fax: 0161 928 7849
E-mail: voice.box@zen.co.uk
Contact *Vicki Robinson*

Established 1984. Personal management representing voiceover artists only. Welcomes queries regarding representation, by telephone only. No unsolicited demo tapes; please check first. *Commission*: 15%

Voice Shop
Bakerloo Chambers,
304 Edgware Road, London W2 1DY
Tel: 0171 402 3966
Fax: 0171 706 1002
E-mail: voiceshop@compuserve.com
Contact *Maxine Wiltshire*

Established 1979. Personal management representing voiceover artists only.

Walmsley Associates
37A Ormsworth Road,
London SW8 4RJ
Tel: 0171 627 4393
Fax: 0171 720 2433
Contact *Peter Walmsley*

Established 1970. Personal management. Represents actors, directors and choreographers. Does not welcome queries regarding representation. *Commission*: 10%–15%

Waring & McKenna
Lauderdale House, 11 Gower Street,
London WC1E 2HB
Tel: 0171 691 1333
Fax: 0171 691 1335
Contact *Daphne Waring, Jefferson
McKenna*

Established 1993. Personal management. Represents actors, voiceover artists, directors and writers. Welcomes written queries regarding representation. Will consider demo tapes and video showreels if 'properly labelled'. 'Give agents plenty of warning if you want them to see your work. We are booked two weeks in advance and we still get letters inviting us to shows with two to three days' notice! Be aware of how people's names are spelled and addresses of agents. So many people get our names wrong.' *Commission*: Theatre 10%; TV, Film and Commercials 12.5%

Newton Wills Management

Utopia Studios, 17 Church Street,
Belton-in-Rutland, Rutland LE15 9JU
Tel: 01572 717314
Fax: 01572 717314
Contact *Newton Wills, Christopher Socci*

Established 1972. Personal management. Represents actors ('those with musical/vocal talent useful, also overseas actors who are able to work in the UK') and directors. Welcomes queries regarding representation. Approach in writing, enclosing cv and photograph. Will consider demo tapes and video showreels. 'Do not send photographs you are not 100 per cent happy with – if you are not happy, neither are we!' *Commission*: Varies according to contract.

The Wendy Wisbey Agency

2 Rupert Road, London W4 1LX
Tel: 0181 994 1210/5378
Fax: 0181 994 5378
Contact *Wendy Wisbey*

Established 1956. Fellow of the Agents Association (Great Britain) Ltd. Represents actors only. Welcomes queries from those seeking representation. Approaches may be made in writing, enclosing an sae or by phone (weekdays before 5 p.m. and not between 1 p.m. and 2 p.m.). 'Will chat to Equity members and experienced actors.' No demo tapes or video showreels. *Commission*: 10%

April Young Limited

11 Woodlands Road, Barnes,
London SW13 0JZ
Tel: 0181 876 7030
Fax: 0181 878 7017
Contact *Miss Lesley Ray, Miss April Young*

Established 1975. Personal management. Represents actors. Does not welcome queries regarding representation. No demo tapes or video showreels. 'We do not seek to extend our present list of personally managed clients.'

Young Casting Agency*

7 Beaumont Gate, Glasgow G12 9EE
Tel: 0141 334 2646/339 5180
Fax: 0141 334 0575
Contact *Freddie Young, Ann McArthur, Jayne Tollan*

Established 1972. Personal management. Represents actors, voiceover artists, walk-on and supporting artists. Welcomes queries from those seeking representation; approach in writing in the first instance. *Commission*: 10%

The Workplace

Casting Directors

Casting directors are the go-betweens for actors and directors. It is their job to interpret how the director visualises his production and then to find the actors who can realise that vision. Casting directors hold a position of strength in the production team which should not be underestimated, and it is important for the actor to know them and vital that his agent has a good relationship with them.

Casting directors generally conduct their business by telephone and work under considerable pressure. Making casual query calls may result in an abrupt response. Check out the following listing and take note of how individuals prefer to be approached – advance performance notices are often welcome, although it has to be said that it is unlikely a London-based casting director will travel out of town to see something on spec.

Dorothy Andrew
– see **Mersey Television Company** in Film, Video and Independent Production Companies, page 299

Penny Barbour Casting
Rosemary Cottage, Etchingham, East Sussex TN19 7DD
Tel: 01580 819306
Contact Penny Barbour

Established 1965. Drama, documentary, corporate and training films. Welcomes written casting queries. No demo tapes or video showreels.

Michael Barnes
25 Old Oak Road, London W3 7HN
Tel: 0181 749 8799
Fax: 0181 742 9385

Commercials and corporate videos. Approach by fax or post in the first instance. No unsolicited demo tapes or video showreels. Welcomes performance notices.

Lesley Beastall
– see **Broadcasting Co.**, page 106

Maureen Bewick
104A Dartmouth Road,
London NW2 4HB

Commercials and corporate work. Does not welcome casting queries; no telephone calls. Approach in writing with performance notices. No unsolicited demo tapes or video showreels.

Sarah Bird
– see **The Casting Company**, page 107

Stephanie Booth
74B St James's Drive,
London SW17 7RR
Tel: 0181 672 4052
Fax: 0181 672 4052

Established 1994. Films, commercials, corporate, television and theatre. Welcomes casting queries 'c/o ansaphone'. Will consider demo tapes and video showreels as long as an sae is provided. Welcomes performance notices. 'No personal callers as I work from home. If I am working on anything new I use SBS or leave a message of casting breakdown on my ansaphone.'

Siobhan Bracke
Upper Flat, 33 Sandy Coombe Road,
East Twickenham TW1 2LR
Tel: 0181 891 5686

Former Head of Casting at the RSC (1985–91). Film, television and theatre. Does not welcome casting queries or demo tapes/video showreels. Happy to receive performance notices.

Wendy Brazington
No. 2 Old School Buildings,
Archdale Road, London SE22 9HP
Tel: 0181 299 9660
Fax: 0181 299 9660
Contact Wendy Brazington, Emily Morrissey

Established 1995. Film, television and theatre. Welcomes casting queries; send cv and photograph with covering letter but please call before sending submissions in response to PCR. No demo tapes or video showreels. Welcomes performance notices.

Broadcasting Co.
Canalot Studios, 222 Kensal Road,
London W10 5BN
Tel: 0171 460 5220
Fax: 0171 460 5223
Contact Lesley Beastall, Sophie North

Commercials. No telephone calls; approach in writing. Performance notices welcome. No unsolicited demo tapes or video showreels.

Malcolm Bullivant
9 Montrose Villas,
Hammersmith Terrace,
London W6 9TT
Tel: 0181 748 4146
Fax: 0181 748 1793

Established 1981. Commercials. No telephone calls or faxes. Approach in writing. Performance notices welcome. Will consider demo tapes; enclose correct postage for return. 'Please ensure letters, cvs and photographs are stapled together.'

Linda Butcher

39 Arlington Road, Surbiton,
Surrey KT6 6BN
Fax: 0181 390 9777

Television drama. No casting queries. Performance notices welcome. No unsolicited demo tapes or video showreels.

Caird Littlewood Casting

PO Box MT86, Wigton Park, Leeds,
West Yorkshire LS17 8YQ
Tel: 0113 288 8014
Fax: 0113 266 6068
Contact *Angela Caird*

Television, commercials and corporate videos. Approach by telephone or letter; no faxes. Performance notices welcome. Will consider demo tapes; enclose correct postage for return.

Laura Cairns

15 Convent Close, Henbury,
Bristol BS10 7XQ
Tel: 0117 950 6488

Established 1982. Covers all areas of production. Welcomes casting queries by letter. No telephone calls. 'Please put name on the back of photographs and send with a short but to-the-point letter.' No unsolicited demo tapes or video showreels. Welcomes performance notices ('but it's not always possible to attend').

Candid Casting

111–113 Great Titchfield Street,
London W1P 7FQ
Tel: 0171 636 6644
Fax: 0171 636 5522
Contact *Amanda Tabak, Andrea Clark*

Established 1992. Film, television and commercials. No casting queries.

Demo tapes and video showreels on request only. Welcomes performance notices.

Cannon, Dudley & Associates

43A Belsize Square,
London NW3 4HN
Tel: 0171 433 3393
Fax: 0171 433 3599
E-mail: dudley@dircon.co.uk
Contact *Carol Dudley, Elaine Fallon*

Established 1981 (UK), 1980 (US). Feature films, television, commercials and theatre. Welcomes casting queries; approach in writing. Will consider demo tapes and video showreels. Welcomes performance notices.

Di Carling

1st Floor, 49 Frith Street,
London W1V 5TE
Tel: 0171 287 6446

Television films, commercials and training films. No unsolicited demo tapes or video showreels.

The Casting Company

22 Great Marlborough Street,
London W1V 1AF
Contact *Michelle Guishe, Sarah Bird*

Feature films, television and commercials. Does not welcome general letters but will try to see actors' work if performance notices are sent.

The Casting Directors

24 Cloncurry Street,
London SW6 6DS
Tel: 0171 731 5988
Contact *Gillian Hawser*

Films, television and theatre. Happy to

receive performance notices; approach in writing in the first instance. No unsolicited demo tapes or video showreels.

Chard Helps Casting
10–14 Macklin Street,
London WC2B 5NF
Contact *Alison Chard, Audrey Helps*

Established 1995. Television, commercials, corporate and occasional theatre. Welcomes casting queries, in writing only. No unsolicited demo tapes or video showreels – 'write asking if we have time to view tape and always include return postage'. Welcomes performance notices – send a letter and flyer for the show. 'We need to see an actor's work before we can properly consider them for future roles.'

Charkham Casting
3rd Floor, 122 Wardour Street,
London W1V 3LA
Tel: 0171 734 0202
Fax: 0171 439 8568
Contact *Beth Charkham*

Feature films, television and commercials. Written casting queries only. No demo tapes or video showreels. Welcomes performance notices.

Creative Casting International
14 Lodge Avenue, Elstree,
Hertfordshire WD6 3ND
Tel: 0181 953 3789
Fax: 0181 953 0800
Contact *Joanne Waterford (Theatre), Hayley O'Brian (Commercials), Angela Reynolds (Extras), Chris Mitchell (Children's Dept), Laura Way (Television), Jonathan Gartland (Radio/Voiceovers), Michael Bradley*

Pierce (Film), Catrin John (Comedy/Light Entertainment), Corinna Edwards (Models)

Established 1992. Theatre, film, radio, voiceover, commercials, television, comedy and light entertainment. Welcomes casting queries by telephone or in writing. Will consider demo tapes and video showreels. Welcomes performance notices. 'Please feel more than welcome to phone any of us and we will gladly help you as best we can. We are a group of nine full-time casting directors – please do not send nine photographs as we use just one casting file. We accept any type of photograph and hold general interviews every three months. We are the friendliest CDs in the business, so don't be afraid to call.'

Crocodile Casting
Unit 7, Spring Villa Park, Spring Villa Road, Edgware, Middlesex HA8 7EB
Fax: 0181 203 7711
Contact *Claire Gibbs, Tracie Saban*

An 'actor-friendly' casting company, run by two actresses, specialising in commercials and pop videos. No telephone calls. Approach in writing in the first instance, enclosing cv and photograph. 'All details are kept on file.' Welcomes performance notices. No unsolicited demo tapes or video showreels.

Johnny Dallas (Casting)
3 Rushden House, Tatlow Road, Glenfield, Leicester LE3 8ND
Tel: 0116 287 9594
Fax: 0116 287 9594
Contact *Johnny Dallas*

Established 1980. Television, theatre and pantomimes. Has no objection to casting queries – send letter with sae for reply. Will consider demo tapes and video showreels if accompanied by sae. Welcomes performance notices. 'While I am happy to hear of and see any actor, I would request that all approaches are made by letter and not by telephone. It is essential that actors, when applying for casting, stick to the criteria described. Nothing is more annoying than to ask for males and get dozens of females replying. Please also ensure that the sae sent for a reply is the same size as the photograph – 10 x 8 photographs with 3 x 5 envelopes mean that invariably the details are "binned".'

Jane Davies Casting
PO Box 680, Sutton, Surrey SM1 3ZG
Tel: 0181 715 1036
Fax: 0181 644 9746
Contact *Jane Davies, John Connor*

Film and television. Casting queries not welcomed. No unsolicited demo tapes or video showreels. Welcomes performance notices – 'they are the most useful information an actor can give me, whether for theatre, film or television'.

Noel Davis Casting
Flat 6, 160 Gloucester Road, London SW7 4QF
Tel: 0171 835 0884
Contact *Noel Davis, Harry Audley*

Established 1976. Feature films, television films and commercials. Does not welcome casting queries from individual actors – prefers to work with agents. No demo tapes or video showreels; no performance notices. 'One-third of photographs sent to me have no name on the back so they go in the bin. We have no

facility for returning unsolicited photographs and tapes; they will not be returned.'

Paul de Freitas
2 Conduit Street, London W1R 9TG
Tel: 0171 434 4233
Fax: 0171 355 1084

Films and commercials. Approach in writing; no telephone calls. No unsolicited demo tapes or video showreels.

Lesley De Pettit
2 Park View, Hatfield, Hertfordshire AL9 5HG

Films, television series and commercials. Write in the first instance. Performance notices welcome. Will consider demo tapes and video showreels; please ensure correct postage is enclosed for their return.

Gillian Diamond
22 Burghley Road, Kentish Town, London NW5 1HE
Tel: 0171 485 6522
Fax: 0171 482 1384

Casting director for the Peter Hall Company. Formerly Casting Director of the RSC and Royal Court Theatre and for 14 years, until 1987, Head of Casting at the National Theatre. Does not welcome casting queries or demo tapes and video showreels. Happy to receive performance notices.

Julia Duff
11 Goodwins Court, London WC2N 4LL

Film, television and commercials. Approach in writing in the first instance; performance notices welcome. No unsolicited demo tapes or video showreels.

Irene East Casting
40 Brookwood Avenue, Barnes,
London SW13 0LR
Tel: 0181 876 5686
Fax: 0181 876 5686
Contact *Irene East*

Established 1989. Feature films, television and theatre. Does not welcome casting queries but will consider demo tapes and video showreels. Welcomes performance notices.

Liz England Casting
193 Wardour Street, London W1V 3FA

Commercials, films and television. Prefers to be approached in writing in the first instance. No unsolicited demo tapes or video showreels.

Richard Evans Casting
10 Shirley Road, London W4 1DD
Tel: 0181 994 6304
Fax: 0181 742 1010
Contact *Richard Evans*

Established 1989. Theatre, television, commercials and corporates. Welcomes casting queries, primarily by letter but telephone is fine 'as long as you have something specific to say'. Will consider demo tapes and video showreels. Send sae with sufficient postage for return. 'We often have a backlog, so please bear with us as it might be some time before it's watched and returned.' Welcomes performance notices – 'We visit the theatre four to six

times a week as well as watching television and films. Seeing an actor's work is always most useful to us. An actor should get to know who people are and what they do; be pleasant and sensible and you'll get on!'

Ann Fielden Casting
5 Rectory Lane, Tooting,
London SW17 9PZ
Tel: 0181 767 3939
Fax: 0181 672 4803
Contact *Ann Fielden*

Established 1970. Film and television. Welcomes casting queries by post or telephone but only once on any production – 'no weekly phone calls, please!' No unsolicited demo tapes or video showreels. Welcomes performance notices.

Susie Figgis
35 Fortess Road, London NW5 1AD

Feature films. Approach in writing in the first instance with performance notices. Credits include: *Wish You Were Here, Gandhi, The Mission, Crying Game, The Full Monty, Michael Collins.*

Bunny Fildes Casting
56–60 Wigmore Street,
London W1H 9DG
Tel: 0171 935 1254
Fax: 0171 486 6437
Contact *Bunny Fildes*

Established 1970. Film, television, commercials and theatre. No casting queries from individual actors; prefers to deal with agents only. 'Sometimes' considers demo tapes or video showreels. Welcomes performance notices.

Allan Foenander
59 North Eyot Gardens, St Peter's
Square, London W6 9NL
Tel: 0181 748 9641

Films, television and documentaries.
Will consider cvs and performance
notices; only send photographs if you
are not in *The Spotlight*. No unsolicited
demo tapes or video showreels.

Celestia Fox
5 Clapham Common Northside,
London SW4 0QW

Feature films. Credits include the
Merchant Ivory films *A Room with a
View*, *Maurice* and *A Handful of Dust*.
Does not welcome unsolicited photo-
graphs and cvs.

Jane Frisby
51 Ridge Road, London N8 9LJ
Tel: 0181 342 4747
Fax: 0181 348 9122

Commercials and films. Approach in
writing in the first instance. Welcomes
performance notices. No demo tapes or
video showreels.

Caroline Funnell
25 Rattray Road, London SW2 1AZ
Tel: 0171 326 4417
Fax: 0171 326 1713

Theatre casting director, including the
English Theater Frankfurt. Welcomes
performance notices. No demo tapes or
video showreels.

Joyce Gallie
37 Westcroft Square, London W6 0TA
Tel: 0181 741 4009
Fax: 0181 748 4682

Film, television and commercials. No

telephone calls. Does not particularly
welcome unsolicited letters from actors
– 'we are inundated' – nor demo tapes
or video showreels.

GB Casting
1 Charlotte Street, London W1P 1DH
Tel: 0171 636 2437
Contact *Karin Grainger*

Mainly commercials. No telephone
calls. Approach in writing with cv and
photograph, and performance notices
where relevant. No unsolicited demo
tapes or video showreels.

Nina Gold
1st Floor, 36B Notting Hill Gate,
London W11 3HX

Film, television and commercials. Does
not welcome casting queries. Happy to
receive performance notices. No
unsolicited demo tapes or video
showreels.

Lesley Grayburn Casting
74 Leigh Gardens,
London NW10 5HP
Tel: 0181 969 6112
Fax: 0181 962 2846
Contact *Lesley Grayburn*

Commercials. Accepts casting queries
during office hours. No demo tapes or
video showreels. Welcomes performance notices ('but not for weekends').

Marcia Gresham Casting
12 Sherbrooke Road,
London SW6 7HU
Tel: 0171 381 2876
Fax: 0171 381 4496

Established 1992. Theatre and television. Casting queries in writing only;

send a letter enclosing cv and, if possible, a performance notice. Will consider demo tapes and video showreels only if postage is enclosed for their return.

Michelle Guishe
– see **The Casting Company**, page 107

Anne Henderson Casting Ltd
93 Kelvin Road, Highbury,
London N5 2PL
Contact Anne Henderson

Established 1983. Film, television, commercials and theatre. Does not welcome casting queries. No demo tapes or video showreels unless requested. Welcomes performance notices – 'actors should only get in touch to let me know about theatre, film or television pieces they are performing'.

Polly Hootkins Casting
37 Berwick Street, London W1V 3RF
Tel: 0171 287 5643
Fax: 0171 287 5640
Contact Polly Hootkins

Established 1988. Film, television and theatre. Prefers to deal with agents only. No unsolicited demo tapes or video showreels. Welcomes performance notices (via post).

Hubbard Casting
1 Old Compton Street,
London W1V 5PH
Tel: 0171 494 3191
Fax: 0171 437 0559
Contact John Hubbard, Ros Hubbard, Daniel Hubbard

Feature films, television and commer-

cials. Approach by letter in the first instance. Will consider demo tapes and video showreels, provided sufficient postage is enclosed for their return.

Simone Ireland and Vanessa Pereira Casting
Rose Cottage, The Aberdeen Centre,
22–24 Highbury Grove,
London N5 2EA
Tel: 0171 288 1880
Fax: 0171 288 1820
Contact Kate Bulpitt

Feature films. Does not welcome casting queries. No demo tapes or video showreels. Welcomes invitations to see an actor's work – 'drama-school productions are of definite interest'.

Jennifer Jaffrey
136 Hicks Avenue, Greenford,
Middlesex UB6 8HB
Tel: 0181 578 2899
Fax: 0181 575 0369

Feature films; specialises in Asian casting. Approach in writing with cv and photograph. No telephone calls. No unsolicited demo tapes or video showreels. Performance notices welcome.

Priscilla John
The Old Mill, Millers Way,
1A Shepherds Bush Road,
London W6 7NA
Tel: 0181 743 8011
Fax: 0181 749 4571

Films and television. Credits include: *Amistad, Saving Private Ryan, Seven Years in Tibet, Cinderella*. Happy to receive cvs, photographs and performance notices. No unsolicited demo tapes or video showreels.

Marilyn Johnson
11 Goodwins Court,
London WC2N 4LL

Television, films and commercials. Does not welcome letters from actors; prefers to receive performance notices. No unsolicited demo tapes or video showreels. Credits include: *Holding On* (BBC), *Tess of the D'Urbervilles* (LWT), *The Life and Crimes of William Palmer* (Yorkshire TV).

Doreen Jones
The Old Mill, Millers Way,
1A Shepherds Bush Way,
London W6 7NA
Tel: 0171 743 1668

Television and film. Approach by letter in the first instance. No unsolicited demo tapes or video showreels.

Sue Jones
35 Plympton Road, London NW6 7EH
Tel: 0171 372 0036
Fax: 0171 372 2740

Feature films, television, commercials and some theatre. Approach in the first instance. No telephone calls. No unsolicited demo tapes or video showreels. Performance notices welcome.

Beverley Keogh Casting
10A Derby Road, Withington,
Manchester M14 6UW
Tel: 0161 224 2226
Fax: 0161 225 0900
Contact *Beverley Keogh*

Established 1980. Feature films, television and commercials. Welcomes casting queries – in writing only. Will consider demo tapes and video showreels. Welcomes performance notices.

Suzy Korel
20 Blenheim Road, London NW8 0LX
Tel: 0171 624 6435
Fax: 0171 372 3964

Commercials, film, television and corporate videos. Approach by letter in the first instance. No unsolicited demo tapes or video showreels. Welcomes performance notices.

Irene Lamb
Flat 4, Avenue House, 97 Walton Street, London SW3 2JY
Tel: 0171 589 6452

Feature films and television. Approach in writing in the first instance, enclosing cv and *Spotlight* number. No unsolicited demo tapes or video showreels.

Jane L'Epine Smith
2 Chertsey Road, St Margaret's,
Twickenham TW1 1JQ
Tel: 0181 891 1685

Film, television, corporate videos and theatre. Welcomes letters and performance notices. No unsolicited demo tapes or video showreels.

Sharon Levinson
30 Stratford Villas, Camden Town,
London NW1 9SG
Tel: 0171 485 2057
Fax: 0171 916 5872

Established 1981. Television, commercials and corporate videos. Does not welcome casting queries.

Judy Loe
60 Thames Village, Hartington Road,
London W4 3UF

Television only. Approach in writing in
the first instance enclosing cv and
Spotlight number. No unsolicited demo
tapes or video showreels.

Christine McMurrich
16 Spring Vale Avenue, Brentford,
Middlesex TW8 9QH
Tel: 0181 568 0137
Fax: 0181 568 0137
Contact *Christine McMurrich*

Established 1993. Television. Welcomes
casting queries by letter. No demo
tapes or video showreels. Welcomes
invitations to see actors' work, if in
London.

Melika Morrison
The Well House, Windsor Road,
Gerrards Cross,
Buckinghamshire SL9 7NW
Tel: 01753 889469
Fax: 01753 891596
Contact *Melika Morrison, Tatijana
Jacobs*

Established 1990. Commercials and
feature films. Welcomes written
casting queries – 'no telephone calls,
please'. Will consider demo tapes and
video showreels. Welcomes performance notices. NB 'We do not deal
with actors without agents.'

Mugshots Ltd
20 Greek Street, London W1V 5LF
Tel: 0171 437 9245
Fax: 0171 437 0308
Contact *Kate Evans, Alison Fernley*

Established 1987. Commercials and
feature films. Does not welcome

casting queries. No demo tapes or
video showreels. Welcomes performance notices.

Joyce Nettles
16 Cressida Road, London N19 3JW

Does not welcome casting queries but
'I do not mind actors writing to me
informing me of their work'. No
unsolicited demo tapes or video
showreels. Tends not to do quick-
turnaround projects and therefore is
not in need of casting suggestions
unlike casting directors whose
turnover is faster.

Sophie North
– *see* **Broadcasting Co.**, page 106

Debbie O'Brien
72 The High Street, Ashwell,
Nr Baldock, Hertfordshire SG7 5NL
Tel: 01462 742919
E-mail: debcast@aol.com

Theatre – mainly musicals. Casting
director for The Turnstyle Group.
Happy to receive performance notices.
No unsolicited demo tapes or video
showreels.

Susie Parriss Casting
91 Regent Street, London W1R 7TB
Tel: 0171 734 5053
Fax: 0171 734 5054
Contact *Susie Parriss*

Established 1991. Feature films and
television. Does not welcome casting
queries unless 'it is for a specific role
they genuinely know is currently being
cast'. Approach in writing only – no
faxes or telephone calls. No unsolicited

demo tapes or video showreels. Welcomes invitations to see an actor's work – 'a postcard listing theatre venue details or television programme is ideal'.

Jill Pearce Casting
6 Langley Street, London WC2H 9JA
Tel: 0171 240 0316

Television and film commercials. Approach by telephone in the first instance. No unsolicited demo tapes or video showreels.

Patsy Pollock
21 First Avenue, London SW14 8SP

Feature films only. Recent credits include: *My Life So Far* (directed by Hugh Hudson, produced by David Puttnam), *Mission Impossible*.

Carl Proctor
15B Bury Place, London WC1A 2JB

Film, television and commercials. Does not welcome casting queries but welcomes invitations to see actors' work.

Liora Reich
The Rotunda Studios, Rear of 116–18 Finchley Road, London NW2 5HT

Feature films only. Does not welcome casting queries but performance notices may be sent.

Simone Reynolds
60 Hebdon Road, London SW17 7NN
Fax: 0181 767 0280
Contact *Simone Reynolds*

Established 1981. Feature films, televi-sion and commercials. Welcomes casting queries by letter only. No unsolicited demo tapes or video showreels. Welcomes performance notices – 'I like to see an actor's work before meeting him/her'.

Mary Selway and Sarah Trevis
Twickenham Film Studios,
The Barons, St Margaret's,
Twickenham, Middlesex TW1 2AW
Tel: 0181 607 8888

Films and television. Credits include: *Dry White Season*, *White Mischief*, *Gorillas in the Mist*, *Paris by Night*, *Lost in Space*. No casting queries or tele-phone calls.

Philip Shaw Casting
29 Morden Gardens, Mitcham,
Surrey CR4 4DH
Tel: 0181 715 8943
Fax: 0181 715 8943
Contact *Philip Shaw*

Established 1994. Feature films, televi-sion, theatre, commercials, corporate videos and music promos. Welcomes casting queries – send letter with full cv and photograph. No telephone calls. No unsolicited demo tapes or video showreels. Welcomes performance notices. Philip Shaw, as a former actor, teacher and theatrical agent, also operates an 'actors' advisory service' on matters relating to theatre, film, television and commercial employ-ment. Also consults with actors about their cvs, photographs, letter-writing and approaching agents, casting direc-tors, producers, etc. Offers audition coaching, sight-reading and voice/ speech training.

Vincent Shaw Associates

20 Jay Mews, London SW7 2EP
Tel: 0171 581 8215
Fax: 0171 225 1079
Contact *Vincent Shaw*

Established 1950. Mainly operate as agents and managers but act as casting advisors two or three times a year. Invitations to see actors' work welcome.

Debbie Shepherd Casting

59 St Martin's Lane,
London WC2N 4JS
Contact *Debbie Shepherd*

Commercials only. No casting queries but welcomes performance notices. Will consider video showreels with sae enclosed.

Hazel Singer

1 Newcastle House, Luxborough Street, London W1M 3LF

Television commercials, corporate videos and training films. No casting queries but happy to receive performance notices.

Suzanne Smith Casting

138 Haverstock Hill, Belsize Park,
London NW3 2AX
Tel: 0171 722 2085
Fax: 0171 483 2202
E-mail: zan@dircon.co.uk

Feature films, television and theatre. Welcomes written casting queries with photograph and cv. No demo tapes or video showreels. Welcomes performance notices.

Liz Stoll

24 Corinne Road, Tufnell Park,
London N19 5EY
Tel: 0171 700 0724
Fax: 0171 700 0724
E-mail: liz.stoll@ndirect.co.uk

Theatre, musicals, films, television, training films, corporate videos and commercials. Welcomes casting queries. No telephone enquiries; approach in writing with cv and performance notices. No unsolicited demo tapes or video showreels.

Emma Style Casting

115 Finchley Road, London NW3 6HY
Tel: 0171 586 4946
Fax: 0171 483 2829
Contact *Emma Style*

Established 1993. Feature films, television and commercials. Written casting queries only. No demo tapes or video showreels. Welcomes performance notices.

Mark Summers Casting at Casting Unlimited

Ava House, 209 Hatton Road,
Bedfont, Middlesex TW14 9QY (also at 4518½ Hazeltine Avenue, Sherman Oaks, Los Angeles, CA 91423, USA)
E-mail: casting@vossnet.co.uk
Contact *Mark Summers, Ben Summers, David Hall*

Established 1988. Film, television, commercials, voiceover, stage pop tours and pop promos. No unsolicited demo tapes or video showreels. Welcomes performance notices.

Shirley Teece

106 North View Road, London N8 7LP
Tel: 0181 347 9241

Television and musicals. Approach in

writing with cv and photograph in the first instance. Welcomes performance notices. No unsolicited demo tapes or video showreels.

Gill Titchmarsh

75 Thornton Avenue, Chiswick,
London W4 1QF
Tel: 0181 994 8173
Fax: 0181 742 2072
Contact Gill Titchmarsh, Gary Davy

Feature films, television, commercials and theatre. Prefers casting queries to come from agents. 'It's very irritating for the same actor to keep phoning on a regular basis.' Will consider demo tapes and video showreels if sae enclosed. Welcomes performance notices.

Rose Tobias Shaw

219 Liverpool Road, London N1 1LX
Fax: 0171 609 9028

Film, television and commercials. Approach in writing in the first instance, enclosing cv and photograph. Will try to cover a show if performance notice sent. No unsolicited demo tapes or video showreels.

Moira Townsend

Unit 011, Canalot Production Studios,
222 Kensal Road, London W10 5BN
Tel: 0181 964 4043
Fax: 0181 960 8907

Commercials, television, corporate videos and theatre. Welcomes casting queries and performance notices. No unsolicited demo tapes or video showreels. Also runs the Casting Couch and the Video File (see Publications and Services, page 370).

Jill Trevellick

123 Rathcoole Gardens,
London N8 9PH
Tel: 0181 340 2734
Fax: 0181 348 7400

Feature films, television, commercials and theatre. Prefers approaches from actors to be specific rather than general – performance notices with cvs and photographs, ideally. Will consider demo tapes and video showreels if sae enclosed.

Sarah Trevis

– see **Mary Selway**, page 115

Jane Walker Casting

Rayleigh House, 2 Richmond Hill,
Richmond, Surrey TW10 6QX
Tel: 0181 940 1117
Contact Jane Walker

Established 1996. Theatre and television. Welcomes casting queries and performance notices; approach by letter. No unsolicited demo tapes or video showreels.

Toby Whale Casting

80 Shakespeare Road,
London W3 6SN
Tel: 0181 993 2821
Fax: 0181 993 8096
E-mail: twhale@dircon.co.uk
Contact Toby Whale

Feature films, television, commercials and theatre. Casting queries to be made in writing. Will consider demo tapes and video showreels. Welcomes performance notices.

Mela White
29 Talbot Road, Twickenham,
Middlesex TW2 6SJ
Tel: 0181 287 2839

Film, television, commercials, theatre
(including fringe) and corporate work.
Approach by telephone. No unsolicited
demo tapes or video showreels.

Also runs an actors' advisory
service, particularly for those seeking a
change of agent. Gives help with
presentation – photographs and cvs.
Telephone for details.

Sharon Young Casting
1 Charlotte Street, London W1P 1DH
Tel: 0171 255 1899
Contact *Sharon Young*

Music videos, corporate videos and
commercials. No telephone calls.
Approach in writing with cv and
photograph. No unsolicited demo
tapes or video showreels.

Jeremy Zimmerman Casting
Canaletto Yard,
43–45 Beak Street,
London W1R 3LE
Tel: 0171 437 4747
Fax: 0171 437 4748
E-mail: zimmcasting@compuserve.com

Established 1994. Feature films and
television. Welcomes written casting
enquiries. No demo tapes or video
showreels. Welcomes performance
notices.

Repertory and Regional Theatres

Repertory theatres continue their struggle for survival in the face of ever-increasing odds. The bricks and mortar are being refurbished with Lottery awards but funding to employ those who stage and perform within them has until recently remained pitifully restricted. However, news of the £5.7 million Arts Council Lottery Fund grant to Birmingham Rep gives cause for cautious optimism. This pilot scheme, designed to fund artistic rather than capital projects, will enable artistic director Bill Alexander to plan ambitious seasons, commission new work and tour the UK and abroad.

Unlike past practice, reps usually hire casts for individual plays rather than a permanent company for a whole season, although Andrew Manley at the Wolsey Theatre in Ipswich manages to buck this particular trend, continuing a style he employed at the Harrogate Theatre.

In 1997, rep salaries were the subject of dispute. A settlement was reached with Equity with the minimum wage for actors increased to £250 a week from April 1998 with a weekly subsistence allowance of £75. Hardly a fortune, considering the actor is likely to be living away from his permanent home. Not surprisingly, some may regard being cast for individual plays a bonus as it can prove financially crippling to accept a four- or five-month contract in rep. Not only does the money get stretched thin but availability for television or commercials can be on hold, particularly if performing at night and rehearsing during the day. However, the chances of being seen by regional television casting directors and neighbouring theatre directors is high and, nowadays, successful rep productions transfer to London.

Basingstoke

Haymarket Theatre Company

Haymarket Theatre, Wote Street,
Basingstoke, Hampshire RG21 7NW
Tel: 01256 355844
Fax: 01256 357130
Theatre Director *To be appointed*
Contact *Maria Hadnett (Assistant to the Director)*

Founded in 1974. In 1993 the theatre was given a £3-million refurbishment and the Haymarket Theatre Company was created. Plays one season per year, from September to June, attracting well-known 'names'. Previous productions have included: *The Lion in Winter* with Brian Blessed, *The Rise and Fall of Little Voice* with Millicent Martin, *The Innocents* with Sarah Brightman, *Aspects of Love* and *All My Sons* with Jean Boht (transferred to Liverpool Playhouse). Does not use casting directors; advertises in SBS; no telephone queries – send letter with cv and photograph. Does not hold general auditions. 'We do not welcome direct calls to the office because of an extremely busy schedule. Well-constructed letters with full cvs and good photographs, either from actors or their agents, are always looked at and considered.'

Belfast

Civic Arts Theatre

41 Botanic Avenue, Belfast BT7 1JG
Tel: 01232 316901
Fax: 01232 316906
Administrator *Anthony Stott*

Seating capacity: 550. Produces approximately 6 in-house shows per year plus an annual pantomime. Also hosts a wide range of touring companies as well as local amateur shows. Home of the Belfast Civic Arts Youth Theatre.

Lyric Theatre

55 Ridgeway Street, Belfast BT9 5FB
Tel: 01232 669660/669463
Fax: 01232 381395
Artistic Director *Robin Midgley*
Administrator *Patricia McBride*
Production Manager *Wallace McDowell*

Founded in 1951. (Present building opened in 1968.) Seating capacity: 305. Northern Ireland's only repertory theatre produces 8–10 productions annually in two seasons – autumn/winter and spring/summer. Also tours the country on average once or twice per year. Theatre policy encourages the production of new Irish writing although the seasons also include classical and European work plus family shows and musicals. Previous productions have included: *Annie, Pygmalion, The Desert Lullaby* by Jennifer Johnston (première), *Philadelphia, Here I Come!* by Brian Friel, *Playboy of the Western World, A Midsummer Night's Dream* and *Jane Eyre*. Does not use casting directors. Welcomes casting queries – call before sending cvs and photographs. Only holds general auditions 'very rarely' and then usually to update directors on 'who's out there'. 'The Lyric gives preference to Irish and Northern Irish actors so if you come into this category, please tell us. Being of another nationality does not rule out working here altogether but it is the theatre's employment/casting policy to look at actors from Ireland first. We cast for a season at a time – autumn casting in late spring/early summer and spring casting in autumn. However, directors tend to have clear ideas of particular people they want and will not take casting suggestions, so please ring first to check. The Lyric has no facility to keep cvs and photographs on file. *Please*, if you send a photo, send an sae to get it back. (We hate putting many pounds'-worth of photos in the bin but we have no place for them.) If you telephone to get information, the admin assistant will usually be able to tell you straight away what the current casting situation is. Our directors will frequently be unavailable for calls.'

Birmingham

Birmingham Repertory Theatre

Broad Street, Birmingham B1 2EP
Tel: 0121 236 6771
Fax: 0121 236 7883
Artistic Director Bill Alexander

Founded in 1913 by Barry Jackson; moved to present modern home in 1970. Seating capacity: 834–899 (flexible stage). At the time of going to press, major changes are under way at the Rep thanks to the award of a £5.7 million stabilisation grant from the Lottery. As a result, submissions for the spring 1998 season are not being accepted as this is a 'holding' season until the Lottery money takes effect in the autumn.

The Old Rep Theatre

Station Street, Birmingham B5 4DY
Tel: 0121 643 9050
Fax: 0121 643 8099
Actor/Manager Neal Foster
Contact Caroline Dunn
(Administrator)

The Birmingham Stage Company is the resident company of the Old Rep Theatre, and since its commencement in 1992 has staged 16 productions which have attracted the largest audiences to the Old Rep for 20 years. Its patrons are Sir Derek Jacobi and Paul Scofield. Stages three plays and one national tour annually – a mixed programme of classical, new and children's shows. Previous productions have included: Hamlet, directed by Richard Dreyfuss, Cat on a Hot Tin Roof, The Crucible, The Glass Menagerie, The BFG, HRH, She Stoops to Conquer and Woof. Advertises in PCR and SBS; does not use casting directors and welcomes casting queries – in writing. Occasionally holds general auditions for local actors only. 'When writing for a part, give specific, clear and where applicable, personal reasons for playing that role. Do not telephone – it never helps with us.'

Bolton

Octagon Theatre Company

Howell Croft South, Bolton,
Lancashire BL1 1SB
Tel: 01204 529407
Fax: 01204 380110
Artistic Director Lawrence Till
Associate Director Joanna Read
Assistant Director Richard Beecham

Founded 1967. The main stage Octagon is a flexible auditorium (five different shapes), seating up to 420. The Bill Naughton Theatre is a flexible auditorium, seating up to 80. A multi-award-winning theatre, it has a strong new writing element to productions and a commitment to community and education work. Lawrence Till has been artistic director since 1991. Produces 9 main-stage shows per year with 4 in the Bill Naughton Theatre and a varying number of youth theatre, education and community events, produced in two seasons: September to January and January to June. Recent productions have included: Edward the Second, Under Milk Wood, The Pitchfork Disney, Top Girls, Candida. Advertises for actors and sometimes uses casting directors.

Casting breakdowns usually available in July and November. Welcomes casting queries; approach in writing enclosing sae. Rarely holds general auditions.

'Invite directors to see productions giving plenty of notice and do not be disappointed if directors can't make it. Read the play before you come for an interview. If it's new, make sure you or your agent know something about it or the writer. Know *why* you want to play a specific part. Know something about the theatre.'

available and then send sae. If sending cv and photograph, please ensure an sae is enclosed for reply.'

Bromley

Churchill Theatre
– *see* **Theatre of Comedy at the Churchill Theatre Ltd** *under* Producing Theatres and Independent Managements, page 153

Bristol

Bristol Old Vic Company
Theatre Royal, King Street,
Bristol BS1 4ED
Tel: 0117 949 3993
Fax: 0117 949 4996
Artistic Director *Andy Hay*
Associate Director *Ian Hastings*
Contact *Hilary Davis (PA to the Artistic Director)*

Founded 1947. One of the country's oldest theatres, built in 1766. Bristol Old Vic Company is committed to producing new plays in both the Theatre Royal (650 seats) and the New Vic Studio (150 seats). Spring and autumn seasons, usually with 4 plays per season. Previous productions have included: *As You Like It*, *A Taste of Honey*, *The Amen Corner* and *Up the Feeder, Down the Mouth* (new play commissioned by the Bristol Old Vic.) *With Love from Nicolae* (world première by Lin Coghlan), *Brief Lives* (with Michael Williams), *Macbeth* (with Pete Postlethwaite in the title role). Very rarely advertises for actors or uses casting directors and does not hold general auditions. 'Telephone to find out when casting breakdown will be

Cardiff

Sherman Theatre
Senghennydd Road,
Cardiff CF2 4YE
Tel: 01222 396844
Fax: 01222 665581
Artistic Director *Phil Clark*
Associate Director *Matthew Bailey*
Contact *Patti Wallis*

Founded 1987. Produces three seasons annually, with approximately 8 shows in total. Also a receiving house for touring productions and hosts a theatre for young people. Main raked auditorium: 474 seats; studio: 163 seats. Previous productions have included: *Julius Caesar* and *Henry V* (cross-cast), *Table Manners* and *Kes* (cross-cast), *The BFG* (Christmas show), *Under the Bed* (Christmas show for under-7s), *Boy* by Roald Dahl. Does not advertise for actors or use casting directors. Welcomes casting queries from actors; 'send cvs for a specific production stating character you think you are suitable for'. Holds general auditions once a year (usually) for *local* actors only. If you come into this category, apply in the summer for inclusion on the audition list.

Chelmsford

Civic Theatre

– see **Newpalm Productions** *under* Producing Theatres and Independent Managements, page 151

Cheltenham

Everyman Theatre

Regent Street, Cheltenham,
Gloucestershire GL50 1HQ
Tel: 01242 512515
Fax: 01242 224305
Chief Executive *Richard Hogger*
Production Assistant *Adam Rowe*

Seating: 658 (main house); 60 (studio). The original theatre opened in 1891 and in the mid-eighties was given a £2.5-million refit. Subsequently the theatre ceased to be a producing repertory theatre and is now mainly a receiving house with only one or two in-house productions per year. In addition to these, it is involved in outreach work and new writing projects which require actors. Advertises in SBS and all casting is dealt with through agents. No casting queries, please.

Chester

Gateway Theatre Trust Ltd

Hamilton Place, Chester CH1 2BH
Tel: 01244 344238
Fax: 01244 317277
Artistic Director *Deborah Shaw*
Administrative Director *Katy Spicer*
Contact *Barbara Eaton (PA to the Directors)*

Founded in 1968. Seating capacity: 440. In 1995, the theatre won the prestigious Granada TV Flying Start award for Good Business Practice in the Arts and, in 1996, the first award from *The Stage* for special achievement in regional theatre was given to Jeremy Raison (Chester Gateway's previous artistic director). The theatre continues to give emphasis in its programming to new writing, including the commissioning of new plays. Runs two rep seasons per year, from September to December (Autumn) and from January to June (Spring), producing eight or nine plays annually. In the past three years, the theatre has produced 10 world premières, one British première and five national tours. Recent productions have included: *All at Sea* by Vanessa Brooks, *Vertigo*, an adaptation by Sean O'Connor from the book which inspired the Hitchcock thriller, *The Star Spangled Girl* by Neil Simon, *Romeo and Juliet*, *George's Marvellous Medicine* by Roald Dahl. Does not advertise for actors and does not welcome casting queries.

Chichester

Chichester Festival Theatre

Oaklands Park, Chichester,
West Sussex PO19 4AP
Tel: 01243 784437
Fax: 01243 787288
E-mail: admin@cftplay.demon.co.uk
Director Andrew Welch
Contact *Paul Rogerson (General Manager)*

Founded in 1962. Festival season from April to October and annual pantomime in the main house, plus a season of plays in the Minerva Studio. 1997 main-house productions: *The Admirable Crichton* (directed by Michael Rudman), *Lady Windermere's Fan* (Richard Cottrell), *Blithe Spirit* (Tim Luscombe), *Divorce Me, Darling!* (Paul Kerryson), *Our Betters* (Michael Rudman), *The Magistrate* (Nicholas Broadhurst). Minerva Studio: *After*

October (Keith Baxter), *Nocturne for Lovers*, British première by Bruno Villien (Kado Kostzer), *Tallulah!* (Michael Rudman), *Suzanna Andler* (Lindy Davies), *Misalliance* (Frank Hauser), *Electra* (David Leveaux), and a British première of Neil Simon's *Hotel Suites*. Always uses casting directors. Does not welcome casting queries.

Colchester
Mercury Theatre
Balkerne Gate, Colchester,
Essex CO1 1PT
Tel: 01206 577006
Fax: 01206 769607
E-mail: mercury.theatre@virgin.net
Artistic Director *Pat Trueman*
Associate Director *Adrian Stokes*

Founded in 1972. Seating capacity: 497. Produces two seasons per year. Recent productions have included: *Northanger Abbey*, *The Deep Blue Sea*, *Homage to Piaf*, *As You Like It*, *The Last Yankee*, *Golden Girls*. Does not advertise for actors. Welcomes casting queries; approach in writing in the first instance enclosing cv and photograph with a covering letter. Does not hold general auditions.

Coventry
Belgrade Theatre
Belgrade Square, Coventry,
West Midlands CV1 1GS
Tel: 01203 256431
Fax: 01203 550680
Artistic Director *Bob Eaton*

Founded in 1958, the Belgrade was Britain's first civic theatre. Seating capacity: 866 (main house); 60 maximum (studio). Produces 8 shows per year. Previous productions: *Silas*

Marner, *Good Golly Miss Molly*, *Relatively Speaking*, *Drink the Mercury*, *Aladdin*, *She Stoops to Conquer*, *Our Day Out*, *Wakey Wakey – In Bed with Billy Cotton* and *Of Mice and Men*. Rarely advertises for actors or uses casting directors. No general auditions. Send letter and cv for consideration.

Cumbernauld
Cumbernauld Theatre
Braehead Road, Kildrum,
Cumbernauld G67 2BN
Tel: 01236 737235
Fax: 01236 738408
Artistic Director *Simon Sharkey*

Founded 1979. Revenue funded by the local authority and Scottish Arts Council, Cumbernauld Theatre produces on a project basis. Usually stages a Christmas show, one in-house production and an educational tour per year. Productions have included: *Onions Make You Cry*, *Being Frank*, *Sweethearts of the Yellow Rose*, *Pied Piper of Hamelin*. Does not advertise for actors. Welcomes casting queries; send letter and cv.

Derby
Derby Playhouse
Theatre Walk,
The Eagle Centre,
Derby DE1 3NF
Tel: 01332 363271
Fax: 01332 294412
E-mail: @derbyplayhouse.demon.co.uk
Artistic Director *Mark Clements*
Associate Director *(Studio Theatre)*
Laura Harvey
Contact *Kathy Willis (PA and Casting Assistant)*

Founded in 1948. Produces two seasons – an average of 10 productions across the main house (535 seats) and studio theatre (approx. 100 seats). Previous productions have included: British première of *Lips Together Teeth Apart* by Terence McNally, *Richard III*, *Miss Julie*, *Blood Wedding*, *Adam Bede*, *The Rivals*, *Assassins*, *Extremities*, *My Mother Said I Never Should*, *A Passionate Woman* and the annual pantomime. Uses casting directors; advertises season breakdowns and open auditions for large musicals. Welcomes accurate submissions for individual productions. Does not hold general auditions. 'We keep a database of local actors for a range of one-off projects and welcome current cvs from Equity members in the Midlands region. These should be marked for the attention of Laura Harvey.'

Dundee

Dundee Repertory Theatre
Tay Square, Dundee DD1 1PB
Tel: 01382 227684
Fax: 01382 228609
Artistic Director *Hamish Glen*
Associate Directors *Richard Baron, Janet Smith (Dance), Michael Duke (Community)*
Contact *Joanna Reid (Admin Director)*

Founded in 1938. Seating capacity: 450. A unique company combining a main-house producing company, Scottish Dance Theatre (Scotland's only full-time producing company) and a year-round community arts provision, including Britain's only mental-health worker based within a theatre. Produces 7 productions over two seasons per year. Previous productions have included: *On the Line* by Alan Spence (TMA Martini award-winner), *Hyde* by Peter Arnott, *Cat on a Hot Tin Roof* and *The Wizard of Oz*. Does not advertise for actors and rarely uses casting directors. Welcomes casting queries from actors; write with sae in the first instance. Does not hold general auditions.

Edinburgh

Royal Lyceum Theatre
Grindlay Street, Edinburgh EH3 9AX
Tel: 0131 229 7404
Fax: 0131 228 3955
Artistic Director *Kenny Ireland*

Founded in 1965. Seating capacity 700. Three seasons – autumn, spring and summer. Four plays in each season, plus a Christmas show. Classics, new Scottish plays, translations and adaptations. Recent productions include: *Much Ado About Nothing*, *The Steamie* by Tony Roper, *Clay Bull* by Stewart Conn. Does not advertise, but welcomes casting queries from actors. Approach in writing in the first instance. Casts for each production but also holds auditions for Scottish-based actors when time permits.

Traverse Theatre
Cambridge Street,
Edinburgh EH1 2ED
Tel: 0131 228 3223
Fax: 0131 229 8443
Artistic Director *Philip Howard*
Literary Director *John Tiffany*

Founded in 1963 in a small venue in Edinburgh's Lawnmarket. Moved to the Grassmarket in 1969 and from there, in 1992, into its present purpose-built building. The Traverse has always been a theatre that pioneered new writing, premièring the work of many famous contemporary writers over the years, including Sam Shepard, Sue Glover, Liz Lochhead and David Greig. Writers currently under commission include Kate Atkinson, Iain Crichton Smith and Stephen Greenhorn. In-house productions are complemented by an extensive programme of visiting work from Britain and abroad. Produces 5 or 6 major new plays plus a Scottish touring production each year. Previous productions have included: *Wormwood* by Catherine Czerkawska, *Widows* by Ariel Dorfman (also toured to Cambridge, Oxford and Newcastle), *Passing Places* by Stephen Greenhorn, *One Good Beating* by Linda McLean and *The Architect* by David Greig. Does not advertise for actors but welcomes casting queries. Approach in writing, sending cv and photograph ('which go into a casting file which we use'). Does not hold general auditions.

Exeter

Northcott Theatre

Stocker Road, Exeter,
Devon EX4 4QB
Tel: 01392 256182
Fax: 01392 499641
Artistic Director Ben Crocker
Contact Julie Hopper (PA to Artistic Director and Administrator)

Founded 1967. The Northcott is situated in the grounds of the University campus. Seating capacity: 433 (main house); 100 maximum (studio). In-house and co-productions from July through to May – two seasons. Previous productions have included: *Single Spies, As You Like It,*

Turn of the Screw, Under Their Hats, Ghosts, Northanger Abbey, Cinderella, The Passion, The Man Who would be King (studio production and tour), *Travels with My Aunt, Twelfth Night, Far from the Madding Crowd, April in Paris, Richard III, Talking Heads* and *Jack and the Beanstalk.* Does not use casting directors. Advertises for actors and welcomes casting queries 'only in response to casting announcements made through the usual channels (SBS, PCR, RepReport, ACID, Castcall, etc.).' Send letter with cv, photograph and sae. 'No information is kept on file as we have insufficient storage space. Keep letters short and to the point; read and consider all casting breakdowns carefully and be realistic with your submissions; do not submit videos or cassettes unless specifically requested.'

Guildford

Yvonne Arnaud Theatre

Millbrook, Guildford,
Surrey GU1 3UX
Tel: 01483 440077
Fax: 01483 564071
Artistic Director James Barber

Founded in 1965. Seating capacity: 590. In the last five years the Yvonne Arnaud has produced 39 productions of which 19 have transferred to the West End and 18 have been new plays. Produces in conjunction with commercial managements and independently – between 6 and 8 plays annually. Previous productions have included: *Tom and Clem* by Stephen Churchett, directed by Richard Wilson and starring Michael Gambon and Alec McCowen, *Life Support* by Simon Gray, directed by Harold Pinter and starring

Alan Bates, *Laughter on the 23rd Floor* by Neil Simon, directed by Roger Haines and starring Gene Wilder. Occasionally uses casting directors; does not advertise for actors. Rarely holds general auditions.

Glasgow

Citizens' Theatre
119 Gorbals Street, Glasgow G5 9DS
Tel: 0141 429 5561
Fax: 0141 429 7374
Artistic Directors *Giles Havergal, Robert David MacDonald, Philip Prowse*
Contact *Sharman Elizabeth Weir (General Manager)*

Founded 1943. Three theatre spaces of 600, 120 and 60 seats. An internationally renowned company which stages a good hard-hitting repertoire of unusual, high-quality plays, a number of which have transferred to the West End. Contemporary drama, little-known classics and European works make up the rich and varied programme of three seasons: autumn, Christmas and spring. Previous productions have included: *Hamlet*, *Seascape* by Edward Albee, *Long Day's Journey into Night* by Eugene O'Neill, *Dracula* by Bram Stoker, *The Wizard of Oz*, *Conversation with a Cupboard Man* by Ian McEwan, *Miss Julie* by Strindberg, *The Country Wife* by William Wycherley, *Widowers' Houses* by Bernard Shaw, *Eva Peron* by Copi and *Cat on a Hot Tin Roof* by Tennessee Williams. Does not advertise for actors and does not use casting directors. Holds general auditions 'by invitation'. Welcomes casting queries; approach by letter or fax.

Harrogate

Harrogate Theatre
Oxford Street, Harrogate, North Yorkshire HG1 1QF
Tel: 01423 502710
Fax: 01423 563205
Executive Director *Sheena Wrigley*

Founded 1900. Seating capacity: 476. At the time of going to press, no artistic director had replaced Andrew Manley following his departure to the Wolsey Theatre in Ipswich, and the future of in-house productions at Harrogate was under review due to a major cut in funding.

Hornchurch

Queen's Theatre
Billet Lane, Hornchurch, Essex RM11 1QT
Tel: 01708 456118
Fax: 01708 452348
Artistic Director *Bob Carlton*

Founded 1952. Seating capacity: 506. Bob Carlton took over as artistic director from Marina Calderone in September 1997. Four/5-weekly rep with a spring and autumn season from September to June plus national tours, West End transfers and 10-week pantomime. Eight plays per year (4 each season); productions tend to be populist and contemporary. Recent productions include: *The Farndale Mystery* and *Just Between Ourselves*. Does not advertise for actors but welcomes casting queries. Write in the first instance enclosing cv, photograph and sae.

Huddersfield

Lawrence Batley Theatre
Queen's Square, Queen Street,
Huddersfield,
West Yorkshire HD1 2SP
Tel: 01484 425282
Fax: 01484 425336
Artistic Director *Ron McAllister*
PA/Secretary *Annette Romain*

Founded 1994. Seating capacity: 440-seat theatre and 125-seat studio. Three in-house productions; 2 community in-house shows; also receives touring productions. Does not particularly welcome casting queries; prefers to deal direct with agents. Occasionally advertises in *The Stage*.

Ipswich

Wolsey Theatre
Civic Drive, Ipswich, Suffolk IP1 2AS
Tel: 01473 218911
Fax: 01473 212946
Artistic Director *Andrew Manley*
Contact *Eileen Kidd*

Founded 1979, the Wolsey is the repertory theatre for Ipswich and the surrounding area. Seating capacity: 410. 'A community of theatre workers working in and for the community, producing as wide a range as possible of exciting, enriching, high-class theatre, plus a range of support/ancillary activities, including TIE, youth theatre, talks, readings and new-writing workshops.' Produces 12 plays each year. Previous productions have included: *Romeo and Juliet*, *Communicating Doors*, *Arcadia*, *Dead Funny* and *Thickness of Skin*. Does not advertise for actors or use casting directors. Welcomes written casting queries (letter or fax). Holds a limited number

of general auditions; apply in May/June for inclusion. Andrew Manley reports that he is 'looking for versatile, energetic, open-minded, imaginative actors to be part of a semi-permanent group'.

Keswick

Century Theatre
Rawnsley Hall, Keswick,
Cumbria CA12 5NE
Tel: 017687 72282
Fax: 017687 74698
Artistic Director *Gregory Doran*
Administration *Frances Wilson*

Founded in 1949. Having won Lottery funding, the Century is currently in temporary accommodation, producing a summer season of 3 plays. It is hoped that the new theatre will open in the late spring of 1999 with the company planning all-year-round production from that time. 1997 season consisted of Noël Coward's *Private Lives*, Ibsen's *A Doll's House*, Neil Simon's *The Good Doctor*. Welcomes written casting queries; send cv, photograph and sae; 'details are kept on file'.

Lancaster

The Dukes
Moor Lane, Lancaster LA1 1QE
Tel: 01524 67461
Fax: 01524 846817
Artistic Director *Ewan Marshall*
Contact *Jacqui Wilson (Theatre Secretary)*

Founded in 1971. The Dukes is Lancashire's repertory theatre and regional film theatre. Presents an in-house season of contemporary plays, an annual promenade production in Lancaster's Williamson Park and youth theatre groups in dedicated arts centres. Six in-house productions per year. Productions have included: *The Importance of Being Earnest, Alice's Adventures in Wonderland* (both promenade productions), *Why Do Bees Buzz?* (children's show), *The Life and Times of Fanny Hill, Someone Who'll Watch Over Me.* Advertises for actors. Welcomes casting queries; send letter with cv and photograph. Does not hold general auditions. 'The Dukes operates an Equal Opportunities policy with regard to casting and particularly welcomes submissions from disabled actors who are currently under-represented.'

Leatherhead

Thorndike Theatre

Church Street, Leatherhead,
Surrey KT22 8DF
Tel: 01372 376211
Fax: 01372 362595

Founded in 1969. Seating capacity: 526. The theatre remains closed due to debts of over £300,000.

Leeds

West Yorkshire Playhouse

Playhouse Square, Quarry Hill, Leeds,
West Yorkshire LS2 7UP
Tel: 0113 213 7800
Fax: 0113 213 7250
Artistic Director *Jude Kelly*
Managing Director *Maggie Saxon*
Head of Casting *Kay Magson*

Founded in 1991. The largest regional repertory company operating outside London and Stratford with one of the most innovative and vibrant artistic policies. Stages over 1,000 performances, workshops, readings and community events each year. Produces between 15 and 17 in-house shows plus two short touring seasons per year, plus schools' shows (*see entry under* Theatre-in-Education (TIE) Companies, page 232). Recent productions have included: *Of Mice and Men, Odysseus Thump, Peter Pan, The Importance of Being Earnest, The Wasp Factory, Popcorn, A Perfect Ganesh, Office Suite, The Pirates of Penzance, Jar the Floor, Don Juan.* Casting details are circulated to agents on their mailing list and to individuals on receipt of an sae. The best approach for actors is to write to Kay Magson, Head of Casting, enclosing an sae. 'I am willing to see people if in the area, but *not* on spec – give warning.' Does not hold general auditions.

Leicester

Leicester Haymarket Theatre

(Managing Lessors: Leicester Treatre Trust Limited)
Belgrave Gate, Leicester LE1 3YQ
Tel: 0116 253 0021
Fax: 0116 251 3310
Artistic Director *Paul Kerryson*
Associate Director *Sita Ramamurthy*
Casting and Scripts Manager *Stephanie Pennell*

Founded in 1973. Seating capacity: 752 (main house); 120 (studio). Programme includes plays, musicals, tours, multicultural and outreach work with occasional concerts and festivals. Past productions have transferred into the West End or played nationally and internationally. 'We audition for specific plays or parts only, rather than holding general auditions. The season is announced in a block and agents generally keep in touch so they are able to send in submissions. We also distribute details through SBS, otherwise actors send in their own details for specific productions. On the whole, we are happy to receive letters with cvs and a photograph (which can be smaller than 10 × 8, which is costly). We will try and return the photographs if an sae is provided. The director will see all the details sent in for consideration but we tend not to file details because of restrictions on space.'

Liverpool

New Everyman Ltd

5–9 Hope Street, Liverpool L1 9BH
Tel: 0151 708 0338
Fax: 0151 709 0398
Executive Producer *Kevin Fearon*
Administrator *Jane Evans*

Since it was founded in 1964, the Everyman has established itself over the years as an important community theatre, presenting new and challenging work. Local writers have always been encouraged and the theatre was the starting point for the famous four – Alan Bleasdale, Chris Bond, Bill Morrison and Willy Russell – who then moved down the road to liven up the Liverpool Playhouse. Since 1995, local-authority funding for these two Merseyside theatres has been cut back and split on a 40:60 basis, favouring the Playhouse. As a result, the Everyman has reduced its in-house productions to just 3 per year, with the rest of the programme made up of middle-scale tours of drama, dance, music and comedy. Recent in-house

productions have included: *Scouse – A Comedy of Terrors* by Andrew Cullen and *Ballad of the Sea* by Andrew Sherlock and Matthew Wood, a co-production with Landing Stage Productions. The artistic policy is, as it has been over the years, to promote new writing, new work and Merseyside. For casting information on in-house productions, actors are recommended to send an sae and casting breakdowns will be mailed out when available. Does not hold general auditions.

Liverpool Playhouse

Williamson Square, Liverpool L1 1EL
Tel: 0151 709 8478
Fax: 0151 709 7113

Founded in 1911, the Liverpool Playhouse is the oldest established repertory company in the country. Seating capacity: 750. The original stucco exterior still survives but in 1968, a drum-like extension – housing restaurant, bars and workshops – was added, offering a stark contrast to the Victorian elegance of the old music-hall architecture.

At the turn of the year, the Playhouse closed for an indefinite period. The administrators were seeking new owners to undertake refurbishment of the building and a commitment to continued in-house production.

London

Greenwich Theatre

– see Producing Theatres and Independent Managements, page 147

Royal National Theatre

Upper Ground, South Bank,
London SE1 9PX
Tel: 0171 928 2033
Fax: 0171 620 1197
Artistic Director *Trevor Nunn*
Casting Director *Serena Hill*

Under the directorship of Sir Laurence (later, Lord) Olivier, the company was founded in 1963. With Peter Hall as director, the National moved from The Old Vic in 1976 to its present home on the South Bank. Contains three separate theatres: the large, open-stage Olivier (seating 1,160), the proscenium stage Lyttelton (890), and the Cottesloe (400), which is a simple and adaptable rectangular room. Plays are presented in repertoire and since opening on the South Bank, the National has staged nearly 400 productions. In 1988, to marks its twenty-fifth anniversary, the National was granted the title 'Royal'. In September of that year, Richard Eyre took over as director and remained with the company until Trevor Nunn took over in October 1997.

The National also has a Studio, based at The Old Vic Annexe, which is used as an experimental workshop for the company and to encourage new writing. At the time of going to press, the future of the Studio was uncertain due to the impending sale of The Old Vic.

'The Royal National Theatre aims to present a diverse repertoire embracing classic, new and neglected plays from the whole of World drama, to present these plays to the very highest standards, to give audiences a choice of different productions at any one time.'

Nineteen new productions are staged annually. Recent productions have included: *King Lear, Othello, John Gabriel Borkman, Amy's View* (new play by David Hare), *The Cripple of Inishmaan* (new play by Martin McDonagh), *Closer* (new play by Patrick Marber), and *The Invention of Love* (new play by Tom Stoppard).

To be considered for productions at the RNT, it is important for the casting department to know your work. The department is happy to accept written invitations to performances and the casting director, casting assistant and casting secretary cover as much work as possible throughout the year. Follow-up calls are discouraged as the office is always extremely busy.

Royal Shakespeare Company

Royal Shakespeare Theatre, Stratford-upon-Avon, Warwickshire CV37 6BB
Tel: 01789 296655
Fax: 01789 294810
Barbican Theatre, Barbican Centre,
London EC2Y 8BQ
Tel: 0171 628 3351
Fax: 0171 374 0818
Artistic Director *Adrian Noble*
Principal Associate Director *Michael Attenborough*
Head of Casting *Maggy Lunn*

The RSC acquired its Royal prefix in 1961, a year after Peter Hall was appointed artistic director. At that time, the company's London base was at the Aldwych Theatre where the repertoire was widened to include modern as well as classical works. Trevor Nunn took over as artistic director in 1968 and in 1974, The Other Place in Stratford was opened as a venue for experimental work. In 1978, the year in which Terry Hands joined Trevor Nunn as artistic director, the RSC commenced touring to the regions and in 1987, Terry Hands became sole artistic director. The move to the Barbican Centre in London took place in 1982 and in 1986, the Swan Theatre opened in Stratford. The new Other

Place was built on the site of the old theatre in 1991 and now plays host to overseas companies, workshops, teaching courses and the RSC's educational work. Adrian Noble succeeded Terry Hands as artistic director in 1991. The RSC is formed around a core of associate artists – actors, directors, designers and others – 'with the aim that their different skills should combine, over the years, to produce a distinctive approach to theatre, both classical and modern'.

Actors wishing to have an audition should ensure that the casting department knows their work, be it theatre, television or film. Approach in writing with performance notices; follow-up calls are not encouraged as the department is extremely busy. Does not hold general auditions.

Manchester

Contact Theatre Company
– see Children's and Young People's Theatre, page 212

Library Theatre Company
St Peter's Square,
Manchester M2 5PD
Tel: 0161 234 1913
Fax: 0161 228 6481
Artistic Director Chris Honer
Associate Director Roger Haines
Contact Louise Coy

Founded 1952. Housed in the basement of the Central Library, the Library Theatre Company exists to 'produce theatre which illuminates the contemporary world'. Seating capacity: 308. Stages 7 productions per year. Previous productions have included: *My Night with Reg* by Kevin Elyot, *Laughter on the 23rd Floor* by Neil Simon, *Broken Glass*

by Arthur Miller, *Company* by Stephen Sondheim, *Blue Murder* by Peter Nichols, *The Resistible Rise of Arturo Ui* by Brecht and *Love! Valour! Compassion!* by Terence McNally. Usually issues cast breakdowns through SBS. Holds general auditions for recent graduates from drama school and other newcomers; apply in March/April for inclusion.

Royal Exchange Theatre
St Ann's Square, Manchester M2 7DH
Tel: 0161 833 9333
Fax: 0161 832 0771
Artistic Directors Braham Murray, Gregory Hersov
Associate Artistic Director Matthew Lloyd
Associate Director Marianne Elliott
Casting Director Sophie Marshall

Founded as 69 Theatre Company by Michael Elliott, Casper Wrede, James Maxwell, Richard Negri and Braham Murray. Changed its name in 1976 when the new theatre opened in the Royal Exchange Hall. A specifically designed 700-seat theatre-in-the-round, currently undergoing rebuilding and refurbishment following eviction due to the 1995 Manchester bomb and subsequent Lottery award. Due to reopen in November 1998, when a 100-seat studio theatre will also open.

Performs from September to August; currently 9 or 10 plays, but subject to review. Also plans to present a season of studio work after the reopening. Produces new plays, classics, translations and devised work. Each play is separately cast with separate directors. Advertises in PCR, at Actors Centres and via agents' mailing list. Contact in-house casting director Sophie Marshall for details of plays/seasons; sae essential. If applying for parts or wish to be kept on file, send cv and photograph. Rarely holds general auditions. 'Read the play before you apply for parts.'

Milford Haven

Torch Theatre Company Limited

St Peter's Road, Milford Haven, Pembrokeshire SA73 2BU
Tel: 01646 694192
Fax: 01646 698919
Artistic Director Mike James
Theatre Secretary Melanie John

Founded 1977. Seating capacity: 297. As with many repertory houses, cutbacks have led to the Torch Theatre offering a mixed programme of in-house repertory productions and visiting companies. Produces 3 in-house plays per year; previous productions have included: *Frankie and Tommy* (2-week run and tour), *Cat on a Hot Tin Roof* (3-week run), *The Amazing Mr Toad* (6-week run), *Duet for One* (2-week run), *The Rise and Fall of Little Voice* and *The Emperor's New Clothes* (both 6-week runs). Advertises for actors in SBS and PCR. Welcomes casting queries, either by letter or telephone. Contact Melanie John for casting schedule. Does not hold general auditions.

Mold

Theatr Clwyd

County Civic Centre, Mold CH7 1YA
Tel: 01352 756331
Fax: 01352 758323
E-mail: drama@celtic.co.uk
Director Terry Hands
Associate Director Tim Baker

Founded in 1976. Seating capacity: Main house: 530–70 (flexible staging);

Emlyn Williams Studio Theatre: 160–250. Wales's première English-language theatre company. Produces around 12 plays per year in 2 auditoria plus TIE productions and tours. Previous productions have included: *Equus, The Importance of Being Earnest, The Cavalcaders* by Billy Roche, *Someone Who'll Watch Over Me* by Frank McGuinness, *The Servant of Two Masters* and Shaw's *Misalliance*. Uses casting directors but sometimes advertises for actors and holds general auditions. Welcomes casting queries.

Musselburgh

Brunton Theatre

Ladywell Way, Musselburgh, East Lothian EH21 6AA
Tel: 0131 665 9900
Fax: 0131 665 7485
Artistic Director David Mark Thomson
Contact Lesley Smith

Founded in 1979. Seating capacity: 312. The only major producing venue between Edinburgh and the Borders, the Brunton Theatre Company stages a season of 5 in-house productions between August and March each year and the theatre hosts touring productions from April to June. Previous productions have included: *Bold Girls* by Rona Munro, *They're Playing Our Song* by Neil Simon, *Driving Miss Daisy* by Alfred Uhry and *Sleeping Beauty*. Uses casting directors but welcomes casting queries; send cv and photograph. Holds general auditions from time to time and recommends that actors contact them in the spring for inclusion.

Newbury

Watermill Theatre

Bagnor, Newbury,
Berkshire RG20 9AE
Tel: 01635 45834
Fax: 01635 523726
Artistic Director *Jill Fraser*

Founded in 1967. Seating capacity: 185. Produces 8 shows per year. Recent productions have included: *Table Manners* directed by Euan Smith, *Little Shop of Horrors* directed by Martin Connor, *Far from the Madding Crowd* directed by Matthew White, *Wait Until Dark* directed by Euan Smith, *The Adventures of Mr Toad* directed by Dilys Hamlett, *Deadwood*, a new play directed by Stephen Rayne, and *Rogues to Riches*, British première of American musical directed by Wendy Toye. Does not advertise for actors and does not use casting directors. Welcomes casting queries. Each play is cast individually – 'find out what the programme is and apply for specific roles. Don't just send cvs generally – they get lost in piles of letters. Be specific and make sure the cv gives full details such as physical (height, etc.), skills and singing range.'

Newcastle under Lyme

New Victoria Theatre

Etruria Road, Newcastle under Lyme,
Staffordshire ST5 0JG
Tel: 01782 717954
Fax: 01782 712885
Theatre Director *Gwenda Hughes*
Associate Directors *Rob Swain,
Chris Martin, Chris Monks*
Contact *Sue Griffiths (Casting)*

Founded in 1955 (touring company), 1962 (Stoke-on-Trent permanent base), 1986 (Newcastle under Lyme). The New Victoria Theatre, a purpose-built theatre-in-the-round, is the ultimate home of Stephen Joseph's theatre-in-the-round company founded in 1955, sister theatre to Scarborough's Stephen Joseph Theatre. Seating capacity: 605. Producing a repertoire season of 10 plays per year, the company has a tradition of presenting new plays, including community-based documentaries. Presents regular ensemble small-scale musicals with classics and revivals of distinguished texts. Actors are usually contracted for more than one production. Rehearsals are a minimum of $4^1/_2$ weeks. Recent productions have included: *HMS Pinafore*, an ensemble production with revised modern libretto, *Overture*, a new play by Peter Whelan, *Intimate Exchanges* by Alan Ayckbourn, *The Hound of the Baskervilles*, a new adaptation by Chris Martin, and *Beauty and the Beast*, a new children's play by Jan Page. Does not advertise for actors and does not use casting directors. Welcomes queries regarding casting; approach in writing with full cv. Does not hold general auditions.

'We like to see two contrasting audition speeches from any actors willing to be modest enough to keep them going. We always ask an actor to read for a part. Auditions are in two stages with a recall session lasting usually no less than one hour in a group with one or two other actors, organised as a workshop working on a scene or scenes from the play being cast. We try and cast an actor for a minimum of two plays at a time, and always hope to establish a long-term relationship.'

Newcastle upon Tyne

Northern Stage

Newcastle Playhouse, Barras Bridge,
Newcastle upon Tyne NE1 7RH
Tel: 0191 232 3366
Fax: 0191 261 8093
E-mail: northern.stage@ncl.ac.uk
Artistic Director *Alan Lyddiard*
Associate Directors *Neil Murray,*
Richard Gregory
Contact *Brenda Gray (PA to the*
Directors)

Founded in 1978. Based at the
Newcastle Playhouse and Gulbenkian
Studio Theatre (owned by the Uni-
versity of Newcastle), Northern Stage
is the largest professional theatre com-
pany in the north-east of England.
Under the artistic direction of Alan
Lyddiard, it has gained a reputation for
producing a distinctive and exciting
brand of physical and visual theatre.
Produces 6 or 7 plays per year.
Previous productions have included:
But the Living are Wrong in the Sharp
Distinctions they Make created by direc-
tor Richard Gregory, *Merlin the*
Magnificent by Stuart Paterson,
directed by Neil Murray, *The Terrible*
Grump written and directed by Chris
Speyer, *Blood Wedding* adapted by
Brendan Kennelly and directed by
Alan Lyddiard, *Animal Farm* adapted
by Ian Wooldridge and directed by
Alan Lyddiard, *The Long Line* by Tom
Hadaway, directed by Neil Murray.
Occasionally advertises in SBS; does
not use casting directors. Casting
queries should be by telephone or send
an sae. Does not hold general auditions. Besides its own productions,
Northern Stage hosts visiting companies such as the Maly Drama Theatre,
the Peter Brook Company and the
Ninagawa Company. An important
aspect of Northern Stage is its work in
education and the community arts.

Northampton

Northampton Repertory Players Ltd

Royal Theatre,
Guildhall Road,
Northampton NN1 1EA
Tel: 01604 638343
Fax: 01604 602408
Artistic Director *Michael Napier*
Brown
Contact *Julie Martell*

The Royal Theatre, built by C. J.
Phipps in 1884, has been the home of
the Repertory Players since 1927.
Seating capacity: 439. Presents 9 shows
per year; recent productions include:
Neville's Island, Mother Goose, Mail
Order Bride, 13 Rue De L'Amour, The
Deep Blue Sea, Ghosts and *Talking*
Heads. Does not advertise for actors
and does not use casting directors.
Queries should be by letter. 'Please do
not send large, expensive photographs
without sending an appropriate-sized
sae for return.' Occasionally holds
general auditions; apply in May/June
for inclusion. Royal Theatre-in-
Education – *see* Theatre-in-Education
(TIE) Companies, page 229

Nottingham

Nottingham Playhouse

Wellington Circus,
Nottingham NG1 5AF
Tel: 0115 947 4361
Fax: 0115 947 5759
Artistic Director *Martin Duncan*

Founded in 1948. Seating capacity:
685–766. Produces approximately 10
shows per year, playing for 3¹/₂ to 4
weeks each. Recent productions:
Measure for Measure directed by

Stéphane Braunschweig, *The Mysteries of Sex* directed by Martin Duncan, *Iced* directed by Felix Cross, *Aladdin* directed by Martin Duncan and Kenneth Alan Taylor. Does not advertise for actors. Casts for each production and prefers to deal with agents.

Oldham

Oldham Coliseum Theatre

Fairbottom Street,
Oldham,
Lancashire OL1 3SW
Tel: 0161 624 1731
Fax: 0161 624 5318
Chief Executive/Artistic Director
Kenneth Alan Taylor
Contact *Ailsa Condon (PA)*

Founded in 1937. Seating capacity: 576. The company has a very northern bias, using as many local actors as possible and is interested in new writing. Presents 10 productions per year, including one musical and a pantomime. Recent productions have included: *Saturday Night at the Crown, Second from Last in the Sack Race, Comfort and Joy* (world première), *Alfie – The Musical* (world première), *A Different Way Home* (world première) and *Dead Funny*. Does not use casting directors; does not advertise for actors. Welcomes casting queries; send *short* letter, photograph, cv and sae. 'We will not reply if there is no sae, unless a very special applicant. Be brief and to the point when applying for auditions. Although we do not hold general auditions, we do audition now and again and will endeavour to see local actors throughout the year.'

Perth

Perth Repertory Theatre

185 High Street, Perth PH1 5UW
Tel: 01738 472700
Fax: 01738 624576
E-mail: theatre@perth.org.uk
Artistic Director *Michael Winter*

Founded in 1935. The oldest repertory theatre in Scotland. A beautiful late-Victorian theatre, extensively renovated in the early eighties. Seating capacity: 470. Autumn and spring seasons with an annual pantomime. Five plays per season, the first production of the autumn is usually a musical. Recent productions: *The Sound of Music, A View from the Bridge, Funny Peculiar, As You Like It, The Lion in Winter, Mother Goose*. Occasionally advertises for actors. Welcomes casting queries; approach in writing, enclosing cv, photograph and sae. Actors should apply to the theatre in the spring.

Pitlochry

Pitlochry Festival Theatre

Port-na-Craig, Pitlochry, Perthshire PH16 5DR
Tel: 01796 473054
Fax: 01796 473054
Artistic Director *Clive Perry*
Associate Director *Ian Grieve*
Contact *Peter MacIntosh (Theatre Secretary), Sheila Harborth (Administrator)*

Founded 1951, Pitlochry Festival Theatre is a unique operation in Britain and the only producing theatre which performs a different production at each of 8 performances during the playing week. It is the only company (excluding the Nationals) which operates with up to 22 actors for 31 weeks, although any one actor does not perform in more than 4 plays. The repertoire consists of Scottish 'classic' and modern texts, with Sunday and foyer musical concerts. Rehearsals commence in March and the season, which consists of 6 or 7 plays, continues until October. 1997 season: *The Flouers o' Edinburgh* by Robert McLellan, *And Then There were None* by Agatha Christie, *Present Laughter* by Noël Coward, *Travels with My Aunt* by Graham Greene, *On Golden Pond* by Ernest Thompson, *Mr Bolfry* by James Bridie and *Long Day's Journey into Night* by Eugene O'Neill.

Advertises in SBS, PCR, etc., usually in December/January. Auditions are held in Edinburgh and London in January and February respectively; actors should apply for inclusion in December. Telephone or write to the theatre secretary. For auditions, 'prepare two contrasting pieces to show your range and versatility (not necessarily from the new season's play list). Some background knowledge of some of the new season's plays would be useful. Please try to be on time, but understand if the auditioning director falls behind.'

Plymouth

Theatre Royal
Royal Parade, Plymouth,
Devon PL1 2TR
Tel: 01752 668282
Fax: 01752 671179
Associate Directors *Nick Stimson, Laurence Boswell, Jennie Darnell*
Contact *Commissioning Producer*

Founded in 1982. Seating capacity: 1,296 (main house); 150–200 (Drum Studio). Most of the main-house productions are done in conjunction with commercial managements. Productions such as *South Pacific,* *Buddy, Jolson* and *Copacabana* have all transferred to the West End and internationally, and in 1989 their production of *Shadowlands* won a Tony on Broadway. Does not advertise; always uses casting directors. Does not welcome casting queries.

St Andrews

Byre Theatre
Abbey Street, St Andrews,
Fife KY16 9LA
Tel: 013344 476288
Artistic Director *Ken Alexander*

Founded in 1933. Currently undergoing complete rebuilding with the new theatre scheduled to open in the autumn of 1999. This will create a 200-seat main auditorium plus a small studio with a seating capacity of 50–60. For the first time, the Byre will have decent wing space, a fly tower and scene dock. Until then, the company is performing in a variety of venues; for example, the 1997/8 pantomime was staged in the town hall in Anstruther. Produces approximately 6 shows per year. Tends to cast from Scottish-based actors but happy to receive written submissions.

Salisbury

Salisbury Playhouse
Malthouse Lane, Salisbury,
Wiltshire SP2 7RA
Tel: 01722 320118
Fax: 01722 421991
Artistic Director *Jonathan Church*
Contact *Rebecca Morland (Executive Director)*

Founded in 1945. Seating capacity: 516 (main house); maximum 140 (Salberg Studio). Two seasons: January to July and September to December; a total of approximately 12 main-house productions. Previous productions have included: *The Merchant of Venice, Neville's Island, Aladdin, Time and Time Again, The Rehearsal, The Double Inconstancy, Rope, Time and the Conways* and *Travels with My Aunt.* Does not advertise and does not use casting directors. Telephone in the first instance to find out who is directing what.

Scarborough

Stephen Joseph Theatre
Westborough, Scarborough,
North Yorkshire YO11 1JW
Tel: 01723 370540
Fax: 01723 360506
E-mail: response@sjt.onyxnet.co.uk
Website: www.webart.co.uk/clients/sjt/
Artistic Director *Alan Ayckbourn*
General Administrator *Stephen Wood*
Casting Director *Sarah Hughes*

Now sited in a two-auditoria site in a recently converted 1930s Odeon cinema. The McCarthy auditorium is a 165-seater, end stage; The Round auditorium is a 403-seater, entirely in the round. The company was created by Stephen Joseph in 1955. Alan Ayckbourn has been artistic director since 1967. Presents a repertory programme (sometimes repertoire) of mainly new plays; 8 to 13 productions annually. Lunchtime and late-night shows are also produced, plus some touring. Recent productions have included: *It Could Be Any One of Us* by Alan Ayckbourn, *All Things Considered* by Ben Brown, *Love Me Slender* by Vanessa Brooks, *Mirandolina* by Goldoni, *Dealing with Clair* by Martin Crimp, *Things We Do for Love* by Alan Ayckbourn, *They're Playing Our Song*

by Hamlish/Simon/Saye, *Lucky Sods* by John Godber. Does not advertise for actors. Welcomes casting queries; send letter with cv and photograph to Sarah Hughes at the theatre. Rarely holds general auditions. 'Let casting director know of shows you are in, particularly in the region, and if you have played Ayckbourn.'

Sheffield

Crucible Theatre and Studio
55 Norfolk Street, Sheffield S1 1DA
Tel: 0114 276 0621
Fax: 0114 270 1532
Artistic Director *Deborah Paige*

Founded in 1971. Seating capacity: 1,000. Produces approximately 6 productions per year in the main house in the autumn and spring, and 3 per year in the Studio, where the emphasis is on new works. Recent productions have included: *The Merchant of Venice, Hay Fever, The Sound of Music, Bouncers, Villette,* and *Bedevilled.* Does not advertise for actors but issues season breakdowns; send postcard with sae for details – no cvs or photographs. Uses freelance casting directors. Does not hold general auditions but has informal meetings with locally based actors. 'Please be realistic. If we are doing a smallish-cast, main-house play, we will be looking for leading actors. We look at all cvs but cannot respond unless an sae is enclosed. We only keep very limited files: i.e. only include those actors we seriously feel we wish to work with if possible at some point. In such a case we will try to inform you that you're "on file". Please do not mark letters "personal" or "private" if it's about casting (unless *genuinely* personal or private).'

Sonning

The Mill at Sonning Theatre

Sonning Eye, Reading, Berkshire RG4 6TY
Tel: 0118 969 6039
Fax: 0118 944 2424
Artistic Director Sally Hughes

Founded in 1982. Seating capacity: 215. This attractive and unusual theatre, which is privately owned, has been created out of a converted watermill. Produces 9 plays per year with each production running for 6 weeks. Recent productions: *Born Yesterday, Noël and Gertie, Run for Your Wife*. Does not advertise for actors. Welcomes casting queries; approach in writing in the first instance.

Southampton

Nuffield Theatre

University Road, Southampton, Hampshire SO17 1TR
Tel: 01703 315500
Fax: 01703 315511
Artistic Director Patrick Sandford

Founded in 1964. Seating capacity: 506. Lively company with a particularly strong reputation for main-stage new work and British premières of contemporary foreign work. Produces about 8 main-stage productions per year plus tours locally and nationally and has a wide education programme. Recent productions have included: *Dead White Males* by David Williamson (British première), *All's Well That Ends Well, Surprise Party*, a new play by Ivan Menchell, Pinter's *The Caretaker, The Last Yellow*, a new play by Paul Tucker, and *Face*, a new musical by Bob Carlton and Philip Whitchurch. Occasionally uses casting directors but mostly gets actors through agents. Particularly welcomes casting queries from local actors. 'We will send a season breakdown on receipt of an sae.' Very rarely holds general auditions; 'costs now prohibit this except for local actors. All letters are read personally by the AD. We cannot reply unless there is an sae. We are always pleased to hear from actors with proven and extensive experience. Realistically, unsolicited submissions from younger actors are unlikely to result in an audition unless very specific skills are involved. We get most of our younger actors through agents.'

Southwold

Southwold Summer Theatre

– see **Jill Freud & Company** in Producing Theatres and Independent Managements, page 146

Watford

Palace Theatre Watford

Clarendon Road, Watford, Hertfordshire WD1 1JZ
Tel: 01923 235455
Fax: 01923 819664
Artistic Director Giles Croft
Contact Alastair Moir (Administrative Director)

Founded in 1908. Seating capacity: 663. A beautiful Edwardian theatre restored to its original splendour. The rep company produces 9 shows per year, including classic drama, adaptations, new and modern plays and pantomime. Recent productions have included: *Outward Bound* by Sutton Vane, *Elton John's Glasses* by David Farr, *Frankie and Tommy* by Garry Lyons, *Mrs Klein* by Nicholas Wright and *Kind Hearts and Coronets*, adapted by Giles Croft. Does not use casting directors and does not advertise for actors. Does not particularly welcome casting queries but will consider cvs if they are sent in respect of a specific role. Send an sae for the season's brochure.

Westcliff

Palace Theatre Trust

London Road, Westcliff-on-Sea,
Essex SS0 9LA
Tel: 01702 347816
Fax: 01702 435031
Artistic Director *Christopher Dunham*

Founded in 1970. Seating capacity: 612 (main house); 100 maximum (studio). Two seasons with a total of 8 or 9 plays annually. Previous productions have included: *Me and My Girl*, *The Creeper*, *Noises Off*, *Passionate Woman* and *Boy Band*, a new musical. Rarely advertises and does not use casting directors. Welcomes casting queries; approach by letter with cv.

Windsor

Theatre Royal

– see Non-Producing Theatres, page 260

Worcester

Swan Theatre

The Moors, Worcester WR1 3EF
Tel: 01905 726969
Fax: 01905 723738
Artistic Director *Jenny Stephens*
Associate Director *Mark Babych*

Founded in 1965. Seating capacity: 350. A professional repertory company has been resident at the Swan since the theatre opened in the sixties. Produces a wide range of work including classics and new writing as well as more traditional plays from the repertoire. There are usually 7 productions per year between September and April. Recent productions have included: *The Malvern Widow*, a new play by Deborah Catesby, *Hard Times* adapted from Dickens by Stephen Jeffries, *Elsie and Norm's Macbeth*, *Peter Pan*, *Educating Rita*, *Romeo and Juliet* and *Blue Remembered Hills*. Usually advertises for actors in PCR. Does not use casting directors. Welcomes casting queries. 'We produce a casting breakdown of our requirements so actors can send an sae in May/June for the autumn season and November for the spring season. Actors can then submit as appropriate. We find it much more profitable if actors can be suggested for specific roles having seen the casting breakdown.' Holds general auditions; apply for inclusion in May/June and November.

York

Theatre Royal (York Citizens Theatre Trust Ltd)

St Leonard's Place, York YO1 2HD
Tel: 01904 658162
Fax: 01904 611534
Artistic Director *Damian Cruden*
Contact *Director's Secretary*

The Theatre Royal has been on its present site since 1744 and was granted a Royal Patent in 1769. The current auditorium is Victorian; four tiers seating 863 in a traditional proscenium-arch theatre. The present company was formed in 1935. Mostly stages in-house productions but also one or two visiting companies each season. Produces 7 or 8 productions, including pantomime, between late

May and late March. Recent productions have included: *Habeas Corpus, Adam Bede, Into the Woods, Macbeth, Bedroom Farce*, adaptations of *Moll Flanders* and *Tom Jones, A View from the Bridge* and the *York Cycle of Mystery Plays*. Does not usually advertise for actors and rarely uses casting directors. Welcomes casting queries. 'Please check before sending any submissions as to whether we are casting and whether there are any suitable roles; this will save you the cost of unnecessary postage, etc. Please note we are not able to return unsolicited submissions unless you enclose an sae.'

Producing Theatres and Independent Managements

Albemarle of London

74 Mortimer Street,
London W1N 7DF
Tel: 0171 631 0135
Fax: 0171 323 3074
Contact *Basil Chritchley, Sulie Branscombe*

Founded in the 1970s, Albemarle's main activity is that of a major ticket agency. Its production company stages pantomime, summer shows and has now formed a new company to promote productions. Also owns and runs large scenic studios and a costume department. Productions are staged in all major venues throughout Great Britain and Ireland. Occasionally advertises for actors in *The Stage*. 'We do not object to actors writing or phoning but cannot guarantee a reply to letters. We do endeavour to return cvs and photographs if sae is provided. Details are not kept on file.' Occasionally holds general auditions which are advertised; apply as instructed.

Almeida Theatre Company Ltd

Almeida Street, London N1 1TA
Tel: 0171 226 7432
Fax: 0171 704 9581
E-mail: almeidatheatre.demon.co.uk
Joint Artistic Directors *Ian McDiarmid, Jonathan Kent*
Contact *Kathy Bourne, Kevin Fitzmaurice*

An international theatre, based in Islington, with 300 seats. Since it became a producing venue in 1990, the Almeida, under the direction of Ian McDiarmid and Jonathan Kent, has forged a reputation as an important centre of new and classical work of the very highest artistic standard. Produces around 7 plays per year. Productions attract leading 'name' actors such as Diana Rigg and David Suchet in *Who's Afraid of Virginia Woolf*, Ralph Fiennes in the title role of *Ivanov* and Eleanor Bron in *Dona Rosita the Spinster*. Always uses casting directors; does not welcome casting queries.

Armada Theatre Productions

8 Bloomsbury Square,
London WC1A 2LP
Tel: 0171 831 1814
Fax: 0171 242 4740
E-mail: armada@globalnet.co.uk
Producer *Andrew Welch*
Assistant Producer *Celia Mountford*

Both a theatre and radio production company. Output varies: in 1997, Armada produced 6 radio plays and 1 documentary and the previous year, 4 theatre plays and 2 radio plays. Productions have included: *Plunder* (West End co-production); *A Month in the Country, Handel's Ghosts, Shadowlands, Hysteria* (all radio plays). Does not advertise for actors and does not welcome casting queries. 'We are too small to deal with queries. Casting suggestions always come from our directors and producers.'

Carnival (Films & Theatre) Ltd

– *see* Film, Video and Independent Production Companies, page 290

Michael Codron Plays Ltd

Aldwych Theatre Office, Aldwych,
London WC2B 4DF
Tel: 0171 240 8291
Fax: 0171 240 8467
Managing Director *Michael Codron*

Michael Codron Plays Ltd manages the Aldwych Theatre in London and produces West End fare such as *Hapgood, Uncle Vanya, The Sneeze, Rise and Fall of Little Voice, Arcadia, Dead Funny.* Does not advertise for actors and does not welcome casting queries. Individual directors tend to know who they want and prefer to deal direct with agents.

C. V. Productions Ltd

83 George Street, London W1H 5PL
Tel: 0171 486 1732
Fax: 0171 224 2215
E-mail: cvtheatre@aol.com
Artistic Director *Charles Vance*
Contact *Jill Streatfeild (Associate Producer)*

Founded in 1960 by Charles Vance, one of the longest-standing theatrical producers in the UK. Produces between 5 and 10 plays per year. Productions have included tours of *Lettice and Lovage* and *Jane Eyre*, and rep seasons at Wolverhampton, Crewe, Bradford, Swindon, Westcliff and Sidmouth. Does not advertise for actors. Does not use casting directors. Welcomes written casting queries; send cv. 'Letters and cvs are held on file for six months, so regular updates are advised. Replies will only be sent if sae is enclosed. We do look at all applications when casting. Phone calls are *not* welcomed. Casting for tours is mainly done through agents via SBS.'

DGM Productions Ltd

3–5 Latimer Road, Teddington,
Middlesex TW11 8QA
Tel: 0181 977 8707
Fax: 0181 977 6909
Artistic Director *David Graham*
Contact *Elizabeth Wallace*

Founded 1993. Commercial national touring company specialising in fifties and sixties retro musicals (*Twist and Shout, Dancing in the Street, Tutti Frutti*) and popular modern plays (*Absent Friends* by Alan Ayckbourn; *A Month of Sundays* by Bob Larbey; *A Taste of Honey* by Shelagh Delaney; *Talent* by Victoria Wood). Four tours per year. Advertises for actors. Does not welcome casting queries. 'Casting is advertised through SBS to agents and occasionally through PCR and *The Stage.'*

Donmar Warehouse

Earlham Street, London WC2H 9LD
Tel: 0171 240 4882
Fax: 0171 240 4878
Artistic Director *Sam Mendes*
Casting Director *Ann McNulty*

Leading off-West End producing theatre with a formidable list of successful productions under the directorship of Sam Mendes. Produces 4 plays per year. Credits include: Sondheim's *Assassins, Translations, Hamlet* and *Cabaret* (both starring Alan Cumming), *Glengarry, Glen Ross, The Glass Menagerie* (transferred to the Comedy Theatre), *Company* (transferred to the Albery Theatre, three Olivier awards and two Critics' Circle awards), *Habeas Corpus* (with Jim Broadbent and Brenda Blethyn) and *The Fix*. Tends to work with agents rather than directly with actors. Unable to deal with casting queries from actors but performance notices are acceptable.

E & B Productions Ltd

Suite 3, Waldorf Chambers,
11 Aldwych, London WC2B 4DA
Tel: 0171 836 2795
Fax: 0171 379 4892
Contact *Paul Elliott, Brian Hewitt-Jones*

West End producers. Productions include: *Buddy, Jolson* (world tour), *Fame* (UK and US tour), *The Goodbye Girl,* as well as up to 20 pantomimes each winter. Advertises in *The Stage* for dancers and welcomes query letters from actors for the Christmas shows.

English Shakespeare Company International

Tyne Theatre and Opera House,
Westgate Road,
Newcastle upon Tyne NE1 4AG
Tel: 0191 222 0710
Fax: 0191 222 0712
(Education Office: 32 Meard Street,
London W1V 6PA)
Artistic Director *Michael Bogdanov*
Contact *Graham Lister (Administrator), Christopher Geelan (Education Director), Malachi Bogdanov (Associate Director)*

Founded 1986. Multi-award-winning, large-scale classical company. Produces one large-scale tour and a full series of education projects throughout the school term. Regionally based youth theatre and community-based projects (young offender). Recent productions: *A Midsummer Night's Dream* (21-week UK and international tour), *Beowulf*. Does not advertise for large-scale work; uses casting directors. Education work advertised in SBS. Welcomes casting queries *for education work* from actors with previous experience of working directly with young people and who can drive; apply in writing to the London office ('an updated fact sheet can be supplied giving details of latest casting requirements'). Holds general auditions for their education work; casting takes place throughout the year.

Façade

43A Garthorne Road,
London SE23 1EP
Tel: 0181 699 8655
Fax: 0181 699 8655
E-mail: facade@compuserve.com
Artistic Director *Richard Andrews*

Founded 1988. Promotes and produces new work in musical theatre.

Advertises for actors. Does not welcome general casting queries. 'Only apply for specific castings and those for which you are suitable. The blunderbuss approach does not work.'

Vanessa Ford Productions Ltd
Upper House Farm, Upper House Lane, Shamley Green,
Surrey GU5 0SX
Contact *Vanessa Ford, Glyn Robbins*

Founded 1979. A production company noted for touring and West End productions (90 to date). Mostly drama: classical and family entertainment. Recent productions have included: *The Hundred and One Dalmatians* (UK tour), *Treasure Island* (West End for two years), *The Lion, the Witch and the Wardrobe* (tour), *A Christmas Carol* (Birmingham Rep, Chichester Festival Theatre, Manchester Opera House and Sadler's Wells). Offers Equity contracts. Advertises for actors and sometimes uses casting directors. Welcomes casting queries; approach in writing with an accurate cv, photograph and sae. Occasionally holds general auditions which are advertised; do not apply before then. 'Our first "loyalty" is to those actors who have worked with us before. All incoming cvs are retained and shown to the artistic directors we employ. The ultimate responsibility for selection has to be theirs. Our advice would be to take this into account.'

Robert Fox Ltd
6 Beauchamp Place, London SW3 1NG
Tel: 0171 584 6855
Fax: 0171 225 1638
Managing Director *Robert Fox*

Founded 1980. West End and Broad-way theatre producer, plus film and television. Produces approximately 3 plays per year. Recent productions have included: *Masterclass* (Queen's Theatre), *Who's Afraid of Virginia Woolf* (Aldwych Theatre), *Skylight* (London and New York). Always uses casting directors and works through agents. Does not advertise for actors and does not welcome casting queries.

Jill Freud & Company
22 Wimpole Street,
London W1M 7AD
Tel: 0171 580 2222
Contact *Jill Freud (Artistic Director), Anthony Falkingham*

Founded 1983. Performs summer seasons at the Summer Theatre in Southwold (9 week season) and the Jubilee Hall in Aldeburgh (4 weeks). The two companies rehearse simultaneously and the productions run for 1 or 2 weeks. The 1997 productions were: *A Funny Thing Happened on the Way to the Forum, Home at Seven* by R. C. Sherriff, Ayckbourn's *Joking Apart, Great Expectations* (adapted by Tal Rubens), *Corpse, The Business of Murder* by Richard Harris. Although the company uses actors who have worked with them before, new actors are auditioned in January and February each year. Cvs and photographs should be sent towards the end of the year and performance notices should be included if the actor is due to appear in a production. Details are kept on file and suitable candidates are considered by the directors for inclusion in the auditions for the season in March/April.

Frinton Summer Theatre

Ashlyns Road, Frinton-on-Sea,
Essex CO13 9BL
Administration address: Jack Watling
Productions Ltd, 21 Queen's Road,
Frinton-on-Sea, Essex CO12 9BL
Tel: 01255 672033
Artistic Director Seymour Matthews
Associate Director Nicola Matthews

Frinton has had a summer theatre since
1934. It was saved from closure in 1974
by actor Jack Watling. Weekly rep
summer season of 7 plays staged in July
and August. 1997 productions: Dial 'M'
for Murder, Communicating Doors,
Natural Causes, See How They Run, I Have
Been Here Before, Birthday Suite and
Deathtrap. Does not advertise for actors
but welcomes casting queries; send
letter with cv and photograph. Holds
general auditions for which actors
should apply in February or March.

Greenwich Theatre

Crooms Hill, Greenwich, London
SE10 8ES
Tel: 0181 858 4447
Fax: 0181 858 8042

Founded 1969. A middle-scale, outer-
London subsidised repertory theatre
with a history of distinguished revivals,
premières and 'Golden Age' classics.
Recent successes have included: Juliet
Stevenson in The Duchess of Malfi,
Maureen Lipman in The Sisters
Rosenweig, adaptations of Northanger
Abbey and A Tale of Two Cities, Side by
Side by Sondheim. Produces 7 or 8 plays
per year. Does not advertise for actors
or use casting directors. Prefers actors
to approach 'with very specific suggestions for particular roles. Actors could
usefully identify lines of reference
between their work and the artistic
director here; i.e. "I was directed by . . .
who you know because of . . ." etc.

Research programmes and target visiting directors. Express an interest in the
work of the company. Never admit to
not having been to Greenwich. Write
with good humour; formulaic letters
get ignored. Only send postcard-size
photographs.' (It has been announced
recently that Greenwich Theatre has
lost its grant and is due to close. It is
hoped that the theatre may re-open as a
receiving house.)

Ivan Hale Ltd

PO Box 337, Rickmansworth,
Hertfordshire WD3 5DX
Tel: 01923 49299
Fax: 01923 492772
Artistic Director Ivan Hale

Founded 1992. Commercial producing
company of middle-scale and No. 1
tours. Now expanding into pantomimes and the West End. One or 2
tours annually. Previous productions
have included: Black Chiffon (with
Susan Hampshire), Gaslight (with
Frank Finlay) and The Constant Wife
(with Fiona Fullerton). Equity
contracts. Does not advertise for actors.
Occasionally uses casting directors.
Does not really welcome casting
queries. 'Sending photos/biogs specu-
latively is rather a waste of time and
money. We cast for specific projects by
invitation and in conjunction with the
director's input.'

The Peter Hall Company

Piccadilly Theatre, Denman Street,
London W1V 8DY
Tel: 0171 287 7122
Director Sir Peter Hall
Associate Producer Gillian Diamond

Founded in 1988 with the aim of
producing both classical and new plays
to the highest possible standard and to

tour them both within the UK and abroad, particularly to America and Europe. The first five productions were in association with Duncan Weldon and, from 1992, in partnership with Bill Kenwright. Productions include: *Orpheus Descending* (also Broadway and film), *The Merchant of Venice* (also Broadway), *Wild Duck*, *Born Again*, *The Homecoming*, *Twelfth Night*, *The Rose Tattoo*, *Tartuffe*, *Sienna Red*, *An Ideal Husband*, *The Gift of the Gorgon*, *Lysistrata*, *Separate Tables*, *She Stoops to Conquer*, *Piaf*, *An Absolute Turkey*, *Hamlet*, *The Master Builder*, *Mind Millie for Me*, *School for Wives*, *A Streetcar Named Desire*. In 1997, the company staged an ambitious and outstanding repertory season at The Old Vic, the productions being: *Waste*, *Cloud Nine*, *The Seagull*, *Waiting for Godot*, *The Provok'd Wife*, *King Lear*, *Snake in the Grass*, *Shining Souls*. Casting is handled by Gillian Diamond (*see entry under* Casting Directors, page 109).

Hampstead Theatre

Swiss Cottage Centre,
98 Avenue Road, London NW3 3EX
Tel: 0171 722 9224
Fax: 0171 722 3860
Contact *Jenny Topper (Artistic Director), Sam Stevenson (Casting Assistant)*

Hampstead Theatre is publicly funded to commission, produce and present new writing for the stage and has consistently maintained its reputation for high-quality productions of new drama and the occasional modern classic. The company currently occupies a 174-seat studio theatre in Swiss Cottage in north London, founded by James Roose-Evans in 1959. Stages 5 or 6 in-house plays per year plus presents a further 2 or 3 visiting productions.

Productions have included: *Dead Funny* by Terry Johnson, *Slavs!* by Tony Kushner, *The Maiden Stone* by Rona Munro, *According to Hoyle* by William Gaminara, *The Eleventh Commandment* by David Schneider, *Chimps* by Simon Block. Does not advertise for actors or use casting directors. Does not generally welcome casting queries but invitations to see an actor's work are welcome. 'Because we receive so many requests from actors asking to meet, we make it an absolute rule only to do so when casting and then only should the actor seem appropriate for the role. However, the artistic director and associate directors do try to see as much work as possible and are happy to be informed of shows (theatre and television) that actors would like them to see.'

Philip Hindin Productions

66 Melbourne Way, Bush Hill Park,
Enfield, Middlesex EN1 1XQ
Tel: 0181 366 2978
Fax: 0181 366 2978
Artistic Director *Philip Hindin*

Founded 1947. Producers of shows for theatre and television such as *The Merry Widow* (Cambridge Theatre) and *The Sunshine Boys* (Piccadilly Theatre), and *Play Your Hunch* and *Call My Bluff* for television. Always uses casting directors and works through agents. Does not welcome casting queries; 'no personal contact is desired'.

The Hiss & Boo Company

1 Nyes Hill, Wineham Lane, Bolney,
West Sussex RH17 5SD
Tel: 01444 881707
Fax: 01444 882057
E-mail: hissboo@msn.com
Artistic Director *Ian Liston*

Founded 1976. Specialises in music hall, variety and light entertainment.

Produces plays for the UK touring circuit and over the last 10 years, presented 7 shows in the West End. Also presents shows overseas and has a particularly thriving market in the Middle East where they frequently stage musical compilation shows. Produces over 200 music-hall/variety shows, 2 or 3 Christmas shows and 2 or 3 plays per year. Productions have included: *Season's Greetings, Christmas Cat and the Pudding Pirates, The Best of Broadway, The Best of the West End, Hooray for Hollywood*. Sometimes advertises in SBS. Does not welcome casting queries except from actors who can offer special skills for music hall – send letter, photograph, cv and tape of act or specific skill. 'Don't even think of contacting us unless you have seen our work or know something about what we do. Those involved with the running of the company are all "working actors" and have no time for time-wasters who know nothing of what we do. We do our utmost to help new performers (we work directly with several drama schools) but casting opportunities are rare. We also operate a strict "no sae, no reply" policy – we can't afford to do otherwise. Sad, but true.'

Bill Kenwright Ltd

55–59 Shaftesbury Avenue,
London W1V 8JA
Tel: 0171 439 4466
Fax: 0171 437 8370

One of the country's most prolific producers, Bill Kenwright has been responsible for over 250 productions on tour in the UK, Europe and the USA; in the West End and on Broadway. Recent West End productions include: Willy Russell's *Blood Brothers, An Ideal Husband* and *The*

School for Wives directed by Sir Peter Hall, *A Streetcar Named Desire* starring Jessica Lange, Stephen Sondheim's *Passion* and *Elvis – The Musical*. On Broadway, he has presented *Blood Brothers, An Ideal Husband, Dancing at Lughnasa* and, most recently, *A Doll's House* which won four Tony awards. Major tours include: *Joseph and the Amazing Technicolor Dreamcoat* and *Blood Brothers*. Bill Kenwright has co-produced two films: *The Day after the Fair* and *Stepping Out*, directed by Lewis Gilbert and starring Liza Minnelli. In 1997 he produced his first solo feature film, *Us Begins with You*, starring Anthony Edwards, Jenny Seagrove and Charles Dance.

All productions are cast by the producer and individual directors. Directors who have worked for the company include Sir Peter Hall, Roger Redfarn, Bob Tomson, Jeremy Sams and Alan Ayckbourn. Bill Kenwright is also Executive Producer of the Theatre Royal, Windsor.

Lyric Theatre Hammersmith

King Street, London W6 0QL
Tel: 0181 741 0824
Fax: 0181 741 7694
Artistic Director *Neil Bartlett*

Theatre with a long tradition of original work. Recent productions include: Iain Banks's *The Wasp Factory*, Tennessee Williams's *The Milk Train Doesn't Stop Here Anymore* (with Rupert Everett), *Treasure Island* (adapted by Neil Bartlett), *The Message* devised in association with Tony Harrison, *Sarrasine* by Balzac, Rattigan's *Cause Celebre*, *The Letter* by Somerset Maugham. Produces 4–5 plays per year. No longer able to produce in-house shows in its 110-seat studio owing to reduced funding but hosts work by some of the best touring companies in the country. Does not advertise for actors. Welcomes casting queries; approach in writing in the first instance. Send cvs and photographs to Neil Bartlett.

Cameron Mackintosh
1 Bedford Square, London WC1B 3RA
Tel: 0171 637 8866
Fax: 0181 436 2683

Founded 1980. Highly successful West End producer of musicals. Credits include: *Cats, Phantom of the Opera* (co-productions with the Really Useful Theatre Company), *Les Misérables, Miss Saigon, Oliver!*. Advertises in *The Stage*. Welcomes casting queries from actors, which should be addressed to the Casting Department. Holds general auditions, which are always advertised in *The Stage*.

The Mull Theatre
Dervaig, Isle of Mull, Argyll PA75 6QW
Tel: 01688 400377
Fax: 01688 400377
Website:
http://www.zynet.co.uk/mull/theatre/
Contact *Alasdair McCrone (Artistic Director); Gill Richey (Secretary)*

Founded in 1966, when actors Barrie and Marianne Hesketh converted an old coach house into an acting space and created the world's smallest professional theatre. Seating an audience of just 43, and with a company usually consisting of no more than 4 actors, the theatre presents a programme of 3 or 4 plays in its summer season. In addition, the company now tours the Highlands and Islands and in 1997, appeared during Mayfest at the Citizens' Theatre and community centres in Glasgow. 1997

season: *Whisky Galore, Retreat, Death and the Maiden, Not About Heroes*. Advertises for actors and welcomes casting queries via agents and post ('not by telephone'). Holds general auditions; apply in January/February for inclusion. 'Actors need to fully understand the nature of the job and the environment, and how much work would actually be involved.'

Museum of the Moving Image: Actors' Company
Museum of the Moving Image, South Bank, Waterloo, London SE1 8XT
Tel: 0171 815 1336
Fax: 0171 928 7938
Director *Julia Munrow*
Company Manager *Andrew Ashmore*

Established in 1988 as an integral part of the Museum of the Moving Image, the actors' company uses first-person live interpretation to literally bring the part to life. Rehearsals focus on creating a believable character and are augmented by film screenings, seminars and in-depth research into social and film history. The character operates in a designed environment to entertain and inform Museum visitors. The areas are Pre-Cinema (c. 1896), Electric Palace (c. 1916), Hollywood Silent Casting (c. 1927), Soviet Propaganda Film Train Carriage (c. 1917–29), Hollywood Studio (c. 1939) and Odeon (1946). Recruits a new cast of 18 actors for a short-term 21-week contract. General auditions, which are advertised in *The Stage* and PCR, are held every 21 weeks. Welcomes casting queries – 'provided actors are aware of the work we do and have considered whether they could contribute'. Send letter, photograph and cv. 'We are looking for a special blend of skills for our company. The ability to research well and in-depth; strong performance and improvisation skills; the ability to think on your feet are all vital. Other qualities are an easy, outgoing manner and an ability to communicate effectively with a wide range of visitors. Previous teaching, TIE and workshop experience is always an advantage, as are language skills. Add to this high levels of enthusiasm, energy and stamina and you are looking at a MOMI actor! Before applying, you really need to see our team at work – some actors relish the challenge, others find it a bit daunting. It is certainly not a fill-in job for "resting" actors but demands great commitment and energy.'

MW Entertainments

48 Dean Street, London W1V 5HL
Tel: 0171 734 7707
Fax: 0171 734 7727
Artistic Director Michael White
Contact Mac Mackenzie

Theatre and film producers. Theatre credits include: Oh! Calcutta, The Rocky Horror Show, Annie, Fame, Crazy for You. Film credits: The Rocky Horror Picture Show, Monty Python and the Holy Grail, Widow's Peak. Sometimes advertises for actors. Uses casting directors and does not welcome casting queries.

New Shakespeare Company Ltd

Open Air Theatre, Regent's Park,
London NW1 4NP
Tel: 0171 935 5756/5884
Fax: 0171 487 4562
E-mail:
106124.3174@compuserve.com
Artistic and Managing Director Ian Talbot
Contact Hilary Dean (Administrator), Sheila Benjamin (General Manager)

The company was founded in 1962–3

by David Conville and David William, but there have been performances at the Regent's Park site since 1932. The theatre has fixed seating for 1,187 and a grass bank for when the house is full. The season runs from May to September each year, consisting of 3 main productions – 2 Shakespeares and 1 other (usually a musical) – plus children's shows and a season of late-night and Sunday concerts/shows. The 1997 season presented A Midsummer Night's Dream, All's Well That Ends Well and Kiss Me Kate. Does not advertise for actors. Prefers to deal with agents but will accept letter with cv, photograph and sae.

Newpalm Productions

26 Cavendish Avenue,
London N3 3QN
Tel: 0181 349 0802/346 8011
Fax: 0181 346 8257
Contact John Newman, Daphne Palmer, Philip Compton

West End producers, and managers of provincial tours of 'thriller seasons', summer seasons at Eastbourne, pantomimes, and a 6-month repertory season at Chelmsford from October to March. Productions have included national tours of Seven Brides for Seven Brothers and Ladies' Night; Eastbourne summer season: Don't Dress for Dinner and Gaslight; In the Small Hours, The Sound of Murder, Towards Zero in the thriller season. Sometimes advertises for actors but 'most come from previous castings'. Prefers actors to approach in writing; no phone calls.

Pola Jones Associates Ltd

2nd Floor, 14 Dean Street,
London W1V 5AH
Tel: 0171 439 1165
Fax: 0171 437 3994
Director André Ptaszynski
General Manager Vanessa Stone

Founded in 1981 by André Ptaszynski. Over 20 plays and musicals in the West End, including: *Tommy* (Olivier award 'Outstanding Musical Production'), *Return to the Forbidden Planet* (Olivier award 'Best Musical'). Also produces tours, including: *Me and My Girl*, *Crazy for You*, *Showboat*. During 1997, presented the West End opening of the Broadway musical *Chicago*, Eddie Izzard in London and on tour, national tours of *Tommy*, *From a Jack to a King* and a major new production of *West Side Story*. As a comedy producer, has presented the live work of Rowan Atkinson, Victoria Wood, Mel Smith and Griff Rhys Jones, Rory Bremner, Dave Allen, Ben Elton and many more. The television division of the company has produced two series of the comedy *Joking Apart*, *The 39,000 Steps* (a documentary about the Edinburgh Festival), two series of the comedy *Tygo Road*, the second series of *Chalk* for BBC1 and a one-hour special with Rowan Atkinson for BBC1. Will accept cvs from actors and keeps a file of details, although casting opportunities are limited and whoever is directing a show will usually make casting requests and decisions. Employs freelance casting directors.

Really Useful Theatre Company Ltd

20 Tower Street, London WC2H 9NS
Tel: 0171 240 0880
Fax: 0171 240 1204

Andrew Lloyd Webber's company which produces West End musicals, plays and comedies. Credits include: *Jesus Christ Superstar*, *Sunset Boulevard*, *Joseph and the Amazing Technicolor Dreamcoat*, *Cats*, *Phantom of the Opera*, *Starlight Express*, *Daisy Pulls it Off*, *Lend Me a Tenor*, *Arturo Ui*, *Aspects of Love*. All casting is handled in-house. Does not welcome casting queries. Open calls are advertised in *The Stage* and agents are mailed with breakdowns.

Royal Court Theatre/ English Stage Company Ltd

St Martin's Lane, London WC2N 4BG
Tel: 0171 565 5050
Fax: 0171 565 5001/2
Artistic Director Ian Rickson
Casting Director Lisa Makin

The English Stage Company at the Royal Court Theatre was founded by George Devine in 1956 to bring serious writing back to the stage. John Osborne, John Arden, Arnold Wesker, Edward Bond, Caryl Churchill, Howard Barker and Michael Hastings are all writers this theatre has discovered. The Royal Court Theatre Downstairs is currently based at the Duke of York's Theatre in the West End while the Sloane Square theatre is being comprehensively rebuilt with Lottery funding, and the Royal Court Theatre Upstairs is at the Ambassadors Theatre. Generally produces 20 to 25 plays over three seasons per year. 1997 productions included: *The Shallow End* by Doug Lucie, *The Wake* by Tom Murphy, *East is East* by Ayub Khan-Din, *Fairgame* by Rebecca Prichard, *The Chairs* by Eugène Ionesco, trans. by Martin Crimp (co-production with Théâtre de Complicité, *Faith* by Meredith Oakes, *Bazaar* by David Planell, trans. by John Clifford.

Does not advertise for actors unless it is for 'something very, very specific'.

In-house casting director. Welcomes queries from actors, preferably by telephone. 'Do not send unsolicited cvs and photographs – find out by phone if there is anything you might be suitable for.'

Sandpiper Productions Ltd

Flat B, Abingdon Court, Allen Street,
London W8 6BP
Tel: 0171 937 9593
Fax: 0171 937 3536
E-mail: sandpipe@dircon.co.uk
Contact Harold Sanditen (Artistic Director)

Founded 1989. Sandpiper is an independent theatre production company specialising in bringing contemporary American drama, musicals and performers to the UK. Produces 1 to 3 shows per year. Productions have included: *Hospitality* by Allan Havis, *The Real World?* by Michel Tremblay, *Being at Home with Claude* by René-Daniel Dubois, *A Shayna Maidel* by Barbara Lebow, *The Boys Next Door* by Tom Griffin. Advertises for actors and uses casting directors. Sometimes holds general auditions. Does not welcome casting queries.

Shakespeare's Globe Theatre

New Globe Walk, Bear Gardens,
Bankside, Southwark,
London SE1 9ND
Tel: 0171 620 0202
Fax: 0171 928 7968
Artistic Director Mark Rylance

Sam Wanamaker's faithful reconstruction of Shakespeare's Globe Theatre opened in August 1996 with a production of *The Two Gentlemen of Verona*. Its first official season in 1997 proved a success with productions of *Henry V*, *The Winter's Tale*, Middleton's *A Chaste*

Maid in Cheapside and *The Maid's Tragedy* by Beaumont and Fletcher. Uses a freelance casting director and does not particularly welcome casting queries to the theatre.

Theatre of Comedy Company

210 Shaftesbury Avenue,
London WC2H 8DP
Tel: 0171 379 3345
Fax: 0171 836 8181
Chief Executive Andrew Welch

Founded 1983 to produce new work as well as classics and revivals for the West End and national tours. Credits include: *Run for Your Wife* and *Out of Order* (both directed by Ray Cooney), *When We are Married* (Richard Eyre), *Plunder* (revival of the Ben Travers farce at the Savoy Theatre), *Staying On* by Paul Scott. Does not advertise. Usually employs freelance casting directors. Welcomes casting queries from actors.

Theatre of Comedy at the Churchill Theatre Ltd

Churchill Theatre, High Street,
Bromley, Kent BR1 1HA
Tel: 0181 464 7131
Fax: 0181 290 6968
General Manager Ian Ross
Production Manager Digby Robinson
PA to the General Manager Alison Carney

Founded 1977. Formerly a subsidised repertory theatre, the Churchill has been managed and programmed by the Theatre of Comedy Company since April 1995. Produces 10 shows per year, many of which transfer to the West End. Productions include: *Tap Dogs, Seven Brides for Seven Brothers, Wallace and Gromit, The Goodbye Girl, South Pacific, Stepping Out, To Kill a*

Mockingbird, Boogie Nights, Jack and the Beanstalk. Advertises for actors and uses casting directors. Welcomes casting queries; send cv and photograph to Alison Carney.

Théâtre de Complicité
– *see* Touring Theatre Companies, page 187

Turnstyle Group Ltd
25 Shaftesbury Avenue,
London W1V 7HA
Tel: 0171 494 0333
Fax: 0171 494 0034
Managing Director *Howard Panter*

Leading West End production company whose credits include: *Smokey Joe's Café*, the Royal Court Classics 3-play season, *A Chorus Line* (with Adam Faith), *Carmen Jones*, *Single Spies* (with Simon Callow, Alan Bennett and Prunella Scales), *A Slip of the Tongue* (with John Malkovich), *Look Back in Anger* (with Kenneth Branagh and Emma Thompson) and Jonathan Harvey's award-winning *Beautiful Thing*. Turnstyle also manages and co-owns the Ambassadors Theatre Group, the company which owns the Duke of York's and Ambassadors theatres in London and other out-of-town venues. All casting is handled by Debbie O'Brien (*see* Casting Directors, page 114).

Jack Watling Productions Ltd
– *see* Frinton Summer Theatre, page 146

Duncan C. Weldon Productions
Suite 4, Waldorf Chambers,
11 Aldwych,
London WC2B 4DA
Tel: 0171 836 0186
Fax: 0171 240 7511

Major producer of West End and touring productions. Director of Chichester Festival Theatre from 1995 until 1997. His first production was *When We Are Married* at the Strand Theatre in 1970 and, since then, he has produced almost 200 shows in the West End. With his late partner, Louis I. Michaels, he acquired the lease of the Theatre Royal, Haymarket in the early seventies and was responsible for the artistic policy of the theatre until 1995, presenting 60 productions in that period, including: *The Aspern Papers* (with Vanessa Redgrave and Christopher Reeve), *Sweet Bird of Youth* (with Lauren Bacall), *You Never Can Tell* (with Michael Hordern and Irene Worth), *Becket* (with Derek Jacobi and Robert Lindsay). Has presented many Broadway and Canadian productions, including: *Strange Interlude* (with Glenda Jackson), *Beethoven's Tenth* (with Peter Ustinov). In 1988 he formed, with Sir Peter Hall, the Peter Hall Company (*see entry*, page 147). Recent West End credits include: Peter Whelan's *The Herbal Bed* (Duchess Theatre) and Simon Gray's *Life Support* (Aldwych). In 1997, co-produced with Carlton Television Robert Goddard's *Into the Blue*, starring John Thaw. Always uses freelance casting directors and does not welcome casting queries.

Touring Theatre Companies

Large- and middle-scale touring can give actors a period of work security. A No. 1 tour of a hit musical is likely to play most of the major venues throughout the UK, resulting in contracts lasting a year or more. A drawback, especially for those with family commitments, is the cost of living away from home for an extended period with the touring allowance (currently £110 per week) barely covering rent for digs and eating out. However, the wages are usually considerably higher than average repertory-theatre pay.

Small-scale touring is tiring work with actors usually required to help with get-ins and get-outs at every venue. Accommodation for the company sometimes causes upsets – the need to share a room may not suit everyone – and the mileage travelled can induce a state of exhaustion, particularly if you have to share some of the driving. In addition, your sparkling performance may remain unseen by potential employers who are thin on the ground in rural areas, while your touring schedule may prevent attendance at auditions for your next job.

Despite this catalogue of drawbacks, the work can be satisfying; living and working as a team, and there is the chance to see beautiful areas of the UK or Europe, or even further afield.

Actions & Words Theatre Company
32 Hoyle Road, London SW17 0RS
Tel: 0181 672 2824
Fax: 0181 672 2824
Artistic Director David Beaton

Founded 1989. Tours classical plays with large casts (usually about 12 actors) to 100–500-seater theatres and arts centres in the south of England. Usually 2 tours per year. Previous productions have included: *Macbeth*, *Twelfth Night* and Christopher Fry's *The Lady's Not for Burning*. 'We are striving to be able to offer Equity contracts but at present are unable to do so – the situation may change, so please enquire.' Advertises for actors and welcomes written casting queries.

'A&W welcomes applicants new to the profession and from all sections of the community. Applicants are advised to suggest themselves for specific roles and to be realistic about their suitability. We try *not* to cast to stereotype, however.'

Action Space Mobile
PO Box 73, Barnsley S75 1NE
Tel: 01226 384944
Fax: 01226 384944
Artistic Director *Mary Turner*

Founded 1982. Action Space Mobile is a community arts theatre company working with specialist groups nationwide and internationally. Tours shows, outside events and special needs theatres. Stages 3 tours annually to venues which include community halls, schools, training centres, hospitals, art centres, galleries and outdoor locations. Previous productions have included: *I Love No Leafless Land, This Year, Next Year, Sometimes, Always* and *It's Our Ball.* Non-Equity contracts. Welcomes casting queries – 'write, ring and visit'. Sometimes holds general auditions. Actors should be prepared to 'work with special needs, on sites, devising workshops'.

Actors Touring Company
Alford House, Aveline Street,
London SE11 5DQ
Tel: 0171 735 8311
Fax: 0171 735 1031
Artistic Director *Nick Philippou*
Executive Producer *Hetty Shand*
Administrator *Craig Dronfield*

Founded 1978. Leading small- to middle-scale touring company renowned for creating new theatre from old stories, plays, myths and legends. Stages 2 new productions per year, touring to small theatres and arts centres. Nick Philippou was appointed Artistic Director in 1993 having formerly worked with the education departments of the Royal National Theatre and the Royal Shakespeare Theatre. Previous productions have included: *Faust* by Mary Ravenhill; *Belle Vue* by Odon Von Morvarth; *Orpheus* by Kenneth McLeish. ITC/Equity contracts. Sometimes advertises for actors and occasionally uses casting directors. Welcomes casting queries; approach in writing with cv. Sometimes holds general auditions – apply for inclusion in early summer.

Age Exchange Theatre Trust
The Reminiscence Centre,
11 Blackheath Village,
London SE3 9LA
Tel: 0181 318 9105
Fax: 0181 318 0060
Artistic Director *Pam Schweitzer*

Founded in 1983. Tours 'reminiscence' shows based on the memories of pensioners on a range of topics such as work and leisure in the twenties and thirties and life in general 50 years ago. Performs in elderly people's homes, sheltered housing units, community centres. Three or 4 tours per year of 7–13 weeks. ITC/Equity contracts. Advertises in *The Stage.* Welcomes casting queries; approach in writing in the first instance, enclosing cv, photograph and sae. Most shows have a musical content and it is important that actors can sing and, preferably, play a musical instrument. Runs training courses in the use of reminiscence, for professionals in community work.

Annexe Theatre Company

The Bishop's House, Porterfield Road,
Kilmacolm, Renfrewshire PA13 4PD
Tel: 01505 874111
Fax: 01505 874111
Artistic Director *Paula MacGee*
Administrator *Gaynor Holmes*

Founded 1986. Annexe's main activity
is to provide a platform for new
writing and writers from Scotland and
to develop creative talent within
individuals or groups. The company
achieves this within the following
areas: mentoring, workshops,
creative-writing development, performance, touring productions and
readings. To date the company has
produced the work of 23 new writers
and 10 of these productions have been
extensive tours. Performs in small- to
middle-scale venues; 2 to 3 tours per
year. Previous productions have
included: *H* by Noel McMonagle and
Spitting in the Face of Eve by Douglas
Esson Moffat. Offers Equity contracts.
Does not advertise for actors.
Welcomes casting queries – send a
letter enclosing cv and photograph.
'Do write and keep us up to date. We
arrange auditions and cast from our
files.'

Ash Productions

8 Valley Road, Streatham,
London SW16 2XN
Tel: 0181 677 6171
Fax: 0181 677 6171
Artistic Director *Anthony Hyland*
Contact *Jason Mullen, James
Harman*

Founded 1985. Tours a wide variety of
productions, from one-man shows to
musicals. Venues can be from 200-
seater to 1,000-seater theatres. Two or
3 tours annually. Previous productions have included: *Oresteia, Deadly
Rivals, Romeo and Juliet* and *The
Mikado.* Non-Equity contracts.
Advertises for actors and welcomes
casting queries. 'Casting is generally
in February/ March or October/
November. Watch the updates for
particulars. Write or fax only, no
telephone calls, please.'

Attic Theatre Company (London) Ltd

– see Fringe and Alternative Theatre,
page 196

Banner Theatre

The Friends Institute,
220 Moseley Road, Highgate,
Birmingham B12 0DG
Tel: 0121 440 0460
Fax: 0121 440 0459
Artistic Director *David Rogers*
Contact *Jan Bessent (Administrator)*

Founded 1973. 'Banner Theatre has a
24-year history of touring dynamic
multimedia theatre, based on recorded
interviews, in many different communities. Creates shows about vital issues
facing people today.' One tour per
year, playing in community centres,
union halls, pubs, clubs and arts
centres. Previous productions have
included: *Criminal Justice* (multimedia
show), *Redemption Song* (anti-racist
show) and *First of May Band.* Offers
Equity contracts ('funding permit-
ting'). Advertises for actors and

welcomes casting queries. Send letter with sae.

Beaver Arts

16 Barracks Square, Barracks Road,
Newcastle under Lyme,
Staffordshire ST5 1LG
Tel: 01782 717326
Fax: 01782 717190
E-mail: barts1@compuserve.com
Artistic Directors *Gill Gill, Hilary Hughes, Susan Clarke*

Founded 1985 as a small-scale touring company run by women, focusing on street work and touring shows. Developed into a broader cross-art form company. Performances take place at non-theatre venues such as car parks, schools, beaches, buses, streets and pubs. Recent productions have included: *Rattling Bones* – a theatrical event incorporating dance, music, visual imagery, physical, verbal and non-verbal performance for indoors and out, *Respect* – a Theatre-in-Education show looking at behaviour in junior schools. No Equity contracts but 'pay and conditions comparable'. Welcomes casting queries; approach in writing in the first instance. 'If you are seriously interested in working in non-theatre settings and in a collaborative and cross-art form approach, and are interested in working *with* non-professionals/community members, then it is worth approaching this company. If you are not, it is not. We will always ask prospective workers to visit us and see our work first, if possible. We work hard, long hours and like to work with comedy, character and the language of theatre. We do not usually work in London or the South-East.'

Besht Tellers

73 Compayne Gardens,
London NW6 3RS
Tel: 0171 624 4343
Fax: 0171 624 4343
E-mail: 100645.3632@compuserv.com
Artistic Director *Rebecca Wolman*
Administrator *Olivia Jacobs*
Education Director *Danny Simmonds*

Founded 1991. Committed to opening up the Jewish world to both Jews and non-Jews alike through open and innovative physical story theatre. 'Our work is driven by the search for the spark within theatre – the magical contact between audience and performers.' Tours to small- and middle-scale theatres; 1 or 2 tours per year. Previous productions have included: *Angels and Demons* (Tricycle Theatre and national tour), *Tales from Home* (national tour) and *Telling Tales* (King's Head, national and international tour). Equity contracts. Sometimes advertises for actors and occasionally uses casting directors. Casting queries in writing only. Sometimes holds general auditions in which case they are advertised.

Big Bubble Theatre Company

111 Norton Way South,
Letchworth,
Hertfordshire SG6 1NY
Tel: 01462 681916
Fax: 01462 484517
E-mail: bigbubble@mail.enterprise.net
Artistic Director *Julian Newman Turner*

Founded 1993. 'High-energy, stylised, visual, total theatre.' One or 2 tours per year to small- to middle-scale theatres and arts centres. Also holds workshops. Previous productions have included: *Knife Games* by Gary Drabwell, *Decadence* and *East* by

Steven Berkoff. Non-Equity contracts. Advertises for actors in *The Stage* and PCR. Welcomes casting queries – send letter with cv and photograph. 'We specialise in "total theatre", so experience in mime and physical theatre and devising is required.'

Big Telly Theatre Co.

c/o Flowerfield Arts Centre,
185 Coleraine Road,
Portstewart BT55 7HU
Tel: 01265 832588
Fax: 01265 832588
Artistic Director *Zoë Seaton*
Contact *Bernadette McGill*

Founded 1987. Northern Ireland's only permanent professional theatre company based in the regions. Premières its work at the Riverside Theatre and has been involved in the local youth theatre since its outset. Tours to middle-scale venues in England, Scotland and throughout Ireland. Two tours per year. Recent productions have included: *To Hell with Faust*, *Stage Your Story* (a story-telling/creative-writing project, leading to a performance workshop), *Navigating Shakespeare* (series of workshops) and *Metamorphosis* by Steven Berkoff. Offers ITC/Equity contracts. Sometimes advertises for actors. Welcomes casting queries – send cv.

Black Mime Theatre Co.

34–6 Colombo Street,
London SE1 8DP
Tel: 0171 928 1311
Fax: 0171 928 1740
Artistic Director *Denise Wong*
General Manager *Felicia Nevins*

Founded 1984. Working as a group, the company researches all its material and maintains a direct link with the Black community which is its source of inspiration. 'Black Mime Theatre aims to provide thought-provoking experiences which incorporate acrobatics, dance, mime, music and drama to create entertaining, hard-hitting, physical theatre.' One tour per year to national and international venues. Previous productions have included: *Mourning Song*, *Dirty Reality, Dirty Reality II* and *Forgotten Heroes*. Offers Equity contracts. Advertises for actors and welcomes casting queries. Send photograph and cv with covering letter. Holds general auditions and actors should apply for inclusion at any time. 'Black Mime considers training a priority and an investment for the future. By finding resources in new, exciting and vibrant techniques, the performers add to the strength and originality of the devised process. Participation in Black Mime's annual training projects is a valuable means of developing a range of skills which broaden actors' experience and development.'

Black Theatre Cooperative

Unit 3P, Leroy House,
436 Essex Road, Islington,
London N1 3QP
Tel: 0171 226 1225
Fax: 0171 226 0223
Artistic Director *Felix Cross*

Founded 1978. Britain's oldest-established Black theatre company. Small-scale touring plus some mid-scale touring co-productions. One or 2 tours per year. Offers Equity contracts. Sometimes holds general auditions. Advertises for actors and welcomes written casting queries. 'Always call to check that you are writing to the correct person and at the correct address – do your homework!'

Bold & Saucy Theatre Company

22 Cleveland Mansions, Widley Road,
Maida Vale, London W9 2LA
Tel: 0171 266 5235
Artistic Director *Sarah Davey*

Founded 1992. Aims to create productions that live up to their name. 'A fresh, original style, inventive storytelling and visual audacity, so conjuring up a magical theatre experience for all.' Currently touring once a year to outdoor spaces, festivals, small- to middle-scale arts centres, theatres and studios. Previous productions have included: *Bold in Her Breeches* (devised work), *The Taming of the Shrew*, *Twelfth Night* and *The Tempest*. No Equity contracts at present but 'we are working towards them'. Advertises for actors in PCR and welcomes casting queries; send letter or invitation to see shows. Holds (free) general workshops and often auditions people from these. Apply for inclusion in January or November. 'We keep all details on file and will contact actors for workshops/auditions. We are looking for actors who can work well physically as well as handle a classic text. Also actors who like working in an ensemble both on and off stage.'

Bootleg Theatre Company

23 Burgess Green, Bishopdown,
Salisbury, Wiltshire SP1 3EL
Tel: 01722 421476
Artistic Director *Colin Burden*
Contact *Colin Burden, David Taylor, Philip Brant*

Founded 1985. Formed by two disillusioned actors with the intention of only one production of Barrie Keefe's *Barbarians*. The show was so success-ful that the company became fully formed with the aim of producing new work by new writers to as wide an audience as possible. Tours 2 plays per year to arts centres, studio theatres, universities and, occasionally, village halls. Previous productions have included: *Different Animal* by Philip Goulding (rhyming monologue about an imprisoned football fan), *Monomania* by Michael Burnham (play about the unsafe conviction of James Hanratty for the A6 murder in 1961 – premièred at the Salisbury Playhouse prior to national tour). Offers Equity contracts 'when financial constraints allow'. Rarely advertises 'as we tend to use actors whose work we know or who have made their desire to work for and with us known previously'. Welcomes casting queries – send cv and photograph with a covering letter expressing interest in new work and desire to work within the constraints of small-cast plays. 'Each cv is given serious consideration before any decision is made. If an actor is deemed unsuitable for this company, their cvs and photographs will be returned to them. We do, however, keep a file of actors we would like to work with in the future and, even if this does not come to fruition, we may recommend them to other companies.' Does not hold general auditions. 'We do not believe auditions are the safest way to assess a person's ability; so we usually meet and discuss the project with them before holding a reading of the script. Our company is built on the solid foundation of working-class theatre, with the likes of Barrie Keefe, Tony Marchant, Vince Foxall and Philip Davis as inspiration. We do *not* welcome "luvvies" or people who put themselves before the work we are committed to.'

Borderline Theatre Company

North Harbour Street, Ayr KA8 8AA
Tel: 01292 281010
Artistic Director *Leslie Finlay*
Contact *Eddie Jackson*

Founded 1974. 'From heady beginnings in the 1970s to ground-breaking touring and education projects in the 1990s, Borderline has continued to produce popular, innovative and accessible theatre.' Tours small- to large-scale venues 3 times per year. Previous productions have included: *The Misanthrope* by Molière, *Broken Angel*, a new play by Lin Coghlan aimed at young people, and a new writing commission by Anita Sullivan. Offers Equity contracts. Does not advertise for actors; uses casting directors. Holds general auditions. Welcomes casting queries – send letter and cv. NB Borderline has a bias towards Scottish-based actors.

Box Hedge Theatre Company

12 Conal Court, Mitcham Lane,
London SW16 6LN
Tel: 0181 769 0300
Fax: 0181 769 2106
E-mail: a.lilley@dial.pipex.com
Artistic Director *Anthony Lilley*

Founded 1991. Large open-air touring theatre company, performing at stately homes, festivals and gardens throughout Britain. One tour per year in the summer. Previous productions have included: *Twelfth Night, As You Like It, A Midsummer Night's Dream, The Tempest, Macbeth* and *Romeo and Juliet*. Does not offer Equity contracts at present, but 'we are striving so to do'. Advertises in PCR in the spring; send cv and covering letter in response to advert. Holds general auditions.

Bright Ltd

10–14 Macklin Street,
London WC2B 5NF
Tel: 0171 242 1882
Fax: 0171 242 1855
E-mail: chapman@dircom.co.uk
Artistic Directors *Guy Chapman, Paul Spyker*

Founded 1996. New writing touring company, playing small-to middle-scale venues. Previous productions have included: *The Twilight of the Gods* by Jonathan Tolius, *Never the Sinner* by John Logan and *Showstopper* by Dan Rebellato. Offers Equity contracts. Advertises in PCR and uses casting directors. Holds general auditions. Welcomes *written* casting queries. 'Don't hassle too much. We file everything and contact people we're interested in.'

British Asian Theatre Company

Star Studios, 38 Lea Bridge Road,
Clapton, London E5 9QD
Tel: 0181 986 4470
Fax: 0181 533 6597
Contact *Raj Patel (Artistic Director), Ashi Asghar, Sarfraz Patel*

Founded in 1982 out of Star Productions, a film and video production company, the British Asian Theatre Company works from an Asian point of view, writing, devising, workshopping and touring both nationally and internationally. Always on the lookout for new plays. Touring venues range from small- to large-scale (100 to 1,000 seats). One or 2 tours per year. Offers Equity contracts. Advertises for actors and welcomes casting queries; approach in writing with cv and photograph. Does not hold general auditions. 'If you have dedication for theatre and are committed to the hard work it demands, do not hesitate to get in touch with us.'

Bruvvers Theatre Company
Ouseburn Warehouse Workshops,
36 Lime Street, Ouseburn,
Newcastle upon Tyne NE1 2PQ
Tel: 0191 261 9230
Fax: 0191 261 9230
Artistic Director *Michael Mould*

Founded 1969. Tyneside touring company which returns to base each day. An ensemble company with 3 shows in repertoire, playing to all age ranges in community centres, pubs, clubs, schools and hospitals throughout the year. Previous productions have included: *Victorian Delights* (for Key Stage 2 schools and family audience), *The Serenaders* (elderly/ OAP audience), *Pigs Meat: A Vision of Utopia* (adult and student audience) and *Mother Goose* (family audience). Does not offer Equity contracts. Welcomes casting queries from actors. 'Come and see our work and understand the style which is heavily music-based. We demand energy of a high order, imagination, sensitivity and creativity.'

Channel Theatre Company
Granville Theatre, Victoria Parade,
Ramsgate, Kent CT11 8DG
Tel: 01843 588280
Fax: 01843 588260
Artistic Director *Philip Dart*
Contact *Claudia Leaf, Associate Director*

Founded in 1980 to serve the southeast of England with professional theatre, the company rapidly expanded and is now a successful national touring company. Performs in middle- and small-scale venues as well as schools and community centres such as village halls. From time to time, produces large-scale community plays. Does not hold general auditions. 'As a relatively small organisation, we regret we cannot process unsolicited applications for work. Actors should look out for advertisements in *The Stage* for TIE work; all other casting is handled direct through agents' casting broadsheets. Please send sae and an envelope large enough to include your photo when applying in response to adverts.'

Cheek by Jowl
In the spring of 1998, Cheek by Jowl is mounting a major national and international tour of *Much Ado About Nothing*, following which the company is taking a sabbatical from producing and is disbanding its management team. The artistic directors, Declan Donnellan and Nick Ormerod, have said: 'This period of reflection will nourish the company, resulting in a Cheek by Jowl for the new millennium. Meanwhile, the essence of the company remains: a dedication to theatre of the highest quality. We look forward to providing more in the years to come.'

The Cherub Company London
5–6 Midland Road, London NW1 2AD
Tel: 0171 383 0947
Fax: 0171 383 0947
Contact *Andrew Visnevski (Artistic Director), Vi Marriott (Administrator)*

Founded in 1978 by Andrew Visnevski. A pioneering company with a 'colourful visual style and a reputation for innovative and challenging productions'. One tour per year to national and international venues. In 1995, launched 'Theatre-alive!', a unique cultural and educational post-guidance training scheme for young theatre practitioners. Previous productions have included: *The Tempest* and Bertolt Brecht's *The Life of Edward the Second of England.* Offers Equity contracts 'when funds are available'. Occasionally advertises for actors. Welcomes casting queries; approach in writing with cv, telephone and fax numbers. Applicants should know the company's work. 'When auditioning, come prepared and do not undersell yourself.'

Clean Break Theatre Company Ltd

37–9 King's Terrace,
London NW1 0JR
Tel: 0171 383 3786
Fax: 0171 380 0308
Contact *Susannah Kraft, Lucy Perman*

Set up by two women in HMP Askham Grange in 1979, Clean Break produces high-quality, original theatre which provides a powerful and unique voice for women prisoners, ex-prisoners and ex-offenders. Tours once a year to theatres, arts centres and prisons. Productions have included: *Goldmines* by Lavinia Murray, *Mules* by Winsome Pinnock, *Another Nine Months* by Louise Page, *Red* by Anna Reynolds. Offers Equity contracts. Advertises for actors in *The Stage* in January; 'we cast women actors who have had personal experience of the criminal justice system'. Cast size of 1–3 performers per production. Auditions held in February from shortlisted actors and rehearsals are usually in February/March.

Communicado Theatre Company

2 Hill Street, Edinburgh EH2 3JZ
Tel: 0131 624 4040
Fax: 0131 624 4041
E-mail: communicado@dial.pipex.com
Artistic Director *Gerry Mulgrew*
Contact *Linda Borthwick (Producer)*

Founded 1983. Leading Scottish touring company. Communicado's aims are to 'break down the barriers between artistic disciplines by bringing artists, performers, poets, playwrights and musicians together to create passionate, explosive theatre'. Tours to national touring houses, producing houses, arts centres, studios, educational venues and village halls. Usually 2 tours per year plus one site-specific. Previous productions have included: *Tales of the Arabian Nights* by Gerry Mulgrew, *Cyrano de Bergerac* adapted by Edwin Morgan, *Portrait of a Woman* by Michel Vinaver and *Tall Tales for Small People* by Gerry Mulgrew. Offers Equity contracts. Does not advertise for actors. Welcomes casting queries. Prefers initial contact to be by telephone, but 'we hold cvs on file and get back to people if there is anything suitable'.

Compass Theatre Company

Carver Street Institute, 24
Rockingham Lane, Sheffield S1 4FW
Tel: 0114 275 5328
Fax: 0114 278 6931
Contact *Neil Sissons (Artistic Director), Deborah Rees (General Manager)*

Founded 1981. Middle-scale ensemble company which tours a classical repertoire twice a year. Previous productions have included: *Endgame* by Beckett, *The Merchant of Venice* by Shakespeare, *Dr Faustus* by Marlowe,

Woyzeck by Buchner and Pinter's *The Caretaker*. Offers Equity contracts. Advertises for actors and welcomes casting queries. Approach in writing, enclosing cv and photograph. No general auditions; sees actors for specific projects. 'We notify our intention to audition through SBS and PCR. All applications we receive in between auditions are kept and considered for the next auditions. We clear our files after each audition and only keep on file permanently those actors we have met and those we are interested in for future projects. Actors who submit details to us and fail to get an audition should resubmit details if they wish to be considered for the next project.'

Custard Factory Theatre Co.

Unit 130, The Custard Factory, Gibb Street, Digbeth, Birmingham B9 4AA
Tel: 0121 766 8083
Fax: 0121 773 0038
Artistic Directors *Rachel Gartside, Juliet Forster*

Founded 1989. Small-/middle-scale touring company which aims to make classic texts accessible to all 'through innovative, dynamic, physical theatre'. Performs in anything from village halls to 600-seater theatres. Two tours per year. Previous productions have included: *Macbeth, Romeo and Juliet, A Midsummer Night's Dream*. Offers Equity contracts. Advertises for actors in PCR. Welcomes casting queries. Approach by phone. Apply for a particular job only once it is advertised. Send cv, photograph and 'most importantly', personal letter. Occasionally holds general auditions which are advertised. 'We are hugely oversubscribed. Read adverts carefully and only apply if you fit all criteria.'

Cwmni Theatr Gwynedd

Theatr Gwynedd, Deiniol Road, Bangor, Gwynedd LL57 2TL
Tel: 01248 351707
Fax: 01248 351915
Contact *Dafydd Thomas*

Founded 1986. Welsh-language, mainstream theatre company, performing at Theatr Gwynedd and major theatres and arts centres throughout Wales. Up to 3 tours per year. Productions have included translations into Welsh of Molière's *The Imaginary Invalid* and *A Doctor in Spite of Himself*, *Y Twr* by Gwenlyn Parry, Welsh classics, and frequent new plays. Offers Equity contracts. Rarely advertises. Welcomes casting queries from actors who can work in Welsh only; approach in writing, sending photograph and cv with covering letter. Does not hold general auditions.

Dead Earnest Theatre

84 Walkley Road, Sheffield S6 2XP
Tel: 0114 231 0687
Fax: 0114 231 0687
Artistic Directors *Ashley Barnes, Mark Ellison*
Contact *Ashley Barnes, Neil Adleman*

Founded 1993. Dead Earnest presents contemporary European theatre with 'a view to exploring the similarities and differences in social perspectives across Europe'. Live music is an integral part of the company, underpinning the emotionally charged nature of many of the productions. Two tours per year to small-scale venues, including arts centres, studio theatres, colleges and pubs. Recent productions have included: *The Nest* by Franz Xaver Kroetz (May 1997 tour), *Swine* by Peter Turrini (October/November 1997), *Bremen Coffee* by Rainer Werner Fassbinder (1996). Does not offer Equity contracts. Advertises in *The Stage* and welcomes casting queries. 'Send a cv to Ashley Barnes which will be kept on file until useful. If a reply is required then enclose an sae and suggest as much in the covering letter.' Audition on a show-by-show basis. 'We welcome contact from actors of all ages, sizes, etc., but give most attention to those who have a base in South Yorkshire or within commuting distance (Leeds or Manchester). This is because we can usually only cover actors' expenses and that will cause difficulty in securing accommodation. When casting, I look for three things: suitability in age and appearance for part; required technical ability and enthusiasm; and, probably most important, whether an actor will fit in with the rest of the company or (in other words) whether or not I like them as a human being and vice versa' [Ashley Barnes].

Druid Theatre Company

Chapel Lane, Galway,
Republic of Ireland
Tel: 00 353 91 568660
Fax: 00 353 91 563109
E-mail: druid@iol.ie
Artistic Director *Garry Hynes*
Contact *Louise Donlon (General Manager), Maria Fleming (Administrator)*

Founded 1975. Acclaimed national and international Irish touring company which has evolved an ambitious repertoire and dynamic style. Under Artistic Director Garry Hynes the company has developed a comprehensive programme of new work. Writers currently under commission include Billy Roche and Martin McDonagh. In 1997, McDonagh's *The Leenane Trilogy (The Beauty Queen of Leenane, A Skull in Connemara* and *The Lonesome West)* transferred to London to the Royal Court Downstairs at the Duke of York's Theatre. Offers Irish Actors' Equity contracts. Uses casting directors. Welcomes casting queries from actors – send letter and cv. Although Druid does not cast Irish actors exclusively, most of the directors are Irish and their casting invariably leans that way. Does not hold general auditions.

Eastern Angles Theatre Company

Sir John Mills Theatre, Gatacre Road,
Ipswich, Suffolk IP1 2LQ
Tel: 01473 218202
Fax: 01473 250954
Artistic Director *Ivan Cutting*
Contact *Rebecca Farrar (Administrator)*

Founded in 1982 by a group of local actors wanting to produce plays for and about the East Anglian region. Artistic Director Ivan Cutting was one of the founding members. The current aims of the company are 'to provide high-quality theatre; to maintain and promote a regional identity; to tour to theatre, non-theatre and community venues; to develop and produce new and original work'. Three tours per year, on average. Previous productions have included: *The Wuffings* by Kevin Crossley Holland and Ivan Cutting (site-specific, non-touring), *Fields* by Ivan Cutting (small-scale tour), *David Copperfield* adapted from Dickens by Alastair Cording (middle-scale tour). Offers ITC/Equity contracts. Advertises for actors in SBS. Welcomes casting queries – send cv, photograph and sae for reply/return if not used. Does not hold general auditions. 'If you have a cast breakdown, be honest – is this part right for you? We get far too many cvs in response to break-downs that are very obviously not suitable.'

ELAN – Wales

Chapter, Market Road, Canton, Cardiff CF5 1QE
Tel: 01222 345831
Fax: 01222 345831
E-mail: http://www.demon.co.uk
Contact *Firenza Guidi (Artistic Director), David Murray*

Founded in 1989, ELAN is a training and production company which creates projects/performances to enable collaboration between perform-ers from different parts of Wales, Europe and beyond, 'in the belief that there is a language, in theatre, which unifies without abolishing differ-ences'. A non-profit, limited company and a charity (No. 1064431). Stages highly visual, small- and large-scale performances/ events not only in theatres, arts centres and schools but also in unusual settings such as medieval towers, crypts, canteens, churches, dockyards and marshlands. One tour per year consisting of 8 to 10 projects, most of them site-specific. Productions have included: *Of Love and Demons*, an international work-shop/montage held in Ireland; *Acqua Nera: In the Underground of Memory*, a site-specific, large-scale performance at the Piazza Vittorio Veneto in Florence. Offers Equity contracts, 'if possible'. Does not advertise for actors; 'our performers come through montage or workshop experience with the company. We are always happy to let actors know about our perfor-mances, workshops or montages in Britain or abroad. For any enquiry, it is best to approach in writing. ELAN operates as an ensemble, with perma-nent members working with the company since its inception. We offer up to two residencies every year which enable performers to know the company better. It is therefore not advisable to send us cvs or photos as it is highly unlikely that we would cast an actor through that route. Should anyone be interested in our work they ought to try and attend one of our training projects and see for them-selves if our style of work suits their artistic needs.'

Empty Space Theatre Company

37 Nasmyth Street, London W6 0HA
Tel: 0181 563 1949
Fax: 0181 563 1949
Artistic Director *Andrew Holmes*

Founded 1985. Empty Space tours ensemble theatre to small-scale venues such as arts centres, studios and universities (up to 350 seats) through-out the UK and abroad. Performs new work with a minimum of set, costumes and props, placing the emphasis on the quality of the acting. The work is physical and increasingly experimen-tal. One or 2 tours per year. In 1997, staged a British Council tour of *The Strange Case of Dr Jekyll and Mr Hyde* to Egypt, Bangladesh, Romania and Malaysia; in 1996, a new play, *Fav'rite Nation* toured to the RSC's Swan Theatre, Edinburgh Traverse Theatre, Bristol Old Vic and the Lyric Hammersmith in London. Offers Equity contracts although not for every production. Advertises for actors in SBS and PCR. Welcomes casting queries at any time – approach in writing, enclosing cv and photograph. Auditions for specific projects only. 'All details sent to us are held on file until we are next casting. Experience of improvisation, ensemble work and physical theatre are all an asset.'

English Chamber Theatre

410 Beatty House, Dolphin Square,
London SW1V 3LX
Tel: 0171 798 8798
Fax: 0171 932 0221
Artistic Director *Jane McCulloch*

Founded 1984. Tours small-cast productions (usually 2–4 characters) with minimal sets. Ideal for festivals, foreign tours, short runs, galas, etc. Often biographical in content and vehicles for stars – Derek Jacobi as Byron and James Bolam as Beethoven, for example. Recent productions have included a new play by Beverley Cross on the QE2 cruise liner, and a British Council tour to Cologne with Jane Lapotaire, Julian Glover and Jasper Britton in an adaptation of *Lamb's Tales from Shakespeare*. Does not advertise and does not welcome casting queries from actors.

English Touring Theatre Ltd

New Century Building, Hill Street,
Crewe, Cheshire CW1 2BX
Tel: 01270 501800
Fax: 01270 501888
E-mail:
admin@englishtouring.demon.co.uk
Artistic Director *Stephen Unwin*
Executive Director *Keith Halsall*
General Manager *Valerie Evans*
Head of Education *Fiona Lesley*

Founded 1993. Arts Council-funded touring company, producing high-quality productions of classic and new work. All tours are supported by a strong education programme. Tours to middle- to large-scale venues; 3 tours per year. Productions include: *Measure for Measure, The Seagull, Design for*

Living, Henry IV Parts I and II, Rupert Street Lonely Hearts Club. Offers Equity contracts. Does not advertise for actors. Uses casting directors (currently, Toby Whale). Does not welcome casting queries; all approaches must be through the casting director.

Enzyme Theatre Company

LJ's Theatre Bar, 140 London Road,
Kingston, Surrey KT2 6QL
Tel: 0181 288 1448
Artistic Director *Scott Matheson*

Founded to promote new writing and take a fresh look at established plays, Enzyme is a touring company committed to the integration of the disabled into the arts. Resident at LJ's Theatre Bar, a multi-purpose arts venue with two performance/rehearsal spaces, the company has an 'open door' policy, welcoming anyone regardless of age, race, sex or disability to take part. As many as 20 productions are staged each year. Recent productions have included: *Ghetto, No Visible Wounds, Some Voices, Decadence* and *Adult Child, Dead Child*. Does not offer Equity contracts. Advertises for actors in *The Stage*, Casting Sheet and the local press. Welcomes casting queries. Holds group auditions – 'all welcome'. 'Enzyme looks for committed actors who will work as part of a group and be aware of all aspects of theatre. Production and practical theatre skills/awareness are appreciated. Open policy means that actors can get involved in all aspects and in that instance receive "profit-share". Don't just send in details; come and see shows to see what we do. Come to us with ideas, favourite projects and roles and we'll consider them. LJ's holds cvs and details on file, not just for Enzyme, but all incoming directors or companies.'

European Theatre Company Ltd

39 Oxford Avenue, London SW20 8LS
Artistic Directors *Adam Roberts, Jennie Graham*

Founded 1992. A unique and innovative professional touring company which performs educational, foreign-language theatre in schools, colleges, theatres and art centres throughout the UK. Their aim is to bring European theatre alive through imaginative productions that are easy to understand, appreciate and enjoy. Three tours per year. Previous productions have included: Molière's *L'Ecole des femmes* in a new version, performed in French, Dürrenmatt's *Die Physiker*, performed in German, *Le Ballon Rouge*, adapted from the French film, performed in a mixture of French and English. Pays above Equity rates. Advertises for actors and uses casting directors. Welcomes queries from actors who speak a second European language other than English, or are native French or German. Send letter with cv and photograph. Does not hold general auditions.

Fecund Theatre

6 Cleland Road, Chalfont St Peter, Buckinghamshire SL9 9BG
Tel: 01753 882692
Artistic Director *John Keates*
Contact *Beverley Reid (Administrator)*

Founded 1992. Touring company which produces innovative, highly physical work which combines visual and aural technology with the performance skills of the actor. Tours once or twice a year to national arts centres. Previous productions have included: *27, Hamlet, Fallen Angels, The End* and *The Pleasure Dome*. Does not offer Equity contracts. Advertises for actors and welcomes casting queries; approach in writing with covering letter, photograph and cv. 'Interested in versatile performers who are "progressive" in their attitude to theatre and have a desire to improve and learn new performance skills.'

Vanessa Ford Productions Ltd

– see Producing Theatres and Independent Managements, page 146

Forest Forge Theatre Company

The Theatre Centre, Endeavour Park, Crow Arch Lane, Ringwood, Hampshire BH24 1SF
Tel: 01425 470188
Fax: 01425 471158
Artistic Director *Kevin Shaw*
Associate Director *(Outreach) Josh Elwell*
Contact *Karen Jeffries, Sharon Lawless (Administrators)*

Founded in 1981. A professional touring community theatre company based in Ringwood, providing theatre and related activities to the greatest possible range of people in their own communities. Tours throughout Hampshire, parts of east Dorset and south Wiltshire to non-theatre venues – arts centres, village halls, community centres, colleges, schools and elderly people's homes. Recent productions include: *Beauty and the Beast, Alice in Wonderland, Pied Piper, Tess of the D'Urbervilles, Much Ado About Nothing, The Mayor of Casterbridge, The Government Inspector*. Offers Equity contracts. Advertises for actors and welcomes casting queries. 'We have, to date, placed an annual advert in *The Stage* (first week of June) for the season's requirements – 4 touring shows from September to May. Also advertise in PCR and SBS. Auditions are held in July in London, by invitation.'

Gay Sweatshop Theatre Company

At the time of going to press, a withdrawal of funding had led to operations being suspended.

Geese Theatre Company

MAC (Midland Arts Centre), Cannon Hill Park, Birmingham B12 9QH
Tel: 0121 446 4370
Fax: 0121 446 5806
Contact *Vivienne Cole (Administrative Director)*

Founded 1987. National touring company working throughout the year in prisons, young offenders' institutions and probation centres. The work includes live performances, residencies, staff training, long-term probation service partnerships. The company's approach is based on the work of Geese Theatre Company USA and John Bergson and uses mask and improvisation. Recent work has included: *Lifting the Weight*, *The Plague Game*, *The Violent Illusion Trilogy* and *Stay* (all devised, original work). Does not offer Equity contracts. Occasionally advertises for actors. Does not welcome casting queries.

Good Company

46 Quebec Street, Brighton,
East Sussex BN2 2UZ
Tel: 01273 606652
Fax: 01273 606926
Artistic Director *Sue Pomeroy*
General Manager *John Owen*

Founded 1986. Well-established No. 1 touring company which aims to provide innovative and accessible theatre to the widest possible audience. Has an interest in new writing and a strong commitment to the educational aspects of its work. Concentrating at present on adaptations of classics such as *Wuthering Heights*, *Pride and Prejudice* and *Hard Times*. Tours are approximately 28 to 33 weeks in length, working from the autumn through to the spring. Performs in large-scale theatres nationwide. Offers Equity/TMA contracts. Mainly deals with agents. Advertises in SBS but happy to receive letters from actors, enclosing cvs and photographs.

Graeae Theatre Company

Interchange Studios, Dalby Street,
London NW5 3NQ
Tel: 0171 267 1959
Fax: 0171 267 2703
E-mail: graeae@aircon.co.uk
Artistic Director *Jenny Sealey*
Contact *Kevin Dunn (Administrative Director)*

Founded 1980. A professional touring theatre company of disabled people. As far as possible, Graeae aims to employ staff, actors, directors, writers and theatre practitioners who are physically disabled or have sensory impairment. The company also provides training for disabled actors and operates a youth and community programme. Tours twice a year to small- to medium-scale theatres and arts centres. Previous productions have included: *What the Butler Saw* by Joe Orton, *Fleshfly*, an adaptation of Jonson's *Volpone* by Trevor Lloyd, *Ubu* adapted by Trevor Lloyd. Offers Equity contracts. Advertises for actors but does not welcome general casting queries. Send cv, photograph and covering letter in response to advertisement.

Midlands. Send letter with cv and photograph.

Green Pavement Theatre Co.
35 Armadale Road, Chichester,
West Sussex PO19 4NR
Tel: 01243 771597
Artistic Director *Peter Waters*

Founded 1988. Small-scale touring of children's shows, new plays, community projects and workshops to studio spaces of main theatres, schools and community centres. One tour per year. Previous productions have included: *Please Don't Feed the Animals, When Water Came to Stay* (both plays for children). Does not offer Equity contracts. Sometimes advertises for actors; does not welcome casting queries.

Heartbreak Productions
72 New Street, Leamington Spa,
Warwickshire CV31 1HL
Tel: 01926 430307
Fax: 01926 426523
E-mail: heartbreak1@m.s.n.com
Artistic Director *Peter Mimmack*
Contact *Maddy Kerr*

Founded 1991. Presents outdoor productions of Shakespeare in the grounds of castles and stately homes, classics and new work in middle-scale arts centres and promotes other professional groups in Leamington. One or 2 tours per year. Does not offer Equity contracts. Sometimes advertises for actors. Welcomes casting queries from locally based actors, i.e. from the West

Hijinx Theatre Cooperative Company Limited
c/o The Arts Council of Wales,
9 Museum Place,
Cardiff CF1 3BG
Tel: 01222 395238
Artistic Director *Gaynor Lougher*
Contact *Val Hill (General Manager), Denise Lord (Tour Booking and Marketing)*

Founded in 1981 as a project company to tour nationally throughout Wales. Now also tours extensively in England. Winner of the BBC Wales Company award in 1994. The company's policy is to create original, innovative and accessible plays, combining music, design and theatre, for people with learning disabilities and for community audiences. Performs in small arts centres, drama studios, community centres, social services day centres and Gateway Clubs. Two tours per year; one of 10 weeks and one of 12 weeks. Recent productions have included: *Wishful Thinking, A Leap in the Dark* (both for people with learning disabilities); *The Dove Maiden* by Charles Way (community tour). Offers ITC/Equity contracts. Sometimes advertises for actors. Welcomes casting queries; send letter, cv and photograph (particular reference to musical skills). 'As we are a small-scale touring cooperative theatre company, we need to know of actors' experience in small-scale touring; we need to know the age of the actor; we need to know of other skills, especially musical or driving skills.'

Hull Truck Theatre

Spring Street, Hull HU2 8RW
Tel: 01482 224800
Fax: 01482 581182
Artistic Director *John Godber*
General Manager *Simon Stallworthy*
Casting/Administrative Assistant
Christine Wild

Founded in 1971. The artistic policy of Hull Truck is 'accessibility and popularity' and it is no surprise that a large proportion of the productions toured by Hull Truck are by artistic director John Godber. Tours to large-/middle- and small-scale venues 2 or 3 times per year. Recent productions have included: *Gym and Tonic, Weekend Breaks, Relatively Speaking, Jump to Cow Heaven* by Gill Adams (winner of a Fringe First and First of the First for 1997). Offers Equity contracts. Advertises for actors. Uses casting directors and welcomes casting queries from actors. Telephone for details. Does not hold general auditions. 'When we cast we send out breakdowns through SBS and PCR and audition as and when required. Although we do keep cvs and photographs sent in on spec, it is best to reply in response to a casting breakdown, so telephone first. Experience of John Godber's work is useful as the bulk of our productions are based on his writings.'

Instant Classics

21 Campion Road, Putney,
London SW15 6NN
Tel: 0181 788 9714
Fax: 0181 788 9714
Artistic Director *David Cottis*

Founded in 1990 in Cardiff, the company moved to London in 1993. Its policy is to present classic plays in an accessible manner, and new plays that have the qualities to become classics. Tours once or twice a year to small-scale theatres and arts centres. Previous productions have included: Molière's *Amphitryon* (British première), *Contested Will* by Olly Figg (première), *The Birds* and *Lysistrata* by Aristophanes – both new translations. Does not offer Equity contracts. Advertises for actors in PCR. Welcomes casting queries. 'Write with cv and photograph. Send leaflets if you're in a show in London (especially on the Fringe). Don't telephone. If you're interested in the company's work, come and see one of our shows and make yourself known to the artistic director.'

Kaos Theatre UK

Brewery Arts, Brewery Court,
Cirencester, Gloucestershire GL7 1JH
Tel: 01285 641781
Fax: 01285 644060
E-mail: kaos.uk@btinternet.com
Artistic Director *Xavier Leret*
Contact *Kayte Potter (Administrator),*
Sharon Schaffer (Company Manager)

Founded 1993. Tours twice a year to arts centres, some schools/colleges and theatres. Previous productions have included: *The Kaos Caligula* (Edinburgh Festival, national tour, Perth in Australia, and Ireland) and a national tour of *The Kaos Importance of Being Earnest*. Does not offer Equity contracts. Occasionally advertises for actors. Welcomes casting queries if actors have 'a special interest and additional training in physical theatre, and would like to be part of a tight, ongoing ensemble'. Approach in writing in the first instance.

approach in writing in the first instance.

Live Theatre Company

The Live Theatre,
Broad Chare,
Newcastle upon Tyne NE1 3DF
Tel: 0191 261 2694
Artistic Director *Max Roberts*

Founded 1973. Extensive touring, both regional and national, of in-house productions, collaborations with other theatre, film and television companies, workshops and community projects. 'Our policy is to perform new work with a commitment to those writers, performers and technicians from the North-East whose work is innovative and challenging. These plays reflect experiences of working-class life, past and present, in a way that is neither exclusive nor parochial.' Recent productions have included: *Falling Together* by Tom Hadaway and Pauline Hadaway, *Twelve Tales of Tyneside*, *A Modern Cycle of Mystery Plays* written by twelve writers (Peter Flannery, Michael Chaplin, Kitty Fitzgerald, Tom Hadaway, Shaun Prendergast, Phil Woods, Lee Hall, Carol McGuigan, Len Barras, Julia Darling, Karen Hope, Steve Chambers, Emily Woof) under the additional direction of Peter Flannery, *Kander and Ebb's Cabaret*, *Here I Come* by Karin Young. Performs in a wide range of community venues and arts centres, small- and middle-scale theatres, as well as in their own 200-seat theatre. ITC/Equity contracts are used. Advertises for actors in SBS and PCR. Welcomes casting queries;

Logos Theatre Company

Unit 1411, Park House, Southbank Commercial Centre, 140 Battersea Park Road, London SW11 4NY
Tel: 0171 498 0009
Fax: 0171 670 4895
Artistic Director *Kenneth McClellan*
Contact *Dermot O'Brien, Norma Dixit, Tracy Russell, Owen Massey, Trevor Rawlins, George Sandes*

Founded 1989. 'Logos's aim is to do simple, straightforward productions of classic plays, the author always being the star of the show, the text never overlaid by infantile stunts and gimmicks such as modern dress.' Tours once or twice a year to arts centres, civic theatres and independent schools. Productions have included: *The Winter's Tale, Life is a Dream, John Gabriel Borkman, I Have Been Here Before, Measure for Measure, Misalliance, Macbeth, The Roman Actor* and *The Tempest.* Does not offer Equity contracts. Advertises for actors and welcomes written casting queries only; do not telephone. Holds general auditions which are advertised in PCR. 'We give pride of place to the spoken word. In doing verse plays the rhythms and metrical patterns must be fully observed. If you wish to do a prepared piece for audition, fine, but this is not obligatory. We will ask you to read from the play and allow time for a second go if you want one. We write eventually to everyone who has auditioned, but we have no paid staff and cannot guarantee that you will hear within a set time. Please do not phone us to ask how your audition went.'

London Bubble Theatre Company

5 Elephant Lane, London SE16 4JD
Tel: 0171 237 4434
Fax: 0171 231 2366
E-mail: londonbubble@.gn.apc.org
Artistic Director Jonathan Petherbridge
Associate Director *Adrian Jackson*
Administrative Assistant *Andrea Mason*

Founded 1972. The company used to tour with the Bubble tent but now does promenade performances in the summer in parks, specific sites and at the Albany Empire in Deptford. One or 2 tours per year. Bubble's policy is to make work for and with new audiences. Previous productions have included: *Once Upon a Time Very Far from England* and *Stories that are Just-So* (both summer Kipling-based tours), *Dealing with Feelings* (interactive piece for under-6s), *The Lower Depths* (site-specific). Offers Equity contracts. Sometimes advertises for actors (on average, once every two years). Welcomes casting queries *only* if people have seen their work first. Holds general auditions; send letter and cv in March or September.

Maverick Theatre Company

Richardson Villas, 32 Highbury Road, Birmingham B14 7QN
Tel: 0121 444 0933
Fax: 0121 443 1426
E-mail: maverick.theatre@virgin.net
Artistic Director *Nick Hennegan*
Contact *John Slater (Technical Director), Robb Williams (Musical Director)*

Founded in 1994, Maverick created and introduced the concept of pub theatre to Birmingham. The company is 'dedicated to increasing access to the performing arts, both for audiences and artists', and its success in this field has resulted in a number of awards. Performs in a wide range of venues, from community centres to No. 1 theatres, depending on the nature of the production. Anything from 1 to 6 tours per year. Previous productions have included: *Henry V – Lion of England* by Nick Hennegan, *Two* by Jim Cartwright, *Same Time Next Year* by Bernard Slade, *A Ghost of a Chance* by Nick Hennegan. Offers Equity contracts for their larger tours. Advertises for actors, usually in PCR or SBS. 'We are about to create a database of Birmingham-based actors, so we'd like to hear from them.' Send cv with covering letter and sae for return, if required. 'Although luck often plays a part in a successful career, the old quote "The harder I work, the luckier I get" is very true. You can never work too hard, or research too much. Try not to get fazed by the lack of money in the early days. If you have a talent and work hard, something will happen. What drama training will not teach you is the pressure you will get from friends and family outside the profession to "get a proper job" in the early days. Be ready for it. Due to lack of funding we generally pay very badly, apart from our commercial tours. But we never compromise our standards and our hard work over the past four years means we are edging closer to financial independence. And many of our original "unknown" artists are now rapidly becoming household names.'

Method & Madness

25 Short Street, London SE1 8LJ
Tel: 0171 401 9797
Fax: 0171 401 9777
Artistic Director *Mike Alfreds*
Contact *Lucinda Harvey (Projects Manager)*

Founded in 1969 as the Cambridge Theatre Company, changed its name to Method & Madness in 1995. Arts Council of England-funded touring company whose work is based on the creation of long-term acting ensembles. Tours a mixture of straight plays and adaptations and new work for 30 weeks each year to venues seating between 400 and 1,000. Recent productions have included: *The Winter's Tale, Ghosts,* an adaptation of Thomas Hardy's *Jude the Obscure, Private Lives* and Philip Osment's *Flesh and Blood.* Offers Equity contracts. Welcomes queries from actors only when casting but 'this won't be until March 2000. Please don't send anything until then as we cannot hang on to details for that length of time. Then call the office to see if we are casting before you send a cv and photograph. Get yourself a good agent – they're always the first people we go to when we're casting. Don't send anything in when we're not casting – it doesn't do any good.'

Mikron Theatre Company

Marsden Mechanics, Peel Street,
Marsden, Huddersfield,
West Yorkshire HD7 6BW
Tel: 01484 843701
Fax: 01484 843701
Artistic Director *Mike Lucas*

Founded 1972. Small-scale touring company staging 2 tours per year, travelling by narrowboat on the waterways in the summer and by van in the autumn. Performs in non-theatre venues such as pubs, arts centres, festivals and rallies. Previous productions have included: *If You Go Down to the Woods . . . Tales from the Newbury Bypass* and *Just the Job* – the story of a family who win a canal holiday. Offers Equity contracts. Prefers actors to approach them in writing in response to their advertisements. Does not hold general auditions.

Millstream Theatre Company

The Workshop, Clayfield Mews,
Newcomen Road,
Tunbridge Wells,
Kent TN4 9PA
Tel: 01892 518868
Fax: 01892 526165
Artistic Director *Christopher Masters*
Contact *Rachel Donnelly*

Founded in 1981, Millstream's artistic policy has always been to provide 'quality performances of critically acclaimed modern plays for audiences throughout the UK, the emphasis being placed on an honest representation of the text'. Tours twice a year to small- middle-scale venues. Productions include: *Blue Remembered Hills* by Dennis Potter, *Death and the Maiden* by Ariel Dorfman, *Lady Macbeth* by Jean Binnie, *Top Girls* by Caryl Churchill. Offers Equity contracts. Advertises in SBS. Does not use casting directors and welcomes queries from actors – 'send cvs'.

Natural Theatre Company

Widcombe Institute, Widcombe Hill,
Bath, Somerset BA2 6AA
Tel: 01225 469131
Fax: 01225 442555
E-mail: naturals@compuserve.com
Artistic Director *Ralph Peryer*
Contact *Dot Peryer (Administrator)*

Founded 1969. Worldwide touring company specialising in highly visual, comic street theatre, featuring well-observed characters acting out a scenario, and medium-scale musical shows, usually featuring classical musicians. The street-theatre performances take place throughout the year, and the indoor shows tour once or twice a year for a period of 10 weeks to arts centres and small theatres. The street-theatre shows have toured recently to Russia, Turkmenistan, Denmark, South and Central America, France, Taiwan as well as the UK. Offers Equity contracts. Advertises for their indoor shows, usually for actors with musical skills. Uses casting directors on occasion. Actors should 'find out what we require and decide if what they have to offer fits the bill; we might need a performer who can play the harpsichord, for example. Send photograph and cv and give good reasons why we should consider you. General enquiries are not really welcomed. Research the company – ask us to send a brochure or get to see our work; not everyone is cut out for our style of work, whether indoors or out. The only way to get on our street-theatre team is to attend our annual newcomers' workshops, usually held in the spring. Please enquire around February. The workshops are free and selected applicants get to work alongside our regular performers and likely ones go on to do a real gig. This may be followed up with offers of more work. If not, it's fun anyway.'

Northern Broadsides

Dean Clough, Halifax,
West Yorkshire HX3 5AX
Tel: 01422 369704
Fax: 01422 383175
Artistic Director *Barrie Rutter*
Contact *Sue Andrews (Administrator)*

Founded in 1992 by Barrie Rutter to produce classics with a northern voice. An award-winning company that performs in a wide range of venues from barns, mills, castles and cattle markets to the more conventional theatre locations. Two tours (a total of 20 weeks) per year. Their 1997 productions of *Romeo and Juliet* and *Antony and Cleopatra* toured throughout the UK, Europe and the USA. First tour of 1998, *Richard III*, offers Equity contracts. Advertises for actors – all must come from the northern area. All queries must be in writing with an sae, otherwise there will be no reply.

Not the National Theatre Company

149 Eglinton Hill, London SE18 3DU
Tel: 0181 855 3258/675 6702
Fax: 0181 855 3258/675 6702
Contact *Roger Gartland, Victoria Little, Jeffrey Perry*

Founded in 1984 by former National Theatre players. A cooperative of 6 actors that tours once a year to small- and middle-scale venues in the UK and abroad. Productions have included: *Not a Game for Boys*, written and directed by Simon Block, and *Someone Who'll Watch Over Me* by Frank McGuinness. Offers Equity contracts. Occasionally advertises for actors. 'We prefer casting enquiries by letter in January. Suggest yourself for a particular role and make clear why.'

NTC Touring Theatre Company

The Playhouse, Bondgate Without,
Alnwick, Northumberland NE66 1PQ
Tel: 01665 602586
Fax: 01665 605837
Contact *Gillian Hambleton (Artistic Director), Anna Flood, Hilary Burns*

Founded 1978. Formerly Northumberland Theatre Company, NTC won a five-year franchise from Northern Arts in 1994 to provide professional touring theatre in particular to predominantly rural areas without theatres. Four tours per year, mainly to village halls and small theatres of under 300 seats. Previous productions have included: *Lindisfarne – The Sword's Edge* (new play with original music), *East of the Sun, West of the Moon* (Christmas tour with music), *On Yer Bike* (new comedy), *The Porter's Daughter* (new play, physical theatre tour to arts centres). Offers Equity contracts. Advertises for actors in SBS and welcomes casting queries. Submit cv and photograph with a covering letter. Holds general auditions for locally based actors only. Those who come into this category may apply at any time during the year. 'Any submission from an actor will automatically be considered for the next production(s) – if unsuitable, they will be placed on file for three years. If, after that time, no further "updates" have been received, actors' "existence" will be checked with *Spotlight* and re-filed or discarded as appropriate. During that time, all files are referred to for casting. NTC is always interested in actor/musicians and authentic "Geordie" actors. NTC works as an ensemble company on a company wage. The majority of tours are of one-night stands and all actors do get-ins and get-outs. The core work of NTC and its *raison d'être* is village-hall tours.'

Open Hand Theatre Company

Dean Clough, Halifax,
West Yorkshire HX3 5AX
Tel: 01422 330101
Artistic Directors *Maureen Lunt, John Barber*
Contact *Angela Saville (Administrator)*

Founded 1985. National small- to middle-scale touring company specialising in shows for young people and family audiences in which actors, puppets, masks and music 'fuse with the surreal, the fantastic and the grotesque'. Three tours per year. Previous productions have included: *The Mouse and His Child* (family show) and *Monster and Frog Mind the Baby* (children's show). Offers ITC/Equity contracts. Advertises for actors in SBS and PCR. Does not welcome casting queries except from actors who are performing in the area. Send cv, photograph and details of local performance. No phone calls. 'Try to see a performance by the company to judge if you are interested in this very specialised work. You can be placed on our mailing list by writing in. When you have seen a show, *then* write in if you are interested in the work – show knowledge of the company's work if you want us to be interested in you.'

Orchard Theatre Company

(At the time of going to press, the company was planning to move office; telephone for details of new address.)
Tel: 01271 371475
Fax: 01271 371825
Artistic Director *Bill Buffery*
Administrator *Frederica Notley*
Administrative Assistant *Pat Jones*

Based in North Devon, Orchard

Theatre Company was founded in 1969. Tours a wide range of plays throughout the South-West and beyond, performing in venues ranging from village halls to No. 1 large-scale theatres. Aims to produce 'stimulating theatre of the highest quality, to engage the imagination of the audience through the use of different theatrical styles and techniques and to present plays that have a contemporary relevance'. Also has a strong commitment to education and working with young people. Runs 3 youth theatre groups and holds workshops in schools, colleges and community groups. Four tours per year of approximately 7 to 10 weeks in length. Offers Equity contracts. Initial approach by actors should be by telephone to ascertain what casting is available.

Out of Joint Ltd

20–24 Eden Grove, London N7 8ED
Tel: 0171 609 0207
Fax: 0171 609 0203
E-mail: ojo@outofjoint.demon.co.uk
Artistic Director *Max Stafford-Clark*
Contact *Sonia Friedman (Producer)*

Founded by Max Stafford-Clark and Sonia Friedman in 1993, following Stafford-Clark's directorship of the Royal Court Theatre. The company's aim is to create and produce new writing for the stage and to tour this work both nationally and internationally. Champions the work of contemporary writers and presents a wide variety of new work. Venues are mainly middle-scale but can include small and large venues, depending on the nature of the production. Two or 3 tours annually. Recent productions have included: *Shopping and Fucking* by Mark Ravenhill, *The Steward of Christendom* by Sebastian Barry, *Blue Heart* by Caryl Churchill, *The Positive Hour* by April de Angelio. Offers Equity contracts. Does not advertise for actors; always uses casting directors. Does not welcome casting queries.

Oxford Stage Company

15–19 George Street,
Oxford OX14 5NW
Tel: 01865 723238
Fax: 01865 790625
Artistic Director *John Retallack*
Contact *Patrick Martin (General Manager)*

Presents a diverse range of productions, from Shakespeare to twentieth-century drama, as well as new writing for young people and devised work. Frequently uses a stunning mix of music and physical theatre. As a national and international touring company, Oxford Stage Company performs throughout the year, playing in middle-scale venues. Three tours per year. Recent productions have included: *Roots* by Arnold Wesker, *Junk* by Melvin Burgess (adapted by John Retallack), *Johnny Blue, Where Are You?* by Jane Buckler, *My Mother Said I Never Should* by Charlotte Keatley, *The Comic Mysteries (Mistero Buffo)* by Dario Fo (all directed by John Retallack), *All's Well That Ends Well* (directed by Irina Brook). Offers Equity contracts. Does not advertise for actors. Uses casting directors; 'we only produce three productions a year so we prefer casting directors to be contacted for specific projects'.

Oxfordshire Touring Theatre Company

Unit 1, St John Fisher School,
Sandy Lane West, Oxford OX4 5LD
Tel: 01865 778119
Fax: 01865 714822
Artistic Director *Jeremy James*
Contact *Julie Walters (General Manager), Nicky Young (Administrator)*

Founded 1979. Professional company which tours a dynamic and varied programme of theatre to a diverse range of audiences in small- to middle-scale venues such as village halls, community centres, theatres and arts centres across Oxfordshire. Now extending its regional and national touring. Particularly keen to encourage more young people, families on limited incomes and older and retired people to see their shows. Produces 3 plays (autumn, winter, spring) plus project work. Previous productions have included: *Teechers* by John Godber, *Once . . . In a Faraway Land*, devised by the company, and *Mrs Beeton's History of the World* by Julie Wilkinson. Offers Equity contracts. Advertises for actors in SBS and PCR. Welcomes casting queries; send cv and photograph with a covering letter. Holds general auditions; apply for inclusion in May or June.

Paines Plough

4th Floor, 43 Aldwych,
London WC2B 4DA
Tel: 0171 240 4533
Fax: 0171 240 4534
E-mail: paines.plough@dial.pipex.com
Artistic Director *Vicky Featherstone*
Contact *Lucy Morrison (Administrator)*

Founded 1974. Paines Plough devel-ops, commissions and produces new plays by both established and unknown writers. Tours nationwide twice yearly to arts centres, studios and theatres of up to 350 seats. Offers Equity contracts. Does not advertise for actors. Occasionally uses casting directors. Does not welcome casting queries, preferring to work through agents only. 'Paines Plough's emphasis is on writers and their development. The artistic director sees a lot of new plays therefore and we have a panel of readers who try to attend all rehearsed readings, short performances, etc.'

Pascal Theatre Company

35 Flaxman Court, Flaxman Terrace,
London WC1H 9AR
Tel: 0171 383 0920
Fax: 0171 383 0920
Contact *Julia Pascal (Artistic Director), Katherine Barazetti, Ian Watts*

Founded 1983. New playwriting company which usually employs multilingual performers. Regional small- to middle-scale tours in the UK plus to France, Germany, Belgium, Poland and Sweden. Two tours per year. Previous productions have included: *St Joan* (cast of 3 actresses), *The Dybbuk* (5 performers) and *Theresa* (5 performers). Offers ITC company contracts. Advertises for actors. Welcomes casting queries; send cv and photograph with covering letter. No telephone calls. Holds general auditions; apply for inclusion at any time during the year.

People Show

St James the Great Institute,
Pollard Row,
London E2 6NB
Tel: 0171 729 1841
Fax: 0171 739 0203
Contact *George Khan, Mark Long,
Chahine Yavroyan (Core Company)*
Associates *Denis Buckley, Fiona
Creese, Jane Devoy, Beth Hardisty,
Vic Kravchenko, Alex Mavro, Amelia
Pimlott, Mark Whitelaw, Nick Tigg*

Founded in 1966 by performers
drawn from a variety of disciplines,
the People Show is one of the first
performance-art companies in the UK
and has established a reputation for
creating shows consisting of mixed-
media, multi-disciplinary, live performance work. Recently awarded
£368,000 from the National Lottery
towards the development of the St
James the Great Institute. As a collective, each show is created by the
company without a director. The
touring shows normally last for
between 6 and 10 weeks with 2-night
runs at each venue. Offers Equity
contracts. Rarely advertises for actors.
Welcomes casting queries from those
who are sympathetic to the aims of the
company and excited by the working
process. Approach in writing in the
first instance; actors should enclose a
cv and information on where they are
next performing. 'We never cast from
a cv and photograph, preferring to see
individuals working and then
meeting them informally. The People
Shows are by artists from a wide
range of backgrounds, including
performance, music and fine art.
Productions are created around the
theatrical skills and artistic concerns
of the people involved, so a
background of devised work of any
kind is useful.'

Perpetual Motion Theatre Ltd

10 Provost Road, London NW3 4ST
Tel: 0171 483 3798
Fax: 0171 483 3798
Contact *Emi Slater (Artistic Director),
Ian Hamilton*

Founded in 1992, Perpetual Motion
stages physical performance work and
youth work, all non-text-based. One
tour per year to international venues in
Russia, USA and Europe, performing
in small-scale studios and site-specific
locations. Currently involved in a long-
term research performance project to
be developed and worked on for the
next 3 years. Does not offer Equity
contracts at the moment but hopes to
'within the year'. Advertises for actors
and welcomes written casting queries,
but 'only if interested in physical
theatre'. Holds general auditions. 'We
are only interested in actors with a
long-term commitment to physical
theatre and alternative, experimental,
site-specific performance work. All our
work is movement-based, devised or
new writing.'

Pilot Theatre Company

– *see* Children's and Young People's
Theatre, page 216

Praxis Theatre Company

24 Wykeham Road,
London NW4 2SO
Tel: 0181 203 1916
Fax: 0181 203 1916
Artistic Director *Sharon Kennet*

Founded 1993. A new-writing touring
company with an emphasis on the
voice of women in the theatre. Tours to
middle-scale venues once a year plus
workshop programmes. Previous
productions have included: *Seed* (Lyric
Theatre, Hammersmith), *Dot* (Chelsea

Centre), and *The Sacred Penman* (DOC).
Offers Equity contracts 'wherever
possible'. Sometimes advertises and
occasionally uses casting directors.
Does not welcome casting queries.
'There is no point in sending general
letters. Only apply if you see an advert
or if you know that we are actually
casting. See our work – or know about
it. Only apply if you are genuinely
interested in the company's programme.'

Prime Productions Ltd

54 Hermiston, Currie,
Midlothian EH14 4AQ
Tel: 0131 449 4055
Fax: 0131 449 4055
Artistic Director *Martin Heller*

Founded in 1985 specifically to mount a
production of Ena Lamont Stewart's
trilogy, *Will You Still Need Me*. The
success of this tour prompted further
productions, including three one-
person plays by John Cargill on
eighteenth-century theatrical personalities: *Uncorking Old Sherry*, *Every Inch a
King*, and *A Wilderness of Monkeys*
(Sheridan, Garrick and Macklin), the
last two receiving an Edinburgh Fringe
First in 1992. Other productions have
included *Herr Bach and Mr Handel* by
John Ringham and *Whisky Galore – The
Radio Version* by Paul Godfrey. Tours to
small- to middle-scale venues in
Scotland, Northern Ireland, England
and Holland. Offers Equity contracts
when in receipt of project funding.
Does not advertise for actors.
Welcomes casting queries; send cv with
covering letter. 'The company is a small
operation dependent on project
funding by the Scottish Arts Council or
other funding bodies. We do one or two
tours per year, if funding allows, and
occasionally fall back on "profit-share".

Cast sizes range from 1 to 6 plus stage
management, although the current
show (*The Merchant of Venice*) has a cast
of 10. The tours usually go out in the
spring/summer and autumn.'

Proteus Theatre Company

Fairfields Arts Centre, Council Road,
Basingstoke, Hampshire RG21 3DH
Tel: 01256 354541
Fax: 01256 356186
Contact *Chris Baldwin (Artistic
Director), Amanda Wilde (Associate
Director)*

Founded 1979. Small-scale touring
company whose work is characterised
by 'new writing/new work, education
and internationalism'. Tours to arts and
community centres and village halls in
the Southern Arts region. Two to 3
main tours and projects per year.
Previous productions have included:
The False Hairpiece by John Constable
(16+ audience), *Pinocchio*, adapted by
Chris Baldwin (family audience), *A
Man with Connections* by Alexander
Gelman and *Through the Leaves* by
Franz Xaver Kroetz (16+). Offers Equity
contracts. Sometimes advertises in SBS
and PCR. Welcomes casting queries;
send letter and cv. Sometimes holds
general auditions which are advertised.

Quest Theatre Company

3C Mecklenburgh Street, Bloomsbury,
London WC1N 2AH
Tel: 0171 713 0342
Fax: 0171 713 0342
Artistic Director *David Craik*

Founded 1990. The aim of the company
is to provide opportunities of viewing
rare international works by producing
overlooked plays, usually by non-
English authors. 'Preference is given to
the stylised and non-naturalistic and

the emphasis is on the production of dynamic and thought-provoking shows in visually stimulating formats.' Tours to venues in London, provincial studio theatres, arts centres, Edinburgh Festival Fringe and Eastern Europe (Poland and Romania). One or 2 tours per year. Recent productions have included: *The Show Must Go On* (AIDS play by William Lawrence), Strindberg's *Creditors*, *Play Strindberg* by Dürrenmatt, *A Phoenix Too Frequent* by Christopher Fry, *Les Justes* and *Le Malentendu* by Albert Camus. 'Intermittently' offers Equity contracts ('when funds permit'). Usually advertises for actors and welcomes casting queries; approach in writing only. 'Do not inundate us as everyone who expresses an interest in Quest is held on file which is always consulted when casting. We are not impressed by photographs which bear little resemblance to their subjects – it is counterproductive and we urge actors to reproduce only very accurate and up-to-date representations of themselves.'

Quicksilver National Touring Theatre

– *see* Children's and Young People's Theatre Companies, page 218

Red Ladder Theatre Company Ltd

3 St Peter's Buildings, York Street,
Leeds, West Yorkshire LS9 8AJ
Tel: 0113 245 4311
Fax: 0113 245 5351
E-mail: red-ladder@geo2.poptel.org.uk
Artistic Director *Kully Thiarai*
Contact *Ann Cross, Stefanie Gascoigne*

Founded 1968. Rooted in the radical socialist theatre movement of Britain in the sixties, Red Ladder has strived to take theatre to audiences which have little access or experience of the performing arts. It is one of the oldest of the few remaining socialist companies in Britain today. With a history which spans 30 years, the company has moved on while remaining cognisant of its original ideals. Tours to youth clubs, community centres, small-scale theatres. Two national tours per year. Recent productions: *End of Season* by Noel Greig, *Kaahini* by Maya Chowdhry, *Crush* by Rosy Fordham. Offers Equity contracts. Advertises for actors and welcomes casting queries. Approach in writing, sending cv and photograph. 'Although Red Ladder has an extensive network of actors who have worked with the company on a regular basis, we are always looking to provide opportunities for new actors.'

Red Shift Theatre Company

TRG 2 Trowbray House,
108 Weston Street,
London SE1 3QB
Tel: 0171 378 9787
Fax: 0171 378 9789
Artistic Director *Jonathan Holloway*
Contact *Sophie Elliott (General Manager), Jess Lammin (Administrator)*

Founded in 1982. London-based theatre company which tours nationally once or twice a year to small-scale (studio) theatres and middle-scale (300-seat+) venues. Red Shift has a distinctive style which has evolved out of the interests of its founding director, Jonathan Holloway. The company's work has a commitment to 'story, character and social issues expressed through a rich combination of spoken and visual languages'.

Productions have included: *Les Misérables* (adaptation of the novel), *Bartleby, Orlando, George Dandin, Crime and Punishment, Le Misanthrope, The Life and Times of Fanny Hill*. Offers Equity contracts. Advertises for actors and welcomes casting queries; approach in writing with cv and photograph. 'We recommend knowledge of the company's work before contact is made.'

Ridiculusmus
The Playhouse, 5–7 Artillery Street, Derry BT48 6RG
Tel: 01504 373800
Fax: 01504 261884
Artistic Directors Jon Hough, David Woods

Founded 1992. Tours to a wide range of venues throughout the UK and Ireland. Two to 3 tours per year. Previous productions have included adaptations of *Three Men in a Boat, The Third Policeman, At Swim Two Birds, The Overcoat and the Nose* and two new works: *All About H. Hatterr* and *The Exhibitionists*. Sometimes offers Equity contracts. Advertises for actors. Welcomes casting queries; approach in writing, enclosing cv and photograph. Holds general auditions in the form of a season of work where those taking part work with the company for a week. Apply for inclusion at any time of the year. 'Ridiculusmus uses free-form improvisation as a devising technique and has no conventional writer/director/actor hierarchy. The performers are self-directing and create their own material. It is essential for performers to take part in the company's experimental-projects sea-

son in order to see if the style of working and lifestyle (which is basic and often apparently disorganised) is compatible. We are looking for performers with excellent naturalistic acting ability, a love of absurd humour and a desire to "play".'

Riding Lights Theatre Company/Riding Lights Roughshod
8 Bootham Terrace, York YO3 7DH
Tel: 01904 655317
Fax: 01904 651532
E-mail: rltc@globalnet.co.uk
Artistic Director Paul Burbridge
Contact Janis Smyth (Riding Lights Theatre Co.), Kate West (Riding Lights Roughshod)

Riding Lights Theatre Company has grown over 20 years from community theatre to middle-scale regional touring. It is a Christian theatre company, 'committed to excellence and truthfulness in both Christian and secular theatre'. One or 2 tours per year. Co-productions have included: *Three Men in a Boat* and *The Fire Raisers* with the Northcott Theatre, Exeter, and *The Winter's Tale* (national tour and the Bridewell Theatre, London). Riding Lights Roughshod is an ongoing community-theatre project, employing 8 to 10 young actors at any one time. Six tours annually to schools, prisons, churches, arts centres and theatres. Previous productions have included *Double Dealing* (national community tour) and *A Different Drum* (national and European community tour). Offers Equity contracts. Does not advertise for actors. Welcomes casting queries by post, with cv and photograph. 'Although Riding Lights is a Christian company, it in no way deems acceptance of the Christian faith as a prerequisite for employment. Roughshod companies are, however, employed to communicate a truthful understanding of Christianity and all the company's productions are likely to involve a largely Christian team.'

7:84 Theatre Company (Scotland) Ltd

2 Port Dundas Place,
Glasgow G2 3LB
Tel: 0141 331 2219
Fax: 0141 332 0109
Artistic Director *Iain Reekie*
Contact *Tessa Rennie (Administrator), John Heraghty (Outreach Director), Robert Thomson (Literary Manager)*

Founded 1973. Well-established Scottish touring company producing political theatre which 'challenges injustice, champions truth and provokes thought'. Carries out a coordinated programme of productions and outreach work, and new writing development that gets new voices and strong messages on to the stage. Between 3 to 6 tours per year throughout Scotland, in cities and the Highlands and Islands, performing in community venues and arts centres. Previous productions have included: *Caledonia Dreaming* by David Greig, *The War in Heaven* by Sam Shepard and *Joseph Chaikin, Talking Bollocks*, a devised community piece, and *Angels in America* by Tony Kushner. Offers Equity contracts. Does not advertise

for actors. Usually casts Scottish actors. Welcomes *written* casting queries – 'we keep cvs on file'.

Shared Experience Theatre Company

The Soho Laundry, 9 Dufour's Place,
London W1V 1FE
Tel: 0171 434 9248
Fax: 0171 287 8763
E-mail:
106250.1562@compuserve.com
Artistic Director *Nancy Meckler*
Contact *Rachel Tackley (General Manager), Jane Claire (Office Administrator)*

Founded in 1976 by Mike Alfreds. Shared Experience 'thrives on breaking boundaries, taking risks and creating distinctive, highly charged performances'. Tours nationally and internationally with classics, adaptations of novels and new work. Two middle-scale tours per year. Previous productions have included: *War and Peace*, *The Tempest* and *Jane Eyre*. Offers Equity contracts. Does not advertise for actors. Uses casting directors. Welcomes casting queries. 'It is best to telephone to find out when we are casting and what for before sending information. If you want a reply and your photograph returned, always include an sae. It is best to apply, though, through an agent.'

Snap People's Theatre Trust

– *see* Children's and Young People's Theatre Companies, page 218

Solent People's Theatre

Heathfield Centre,
Valentine Avenue,
Sholing, Southampton,
Hampshire SO19 0EQ
Tel: 01703 443943
Fax: 01703 440752
Artistic Director *Mollie Guilfoyle*
Contact *Caroline Routh*
(Administrative Director)

Founded 1976. Solent is a professional community theatre company, aiming to create theatre both with and for the communities of Southampton, Hampshire and Portsmouth and to place it in expected and unexpected places. Aims to encourage those with little experience and contact with live theatre to 'broaden their expectations of it, to develop their theatre and related skills and use them as a means of self-expression within their communities'. Three tours per year to arts centres, village halls, community and sports centres, parks and playing fields. Previous productions have included: *Pot Luck* (devised), *Dead Rise and Tumble Home* (new commission), *The Trojan Women* (theatre of the deaf), *The Magic Storybook* (Christmas show) and *Educating Rita*. Offers Equity contracts. Advertises for actors in SBS and PCR. Welcomes casting queries; send cv with covering letter following initial call to ascertain whether they are looking for submissions or not. Holds general auditions, usually three months prior to commencement of rehearsals. 'A personally addressed letter shows that you have at least taken a little time to research the company for whom you want to work. If responding to PCR, be sure that you fit the breakdown.'

Spare Tyre Theatre Company

West Greenwich House,
141 Greenwich High Road,
Greenwich,
London SE10 8JA
Tel: 0181 305 2800
Fax: 0181 305 2800
Artistic Director *Clair Chapman*
Contact *Liz Hannah*

Founded 1979. A community theatre company that works with specific groups to produce a musical performance based on the group's experience. Tours to schools, community centres and theatres. Three tours per year. Does not offer Equity contracts. Does not advertise for actors and does not welcome casting queries. Holds general auditions. 'The actors used in our productions are volunteers, usually aged between 16 and 25. We do not employ professional actors.'

The Sphinx Theatre Company

25 Short Street,
London SE1 8LJ
Tel: 0171 401 9993
Fax: 0171 401 9995
Artistic Director *Sue Parrish*
Contact *Alison Gagen (Administrator)*

Founded 1973. Formerly the Women's Theatre Group. National touring company specialising in new writing by women. One to 2 tours per year performing in small- to middle-scale theatres, studios and arts centres. In 1997, staged *Goliath*, based by Bryony Lavery on Beatrix Campbell's book, with a solo performance by Nichola McAuliffe, directed by Annie Castledine. Offers Equity contracts. Sometimes advertises for actors; does not welcome casting queries.

Springboard Theatre Company

20 Lansdowne Road, Muswell Hill, London N10 2AU
Tel: 0181 883 4586
Fax: 0181 883 7142
Artistic Director *Clive Wolfe*

Founded 1987. As a result of early financial support from BP and in more recent years, the UK Charity Lotteries, former National Student Drama Festival and National Student Theatre Company successes have been able to work together professionally, forging a unique direct link between student drama and the profession. Casting and, to date, choice of directors is restricted to former NSDF and/or NSTC participants. Tours once a year, performing in small- to middle-scale venues. Previous productions have included: *Handle with Care* by Jane Thornton, and *Tchaikovsky in the Park* by Tim Fountain. Sometimes offers Equity contracts. Does not advertise for actors and does not welcome casting queries. 'Get involved with the National Student Drama Festival and/or the National Student Theatre Company when at school, college, university, drama school or youth theatres.'

TAG Theatre Company

– see Children's and Young People's Theatre, page 219

Talawa Theatre Company

3rd Floor, 23–5 Great Sutton Street, London EC1V 0DN
Tel: 0171 251 6644
Fax: 0171 251 5969
Artistic Director *Yvonne Brewster*

Talawa was founded in 1985 by Yvonne Brewster, Mona Hammond, Carmen Munroe and Inigo Espejel, moving from the back bedroom of Yvonne's house into the forefront of Black European theatre over the last 12 years. Talawa has sought to provide middle-scale, high-quality productions, reflecting the significant role Black theatre plays within the UK. Previous productions have included: *Zebra Crossing, Medea in the Mirror, Beef, No Chicken, Flying West* and *Othello*. Offers Equity contracts. Does not advertise for actors. Welcomes casting queries – send cv. Holds general auditions; apply three to four weeks in advance.

Tamasha

184 Victoria Road, London N22 4XQ
Tel: 0181 889 6432
Fax: 0181 889 6432
Artistic Directors *Kristine Landon-Smith, Sudha Bhuchar*

Founded 1989. Project-funded company, producing Asian-influenced work. One show per year, touring to small- and middle-scale venues. Previous productions have included: *A Tainted Dawn* by Sudha Bhuchar and Kristine Landon-Smith, *Shafts of Sunlight* by A. Jeshi, *A Yearning* by Lorca, adapted by Ruth Canter, and *East is East* by Ayulo Khan Din. Offers Equity contracts. Advertises for actors in SBS. Welcomes casting queries; either telephone or send a letter.

Tara Arts Group Ltd

356 Garratt Lane, London SW18 4ES
Tel: 0181 333 4457
Fax: 0181 870 9540
E-mail: tara@tara-arts.com
Artistic Director *Jatinder Verma*
Contact *Matthew Jones (Administrative Director), Sophie Robson (Projects Coordinator)*

Founded 1977. Starting out as a community theatre group, Tara Arts is now

Britain's leading Asian theatre company, touring nationally and internationally with productions for adults and children. On average, stages 4 tours per year, performing in small- and middle-scale venues and also schools. Recent productions have included: *A Midsummer Night's Dream*, co-production with the Lyric Theatre, Hammersmith, *Bottom's Dream*, an adaptation for children, *Jasma Odan*, co-production with the Haymarket Theatre, Leicester, *Cyrano*, co-production with the Royal National Theatre. Offers Equity contracts. Occasionally advertises for actors. Welcomes written casting queries – 'Tara considers all applicants and regularly uses their files as a means of casting. We principally use actors of Asian origin – the company's definition of Asian extends to the entirety of Asia, including China and Japan, and includes all those who think of themselves as Asian. Occasionally cast white and Afro-Caribbean performers but they are mostly known to the company.'

Coventry and Warwickshire schools. Has now introduced 'The Writing House' in partnership with the Belgrade Theatre, Coventry, which works with young writers. Recent productions have included: *She's Electric* (premièred at the Belgrade prior to London venue), *Big Burger Chronicles* (premièred at the Belgrade, then Edinburgh Festival), *Strike it Lucky* (schools tour), *Between* (Belgrade and UK tour). Does not offer Equity contracts. Advertises for actors in PCR, *The Stage* and ACID. Welcomes specific show queries; send cv, sae and photograph with covering letter. 'If you can see our work we are more likely to be interested in seeing you for an audition.' Does not hold general auditions but operates 'Audition Weekends' 4 times a year where actors work on audition speeches with professional directors working with Theatre Absolute; apply any time during the year. 'Apply for jobs that are *really* suited to you. Always have a speech ready even if your agent doesn't tell you to prepare one. Do your homework – ask questions before auditioning.'

Theatre Absolute

16 St Thomas Road,
Longford, Coventry,
West Midlands CV6 7AR
Tel: 01203 680125
Fax: 01203 680125
Artistic Director *Chris O'Connell*
Contact *Julia Negus*
(Producer/Associate Artist)

Founded 1992. Theatre Absolute commissions, produces and tours new writing throughout the UK. One to 2 tours per year plus outreach work – usually two school/college residencies and a community pantomime for

Theatre Alibi

Northcott Studio Theatre, Emmanuel Road, Exeter, Devon EX4 6DA
Tel: 01392 217315
Fax: 01392 217315
E-mail: alibi@mail.zynet.co.uk
Artistic Directors *Daniel Jamieson, Nikki Sved*
Contact *Maggie Fisher, Annemarie Macdonald (Joint General Managers)*

Founded 1982. Produces contemporary theatre for adults and children in the form of story theatre, using writing as a basis for devising. The work uses the full physical and vocal resources of its performers and often integrates other art forms. Alibi aims 'to work as an ensemble and employs performers for a number of end-to-end contracts. We are committed to performer training and organise one to two weeks of training each year.' Performs in small- to middle-scale venues such as studio theatres, arts and community centres, village halls as well as site-specific work in non-theatre spaces in Exeter. Tours an adult show in the spring and a children's show in the autumn, plus a site-specific non-touring pilot production in the summer. Recent productions have included: *Sea of Faces* – families, photos and fiction – a show tracing one family through a remarkable collection of photos found in a pile of rubbish, *Egg!* – for 5–12-year-olds – and *The Swell*, a pilot production for adults, staged in a disused Victorian warehouse in collaboration with a contemporary folk band prior to touring. Offers Equity contracts as well as an incremental pay scheme. Sometimes advertises in *The Stage*, usually in the spring, but the company often invites people to audition through other contacts, such as receiving an approach from a performer. Auditions run for 2 days as workshops. 'If a performer is familiar with or interested in our style of work we would be interested in hearing from them.' Send letter and cv (photograph not necessary). 'We recommend that you try to see our work if you can. We're happy to let you know where we are performing. Because we use an ensemble approach we are looking for performers who are interested in committing themselves for about a year's work.'

Théâtre de Complicité

20–24 Eden Grove, London N7 8ED
Tel: 0171 700 0233
Fax: 0171 700 0234
Artistic Director Simon McBurney
Contact Judith Dimant (Administrative Producer)

Founded 1983. A much-acclaimed versatile touring company which specialises in stunningly visual, physical theatre (most company members have trained at the Jacques Lecoq School in Paris). Recent productions have included: *The Three Lives of Lucie Cabrol*, devised by the company after a story by John Berger, and *The Caucasian Chalk Circle* by Brecht in a new translation by Frank McGuinness, in collaboration with the Royal National Theatre. Does not advertise for actors. Prior to a new production, the artistic director holds casting workshops, which are by invitation only. Each spring, the company holds educational workshops which are open to actors. Those who wish to be considered for these sessions should apply for inclusion on the workshop mailing list.

Theatre Rotto

Nanscawen Barn, Newmill, Penzance, Cornwall TR20 8XN
Tel: 01736 365158
Fax: 01736 330704
E-mail: 106275.35@compuserve.com
Artistic Director Julia McLean
Contact Melanie Smith, Tim Wellard

Founded in 1981, the company has developed its own range of puppetry, performing at puppet festivals abroad, arts centres, theatres, British festivals and schools. Productions have included

The Illustrated Tales – a programme of Cornish folk tales brought to life with puppetry, music and song. Does not offer Equity contracts. Advertises for actors and welcomes casting queries. Send cv and accompanying letter to the artistic director.

Theatre Venture
The Resources Centre,
Leywick Street, Stratford,
London E15 3DD
Tel: 0181 519 6678
Fax: 0181 519 8769
E-mail: tventure@ecna.org
Artistic Director *John Edward McGrath*
Contact *Rosemary Evans (Administrator)*

Founded 1981. A community theatre and arts company based in the East End of London. The company's programme combines touring London boroughs with outreach and participatory projects located in Newham. 'Committed to creating access to theatre, drama and arts-related activity for individuals, groups and new audiences who have been excluded from participation.' Two to 3 tours per year with venues including schools, community centres, small- and middle-scale theatres. Offers Equity/-ITC contracts. Advertises for actors and only welcomes queries in response to adverts. 'Actors should apply with photo, cv and covering letter. Experience of or specific interest in small-scale touring, including schools tours and the hard work involved – teamwork, get-ins, get-outs, etc. – would be an advantage.'

Theatre West Glamorgan/ Theatr Gorllewin Morgannwg
Unit 3, Milland Road Industrial Estate,
Neath SA11 1NJ
Tel: 01639 641771
Fax: 01639 644213
Contact *Gronw ab Islwyn (Administrator), Geinor Jones (Associate Director)*

Founded in 1982, the company has established a popular professional local and national theatre providing a much-valued service to the schools and communities within the County Borough of Neath – Port Talbot and the City and County of Swansea, and nationally throughout Wales. Productions are in both Welsh and English. Two tours per year, performing in school halls, community centres, small- and middle-scale theatres. Productions have included: *It'll All be Over by Xmas/Ac Abertawe 'n Fflam* (English/Welsh TIE production for 5–6-year-olds), *Rape of the Fair Country* (co-production with Swansea Grand Theatre). Offers Equity contracts. Rarely advertises for actors. Occasionally holds general auditions; welcomes casting queries; approach in writing enclosing cv.

Theatre Workshop
34 Hamilton Place,
Edinburgh EH3 5AX
Tel: 0131 225 7942
Fax: 0131 220 0122
E-mail:
mail@theatreworkshop.ednet.co.uk
Artistic Director *Robert Rae*
Contact *Anne Fleming*

Founded in the mid-sixties, Theatre Workshop has developed into Scotland's foremost exponent of community theatre, specialising in large-scale community projects. As a year-round producing and receiving theatre and arts centre, it aims to 'give voice to the concerns, interests and cultures of those communities that find themselves relegated to the margins of society'. Tours once or twice a year to a wide range of venues such as The Wynd in Melrose, The Tramway, Glasgow or the Crucible Theatre in Sheffield. Recent projects have included: *Stochareel* (large-scale community show), *Nettles and Roses* (professional Christmas show), *I Diriamba!* (co-production with Teatro Nixtayotero, Nicaraguan theatre company). Offers Equity contracts. Does not advertise for actors. Welcomes casting queries; write, enclosing cv and current photograph. 'Actors should demonstrate a commitment to community theatre.' Does not hold general auditions.

Theatrestorm

23 Sherborne Avenue, Norwood Green, Middlesex UB2 4HX
Tel: 0181 574 2553
Fax: c/o 0181 840 3983
Artistic Director Nicholas Jonne
Contact Sarah Lermit (Administrative Director)

Founded 1992. Theatrestorm's style allows 'the image equal importance to the word'. A small ensemble company which requires actors who have good movement skills, including mime. One tour per year to fringe theatres, studios, arts and community centres, festivals, small-scale regional theatres and universities. Previous productions have included: *Stifled, The Dark – A Macbeth, House of Cords* and *Telling Rashomon.* Does not offer Equity contracts. Advertises for actors in PCR. Welcomes

casting queries but only if 'they feel they are suitable/enthused by our stylised, visual and physical type of work'. Send letter and cv. 'Working *together* as a whole is of the utmost importance when we are casting.'

Theatr Gorllewin Morgannwg
– see **Theatre West Glamorgan**, page 188

Theatr Powys

Drama Centre, Tremont Road, Llandrindod Wells, Powys LD1 5EB
Tel: 01597 824444
Fax: 01597 824381
Artistic Director Ian Yeoman

Founded in 1972, Theatr Powys is a small-/middle-scale community and Theatre-in-Education touring company. Also manages and runs the local youth theatre. Tours to small community halls and schools and to middle-scale mainhouse theatres; 4 tours per year. Productions have included: *Andorra* (Welsh-language community tour), *Maria's Baby* (TIE – primary schools), *Ladies Ladies* (community tour), *The Constitution of the People* (TIE – secondary schools). Offers Equity contracts. Advertises for actors and welcomes casting queries; approach in writing in the first instance enclosing cv.

Trestle Theatre Company

47–49 Wood Street, Barnet, Hertfordshire EN5 4BS
Tel: 0181 441 0349
Fax: 0181 449 7036
Joint Artistic Directors Toby Wilsher, Joff Chafer

Founded 1981. Since its inception, Trestle has developed its own original style of popular mask theatre. Presents on average 300 performances a year to over 40,000 people. Tours one new show and one revival per year to community and arts centres and schools, as well as middle-scale theatres. Recent productions have included: *Fool House* (new show, small-scale), *Beyond the Blue Horizon* (new show, middle-scale), *Top Storey* and *Passionfish* (both small-scale tours). Offers Equity contracts. Advertises for actors in *The Stage*. Welcomes casting queries by telephone 'because we don't keep details on file'. Does not hold general auditions. 'Ring at the beginning of the year for advice as to when to ring and look out for an advertisement.'

Tudor Rose Theatre Company

The Grange,
Wakefield Road,
Rothwell Haigh, Leeds,
West Yorkshire LS26 0RZ
Tel: 0113 282 8880
Artistic Director *David Sinfield*
Contact *Martina McClements,*
Richard Auckland

Founded in 1996 to perform classic plays in classic settings such as stately homes and museums where they would have been performed originally. One tour per year, mainly in the north of England although hoping to go further afield. Recent production was *The Marriage of Figaro* by Beaumarchais. Does not offer Equity contracts. Sometimes advertises for actors. Welcomes casting queries from very experienced, northern-based actors only. No phone calls; send cv,

photograph and sae. 'Actors must be prepared to help with all get-ins and the technical side of the productions. Being in stately homes is *not* like performing in a theatre so you need to be extremely disciplined and professional at all times.'

West 28th Street

Company in Residence,
Fairfield,
Park Lane,
Croydon CR9 1DG
Tel: 0181 681 0821
Fax: 0181 686 7944
E-mail:106020.2442@compuserve.com
Artistic Director *Mark Helyar*

Founded 1992. First ever theatre company in residence at the Fairfield in Croydon. Wide range of output from educational projects to musicals, with a particular focus on work for young people and the production of classic texts. Usually 2 tours per year to venues ranging from studio spaces to No. 1 theatres, predominantly in the south-east of England. Also stages performances and workshops at Fairfield. Recent productions have included: *Starting Here, Starting Now, The Taming of the Shrew, Great Expectations, Romeo and Juliet*. Sometimes offers Equity contracts. Advertises for actors in SBS and PCR. Welcomes casting queries, 'although actors stand a better chance of being seen when we are casting a specific show'. Send cv and photograph with covering letter. Phone calls are discouraged but invitations to see a production are acceptable. 'Please make sure your photos are up to date and honest. Read casting breakdowns thoroughly and do not submit an application unless you fulfil the criteria.'

Wigan Pier Theatre Company
Wigan Pier, Wallgate,
Wigan,
Lancashire WN3 4EU
Tel: 01942 323666
Fax: 01942 322031
E-mail: 100620.1244@compuserve.com
Artistic Director *Edward Applewhite*

Founded in 1986, the company has progressed from performing improvised historical scenes to performing daily promenade plays, Theatre-in-Education work and theatre in the community. Tours to schools and libraries but 98 per cent of their work is performed at Wigan Pier itself. Stages large-scale Christmas musicals, corporate events, musical hall and murder weekends and also works with Wigan Pier Youth Theatre. Offers Equity contracts. Advertises for actors and welcomes casting queries; approach in writing (no telephone calls). Holds general auditions, usually between April and June – apply for inclusion in February or March or look in *The Stage* or PCR. 'It is useful to find out a little about the company before applying. Wigan Pier, for example, is not on the coast – it is not an end-of-the-pier show. The contract is hard work but very rewarding. The work is varied and musical skills are an advantage. I [Edward Applewhite] am always interested to hear from actor-pianists. Actors with excellent singing voices are also encouraged to apply.'

Wildcat Stage Productions
135 Moffat Street, Glasgow G5 0NG
Tel: 0141 420 3151
Fax: 0141 420 3161
Website: http://cbcweb.con/wildcat
Artistic Director *David Maclennan*
Contact *Hilary Weir (General Manager), David Anderson (Musical Director)*

Founded in 1978, Wildcat, Scotland's leading music-theatre company, has had its revenue grant withdrawn by the Scottish Arts Council. However, the company, one of the main employers of actors in Scotland for the past 20 years, has launched a vigorous appeal which is being supported by the profession throughout the country. The magazine, *The Big Issue*, is also committed to saving Wildcat and is hosting the Wildcat Website. A benefit concert was staged in February at the King's Theatre in Edinburgh, featuring, among others, Gregor Fisher, David Rintoul and Elaine C. Smith.

The Wrestling School
42 Durlston Road, London E5 8RR
Tel: 0181 442 4229
Fax: 0181 442 4229
Artistic Directors *Kenny Ireland, Howard Barker*
Contact *Christopher Corner*

Founded in 1988 by actors who had worked on Howard Barker plays at the RSC and the Royal Court and who wanted to develop new methods of presenting these rich, complex and inspiring texts. Through Barker's work, the company aims to explore the relationship between language and communication, performer and audience, and develop new forms of expression for text-based drama. It has established a reputation for mounting outstanding productions of Barker's works, touring them all over the UK and into Europe where it is seen as the principal exponent of Barker's work. Generally 1 tour per year of 6 to 8 weeks' duration, to middle-scale venues. Productions have visited Paris, Berlin, Copenhagen, Sienna, Luxembourg, Lille, Gothenburg, Amsterdam, Stockholm, Limoges and Riga. Recent productions have included: *Wounds to the Face*, *(Uncle) Vanya*, *Judith* (Howard Barker nominated Best Director, TMA Regional Theatre awards), *Hated Nightfall* (TMA Regional Theatre award for Best New Play), *The Castle*. Does not advertise for actors. 'The company only uses actors who can demonstrate significant ability to understand, interpret and express complex text. Most have considerable experience performing in Shakespeare or Restoration work. Prospective actors should have a genuine desire to work on Barker texts, be familiar with the work of the company and demonstrate an awareness of Barker's underlying theory. Howard Barker uses casting directors; other directors generally cast direct from known actors or through auditions. Each production will have some actors who have worked for the company before. Does not hold general auditions. Actors interested in working for the company should phone Chris Corner first to find out when we are next auditioning and then submit details approximately three weeks beforehand with a letter outlining reasons for wanting to work with the company. These will be passed on but we cannot see everyone who contacts us. General mailout details are not welcome.'

Yellow Earth Theatre

47 Croxley Road, London W9 3HJ
Tel: 0181 968 4074
Fax: 0181 968 4074
E-mail: yellow earth@lineone.net
Artistic Director *David K. S. Tse*
Contact *Kwong Loke, Andrew Mallett, Kumiko Mendl, Veronica Needa, Tom Wu*

Founded in 1995, Yellow Earth Theatre is an international touring company whose 6 members are British-East-Asian performers. Committed to producing highly physical, popular performance which brings together traditions from both East and West to create 'a new style that reflects the duality of our cultural heritage'. Stages 3 productions per year. Offers Equity contracts (dependent on project funding). Advertises for actors and welcomes written casting queries.

Yorick Internationalist Theatre Ensemble

5E Peabody Buildings, Rodney Road, London SE17 1BT
Tel: 0171 701 6385
Fax: 0171 701 6385
Contact *Michael Batz (Artistic Director), Nishita Sharma, Karzan Krekar*

Founded 1986. An international theatre group which concentrates on British and world premières. Up to 2 tours per year, usually to venues in London and festivals, playing in middle-scale theatres. Previous productions have included: *The House of the Spirits* by Isabel Allende, adapted for the stage by the author and Michael Batz (cast of 20, including 5 musicians); won a Fringe First award for their production of Lorca's last play, *Comedy Without Title*. Offers Equity contracts 'whenever we have the funds'. Rarely advertises. Welcomes 'intelligent casting queries that show he/she has done some research about us. Come to see our work and get to know us slowly. Especially interested in non-English actors, actors from Asia, Latin America and Africa. No US actors.' Approach in writing. Occasionally holds workshops. 'Learn about history, politics, the world we live in as well as honing your craft. Art is political or it is wallpaper. Don't bother if you're not prepared to work very hard, undergo crises and tough times, be totally committed, able to work in a collective but also able to take instructions even, and especially, if you don't agree with them. Have a complete lack of inhibition (you must be prepared to work fully naked in body and soul!)'.

Yorkshire Women Theatre

Unit 10, 231–5 Chapeltown Road,
Leeds, West Yorkshire LS7 3DX
Tel: 0113 262 6900
Fax: 0113 262 6900
Contact *Julie Courtney (Company Manager)*

Founded in 1986, the company has established a strong track record of high-quality theatre which presents complex health issues in a clear, entertaining and accessible form. Performs in community centres, women's centres, colleges, small-scale theatres, youth clubs and schools. Two to 3 tours per year. Previous productions have included: *Broken Angel* by Lin Coghlan, *Drugs Education* (for 5–6-year-olds),

Through the Shadows by Jane Pearson. Does not offer Equity contracts. Advertises for actors and welcomes casting queries; send cv and photograph.

Zip Theatre

Dunkley Street, Wolverhampton,
West Midlands WV1 4AN
Tel: 01902 712251
Fax: 01902 713494
Artistic Director *Jon Lingard-Lane*
Contact *Cathy Pemberton (Company Secretary)*

Founded 1980. Zip provides professional theatre, music and training to a wide range of people. 'As an arts and education facility, Zip is unique in offering the opportunity to explore and develop skills in a variety of activities in an original and exciting style.' Four to 5 productions a year are toured to 'anywhere a piece of theatre can be performed'. Previous productions have included: *Alice in Wonderland* (panto), *Hold Back the Night* (musical thriller), *Take Me Too* (commissioned work looking at sex and sexuality, for schools audience) and *Ananse the Spiderman* (African/Caribbean folk tales for primary and middle schools). Offers Equity contracts. Advertises for actors in *The Stage*. Welcomes casting queries; send photograph and cv with covering letters. Holds general auditions. 'Midlands-based performers are of interest. Existing company members have been employed for some time. Zip does not recast for each production. However, enquiries are always welcome.'

Fringe and Alternative Theatre

Fringe theatre can provide an excellent showcase, particularly if it offers a leading role in a production in one of the prestigious London venues which potential employers and casting directors are happy to attend. However, it may prove to be an expensive experience. Many fringe companies pay little more than travel expenses. Do not be misled by the well-known term, 'profit share'. In many instances, once production and publicity costs have been met, the handout of a share of the profits to the actors can be minimal, if anything at all, particularly if the venue seats no more than a handful of people and the publicity machine has failed to attract the all-essential *Time Out* reviewer.

Working in Fringe theatre can prove to be an uncomfortable experience and requires great commitment from those involved. Dressing rooms are almost non-existent and often it is a great luxury to have access to water; a considerable problem if the show is physically demanding or involves body make-up. Despite this, a lot of exciting theatre is created and the Fringe is frequently the seed bed of new talent for actors, writers and directors.

Aba Daba Productions

30 Upper Park Road,
London NW3 2UT
Tel: 0171 722 5395
Fax: 0171 722 5395
Contact *Aline Waites (Artistic Director), Robin Hunter*

Founded 1969. Originally produced music hall at the Pindar of Wakefield and revues, pantomimes, musicals at venues such as the Canal Café and Star and Garter. Recent productions have included: *Gone with the Wind 2* at Brick Lane and *Stairway to Heaven*, the story of Marilyn Monroe. Occasionally advertises for actors and uses casting directors. Does not welcome casting queries. 'Mostly, we use actors who are recommended by current company members. We use very small casts and the style is very particular to us. See as many of our shows as possible before you even think of applying.'

Albany Empire

Douglas Way, Deptford, London SE8 4AG
Tel: 0181 691 3277
Fax: 0181 469 2253
Artistic Director *Andrew Broadley*

The Albany moved to its new, purpose-built home in 1981. A highly flexible performance space specialising in new work in the following areas: gay/lesbian performance, British Chinese work, contemporary Black dance, disability arts and new writing. Stages 2 or 3 in-house shows per year as well as acting as a receiving house. Recent productions have included: *Bull!* and *Hungry For It*. Does not offer Equity contracts. Occasionally advertises for actors. Welcomes casting queries – send photograph and cv. Telephone for information on future seasons.

Alternative Theatre Company Ltd

Bush Theatre, Shepherd's Bush Green, London W12 8QD
Tel: 0171 602 3703
Fax: 0171 602 7614
Artistic Director *Mike Bradwell*

Founded 1972. Trading as the Bush Theatre, the company produces about 6 new plays a year (principally British) and hosts up to 4 visiting companies

also producing new work. Winner of the 1997 Peter Brook Empty Space Award. Productions include: *Kiss of the Spiderwoman* by Manuel Puig, *More Light* Snoo Wilson, *Raping the Gold* Lucy Gannon, *Handful of Stars* Billy Roche, *Boys Mean Business* Catherine Johnson, *The Pitchfork Disney* Philip Ridley, *Beautiful Thing* Jonathan Harvey, *Killer Joe* Tracy Letts, *Love and Understanding* Joe Penhall, *Caravan* Helen Blakeman. Does not use casting directors and does not advertise for actors. Happy to receive cvs and photographs; 'no telephone calls, please'.

Attic Theatre Company (London) Ltd

Wimbledon Theatre, The Broadway, London SW19 1QG
Tel: 0181 543 7838
Fax: 0181 543 7838
Contact *Jenny Lee (Artistic Director), Caroline Goodwin*

Founded 1987. Attic's policy is to 'present new work, contemporary plays with a cutting edge and reworked classics whose form is theatrical in concept and appealing to a wide audience'. Emphasis is given to the work of women writers, performers and designers. Initially, Attic just ran a 3-to-5-month season at the Wimbledon Studio Theatre but now also tours to outer-London venues and plans to tour nationally. Two or 3 plays produced each year. Previous productions have included: *The Grannie (La Nona)* by Roberto Cossa (LWT award-winning production), *The Seal Wife* by Sue Glover (outer-London tour), *Rosmersholm* new translation by David Rudkin of the play by Henrik Ibsen.

Does not offer Equity contracts 'at present'. Advertises for actors in SBS and, occasionally, PCR. Sometimes uses casting directors. Does not welcome casting queries. 'We are a small fringe company so we do not have the resources to deal with unsolicited cvs and photographs. What we can't offer in wages we hope to make up for in good experience and exposure in good productions.'

BAC (Battersea Arts Centre)

Lavender Hill, Battersea,
London SW11 5TF
Tel: 0171 223 6557
Fax: 0171 978 5207
E-mail: mailbox@bac.org.uk
Artistic Director Tom Morris
Production Manager Hilary Shearing
Programme Manager Geraldine Collinge

Founded in 1981, BAC is the second-largest arts centre in the country with around 1,200 performances or events taking place each year, from opera to comedy and international drama to young people's theatre. The centre was awarded a Lottery grant of £810,000 which has enabled it to equip the theatre spaces with new lighting and sound, upgrade the dressing rooms and refurbish the Arts Café. Produces a number of in-house shows. Occasionally holds general auditions which are advertised. Does not welcome casting queries from actors; 'it is best to invite us to see them in something'. The BAC Young People's Theatre takes 16- to 30-year-olds, involving them with professional performers. Phone the Education Department for more details.

Tristan Bates Theatre

The Actors Centre, 1A Tower Street,
London WC2H 9NP
Tel: 0171 240 3940
Fax: 0171 240 3896
Artistic Director To be appointed
Contact Pippa Bound (Theatre Manager)

Established in 1994 by actor Alan Bates in memory of his son, the theatre is part of the Actors Centre (*see* Organisations, Associations and Societies, page 329). Seating capacity: 78. Used by professional actors for classes during the day, the theatre acts as a receiving house at night with a platform slot at 6.15 p.m. and a main show at 8 p.m. It is also used to showcase work by The Actors Centre. Sometimes advertises for actors; uses casting directors 'via our contacts at The Actors Centre'. Welcomes casting queries from actors who are members of the Centre. 'Once people become members we keep a copy of their cv/photo. We would then put them forward for something when we are asked to advise casting directors. Members who are familiar often get first chance at castings.'

Bird's Nest Theatre

– see **Flying the Nest**, page 200

The Bridewell Theatre

Bride Lane, Off Fleet Street,
London EC4Y 8EQ
Tel: 0171 353 0259
Fax: 0171 583 5289
E-mail: bride@irational.org

Seating capacity: varies according to production. Originally a Victorian swimming pool, last used in 1972. Left derelict until 1993 when the pool was covered and the space used as a theatre (the pool can still be seen and is sometimes used as an orchestra pit). One of the most flexible and versatile spaces in London, it is the only fringe venue in the City. Stages both in-house and visiting shows. Recent in-house productions include: *Antony and Cleopatra*, *Marry Me a Little*, *On the Twentieth Century* and *Damn Yankees*; visiting productions: *Cogmagogues* (part of the City of London Festival) and *Romance Romance*.

Funding: St Bride's Institute/sponsorship.

Bridge Lane Theatre Company Ltd

Bridge Lane, Battersea,
London SW11 3AD
Tel: 0171 229 5185
Fax: 0171 228 5185
Contact *Terry Adams (Artistic Director), Sandie Cunningham*

Founded 1908. The theatre is both a producing and receiving house with the company's programme made up of approximately 60 per cent new work and 40 per cent revivals. Two or 3 in-house productions per year. The company has a loose amalgam of associate members from which the in-house company is drawn for particular productions. Offers Equity contracts. Advertises for actors. Welcomes casting queries; approach in writing. Occasionally holds general auditions – 'see press for details'. 'While Bridge Lane continues to adapt to changing forms of theatre, we believe the actor is best served by the acquisition of a sound and extensive technique.'

Bristol Express Theatre Company

24 Wells House Road, East Acton,
London NW10 6EE
Tel: 0181 838 4482
Fax: 0181 838 4482
Artistic Director *Andy Jordan*

Founded 1978. Mainly committed to new writing and the development of new writers but Bristol Express also produces more commercial plays. Has produced over 100 new plays since the company was established. Previous productions have included: *A Meeting in Rome* by Michael Meyer (Edinburgh Festival), *Heaven* by Sarah Aicher (Lilian Baylis Theatre, London), *Winter Darkness* by Alan Cubitt (New End Theatre, London). Offers Equity contracts 'when we can'. Rarely advertises for actors. Welcomes casting queries – send cv and photograph with covering letter. At the time of going to press the company had not been in production for three years due to lack of funding but there are hopes of a revival of fortunes in 1998.

The Brix Theatre

The Brix at St Matthew's, Brixton Hill,
London SW2 1JF
Tel: 0171 733 4443
Fax: 0171 733 6604

Reopened in 1995 having formerly been known as the Shaw at the Brix. Seating capacity: 250. Receiving house only. Recent shows have included: *Timon of Athens*, staged by the Andrew Jarvis Theatre Company in association with the English Shakespeare Company, *The Suitcase Kid*, staged by Peter Burke.

Bush Theatre

– see **Alternative Theatre Company Ltd**, page 196

Camden People's Theatre

58–60 Hampstead Road,
London NW1 2PY
Tel: 0171 916 5878
Fax: 0171 916 5878
Artistic Director Sheridan Bramwell
Contact Lynne Kendrick (Associate Director), Shaun Glanville (Associate Director), Martin Sutherland (Administrator)

Founded 1994. Run by theatre professionals working on a voluntary basis, demonstrating a commitment to 'developing the creativity of professionals and non-professionals alike'. Stages 3 or 4 in-house productions per year as well as hosting incoming shows. Fifty per cent is physical theatre/new writing and 50 per cent community work. Offers Equity contracts, if funding permits. Advertises for actors and welcomes casting queries. Send introductory letter and cv. Holds workshops 'which we tend to use as auditions' and these are advertised in PCR and *The Stage*. Applications for inclusion are taken at all times.

Canal Café Theatre

The Bridge House, Delamere Terrace, Little Venice, London W2 6ND
Tel: 0171 289 6036
Fax: 0171 266 1717
Artistic Director Ali Robertson
Contact Robert Lloyd Parry (Press and Marketing Officer)

Founded 1984. A 60-seater pub theatre with a 'cabaret-style' layout – tables and chairs where you can eat, drink and smoke during performances. Presents a wide variety of shows – comedy, drama, cabaret, music, including *Newsrevue*, London's longest-running comedy sketch show. Both a receiving and producing house; 'we are aiming to produce more and more in-house'. Recent productions have included: *The Double Bass* by Patrick Suskind (in-house), *Lulu Liebling* after Frank Wedekind and *Araby and Eveline* after James Joyce. Does not offer Equity contracts. Advertises for actors. Welcomes casting queries; send cv and photograph. Advertises in PCR for *Newsrevue*.

Cockpit Theatre

Gateforth Street, London NW8 8EH
Tel: 0171 258 2920/262 7907
Fax: 0171 258 2921
Contact David Wybrow (Artistic Director), Denise Humphreys

Built and still run as a professional training venue but often used as an off-West End professional showcase. Produces 10 plays a year. Does not offer Equity contracts. 'All/any open auditions would be advertised in *The Stage*.' Do not welcome casting queries.

Conla Productions

– see **Old Red Lion Theatre**, page 203

The Drill Hall Arts Centre

16 Chenies Street,
London WC1E 7EX
Tel: 0171 631 1353
Fax: 0171 631 4468
Artistic Director Julie Parker

Seating capacity: 200. Regularly stages in-house productions (often co-productions) as well as receiving shows. The Drill Hall is noted for its gay and lesbian productions but it also stages a wide range of other work such as Talawa Theatre Company's production of *Othello* and Music Theatre London's *La Bohème* and *Cosi Fan Tutte*. Advertises in *The Stage* as and when they require actors for in-house shows.

Also holds courses and workshops – *see* Additional Skills, page 374.

Etcetera Theatre

Oxford Arms Pub, 265 Camden High Street, London NW1 7BU
Tel: 0171 482 4857
Fax: 0171 482 0378
Artistic Director *David Bidmead*
Contact *Suzanna Rosenthal, David Cottis, Dominic Burnham*

Founded in 1986, the Etcetera Theatre is mainly a receiving house although approximately 3 in-house shows per year are produced. Primarily interested in new works or classic pieces performed in a new and innovative style. In 1997, hosted London's second One Person Play Festival which consisted of 20 new plays over a period of 5 weeks. Previous in-house productions have included: *Great Pretenders* (a lookalike musical which transferred to the Edinburgh Festival) and *Contested Will* (new drama). Does not offer Equity contracts. Advertises in PCR and *The Stage*. Welcomes casting queries – send letter and cv.

Finborough Theatre

– *see* **The Steam Industry**, page 207

Flying the Nest

Bird's Nest Theatre, 32 Deptford Church Street, London SE8 4RZ
Tel: 0181 694 2255
Artistic Director *Nigel Ward*

Founded 1995. Flying the Nest is the in-house production company at the Bird's Nest Theatre, a 70-seat, proscenium-arch fringe venue. Dedicated to presenting new work only, it stages between 6 and 10 plays per year. Recent productions have included: *Heavy Smoking* (musical comedy), *Buskers* (comedy) and *The Tender Mercies* (psychological thriller). Does not offer Equity contracts. 'All shows for which we require actors are advertised in PCR and *The Stage*. We will sometimes place a general advert to cover a season (i.e. 4 months/plays).' Only welcomes casting queries in response to adverts.

Galleon Theatre Company Ltd

The Prince Theatre, Greenwich BR Station Forecourt, 189 Greenwich High Road, London SE10 8JA
Tel: 0181 858 9256
Fax: 0181 969 2910
Contact *Alice de Sousa (Artistic Director), Bruce Jamieson*

Founded in 1988, the Galleon Theatre Company is the resident company at the Prince Theatre, a venue which receives visiting companies and aims to specialise in revivals of classic and modern European plays, and actively encourages and supports the integration of theatre-school graduates into the profession. Galleon produces around 15 plays per year. Previous productions have included: *Anne of the Thousand Days* by Maxwell Anderson, *Pericles* by Shakespeare, *The Zoo Story* by Edward Albee, *Celestina* by Fernando de Rojas. Occasionally offers Equity contracts. Advertises for actors. Uses in-house casting director. Only welcomes casting queries if relevant to current casting/project needs when advertised. 'Attention to accurate detail, timekeeping and perseverance are needed, and always retain an open and pleasurable attitude to work. When auditioning, show previous knowledge and interest in the organisation and individuals interviewing you and the project for which you are being seen.'

The Gate Theatre

11 Pembridge Road, Notting Hill, London W11 3HQ
Tel: 0171 229 5387
Fax: 0171 221 6055
Artistic Director *To be appointed*

Founded 1978. Leading fringe venue which can rightfully claim to be the London home of international drama. Aspires to produce the best of undiscovered world drama, and to provide a platform for the emerging talents of actors, directors, designers and translators. Produces at least 9 in-house productions per year plus receiving some incoming shows. Recent productions have included: Voltaire's *Candide*, Aristophanes' *The Birds*, Gregory Motton's *Little Satire on the '97 General Election*, Kalidasa's *Shakuntala*, Georg Büchner's *Danton's Death*. Does not offer Equity contracts. Does not advertise for actors; uses casting directors. Welcomes casting queries; approach by telephone in the first instance and then send cv and photograph and 'we will contact you as parts come up'. (At the time of going to press, it had been announced that there was a problem with future funding of The Gate.)

GRiP Theatre

59–61 High Street, Hampton Wick, Surrey KT1 4DG
Tel: 0181 296 0242
E-mail: gripthtr@aol.com
Artistic Director *Martin Richards*
Contact *Chantal Richards, Tim Williams*

Founded in 1993, GRiP Theatre is the resident company at the Rose and Crown Club Theatre, a 'black box' space above the Rose and Crown pub. Produces between 7 and 10 plays per year. In 1996, staged the 'All-Encompassing Season' (alternate-night repertory performances over a 6-week period of Berkoff's *East* and *West* coupled with two new plays, also in repertory, entitled *North* and *South*. Recent productions have included *Fire Flies* (shortlisted for the Verity Bargate award), and a new play by writer-in-residence Chris Chibnall entitled *Best Daze*. Does not offer Equity contracts. Advertises for actors and welcomes casting queries; send cv and photograph with covering letter. 'We are particularly interested in actors based nearby but welcome any enquiry from professional actors seeking to work with a growing small-scale company with an equally growing reputation for new work and new productions of contemporary authors.'

The Ideal Theatre Company

94 Gordon Road, London SE15 3RP
Tel: 0171 564 3384
Fax: 0171 564 3147
Contact *Ms Pat O'Toole, Mark Shayle*

Founded 1992. Production company, staging new plays and musicals in London fringe venues. Also runs rehearsed readings and workshops for writers and actors. Productions have included: *These Men* (Old Red Lion), *Dead Dogs and Englishmen*, *Haven* and *Dearly Beloved* (Bridewell Theatre). Does not offer Equity contracts. Advertises for actors and sometimes uses casting directors. Welcomes *written* casting queries. 'We keep photos and cvs on file. An interest in new work is an advantage.'

Jermyn Street Theatre
16B Jermyn Street,
London SW1Y 6ST
Tel: 0171 434 1443

Opened in 1994. Originally a restaurant, this tiny theatre has recently been awarded Lottery funding and will undergo a complete refurbishment. With a seating capacity of just 70, the theatre is mainly a receiving house.

King's Head Theatre
115 Upper Street,
Islington,
London N1 1QN
Tel: 0171 226 8561
Fax: 0171 226 8507
Artistic Director Dan Crawford

The first pub theatre since Shakespearean times and the first venue in the UK for dinner theatre, the King's Head produces a wide range of work, including previously neglected pieces by playwrights such as Terence Rattigan and Vivian Ellis. Noël Coward's work also has a strong presence; Cavalcade was toured in 1995. Produces a minimum of 6 in-house productions each year as well as receiving visiting companies. Recent in-house productions have included: The Boys in the Band, Frankly Scarlet, Romeo and Juliet. Advertises for actors in SBS and PCR. No telephone calls. Approach in writing in the first instance. (At the time of going to press, the future of the King's Head Theatre was uncertain due to cuts in funding.)

Komedia
Manchester Street, Brighton,
East Sussex BN2 1TF
Tel: 01273 277070
Fax: 01273 277010
Website:
http/www.brighton.co.uk/listings/komedia
Artistic Directors David Lavender,
Colin Granger
Contact Jathan Granger
(Administrator), Sally Moulsdale
(Press Officer)

Founded 1994. Komedia is a purpose-built studio theatre with a cabaret bar which is both a producing and receiving house, dedicated to staging new work. Previous productions have included: What's to be Done with Algernon? by Michael Allen, which also toured regionally and played at the Croydon Warehouse. Offers Equity contracts. Advertises for actors and welcomes casting queries – send cv.

LJ's Theatre Bar
– see **Enzyme Theatre Company** under Touring Theatre Companies, page 167

Louder Than Words Productions
115A Liverpool Road,
London N1 0RG
Tel: 0171 837 4137
Artistic Director Ruth Ben-Tovim

Founded 1991. Performs primarily at the Young Vic Studio and non-theatre venues in London. Creates installation/performance work and experiments in narrative structure and theatrical convention with writers, designers, composers, lighting and performers. Previous productions have included: Dream Time (Young Vic Studio), Counting of Years (Young Vic

Studio and BAC), *Navigators, Elephant in a Rhubarb Tree* and *Ballad of the Limehouse Rat*. Offers Equity contracts. Sometimes advertises for actors. Does not welcome casting queries unless the actor knows the company and has seen their work.

Man in the Moon Theatre

392 King's Road, Chelsea,
London SW3 5UZ
Tel: 0171 351 5701
Fax: 0171 351 1873
General Manager *Nick Eisen*
Administrator *Pete Staves*

The Man in the Moon Theatre opened in 1982 as a forum for advertising new work, either through new writing or through ground-breaking productions of established plays. Continues to focus on new drama that explores the relationship between performance and audience and the essential spontaneity of live theatre. Presents in-house plays as well as receiving visiting companies. Recent in-house productions have included: *Hitting Home* and *Come Together*. Does not offer Equity contracts. Does not advertise for actors but welcomes casting queries. 'Telephone as an introduction then send cv and photograph for our files.'

Millfield Theatre

Silver Street, London N18 1PJ
Tel: 0181 807 6186
Fax: 0181 803 2801
Artistic Director *Graham Bennett*

Founded 1988. The Millfield is a modern, purpose-built theatre which produces an annual pantomime on Equity contracts and is home to two profit-share companies: Millfield Theatre Company and Millfield Musical Productions. The former

company produces 4 or 5 plays per year; recent productions have included: *Alfie, A Midsummer Night's Dream, Daisy Pulls it Off, Having a Ball* and *Macbeth*. Musical productions include *Godspell, Rock Hard* and *Little Shop of Horrors*. Advertises for the pantomime only. Does not welcome casting queries. 'Do not send unsolicited cvs and photographs. Always look out for casting calls. Assess your appropriateness for specific roles – do not put yourself up for singing roles if you can't sing. Take note of height and playing-age requirements – are you *sure* you can play a teenager still?!'

New End Theatre

27 New End, Hampstead,
London NW3 1JD
Tel: 0171 794 0022

Seating capacity: 80. Housed in a building that was once a mortuary, the theatre first opened in 1974. Mainly a receiving house for fringe theatre companies but stages the occasional co-production.

Old Red Lion Theatre

418 St John Street,
London EC1V 4QE
Tel: 0171 833 3053
Fax: 0171 833 3053
Artistic Director *Ken McClymont*

Founded 1977. The Old Red Lion, one of London's oldest-established fringe venues, is a 60-seat theatre in Islington. Concentrates on premièring new work by new writers, directors, actors, etc. or work that has not been seen in London or the South-East for at least five years. Both a receiving house and home to two resident companies: Conla Productions and Ken Sharp Productions. Produces 3 or 4 in-house plays per year. Previous productions have included: *Black Dove*, a world première by Robin Keys (Attic Theatre and Ken Sharp Productions), *Golden Own Goal*, a world première by Paul Pavht (Conla Productions), *Humming Bird*, a world première by Chris Lee (Ken Sharp Productions). Does not offer Equity contracts. Advertises for actors and occasionally uses casting directors. Welcomes casting queries; send cv and photograph 'for our file, which we do use'. Holds general auditions. 'Be prepared to work very hard, especially if on a new play. Go to rehearsals with ideas as the directors we generally use are more open and appreciative of this type of input. New plays need diligent, experienced, enthusiastic, controlled performers. Be prepared to do the show to an audience of *one*, if needs must.'

Orange Tree Theatre

1 Clarence Street, Richmond,
Surrey TW9 2SA
Tel: 0181 940 0141
Fax: 0181 332 0369
Artistic Director *Sam Walters*

Founded in 1971, the theatre began in a room above the Orange Tree pub, presenting lunchtime plays by daylight. In 1975, the pub was renovated and the theatre began evening performances, developing into a theatre-in-the-round. In 1991, the company moved to a new purpose-built theatre-in-the-round nearby. Produces between 6 and 8 plays per year. Previous productions have included: *Love Me Slender* (new play by Vanessa Brooks), *The Power of Darkness* by Leo Tolstoy and *Inheritors* by Susan Glaspell. Offers Equity contracts. Very seldom advertises and then only for specialist skills. Welcomes *written*

casting queries only; letters and cvs are kept on file. 'Write, but don't pester. Be patient. Visit the theatre – there are Equity concessions. The problem we have today is that the profession is so overcrowded that if a theatre opens its doors a chink then it risks being swamped by the deluge. So casting tends to be done more and more via recommendation from actors, etc. or by visiting, trusted agents.'

Oval House Theatre

52–4 Kennington Oval, London SE11
Tel: 0171 735 2786

Seating capacity: 100 (downstairs studio); 50 (upstairs studio). A receiving house for fringe theatre companies. Also holds workshops and classes for young people (for those aged 13 and over).

Oxford Street Theatre

Sedley Place, 361 Oxford Street,
London W1N 3HG
Tel: 0171 629 5343
Fax: 0171 629 2462
Artistic Director *Christopher Ager*
Contact *Fiona Cooper (Press and Marketing)*

Founded 1997. Fringe venue which accommodates small- to medium-scale lunchtime and early-evening productions. Housed in the dinner-cabaret ballroom of the famous Rheingold Club (established in 1959), the theatre boasts a stage area, dance floor, pa, lighting and a golden baby-grand piano. There are two bars and the club is licensed until 3 a.m. Hosts about 9 cabaret shows per year. The venue is available on a rental- or box-office split for a variety of productions. Help is given with listings and fliers.

Pentameters Theatre

Three Horseshoes, 28 Heath Street,
London NW3
Tel: 0171 435 6757

Founded in 1968 to promote poetry and new writing. Seating capacity: 100. Generally profit-share productions.

Pleasance London

40 North Road, Islington,
London N7 9DP
Tel: 0171 700 6877
Director *Christopher Richardson*

Opened 1996, the Pleasance London is a modern, 300-seat theatre housed in the General Omnibus Company's timber store in Carpenter's Mews. Also manages the Edinburgh Festival Fringe Pleasance venue during August. Mainly a receiving house but co-produces occasionally. Recent co-production credits include: *Swan Song* by Jonathan Harvey, *Richard II* (with Rubicon Theatre). Home of the resident youth-theatre company, Young Pleasance, which stages productions on a regular basis at the theatre and also at the Edinburgh venue.

The Prince Theatre

– *see* **Galleon Theatre Company Ltd**, page 200

Riverside Studios

Crisp Road, Hammersmith,
London W6 9RL
Tel: 0181 741 2251
Fax: 0181 563 0336
Artistic Director *William Burdett-Coutts*

Founded in 1976 by Peter Gill as its first director, who established its reputation as an international theatre.

Mainly hosts visiting companies. Recent productions include: *An Enchanted Land* by Dale Wasserman, *Caliban* by Marcus Azevedo and the Wrestling School's production of *Wounds to the Face* by Howard Barker.

Rosemary Branch Theatre

2 Shepperton Road, London N1 3DT
Tel: 0171 704 6665 (Box Office)
Artistic Directors *Cecilia Darker, Angela Neustatter, Cleo Sylvestre*

Seating capacity: 70. The present Victorian building, which was renowned for its music hall, was completely refurbished by its present owners in 1992. As well as theatre, there is a constantly changing exhibition of sculpture, paintings, photographs and 'uncategorisable' artworks by local artists. Recent shows have included: *The Birth of Pleasure* (Wonderful Beast Co.), *The Prod* and *Let's Dig Up Dad* by Charles Smith (Kew Bridge Productions), *Paraphernalia* (Aba Daba).

Serio Ensemble

The Pigeon Loft, 443–445 Holloway Road, London N7 6LJ
Tel: 0171 281 7683/7745
Artistic Director *Charles Serio*
Contact *Karin Serio, Mari Cardew-Richardson*

Resident at the Pigeon Loft (a 5,000-sq-ft warehouse space directly behind the National Youth Theatre), Serio Ensemble is a Registered Arts Charity (No. 1002458) founded in September 1987. The aims of the group are twofold: to mount professional arts productions at its resident venue and to offer training in arts-related skills. The focus is on new writing with 2 or 3 productions each year. Previous productions have included: *The Men in Black* (surreal sci-fi), *Circus Minimus* (circus skills) and *Heart Break* (a focus on contemporary attitudes to love). Does not offer Equity contracts. Advertises for actors and welcomes casting queries; send cv and photograph with covering letter. Holds general auditions in July; apply for inclusion by the end of March. 'The ensemble works collaboratively, with over forty full-time members. New writing is stressed, with most productions utilising movement skills. Technical innovations in design, either in sound applications or visual elements, are a focus. Most productions demand musical abilities. One-off experimental work is also offered and new actors are generally given an opportunity on these before consideration for major production work.'

Ken Sharp Productions
– see **Old Red Lion Theatre**, page 203

Show of Strength Theatre Company
Hebron House, Sion Road,
Bristol BS3 3BD
Tel: 0117 963 7634 ext 239
Fax: 0117 963 1770
Joint Artistic Directors *Alan Coveney, Sheila Hannon*

Founded in 1989 as a pub theatre company but now in the process of developing a new space in an arts/community centre being built in a former tobacco warehouse in Bristol. A new writing company, which recently staged the world première of Peter Nichol's new play, *Blue Murder*, subsequently taking it on tour. Other productions include: *Good Works* by

Nick Enright, *The Mystery of the Rose Bouquet* by Manuel Puig, *The Illusion* by Tony Kushner. Produces an autumn season of 4 plays each year. Unable to pay the full Equity rate at present. Advertises for actors in *The Stage*, SBS and PCR. Only interested in actors based in the south-west of England as the company does not pay subsistence. Those who come into this category are welcome to submit cvs and photographs.

Soho Theatre Company
21 Dean Street, London W1V 6NE
Tel: 0171 493 8050
Fax: 0171 493 8051
E-mail: sohotheatre.co.uk
Artistic Director *Abigail Morris*

In 1972, Verity Bargate and Fred Proud established the Soho Theatre Company at the 50-seat Soho Poly. The mission was to produce new plays and discover new playwrights, and the company was to become a pioneering force in British Theatre. In 1992, the company moved again and under the artistic direction of Abigail Morris was relaunched at the 240-seat Cockpit Theatre where, in three years, the company presented more than 35 new plays, winning a host of awards. Following Westminster College's termination of their tenancy of the Cockpit Theatre, the company plans to receive plays when their new theatre is up and running in 1999, but at the moment they are a producing company only, presenting 3 or 4 plays per year. 1997 productions: *Watching* by Lin Coghlan (Irish contemporary classic), *Noise* by Alex Jones (contemporary play of injustice, society and the individual), *Gabriel* by Moira Buffini (set in World War II Guernsey), *Skeleton* by Tanika

Gupta (early-twentieth-century play set in a Bengali village), and *Food for Thought* (six short plays all around the theme of food). Offers Equity contracts. Does not advertise for actors. All casting is done through casting director, Marcia Gresham (*see entry* in Casting Directors, page 111).

Southwark Playhouse

62 Southwark Bridge Road,
London SE1 0AS
Tel: 0171 620 3494
Fax: 0171 261 1271
Contact *Mehmet Ergen (Artistic Director), Juliet Alderdice*

Founded 1993. Produces and receives a diverse repertoire of theatre, music theatre and opera. Plays range across classic texts and new writing. Produces 4 in-house plays per year. Does not offer Equity contracts but actors receive payment. Occasionally advertises for actors in PCR. Sometimes employs casting directors. Welcomes casting queries; approach in writing with cv and photograph in response to adverts.

The Steam Industry

Finborough Theatre,
118 Finborough Road,
London SW10 9ED
Tel: 0171 244 7439
Fax: 0171 835 1853
Artistic Director *Phil Willmott*
Administrator *Mervyn Millar*

Founded in 1994 at the Finborough Theatre, an award-winning venue for new writing, the Steam Industry produces a high percentage of new writing alongside radical adaptations of classics and musicals. The company regularly workshops new work and recent development successes have included David Eldridge's *Serving It Up* (produced by the Bush Theatre), Mark Ravenhill's *Shopping and Fucking* (produced by the Royal Court), Naomi Wallace's *Slaughter City* (produced by the RSC). For two years running, the Finborough has benefited from a Guinness Theatre Ingenuity award and in 1997 this allowed the venue to play host to a major season of new writing. Recent Steam Industry projects have included a revival of *Inherit the Wind* at BAC, a co-production with the King's Head, a TIE project on homelessness in association with the charity CRISIS and a Christmas production of *The Sound of Music*. Does not offer Equity contracts. Advertises for actors; has an in-house casting director, Tom Barrie. Prefers actors to respond to adverts rather than make general casting queries. Does not hold general auditions.

Tabard Theatre

2 Bath Road, London W4 1LW
Tel: 0181 995 6035
Fax: 0181 747 8256
Artistic Director *Kate Bone*

Founded in 1985 as a theatre of new writing. Now concentrating on contemporary work from the fifties onwards. Both a producing and a receiving house. Four to 6 in-house plays per year. Previous productions have included *Mary Rose* by J. M. Barrie, *Frankenstein the Panto* and *Sell Out* by Tony Corkran. Does not offer Equity contracts. Advertises for actors and occasionally uses casting directors.

Does not welcome casting queries; welcomes cvs and letters in response to specific adverts only.

Theatre Royal Stratford East

Gerry Raffles Square,
Newham,
London E15 1BN
Tel: 0181 534 7374
Fax: 0181 534 8381
Artistic Director *Philip Hedley*
Contact *Kerry Michael (Associate Director)*

The Theatre Royal Stratford East has been successfully running since its opening in 1884. Joan Littlewood's Theatre Workshop moved there in 1953, but the high ideal of 'A British People's Theatre', which she had hitherto pursued with commendable single-mindedness, soon gave way to the many attractions – not least financial – of staging West End transfers. Popular and critical success followed with such productions as *The Hostage*, *A Taste of Honey* and *Oh What a Lovely War!*. For the last twenty years, under the artistic leadership of Philip Hedley, the theatre has firmly established itself as a centre of high-quality work for all aspects of the community. Its strength lies in its very strong support from the multicultural audiences, locally, nationally and internationally, that frequent the theatre. Produces 8 new plays per year. Productions include: *Throwaway* by Danny Miller and *Variety Nights* – a monthly event that attracts audiences from across the board. Offers Equity contracts. Advertises for actors. Does not use casting directors. Welcomes casting queries; send cv, sae and covering letter.

Tricycle Theatre

269 Kilburn High Road,
London NW6 7JR
Tel: 0171 372 6611
Fax: 0171 328 0795
Artistic Director *Nicolas Kent*
Contact *Mary Lauder (General Manager)*

Founded 1980. The Tricycle plays to a very mixed audience in terms of both culture and class, with a bias towards new work, multicultural work and work for women. Stages approximately 3 in-house productions each year as well as receiving visiting companies. A £2.05 million Lottery award means that the theatre will be developed and a 280-seat cinema and painting studio for children will be built. Productions have included: *The Mai* by Marina Carr, *Two Trains Running* August Wilson, *The Day the Bronx Died* Michael Henry Brown, *Half the Picture* Richard Norton-Taylor and John McGrath, *Nativity* Nigel Williams, *Playboy of the West Indies* Mustapha Matura, *Three Hotels* Jon Robin Baitz, *Nuremberg* adapted by Richard Norton-Taylor from transcripts of the trials, *Srebrenica* adapted by Nicolas Kent. Offers Equity contracts. Does not advertise for actors as they always use casting directors. Welcomes casting queries from Black, Irish and Asian actors; approach in writing only.

Tron Theatre Company

63 Trongate, Glasgow G1 5HB
Tel: 0141 552 3748
Fax: 0141 552 6657
E-mail: www.tron.co.uk
Artistic Director *Irina Brown*
Contact *Neil Murray (Administrative Director), Yvonne Innes (Administrator)*

Founded 1981 as a theatre club. Based

in the eighteenth-century Tron Church in the centre of Glasgow, the theatre became public in 1989. Seating capacity: 272. Both a producing and a receiving house. Usually stages 3 or 4 plays annually but cuts in 1997/8 led to only 2 in-house productions. Lottery funding, awarded in 1997, has enabled the building to be upgraded. Plays to a broad cross-section of Glasgow and beyond, including international tours (Toronto 1996, Montreal 1992). Previous productions have included: *Lavochkin-5* by Alexei Shipenko, translated by Iain Heggie and Irina Brown (UK première), *Dave's Last Laugh* by David Stirling, *The Trick is to Keep Breathing* by Janice Galloway and *Endgame* by Samuel Beckett. Actors are employed for specific projects. Periodically uses casting directors. Does not advertise for actors. Does not normally hold general auditions. Welcomes casting queries; approach in writing, enclosing cv and photograph.

and co-produces with companies who share their commitment to new work. Regular professional staged readings of new writing through 'Writers in the Wings' and the annual International Playwriting Festival. Productions have included *Iona Rain* by Peter Moffat (winner of the International Playwriting Festival, 1995), *Fat Janet is Dead* by Simon Smith (winner of the IPF, 1996) and *The Blue Garden* by Peter Moffat. Offers Equity contracts. Advertises when special skills are required. Welcomes casting queries – 'send letter with sae. General letters can only be filed for further reference when casting. By far the most useful letter is one informing us of an appearance in a play or production which we are able to cover.' Does not hold general auditions 'as we need to cast specifically for each play'.

Warehouse Theatre Company

Warehouse Theatre,
Dingwall Road,
Croydon CR0 2NF
Tel: 0181 681 1257
Fax: 0181 688 6699
Artistic Director *Ted Craig*
Contact *Evita Bier (Administrative Director)*

Founded 1977. Major fringe theatre with a successful policy of producing new writing. The theatre is a flexible performance space with seating up to 120. Produces up to 6 new plays a year

White Bear Theatre Club

138 Kennington Park Road,
London SE11 4DJ
Administration: 3 Dante Road,
Kennington, London SE11 4RB
Tel: 0171 793 9193
Fax: 0171 277 0526
Artistic Director *Michael Kingsbury*
Administration *Julia Parr*

Founded 1988. Fringe venue which concentrates primarily on new work. Holds readings throughout the year. Produces 4 in-house plays each year. Advertises in SBS and PCR. Welcomes casting queries; approach in writing – 'details are kept on file'. Over the past

2 years, 7 productions have been named as *Time Out* Critics' Choice. Recent production: *Absolution* by Robert Sherwood (nominated by The Writers' Guild for 'Best Fringe Play' award). 'We are a good venue for actors being seen by casting directors and agents.'

Wimbledon Studio Theatre
103 The Broadway
(next to Wimbledon Theatre),
Wimbledon,
London SW19 1QG
Tel: 0181 542 6141
Fax: 0181 543 6637
Contact *Jonathan Kennedy (Administrator)*

Founded in 1994 (known before as the Attic Theatre Club), Wimbledon Studio Theatre is a converted ballroom in the beautiful Edwardian Wimbledon Theatre complex. Presents new works, classic revivals, Sunday one-night stands, musicals and comedy, arranged into seasons throughout the year. Both a receiving and producing house with the Attic Theatre Company producing an annual in-house season (*see entry*, page 196).

Young Vic Company
66 The Cut,
London SE1 8LZ
Tel: 0171 633 0133
Fax: 0171 928 1585
Artistic Director *Tim Supple*
Contact *Caroline Maude (Administrative Producer), Sue Emmas (Artistic Associate)*

Founded in 1970, under the direction of Frank Dunlop, as an offshoot of the National Theatre (at the time, based almost next door at The Old Vic). It went independent in 1974 and reaffirmed its reputation under directors Michael Bogdanov and David Thacker. Leading fringe venue with an adaptable purpose-built theatre-in-the-round main house (seating 500) and a studio theatre seating 114, which offers great opportunities for intimate ensemble performances. The company's policy is to create high-quality, innovative and imaginative theatre for a wide and, in particular, young audience. Both a receiving and a producing house with 3 or 4 in-house productions per year. Recent productions have included: *American Buffalo, Animal Farm, King Lear* and *The Comedy of Errors*. All casting is done through casting director, Toby Whale (*see entry* in Casting Directors, page 117). Welcomes casting queries; send cv and photograph with covering letter. Holds general auditions. 'The work is ongoing – we keep actors' details on file and call them.'

Children's and Young People's Theatre

Working in children's theatre should not be seen as an easy option or just a means of getting a foothold in the business. Those companies devoted to this particular field of work require performers who are committed to bringing theatre to what is, after all, the audience of the future. Actors who are multi-talented and can also offer devising skills are likely to be preferred. The young audiences can be demanding. They are quick to spot any lack of sincerity in the performer and have no inhibitions in making their feelings apparent. But, equally, the rewards can be great, such as when a sullen 'entertain me' attitude by an audience of restless adolescents greeting the opening of a performance is replaced by rapt attention and spontaneous warm applause at the end.

Much of the work is extremely demanding. Considerable commitment and energy is required when asked to perform a fast and energetic show first thing in the morning with the prospect of a repeat show in the afternoon. Not to mention the get-in and get-out required at each venue.

Theatre-in-Education is a shrinking world. Once a majority of reps had TIE companies attached to them but, sadly, only a handful remain, thus removing what for the young actor often proved a stepping stone into the main company. A small number of independent TIE companies are still offering this specialised educational work in schools and they are likely to require actors with an understanding of the educational process.

BAC Young People's Theatre
– *see* Fringe and Alternative Theatre, page 197

Belfast Civic Arts Youth Theatre
– *see* Repertory and Regional Theatres, page 120

Booster Cushion Theatre

Selby Centre, Selby Road,
London N17 8JN
Tel: 0181 365 0243
Fax: 0181 885 2767
Contact *Franz Shealy (Artistic Director), Philip Sherman*

Founded 1990. Booster Cushion Theatre 'brings books to life'. Their aim is to get children more interested in books and reading by making their own stories. Plays to children aged 4–10 years old. Tours all year throughout the UK and Ireland, performing in schools, arts centres and theatres. Productions include: *Never Judge a Book by its Cover* for 5–9-year-olds and *Red Riding Hood and Friends* for 4–8-year-olds. Offers ITC contracts. Holds general auditions. Advertises for actors and welcomes casting queries – send cv with photograph and sae. 'All cvs are kept on file.'

Caught in the Act

– *see* Theatre-in-Education (TIE) Companies, page 223

Celebration Theatre Company for the Young

48 Chiswick Staithe, London W4 3TP
Tel: 0181 994 8886
Artistic Director *Neville Wortman*
Contact *Vicki Courtney*

Founded 1994. Produces traditional and classic plays, training young people in all aspects of theatre craft. Plays to all age ranges. Also involved in television and corporate video production through Wortman Productions UK (*see entry under* Film, Video and Independent Production Companies, page 306). Produces 1 or 2 plays per year; *The Winter's Tale* was

staged at the Bloomsbury Theatre in London. In 1996/7, held an introductory drama and music course. Sometimes advertises for actors and occasionally uses casting directors. Does not welcome casting queries. 'We use *Spotlight* for casting and for "new faces", information from drama schools and agents also for specific roles.'

Contact Theatre Company

Oxford Road, Manchester M15 6JA
Tel: 0161 274 3434
Fax: 0161 273 6286
Artistic Director *Benjamin Twist*
Associate Director *Benedict Ayrton (Community and Education)*
Casting *Nicola Sweeting*

Founded 1972. Young people's theatre company currently producing 6 or 7 shows each year, ranging from classics to new work, aimed at audiences aged from 5 to 25. Recent productions have included: *The Birthday Party* (Pinter), *Speed the Plow* (Mamet), *The Trial* (Kafka, adapted by Berkoff), *A Midsummer Night's Dream*. Does not advertise for actors; casting done in-house by Nicola Sweeting. Welcomes casting queries by telephone; send letter and cv. Casting breakdowns will be sent on receipt of an sae. Holds general auditions 'when time allows'; actors should apply for inclusion at any time of the year. Following a Lottery award, Contact's new theatre building opens in the autumn of 1998. Until then, work is being presented in other Manchester venues.

Green Pavement Theatre Co.

– *see* Touring Theatre Companies, page 170

GYPT – Greenwich and Lewisham's Young People's Theatre

Burrage Road, Plumstead,
London SE18 7JZ
Tel: 0181 854 1316
Fax: 0181 317 8595
Contact *Vivien Harris (Artistic Director), Bryan Newton (Admin/Director)*

Founded in 1971, since when GYPT has operated from its base in Plumstead offering professional Theatre-in-Education programmes to schools and colleges, providing evening drama workshops for young people aged 11–25 years and running accredited courses for young unemployed people and for young people with learning difficulties. The company has a deep commitment to creating the widest range of opportunities possible for young people to learn through theatre and drama. Offers Equity contracts. Advertises for actors and holds general auditions. 'Look for our adverts in *The Stage* and submit application accordingly. Actors must have experience of work in Theatre-in-Education and of leading drama workshop sessions. Because we operate with a permanent company there is no point in sending unsolicited letters, photos and cvs. Please watch for our advertisements.'

Half Moon Young People's Theatre

43 Whitehorse Road, Stepney,
London E1 0ND
Tel: 0171 265 8138
Fax: 0171 702 7220
Artistic Director *Chris Elwell*
Contact *Sophie Hunter, Dee Brecker, Daniel Long*

Founded in the seventies, the Half Moon has been resident in Tower Hamlets for over twenty years. Committed to celebrating and developing the cultural diversity of London, the company provides a programme of work for young people, teachers, youth leaders and artists through theatre, training and youth arts, developing potential and creative ambitions regardless of ability. Produces a minimum of 2 shows per year; one primary and one secondary. Offers Equity contracts and advertises for actors through SBS. Occasionally uses casting directors. Welcomes casting queries; send cv and photograph with covering letter, highlighting work with young people and workshop experience. Does not hold general auditions. 'Half Moon YPT has an integrated casting policy. Some future work will be focused on theatre for the very young (under 6) and work with and for the disabled community.'

Magic Carpet Theatre

18 Church Street, Sutton-on-Hull,
Hull HU7 4TS
Tel: 01482 709939
Fax: 01482 787362
E-mail: jon@magiccarpet.demon.co.uk
Artistic Director *Jon Marshall*
Contact *Steven Collison (Company Manager)*

Founded 1982. Children's touring theatre company which plays in schools, theatres and festivals throughout the UK and abroad. Produces 1 show per year. Productions have included: *The Wizard of Castle Magic* (devised by the company) and *Mr Shell's Seaside Spells* by Anthony Peters. Offers Equity contracts. Does not advertise for actors. Welcomes casting queries – 'ring to see if we are casting'.

Magic Mirror Theatre Company (UK) Ltd

17 Short Road, Leytonstone,
London E11 4RH
Tel: 0181 556 7216
Fax: 0181 556 7216
E-mail:
dormouse@magicmirror.demon.co.uk
Artistic Director *Mandy Holliday*

Founded 1992. Tours musical theatre to primary schools, arts centres, festivals, etc. throughout the year. Original writing, based on classics, strong on singing, comedy and audience participation. Shows are aimed at children aged 5–11. Also holds drama workshops. One new production each year. Previous productions have included: *The Water Babies, The Railway Children*. Does not offer Equity contracts ('But Equity know about us and have supplied cards to about 6 actors.') Advertises for actors and welcomes casting queries – apply any time during the year, although no later than September for the Christmas season. Send cv and photograph. 'Actors must be strong singers and good on harmonies. High-energy performers essential who mustn't mind early mornings, lots of travel and mucking in. Musical instruments a bonus; drivers a bonus. Performers *must* have training or previous experience.'

Merseyside Young People's Theatre Company

13 Hope Street, Liverpool L1 9BH
Tel: 0151 708 0877
Fax: 0151 707 9950
E-mail: k.odonnell@mypt.uk.com
Contact *Karen O'Donnell (Administrator)*

Founded in 1978 by actors and teachers to provide a professional theatre service to the Merseyside region. The company tours throughout the area, nationally and internationally, reaching around 50,000 young people in a year. Age range is between 3 and 19 years old. Between 3 and 5 productions per year. Previous shows have included: *Chasing Shadows* (8–12-year-olds), *Ferdinand* (under 7s), *Flight* (11+) also toured Yorkshire, *In the Frame* (11+). Offers Equity contracts. Advertises for actors. 'MYPT only employs actors from the North-West and those who come into this category are welcome to send cv and photograph. We acknowledge receipt and keep details on file and refer to them each time we audition.'

National Youth Music Theatre

5th Floor, Palace Theatre, Shaftesbury Avenue, London W1V 8AY
Tel: 0171 734 7478
Fax: 0171 734 7515
Contact *Jeremy James Taylor (Artistic Director), Felicity Bunt (General Manager)*

Founded 1976. The National Youth Music Theatre gives young people aged 11–19 throughout the UK the opportunity to participate in all aspects of music theatre. Stages productions, workshops and holds an annual audition programme (open-access) every autumn.

National Youth Theatre of Great Britain

443–445 Holloway Road,
London N7 6LW
Tel: 0171 281 3863
Artistic Director *Edward Wilson*

Founded in 1956 by Michael Croft who was the company's director until his death in 1986. Starting in the East End of London, the NYT proved so successful that soon young people from all over the country were applying to join. It reached the West End in 1959 and, in 1960, was given national status and financial support by the Department of Education and Science, which has grant-aided it ever since.

The NYT's record has been one of continual development and expansion, despite limited resources. It now presents a season of both contemporary and classical plays in London every summer, and has toured abroad many times with the British Council to such places as Moscow Art Theatre and Valencia's Principal Theatre. The NYT also mounts national and regional tours, performing in such venues as the Tramway in Glasgow, Buxton Opera House and Cambridge Arts Theatre. From its earliest days, it has also played a key role in developing youth theatre in the provinces, and has helped to set up many of the regional youth theatres in Great Britain.

The NYT's aims are to give young people practical experience of the theatre, to set them high standards and, in doing so, offer them a valuable form of teamwork. Membership is open to young people aged between 14 and 21. Selection is by interview and audition, but the latter is often of secondary importance. Members are often selected because they have lively personalities or show qualities that seem to be suited to the teamwork essential in the NYT. It is hoped that technical team members will show more evidence of ability, but this is not essential. Applications should be made in October of each year.

Open Hand Theatre Company
– *see* Touring Theatre Companies, page 176

Oxfordshire Touring Theatre Company
– *see* Touring Theatre Companies, page 178

Parasol Theatre for Children
Garden House, 4 Sunnyside,
Wimbledon, London SW19 4SL
Tel: 0181 946 9478
Fax: 0181 946 0228
Artistic Director *Richard Gill*
Contact *Mike McCormack (Associate Director)*

From 1967 to 1988, the company's work was presented under the name of Polka, the children's theatre formed by Richard Gill. Now mostly playing light classics to 'family' audiences with children aged 5 and upwards. Performs in theatres – usually 4 shows each year with 1 or 2 being new productions. Previous shows have included: *The Wonderful Lamp, Peter and the Wolf, Hansel and Gretel, The Snow Queen, New Adventures of Pinocchio, The Magic Spell*. Does not offer Equity contracts ('but we exceed Equity conditions on all points'). Advertises for actors and welcomes casting queries if actors are 'truly interested in classical stage acting and visual theatre (i.e. mime, puppetry, masks, etc.).' Approach in writing with cv and photograph. No telephone calls. Holds general auditions, usually in August; apply for inclusion in July/August. 'We play in medium-size theatres so you must have the desire and ability to produce a suitable "size"; this is very rare in actors straight from college. If you are not visual or physical in your acting, Parasol is not for you. Good mimes, dancers and acrobats often do well with us, but it is fine, classical stage actors we principally use and seek.'

Pied Piper Theatre Company (in association with the Yvonne Arnaud Theatre)

Millbrook, Guildford,
Surrey GU1 3BR
Tel: 01483 505505
Fax: 01483 564071
Artistic Director *Tina Williams*

Founded in 1984. Produces two tours a year for primary schools; plays for juniors on the main stage of the Yvonne Arnaud Theatre and productions in the Mill Studio. New writing and issue-based plays; 'history alive' workshops for 4–18-year-olds. Offers Equity contracts. Advertises for actors and welcomes casting queries. Approach in writing with cv and photograph. 'Actors with singing and instrumental ability are most likely to be offered auditions; also local actors.'

Pilot Theatre Company

Glasshoughton Cultural Centre,
Redhill Avenue, Castleford, West
Yorkshire WF10 4QH
Tel: 01977 604852
Fax: 01977 512819
E-mail: pilot.theatre@geo2.poptel.org.uk
Artistic Director *Marcus Romer*
Contact *Veronica Bailey*
(Administrative Director)

Founded 1980. Theatre for young people, touring nationally from September to March each year. 'The work is combative, explosive, dangerous and direct, using highly stylised physical-theatre techniques, continuous soundtrack and high production values.' Target age range is 14+. Performs in a wide range of venues – schools, colleges, youth centres, arts centres and small-scale theatres. Previous productions have included: *Who's Breaking?*, award-winning Phillip

Osment play looking at issues surrounding sexuality and HIV/AIDS, *Taken Without Consent*, a devised piece about car crime, teenage pregnancy and cycles of reoffending, *Out of Their Heads*, a devised piece looking at issues of drug and substance abuse. Offers Equity contracts. Advertises for actors and uses casting directors. Welcomes casting queries; send cv and photograph with covering letter. 'Pilot is always interested in hearing from actors, particularly those with experience of small-scale touring theatre for young people and workshops.'

Playtime Theatre Company

18 Bennells Avenue, Whitstable,
Kent CT5 2HP
Tel: 01227 266272
Fax: 01227 266272
Artistic Director *Nickolas Champion*
Contact *Sara Kettlewell*
(Administrator)

Founded 1983. A small touring theatre company for children aged 5–17 years, playing in schools and small theatres in the south-east of England, Yorkshire, Hungary, the Czech Republic, Germany and Portugal. Produces 3 shows annually – new works covering everything from fairy tales to historical dramas to social problems. Does not offer Equity contracts. Advertises for actors and welcomes casting queries – send cv and photograph with covering letter. Holds general auditions, usually around August/September. 'It is useful when applying for work for us to know what else you can do besides act as most of our actors also need to know how to drive, ASM and possibly work lights and sound on tour. Musical ability and good mime technique are also very useful.'

Polka Theatre for Children

240 The Broadway, Wimbledon,
London SW19 1SB
Tel: 0181 542 4258
Fax: 0181 542 7723
E-mail: polkatheatre@dial.pipex.com
Contact *Vicky Ireland (Artistic Director), Stephen Midlane*

Founded in 1967, Polka was a touring company before making its home in Wimbledon in 1978. The only purpose-built theatre for children in Britain, it has a small studio seating 80 for shows for under-5s, and a main auditorium which seats 300 and produces plays for children aged 6 and over. Polka produces 5 shows and plays host to 2 visiting productions per year in the main house, while in the studio 2 under-5s' shows are produced in-house annually plus regular visiting companies each Saturday. Recent productions have included: *Dreams of Anne Frank* by Bernard Kops, *Down Among the Minibeasts* by Bryony Lavery and *The Secret Garden*, adapted by Neil Duffield from the book by Frances Hodgson Burnett. Offers Equity contracts. Advertises in SBS and occasionally uses own casting director. Welcomes casting queries – send cv and photograph with covering letter. 'We save letters over a year then invite people to come over two days for general auditions. Include in your letter details of training and special skills. Make sure with your agent that they are happy for you to work in children's theatre. A lot of agents are very narrow-minded and prejudiced unfortunately and block actors from working in this field. Please explain, it is a tremendous learning ground, it is well paid in our theatre and we demand excellence. We only take the best, therefore a Polka credit is one to be proud of. You need energy, professionalism and a sense of humour.'

Pop-up Theatre Ltd

404 St John Street,
London EC1V 4NJ
Tel: 0171 837 7588
Fax: 0171 837 7599
Artistic Director *Michael Dalton*
Contact *Jackie Eley (Administrative Director), Jane Wolfson (Producer)*

Founded 1982. Produces new plays which explore important issues in children's lives. To date, the work has been aimed at under-12s. Tours include schools and theatres although the company sometimes produces plays for larger venues or studio spaces. Stages 2 3-month national tours per year. Recent productions have included: *Iron Dreams* by Tim Newton (for 7–11-year-olds), *What About Me?* – toured to the Young Vic Studio, Birmingham Rep Studio, Derby Playhouse Studio (for under 5s). Offers Equity contracts. Does not advertise – 'usually go to agents for suggestions'. Welcomes casting queries; send cv and photograph.

Quem Quaeritis Theatre Company

c/o 11 Adelphi Court, Thames Park Gardens, Garter Way, Surrey Quays, London SE16 1XB
Tel: 0171 231 6083
Joint Artistic Directors *Samantha Giblin, Alison Gill*

Founded in 1997. Formerly known as 'Hellraisers Stage Fight Company, Quem Quaeritis (Latin for 'Whom seek ye' and the title of the first Christian play) merged with Samantha Giblin Productions to provide children's and 'swashbuckling' theatre. Produces one or two shows per year for audiences of 5+. Offers Equity contracts. Sometimes advertises for actors and welcomes casting queries, particularly from those with fight qualifications. Approach in writing in the first instance. 'If actors contact the company details will be kept on file. For the stage fight side of our work, actors must have SBFD or BADC qualifications. For our education work, actors must be fully committed to education through theatre.' Also holds children's Drama Clubs; details available on request.

Quicksilver National Touring Theatre

4 Enfield Road, London N1 5AZ
Tel: 0171 241 2942
Fax: 0171 254 3119
E-mail: qsilver@easynet.co.uk
Joint Artistic Directors *Guy Holland, Carey English*
General Manager *Paula van Hagen*

Founded in 1977 to promote new writing. Quicksilver is funded on a franchise basis by the Arts Council of England and the London Arts Board. Plays are aimed at children as well as adults and tour to theatres, arts centres nationwide and also to schools in London. Produces between 2 and 4 plays per year. Previous productions have included: *Baby Love* by Carey English (for 7-year-olds and under), *One Hundred Million Footsteps* by Diane Samuels (for 7 and over). Offers Equity contracts. Advertises for actors and welcomes *written* casting queries only. 'We seek multi-talented actors, i.e. they must be able to sing and play an instrument(s) to a high standard. Movement skills are essential too.'

Royal Court Young People's Theatre

309 Portobello Road,
London W10 5TD
Tel: 0181 960 4641
Artistic Director *Carl Miller*

Youth, Community and Education Department of the Royal Court Theatre. Professional actors are occasionally required; all casting is handled by the Royal Court (*see entry under* Producing Theatres and Independent Managements, page 152).

6.15 Theatre Company

72 Tottenham Street,
London W1P 9PG
Tel: 0171 580 6784
Fax: 0171 580 6705
Contact *James Tillitt (Artistic Director), Amanda Govey*

Founded 1984. Producers of TIE projects and theatre for young people on health and environmental issues. National small-scale touring to schools, conferences and exhibitions. Three 10-week tours per year on average. Previous productions have included: *Bottle Busters, Wise Up, The Energized Guys* and *Operation KBT*. Offers Equity contracts. Advertises for actors in SBS. Welcomes casting queries; send photograph and cv with covering letter. Holds general auditions – actors can apply for inclusion at any time during the year.

Snap People's Theatre Trust

Causeway Business Centre, Bishop's Stortford, Hertfordshire CM23 2UB
Tel: 01279 504095
Fax: 01279 501472
Artistic Director *Andy Graham*
Contact *Mike Wood (Administrative Director), Mark Storer (Assistant Director, Educational Drama)*

Founded 1979. Snap is a young people's theatre company carrying out

TIE work in schools and on national tours for adults and children. Produces 8 shows per year. Previous productions have included: *Pride and Prejudice, Five Children and It, The Owl Who was Afraid of the Dark, Tom Jones.* Does not offer Equity contracts. Advertises for actors and welcomes written casting queries.

TAG Theatre Company

18 Albion Street, Glasgow G1 1LH
Tel: 0141 552 4949
Fax: 0141 552 0666
E-mail: tt003@post.almac.co.uk
Artistic Director *James Brining*
Contact *Jon Morgan (General Manager), Wendy Rouse (Education Officer)*

Founded in 1967 as a touring theatre company, TAG enjoys a close relationship with the Citizens' Theatre. TAG's target audience is young people aged between 7 and 25 although most of their work appeals to people of all ages. Tours primary and secondary schools, arts centres, large theatres and community venues with a mixture of new plays, classics and adaptations. Produces 3 shows per year. Previous productions have included: *Peter Pan* – Scottish tour (cast of 9), *Running on Empty* – dance piece about asthma (schools tour for 12–14-year-olds). Offers Equity contracts. Advertises for actors and welcomes casting queries; send cv and photograph with covering letter. 'Apart from initial contact with letter, cv and photograph, it is useful to let us know if an actor is appearing anywhere in Scotland.'

Theatre Centre Ltd

Unit 7–8 Toynbee Workshops, 3 Gunthorpe Street, London E1 7RQ
Tel: 0171 377 0379
Fax: 0171 377 1376
Artistic Director *Rosamunde Hutt*
Contact *Jackie Alexis*

Founded in 1953, Theatre Centre is a national touring young people's theatre company producing age-specific shows for schools, studio theatres and small-scale venues. Four or 5 tours per year. Productions have included: *Joshua's Egg* (by Jacqui Shapiro; for 5–7-year-olds), *Wise Guys* (Philip Osment; co-production with Red Ladder Theatre Company for 15+). Offers Equity contracts. Advertises for actors in *The Stage*. 'Theatre Centre welcomes and prefers written applications directly from actors.' Holds general auditions once a year; check *The Stage* advertisement for dates.

Ticklish Allsorts

31 Highfield Road, Salisbury, Wiltshire SP2 7LZ
Tel: 01722 335654
Fax: 01722 335654
Artistic Director *Gary A. Nunn*

Founded 1981. A husband and wife team of children's and family entertainers, staging performances, environmental projects and workshops. The main elements of their shows are clowning, music, song and dance, puppetry, live action and 'tomfoolery'. Plays to all ages, but mostly 4–11-year-olds in all kinds of venues, indoors and out, at arts and community festivals, schools, etc. Occasionally advertises for actors during the busy summer season or for Christmas touring. 'Actors would have to be pretty good all-rounders with some musical ability and enjoy working with children.' Send cv, followed by phone call or fax.

Travelling Light Theatre Company
– see Theatre-In-Education (TIE) Companies, page 231

Unicorn Theatre for Children
6–7 Great Newport Street, London WC2H 7HB
Tel: 0171 379 3280
Fax: 0171 836 5366
Artistic Director Tony Graham
Contact Chris Moxon (Administrative Director)

Since it was founded in 1947, the Unicorn Theatre has presented high-quality professional theatre for children up to 12 years old, both in school parties and family groups. Presents new plays, adaptations and children's classics. From September to May each year, the company produces 6 plays and hosts visiting companies with similar aims. Multi-racial casting and ensemble work characterise the nature of the programme. Has a full range of drama workshops, both outreach and in-house, to complement the programme of work. Recent productions have included: The Mysteries, Alfie (also toured), Pinocchio, Happy Families and Twelfth Night (both in repertoire). Offers Equity contracts. Occasionally advertises for actors. Welcomes written casting queries – send cv, photograph and details of current performance. 'A letter will be read and filed; an sae will be replied to.' Occasionally holds general auditions; apply for inclusion from March to June, 'i.e. at the end of our season when considering next year's programme'.

Whirligig Theatre
14 Belvedere Drive, Wimbledon, London SW19 7BY
Tel: 0181 947 1732
Fax: 0181 879 7648
Artistic Directors David Wood, John Gould
Contact Barry Sheppard (Administrator)

Founded 1979. Whirligig tours large-scale productions for children to major theatres in Great Britain, playing full weeks, mainly to parties of primary-school children, with family performances at weekends. Tours can be from 10 to 30 weeks in length. The aim is to provide theatre for children at the lowest possible seat price to enable as many children as possible to attend. Most Whirligig productions are aimed at primary-school age. For many years, Sadler's Wells Theatre in London was a regular venue. Arts Council Touring has supported many of the tours. Produces 1 show per year, usually with a cast of between 8 and 10 actors. Productions have included: The Gingerbread Man, Save the Human, The Selfish Shellfish, The See-Saw Tree, The Ideal Gnome Expedition, The Papertown Paperchase, The Owl and the Pussycat Went to See . . ., Nutcracker Sweet, The Plotters of Cabbage Patch Corner. Offers Equity contracts. Advertises for actors in SBS. Welcomes casting queries but 'we cannot afford to reply unless a stamped addressed envelope is enclosed. Send cv and photograph; telephone calls are not welcome.'

Sometimes holds general auditions; since productions often open in the autumn, auditions tend to be in the summer.

'Whirligig looks for actors who will be committed to working for children. For the right actors, the work is extremely rewarding. But if the thought of facing 900 children at 10.30 a.m. is terrifying, don't apply! We look for actors who will give big acting performances. Subtlety is also necessary, but a willingness to create characters with broad, bold strokes is essential. Physical skills, movement, mime, puppetry and singing are a huge advantage. Actors who think they are rather short should not be embarrassed by this or tempted to lie about their height. Whirligig likes to find people of contrasting size – and shape! Don't come to Whirligig if you think that children's theatre is just a jolly romp. It really can be much more serious than that. We aim to involve children emotionally and trigger their imaginations. This needs performances of great truth and sincerity. But we have a lot of fun too, and the plays are highly entertaining.'

Y Touring Theatre Company

10 Lennox Road, Finsbury Park,
London N4 3NW
Tel: 0171 272 5755
Fax: 0171 272 8413
Artistic Director *Nigel Townsend*
Contact *David Jackson*
(Administrator), Lizi Han (Education Director)

Founded 1989. Commissions, develops and produces new plays by leading contemporary writers for audiences aged under 30. Y Touring doesn't see itself as a Theatre-In-Education company but believes that theatre is intrinsically valuable and educational. Produces 3 or 4 national tours per year, usually of 10 weeks' duration. Previous productions have included: *Cracked*, a new play about mental illness by Nicola Baldwin for schools and studios, *Connected*, a new play about adolescent relationships by Judith Johnson for schools, *The Gift*, a play about human genetics by Nicola Baldwin for schools and studios, *The Inner Circle*, a play about HIV/AIDS by Patricia Laughrey. Offers Equity/ITC contracts. Advertises for actors in PCR and SBS and, when appropriate, *The Stage*. Welcomes casting queries – 'by post, including their cv and photo with a letter saying why they are interested in working for Y Touring'.

'Throughout the year, Y Touring produces up to 4 national tours in schools and studios. We also give showcase performances for invited audiences at our London base. If you are interested in working for the company or finding out more about us, ring the office and ask to be put on our mailing list for showcase performances, also ask about performances local to you.'

Young Pleasance
– see **Pleasance London** *under* Fringe and Alternative Theatre, page 205

Theatre-In-Education (TIE) Companies

Action Transport Theatre Company Ltd

Whitby Hall, Stanney Lane, Ellesmere Port, South Wirral L65 9AE
Tel: 0151 357 2120
Fax: 0151 356 4057
Contact *Karen Simpson (Artistic Director), Margaret Housley*

Founded 1986. TIE company which tours projects for audiences ranging from 3- to 21-year-olds on a wide range of issues of social and educational importance to young people. Produces 5 shows per year. Productions have included: *One Small Step* (infants), *Glory* (junior), *Sorted* (14+) and *Sun Princess* (family Christmas show toured to civic venues). Offers Equity contracts. Advertises for actors; welcomes casting queries. Send cv and letter to the artistic director.

Arc Theatre Ensemble

Eastbury Manor House, Eastbury Square, Barking Essex IG11 5SN
Tel: 0181 594 1095
Fax: 0181 594 1052
Artistic Director *Carole Pluckrose*

Founded 1995. Presents drama which deals with difficult issues such as racism, drug abuse, relationships and individual responsibility. Arc aims to inspire young people to look beyond their own lives and develop their dreams and aspirations. Tours 3–6 shows per year. Productions have included: *Kicking Out,* a piece about football and racism for children aged 14+, *The Emperor's Birthday Suit* (5–11 years). Offers Equity contracts. Advertises for actors and welcomes casting queries. Send cv and covering letter.

Cambridge Syllabus Players

– *see* **Off The Shelf Theatre**, page 227

Caught in the Act

The Brix, Brixton Hill, London SW2 1JF
Tel: 0171 733 2950
Fax: 0171 733 2950
E-mail: caughtintheact@msn.com
Artistic Director *Christopher Higgins*
Contact *Jenny Dee, Mark Jennett, Bryan Savery*

Founded in 1989, Caught in the Act (CITA) produces educational theatre for young people, 'in the belief that it is the most effective and inspiring medium with which to communicate awareness about health issues. The company's work aims to reflect the cultural and ethnic diversity of its audiences. It considers the needs of teachers alongside those of pupils, the concerns of purchasers as well as parents and governors. Above all, it provokes thought and laughter, speaking to young people in ways they respond to and respect.' Produces 3 sexual-health shows, 3 drug-awareness shows, 1 special needs plus workshops for all 7 productions. Recent productions included: *A Word in Your Ear* (a drug-awareness performance and a project on bullying). Offers Equity contracts. Advertises for actors and welcomes written casting queries. 'Work takes the form of TIE. Experience in this area would be helpful; workshop skills also a bonus.'

Channel Theatre Company TIE
– *see* Touring Theatre Companies, page 162

Crucible Theatre in Education
Crucible Theatre, 55 Norfolk Street, Sheffield S1 1DA
Tel: 0114 276 0621
Fax: 0114 270 1532
Artistic Director *Amanda J. Smith*
Contact *Sue Burley (Education Administrator)*

Founded 1971. The company tours 3 professional productions to schools each year with additional public performances in the Crucible Studio. Each piece is targeted at a specific age group and accompanied by participatory workshops and extensive educational support in the form of teachers' resource packs and teacher inset days. During 1996, the company worked with 7,000 children in Sheffield schools

and performed to over 16,000 through 4 touring productions. Previous shows have included: *Slap* by Lisa Evans, *Flight* by Andrea Earle, *Broken Angel* by Lin Coghlan, *Grandpa's Shed* by Chris Mellor, *A World Turned Upside Down* by Hijinx Theatre Co. Offers Equity contracts. Advertises for actors and welcomes casting queries. Send cv and photograph with covering letter. 'We look to work with skilled professional actors who are positively alive to the challenge of creating dynamic and contemporary theatre for young people.'

English Shakespeare Company International
– *see* Producing Theatres and Independent Managements, page 145

First Bite Theatre-in-Education Company
Pope John Paul RC High, Alderwood Avenue, Speke, Liverpool L24 2UB
Tel: 0151 448 1818
Fax: 0151 448 1818
Artistic Director *Freda O'Byrne*
Contact *Rebecca Kilbey (Administrative Manager)*

Founded in 1988 by Freda O'Byrne and Rebecca Kilbey, both graduates of the Middlesex (Poly) University BA(Hons) Performing Arts degree course. The company works in the field of personal and social education, creating physical, visual TIE programmes for 8–11-year-olds and 13–15-year-olds. First Bite tours north-west England and central Scotland, where the company is also based. One new play is staged each year plus 1 re-toured. Plays stay in repertoire for 2 years. Productions have included: *Insideout*, which looked at substance abuse and sexual health (for 13–15 years), *One-to-One*, which looked at smoking, alcohol and relationships (8–11 years). Offers Equity contracts. Advertises for actors. Welcomes casting queries, if they are appropriate; 'We are a physical Theatre-in-Education company. Actors not interested in those areas should not apply. We prefer actors to see our work before approaching us re auditions. Actors are welcome to ring the office for performance dates, and can also send details in at any time. Those without an sae will not be replied to. We tend to offer work only to actors based in Liverpool or Edinburgh.' Holds general auditions, usually in July/November. Apply 6 weeks before then.

GYPT – Greenwich and Lewisham's Young People's Theatre
– *see* Children's and Young People's Theatre, page 213

Gwent Theatre
The Drama Centre, Pen-y-Pound, Abergavenny, Monmouthshire NP7 5UD
Tel: 01873 853167
Fax: 01873 853910
e-mail: gwenttie@aol.com
Artistic Director *Gary Meredith*
Contact *Julia Davies (Administrator)*

Founded in 1976 to provide a high-quality Theatre-in-Education service for schools and small-scale community touring. Productions are designed for specific age groups from 6 to 18 years in schools enhancing and supporting areas of study in the National Curriculum. The company also provides a youth theatre for young people (10–20 years) under the direction of professionals. Produces four plays a year. Productions have

included: *The Good Old Days – Victorian Era* (for 9–12-year-olds); *Gwrthryfel* (Welsh language show for 9–12-year-olds); *Land of Dreams* (folk tales for 6–8-year-olds); *Words, Words, Words – The Romantics* (14–18-year-olds). Offers Equity contracts. Advertises for actors and welcomes casting queries. Approach in writing with cv. Occasionally holds general auditions which are advertised.

Harrogate Theatre-in-Education
Harrogate Theatre, Oxford Street, Harrogate, North Yorkshire HG1 1QF
Tel: 01423 502710
Fax: 01423 563205
Artistic Director *Kate Vaughan*
Contact *Tricia Preston (Education and Administration Assistant)*

Founded in 1970, the company is funded by the county council and has established a reputation for innovative work supporting the National Curriculum. Most projects employ a company of 3 or 4 actors with a strong emphasis on participatory work. Although some secondary-level work is involved, most projects are aimed at Key Stages 1 and 2. Usually produces 3–5 projects per year. Offers Equity contracts. Does not advertise for actors. Welcomes casting queries; send cv and photograph with covering letter. 'Only apply if you have a *genuine* interest in and, ideally, some experience of TIE, especially participatory work. We *do* look at and keep on file all applications.'

Humberside Theatre-in-Education Company
– *see* **Making Space Theatre Company**, page 226

Kinetic Theatre Company

1 Bickersteth Road,
London SW17 9SE
Tel: 0181 672 8609
Fax: 0181 672 8609
Artistic Director *Graham Scott*
Contact *Karen Harley*

Founded 1988. Performs in schools and theatres throughout the UK. One new show is produced annually with 4 productions running concurrently, each geared to the National Curriculum for Science. Each show has two levels: infants (5–7) and juniors (8–12). All are musicals, so good singers are essential (but not necessarily instrumental skills). Productions have included: *The Hospital Force* (a 'Carry-On'-style spoof on forces), *The Bunsen Towers Mystery* (a spoof 'whodunnit'), *Lady Cecily's Sound Box* (a Victorian melodrama). Does not offer Equity contracts ('but our contracts are Equity-based'). Advertises for actors in August, November and February in SBS and PCR and, sometimes, *The Stage*. Does not welcome casting queries – 'not until advertisements have appeared'. 'TIE is *not* a pretty option. Actors must be prepared for early starts, heavy lifting and are usually expected to drive vans.'

Learning Through Action

Learning Through Action Centre,
Fair Cross, Stratfield Saye, Reading,
Berkshire RG7 2BT
Tel: 01256 883500
Fax: 01256 883700
E-mail:
100045.3465@compuserve.com
Artistic Director *Annette Cotterill*

Founded 1984. Learning Through Action works in primary-, secondary- and special-school communities. Its aim is to help counter the causes of alienation and antisocial behaviour.

Some two-thirds of the work is on behavioural issues (drugs and alcohol awareness, bullying, peer counselling, better parenting for the next generation of parents). Also presents a range of curriculum-supporting projects, some of which are held in museum venues. The company has a repertoire of over 30 interactive projects which is constantly being reviewed and added to. Does not offer Equity contracts. Does not advertise for actors. 'We advertise for interactive teacher/presenters in, for example, *Guardian Education*.' Does not welcome queries from actors. 'We employ people who can teach through role-play and simulation in conjunction with a range of specialist interactive skills. Our work is totally participatory; we do not present plays in the general sense of the word. That being said, many of our staff have experience and training as actors in addition to other essential communication skills.'

Making Space Theatre Company

Cultural Enterprise Centre, Middleton
Street, Hull HU3 1NB
Tel: 01482 324256
Fax: 01482 326190
Artistic Director *John Hazlett*

Founded in 1983, the company provides Theatre-in-Education and related services to schools in Hull, the East Riding of Yorkshire and North Lincolnshire. Formerly known as the Humberside Theatre-in-Education Company. Audience ages range from 4 to 30. Produces 3 shows per year. Previous productions have included *A Midsummer Night's Dream, Beauty and the Gaze* by Linda Taylor, *Our Bodies* (a devised piece for infants). Offers Equity contracts. Advertises for actors and uses casting directors. Welcomes casting queries; prefers actors who send a letter and who try to see the company's shows. 'Write a full letter and make personal contact.'

M6 Theatre Company
Hamer CP School, Albert Royds
Street, Rochdale,
Lancashire OL16 2SU
Tel: 01706 355898
Fax: 01706 711700
Artistic Director *Dorothy Wood*

Founded 1977. M6 tours mainly in the north-west of England, primarily to schools but also to some arts centres and community venues. Plays to the whole school age range, targeting projects to a 2- or 3-year-school age band. The work explores themes and issues of special interest to young people and the company works closely with teachers and specialist workers to develop its projects. Produces 3 projects per year. Offers Equity contracts. Sometimes advertises for actors. Welcomes casting queries – send photograph, cv and covering letter, with information of any performances in the North-West in which they can be seen. 'Please only apply to touring companies if you feel positive about this area of work. It has many rewards, if you're open to receive them, but absolutely no glamour.'

Quem Quaeritis Theatre Company
– *see* Children's and Young People's Theatre, page 217

Off The Shelf Theatre
12 Guildford Street,
London WC1N 1DT
Tel: 0171 242 1046
Artistic Director *Tim Seward*
Contact *Kim Hart (Design/Business Manager)*

Started in 1981 as Cambridge Syllabus Players. Tours secondary schools with syllabus texts and offers workshops and student participation in productions. Also has a broad-based community audience in central London. Produces 1 or 2 shows annually. Productions include: *Great Expectations, Silas Marner, Hear My Cry, Sing a Song of Shellshock* (original curriculum-related piece about First World War poets). Does not offer Equity contracts but 'we pay a modest wage on tour and observe ITC guidelines'. Advertises for actors and uses casting directors. Welcomes casting queries. 'Material is kept until we next cast. Updates are appreciated once an audition notice has gone out. We look for appropriate experience and a pattern of casting . . . Auditions take the form of a 20-minute interview with prepared pieces and a reading of the part(s) being offered. We always work on a piece together so that the actor can get an idea of how the director works. We answer questions about the company and make financial and other matters as clear as possible Unsuccessful auditionees are always informed. Final choices are made by workshop; explanations for *not* casting are given, if desired. We genuinely strive to operate Equal Opportunities in our casting and are members of ITC.'

Rent-a-Role at the Barbican Theatre

Castle Street, Plymouth,
Devon PL1 2NT
Tel: 01752 267131
Fax: 01752 222209
Artistic Directors Sheila Snellgrove, Mark Laville
Contact Sarah Pym (General Manager)

Founded 1983. Rent-a-Role tours Theatre-in-Education and Theatre-in-Health-Education throughout the South-West region. Presents interactive, issue-based theatre for primary and secondary schools, community and youth groups. Two or 3 projects per year. Productions have included: *What's Your Poison?* – drug/alcohol awareness project which toured to all 33 secondary schools in Cornwall. Offers Equity contracts. Advertises for actors and welcomes casting queries; send cv and covering letter.

Replay Theatre Company

Old Museum Arts Centre, 7 College Square North, Belfast BT1 6AR
Tel: 01232 322773
Fax: 01232 322724
Contact Janice Jarvis (Artistic Director), Ali Fitzgibbon (Administrator)

Founded in 1988, Replay is Northern Ireland's professional Theatre-in-Education company, touring to primary, secondary and special-needs schools. Aims to provide a high-quality theatre experience and also provides study materials relating to themes. Scripts are often commissioned from local writers. Produces 3 shows annually, 1 for each sector: 2 plays (primary and secondary) and 1 tour of workshops (special needs). Productions have included: *Mirad, A Boy from Bosnia* by Ad de Bont (for 14+), *Forging Ahead* by John McClelland (8–11), *Sinking* by Gary Mitchell (11–14). Offers Equity/ITC Small-scale Touring contracts. Occasionally advertises for actors. Welcomes casting queries; send letter of application with cv and photograph. Occasionally holds general auditions; apply for inclusion at any time.

'Touring with Replay demands not only acting skills but also good teamwork and a willingness to participate in various aspects of schools touring – get-ins/get-outs, fit-ups and striking of set, plus an interest in making theatre accessible to young people. Standards of performance, writing and set design are high in Replay's work. We make no concessions to standards because we are not working in theatre venues. Our tours usually include some performances in local arts centres as well as schools, and we always showcase our productions at the Old Museum Arts Centre in Belfast.'

Roundabout Theatre-in-Education

College Street Centre for Performing Arts, College Street,
Nottingham NG1 5AQ
Tel: 0115 947 6202
Fax: 0115 953 9055
Director David Johnston
Contact Kitty Palmer (Administrator)

Founded 1973. The Theatre-in-Education company of Nottingham Playhouse, Roundabout provides a TIE and YPT service to young people aged 4–16 years in Nottinghamshire local-authority maintained schools. Produces 4–6 shows per year, with projects dealing with subjects such as drug education, young people and crime.

Presents a wide range of issue-based and story-based work. Offers Equity contracts. Usually holds one general audition per year but there is no fixed time for these – adverts appear in *The Stage.* 'Casting is done by our artistic directors, who are freelance artists coming in for specific projects. We prefer actors to respond to our advertisements [rather than make general enquiries]. We get a great many casting enquiries, which we can only put on file. Sending unsolicited cvs takes time and effort and costs money. We would advise actors seeking work to check with some of their "target" theatres and directors, whether or not people ever actually get jobs that way. We advertise all our casting requirements and this is the only time we see people at audition.'

Royal Theatre-in-Education

Royal Theatre, 15 Guildhall Road, Northampton NN1 1EA
Tel: 01604 27566
Fax: 01604 602408
Artistic Director Sean Aita
Contact Janet Humphrey (Education Officer), Mary Jennings (Administrative Assistant)

The TIE/community company attached to the repertory theatre in Northampton. Works with schools at all Key Stages and with community audiences of all ages. Established in 1985 on a per-project-basis, the company now has permanent members of staff, with actors and technical support employed on a freelance basis as required. Three TIE and 2 village-hall tours per year. Productions have included: *Bretevski St* by Lin Coghlan (ages 11–13), *Under the Influence* (Electric Theatre Co., 14+), *Caucasian Chalk Circle* (community tour

and 14+ in schools), *The Lost Child* by Milee Kenny (4–6). The company is a member of the TMA and offers Equity contracts. Sometimes advertises for actors and holds general auditions. Details are issued via SBS. Does not welcome casting queries; 'replying takes time and resources'. 'We prefer actors with a genuine interest in work with/for young people and in community settings. Workshop experience preferred but not essential.'

Salamander Theatre Company

333 Chiswick High Road, Chiswick, London W4 4HS
Tel: 0181 994 4969
Fax: 0181 742 3923
Artistic Director Stephen Christopher
Contact Helen Lewis, Candy Coe

Founded 1978. Salamander's aims are 'to raise self-esteem by developing communication skills and encouraging an individual to make his/her own choices'. Presents educational projects which include introductory teachers' session, performance, accompanying children's workshop and cross-curricula teachers' pack. Produces approximately 6 shows per year – issue-based plays on topics such as drug education and anti-bullying, and performances aimed at children aged 4–11 years. Offers Equity contracts, usually of around 14 weeks. Advertises for actors twice a year in SBS, PCR and *The Stage.* Welcomes casting queries. Prefers to receive 'letters describing interest in educational theatre and special skills along with photo and cv. Also invitations to shows actors are in to see them "in action". We have a team of approximately twenty actors who are auditioned individually and in groups for workshop technique.'

Snap People's Theatre Trust

– *see* Children's and Young People's Theatre, page 218

Solo Plus Theatre Company

23 Foley Road, Ward End,
Birmingham B8 2JT
Tel: 0121 786 2488
Artistic Director *Linda Mae*

Founded 1988. Performs a variety of plays for different age ranges and offers drama workshops throughout the year. Venues include playschemes, schools, community centres, theatres, youth clubs and churches. Previous productions have included: *The Selfish Giant, Pied Piper in Nursery Rhyme Land, Rachel Weeping* (on the topic of abortion), *Snakebite* (on alcohol abuse), *The Taming of the Shrew, Patchwork Quilt* (disability). Does not offer Equity contracts. Advertises for actors and welcomes casting queries. Telephone or send cv and photograph with covering letter. Holds general auditions. Particularly interested in hearing from actors based in the Midlands; musical skills and actors who can drive are a plus.

Theatre Company Blah Blah Blah!

East Leeds Family Learning Centre, Brooklands View, Leeds, West Yorkshire LS14 6SA
Tel: 0113 224 3171
Fax: 0113 274 4759
Artistic Director *Anthony Haddon*
Contact *Maureen McGough (Administrator)*

Founded in 1985 to produce educational theatre and drama projects for children and young people in schools and youth centres, the company aims to forge an exciting path into children's and young people's education with original and thought-provoking artistic consequence. Generally, produces 1 play and 1 participatory drama project per year, although there are plans to extend output over the next 2 years. Projects have included: *Thin Skin* by Mike Kenny – a package of work (play, workshop and education pack) dealing with the issue of bullying for 12+, *Stuck* by Mike Kenny, based on the story of original Siamese twins, *Julius Caesar* – collaborative project with Oldham Theatre Workshop with young people working in character as archaeologists. Offers Equity contracts. Advertises for actors in *The Stage* and mailout to actors held on company database. Does not welcome casting queries.

Theatre West Glamorgan/Theatr Gorllewin Morgannwg

– *see* Touring Theatre Companies, page 188

Theatr Iolo Ltd

The Old School Building, Cefn Road, Mynachdy, Cardiff CF4 3HS
Tel: 01222 613782
Fax: 01222 520786
Artistic Director *Kevin Lewis*
Contact *Gillian Dale (Administrative Director)*

Founded 1987. Theatr Iolo presents devised and scripted work, new and extant, targeting age groups 4–18 years, plus some local community performances. Shows have strong themes – storytelling, multicultural, Shakespeare. Produces 3 or 4 shows annually. Previous productions have included: *Days with Frog and Toad* (devised for infants), *Gwrthryfel* (Welsh-language, historical, top-junior/lower-secondary and community show), *The Party* (devised secondary piece, addressing issue of alcohol misuse). Offers Equity contracts. Advertises for actors and welcomes casting queries; send letter and cv. Occasionally holds general auditions. 'We can only offer a small number of fixed short-term contracts per year. Prefer Wales-based actors. Always interested in Welsh-speaking actors.'

Theatr Powys
– *see* Touring Theatre Companies, page 189

Tiebreak Theatre Company Ltd
Heartsease High School, Marryat Road, Norwich, Norfolk NR 7 9DF
Tel: 01603 435209
Fax: 01603 435184
Artistic Director *David Farmer*
Contact *Anne Giles (Administrator)*

Founded 1981. Also known as Tiebreak Touring Theatre, the company aims to provide high-quality theatre for children and young people, performing in schools, youth centres, museums and other non-theatrical venues. Productions are issue-based and supported by teachers' resource material, follow-up workshops and teacher training days. Usually produces 3 plays per year – 1 per school term. Previous productions have included: *Frog and Toad*, adapted by David Farmer for 5–8-year-olds, *Almost Human* by Robert Rigby (animal welfare issues, for 10–14 years), *My*

Friend Willy by Robert Rigby (growing up for boys, 14–18 years). Offers ITC/Equity Small-scale Touring contracts. Advertises for actors and only welcomes queries in response to specific casting-breakdown requirements. 'Casting requirements are included in PCR and also circulated to agents via SBS. We do not have a permanent acting company and actors are employed on short-term contracts (approximately 12–14 weeks) for specific productions. We are particularly interested in actors with experience of working in TIE or touring children's and young people's theatre to small-scale venues and non-theatrical venues. Also, those who feel that CYPT is important in its own right and not merely a stepping stone or fill-in until a TV part comes up!'

Travelling Light Theatre Company
St George Community School, Russell Town Avenue, Bristol BS5 9JH
Tel: 0117 955 0086
Fax: 0117 955 0475
Artistic Director/General Manager *Jude Merrill*
Contact *Avril Page (Administrator)*

Founded 1984. Aims to produce theatre which stimulates children and young people between 4 and 18 years of age. Usually produces 2 shows per year. Productions have included: *Sorted* (TIE piece for 14–18 years), *Tir Na N-Og* (tour of primary/secondary schools and theatres for audiences aged from 7 to 90), *The Melon Boat* (play for 4–7s and families). Offers Equity contracts. Advertises for actors. Does not welcome casting queries as casting requirements are too small (1 or 2 a year, on average).

The West Yorkshire Playhouse Schools Company

The West Yorkshire Playhouse,
Playhouse Square, Quarry Hill, Leeds,
West Yorkshire LS2 7UP
Tel: 0113 244 2141
Fax: 0113 244 8252
Contact *Gail McIntyre (Schools Company Director), Lisa Parrot (Community and Education Assistant)*

The permanent Theatre-in-Education company of the West Yorkshire Playhouse is funded to tour to schools in the Leeds area. Commissions new work and also presents established plays for young people. Produces between 2 and 4 shows per year. Previous productions have included: *How High is Up?* by Brendan Murray (5–7 years), *Moor Masterpieces* by Sol River (16–18 years). Offers Equity contracts. Advertises for actors and uses casting directors. Welcomes casting queries – send letter or cv. Holds general auditions. 'Applicants are welcome any time. They are included on our files and considered when we hold our next set of auditions.'

The Young National Trust Theatre

Sutton House, 2 & 4 Homerton High Street, London E9 6JQ
Tel: 0181 986 0242
Fax: 0181 935 2343
Artistic Director *Matthew Townshend*
Contact *Sally Littlefair (Administrator)*

Founded 1977. The YNTT is the National Trust's professional Theatre-in-Education company, working with over 8,000 schoolchildren aged between 7 and 14 at 9 different National Trust properties each year, on productions linked to the National Curriculum History Key Stages 2 and 3. One play produced annually. Offers Equity contracts. Advertises for actors and welcomes casting queries. Send letter with cv. Holds general auditions which are advertised in January.

English-Language, European Theatre Companies

Austria

Vienna's English Theatre

Josefsgasse 12,
A-1080 Vienna
Tel: 00 43 1 402 8284
Fax: 00 43 1 408 8083
Artistic Director *Julia Schafranek*
English Agent *Vanessa Mallatratt*
(16 The Street, Ash, Canterbury,
Kent CT3 2HJ)

Founded 1963. Well-established English-speaking theatre company which produces an international season each year. Presents 5 English plays (each playing for 6 weeks), 1 Italian play, 1 French and 1 or 2 guest productions of 1–2-week runs. Recent productions have included: *A Midsummer Night's Dream, The Dresser, The Rivals, Travels With My Aunt, Having Our Say.* Offers Equity contracts. Advertises for actors. All casting is dealt with in Britain through Vanessa Mallatratt. Casting queries are not welcome.

Denmark

London Toast Theatre, The English Theatre of Copenhagen

Kochsvej 18, 1812 Fred. C.,
Copenhagen
Tel: 00 45 31 22 8686
Fax: 00 45 31 22 7370
Artistic Director *Vivienne McKee*
Contact *Vivienne McKee, Søren Hall*

Founded in 1982 by Vivienne McKee and Søren Hall. Over the years, the repertoire has included not only modern plays by playwrights such as Wesker, Pinter, Berkoff and Ayckbourn, but also productions of Shakespeare, musical cabarets, stand-up comedy shows and drama workshops. The company consists of its 2 founding directors, a team of Danish technicians and a nucleus of professional British actors and directors, some of whom are now permanently based in Denmark. The theatre is a flexible 300-seat playing space which is part of a larger theatre complex – the Det Ny Teater. The company's voiceover agency, Speaker's Corner, provides English and American voices for dubbing and narration on commercials and films. Stages 2 or 3 plays in-house and also tours 1 or 2 shows per year. Recent productions have included: *Intimate Exchanges, Betrayal, Macbeth, The Scarlet Fingernail* (Christmas comedy show). Offers the Danish equivalent of Equity contracts. Advertises for actors and uses casting directors. Casting is done in May/July so any cvs should be sent early in the year. Welcomes casting queries; by letter, enclosing cv and photograph or by telephone if the actor is visiting Denmark, but *not otherwise*.

France

ACT Company

84 rue Pixérécourt, 75020 Paris
Tel: 00 33 1 40 33 64 02
Fax: 00 33 1 40 33 64 02
E-mail: awilson@pratique.fr
Contact *Andrew Wilson (Artistic Director), Anne Wilson*

Founded in 1981, ACT is an English-speaking theatre company which tours throughout France, performing in small- and middle-scale theatres. Since 1981, the company has produced over 40 plays, developing theatrical approaches which allow English- and non-English-speaking people to appreciate the English language, culture and people. Presents 2 touring projects, 1 pantomime and a variety of short-term projects per year. Previous productions have included: *The Canterville Ghost* by Oscar Wilde, *Wuthering Heights* by Emily Brontë, *Kes* by Barry Hines, *Animal Farm* by George Orwell. The company is recognised by Equity as being professional. Advertises for actors and uses casting directors.

Welcomes casting queries; send cv and photograph with covering letter detailing motivation and personal experience. Previous contact with France and the French language a great advantage, and an openness to physical theatre is important.

'Actors working for ACT need to be young enough to cope with the rigorous touring timetable and mature enough to sustain the responsibility of producing good-quality work in all sorts of settings, with all sorts of audiences. They need to be ready to enjoy the challenge of being away from the English scene for a few months and prepared to live in another country with its different ways of doing things. A command of the French language and friends or relatives living in Paris can suddenly become a very useful asset. The whole team, actors and technicians alike, share in the responsibility of the set-ups and strikes, looking after the costumes and props. Early-morning calls are a regular feature.'

Germany

English Pocket Theatre, Internationales Theater Frankfurt (Main)

Hanauer Landstrasse 7–9, G-60314
Frankfurt am Main
Tel: 00 69 499 0980
Fax: 00 69 499 0980
Artistic Director *Kerstin Hailer*
Contact *Werner Andreas (Head of Departments)*

Founded 1987. Seating capacity: 150. A receiving house for English-language productions. 'Personal, friendly, co-operative atmosphere, but little money!' Generally interested in affordable productions of 'literary' theatre.

English Theater Frankfurt

Kaiserstrasse 52, 60329 Frankfurt
am Main
Artistic Director *Judith Rosenbauer*
Casting Director *Caroline Funnell*
see Casting Directors, page 111

Founded 1981. The company is based
in a 6-year-old, 230-seater theatre in
central Frankfurt, staging 4 plays per
year. Productions have included: *Killer
Joe, Sweet Charity, Separation, Don't
Dress for Dinner.* Offers German Guild
contracts. Does not advertise for actors.
All casting is dealt with in Britain by
casting director Caroline Funnell, who
will take telephone queries during
office hours *only.* No showreels.

The English Theatre of Hamburg

Lerchenfeld 14, 22041 Hamburg
Tel: 00 49 4022 77089
Fax: 00 49 4022 77927
Artistic Directors *Robert Rumpf,
Clifford Dean*

Founded and run since 1976 by Robert
Rumpf and Clifford Dean, the theatre
seats 160 with 8 performances per
week. Produces a wide range of plays,
usually 4 to 6 annually, all performed
in English, with runs of 8 to 12 weeks
per show. Productions have included:
*Private Lives, Table Manners, Mr
Fothergill's Murder, Last of the Red Hot
Lovers.* Does not offer Equity contracts.
Advertises for actors in SBS and PCR.
Uses casting directors, 'but we do the
final casting in London'. No general
casting queries. 'Do not write to
Hamburg. Wait until we advertise.
Responses to adverts should be made
only to the casting director in London,
whose name and address are always
listed when we advertise.'

White Horse Theatre

Böerdenstrasse 17,
59494 Soest-Müllingsen
Tel: 00 49 2921 76488
Fax: 00 49 2921 76581
E-mail: white horse theatre@-online.de
Contact *Peter Griffith (Artistic
Director), Michael Dray*

Founded 1978. Multiple small-scale
touring (at present, 10 companies, each
with 3 actors with a repertoire of 2
plays) on 10-month contracts, performing English-language theatre for
audiences of people learning English.
Plays are graded into 3 levels –
abridged Shakespeare and modern
classics (Wilde, Pinter, Shaffer, etc.) for
advanced pupils and universities;
plays in simple English dealing with
social topics for teenage audiences;
movement-based interactive comedies
in extremely simple English for beginners. Tours mainly to schools in
Germany (where the company has
been based since 1985), with annual
visits by some groups to Scandinavia
and (since 1996) Japan. The company
was originally based in Somerset and
was first invited to Germany in 1980.
Now plays to over 300,000 people per
year which means that White Horse
Theatre is probably Europe's largest
educational   touring   company.
Contracts are accepted by the GDBA
(Equity's sister organisation in
Germany). Advertises for actors,
usually in *The Stage*, PCR and
sometimes in Castcall, ACID and SBS.
Normally holds auditions in June.
Welcomes casting queries; 'we receive
enquiries and cvs from actors most
weeks and these are kept until our next
casting. Send cv with photograph and
sae (British stamps) to reach us by mid-
May at the latest each year.
   'All actors will be taking part in two
plays, so acting talent and versatility

are essential. All applicants should have a full clean driving licence. One member of each company should speak a few words of German. The most important quality is the desire to do the job! Those who are cast will find themselves in a foreign country for some nine months; will be relatively isolated in a very small group with whom they will live and work and socialise; will have to get up very early most mornings; will have to drive long distances every day; will have to load and unload vans and participate in all aspects of touring. We are therefore looking for people who are physically and emotionally healthy and robust, who don't mind hard work, and who are prepared to enjoy (not just endure) the experience of living and working in Germany.'

Hungary

Merlin International Theatre

1052 Budapest, Gerloczy Utca 4
Tel: 00 36 4 117 9338/118 9844
Fax: 00 36 4 117 9338/118 9844
E-mail:
merlin.theatre@budapest.blackbox.at
Contact László Magács (Director of the English Section)

Founded 1991. 'The Merlin International Theatre is Budapest's premier English-language theatre venue. The theatre has earned its reputation by its commitment to high-quality performances during the past five years.' Audiences range from international expatriates to English-speaking business people, as well as tourists and Hungarian-language student groups. Produces 7 in-house shows per year and the theatre plays host to 20 to 30 visiting touring productions. Previous productions have included: *One Minute Stories* by István Orkény, *Anthem* by Gyorgy Schwafda, *Bunbury* by Oscar Wilde, *Blithe Spirit* by Noël Coward, *Those Good Old Days* – cabaret and physical-theatre performances. Offers Equity contracts. Sometimes advertises for actors and uses casting directors. Welcomes casting queries; send cv and photograph.

Sweden

The English Theatre Company Ltd AB

Nybrogatan 35, 114 39 Stockholm
Tel: 00 46 8 662 4133
Fax: 00 46 8 660 1159
Contact Christer Berg (Artistic Director), Yvonne Åsebol

Founded in 1981, the company, which is a member of the British and Swedish TMA, aims to present good, representative English theatre in Sweden, for Swedes, using native British actors only. Presents 2 seasons per year. Previous productions have included: *A Christmas Carol* by Charles Dickens, *Educating Rita* by Willy Russell, *Good Morning Bill* by P. G. Wodehouse. Offers Equity contracts. Advertises for actors in SBS. Welcomes written casting queries.

Non-Producing Theatres

Non-producing theatres do not mount in-house productions. They are available for rent to production companies. The telephone and fax numbers noted below are for the administrative offices, not the box office.

London

Adelphi Theatre
411 Strand, London WC2E 7NA
Tel: 0171 836 1166
Fax: 0171 379 5709

Seating capacity: 1,476. Built in 1814, renovated in the 1850s and again in 1900 and 1929 with an art deco interior. Refurbished in 1993. One of the leading musical houses, staging hits such as *Me and My Girl, Sunset Boulevard, Damn Yankees* and *Chicago*. *Funding*: self-financing.

Albery Theatre
St Martin's Lane, London WC2N 4AH
Tel: 0171 867 1125
Fax: 0171 867 1131

Seating capacity: 900. Renowned for the Olivier/Richardson season of the forties. Other successes include *Blood Brothers, Oliver!* (which ran for 5 years from 1960, returning to sweep the board again in 1977), and a number of transfers from the subsidised sector. Part of Mayfair Theatre & Cinemas Ltd. *Funding*: self-financing.

Aldwych Theatre
Aldwych, London WC2B 4DF
Tel: 0171 836 5537
Fax: 0171 379 5776

Seating capacity: 1,200 (variable). The Aldwych was originally built in 1905 as a companion to the Strand Theatre which had opened 7 months earlier as the Waldorf. Between 1925 and 1933 the theatre was renowned for the famous 'Aldwych farces', many by Ben Travers (*Rookery Nook, A Cuckoo in the Nest, Plunder*). At the end of 1960, the theatre became the London base for the Royal Shakespeare Company until their move to the Barbican 21 years later. During the RSC's tenure the Aldwych was also the annual home of the late Sir Peter Daubeny's World Theatre Season from 1965 to 1975. The theatre was bought by James Nederlander, the Broadway producer, in 1982 and is operated on his behalf by Michael Codron Plays Ltd. Recent productions have included: *Who's Afraid of Virginia Woolf?*, *Tom and Clem* and *Amy's View*. *Funding*: self-financing.

Ambassadors Theatre
West Street, London WC2H 9ND
Tel: 0171 565 5050
Fax: 0171 565 5001

Seating capacity: 450. Opened in 1913, the theatre initially made its name with the London debuts of Vivien Leigh and Ivor Novello. But it is chiefly remembered as the home of London's longest-running play, *The Mousetrap*, which was here for 22 years before transferring to the St Martin's Theatre next door. Currently the home of the Royal Court Theatre Upstairs.

Apollo Theatre
Shaftesbury Avenue,
London W1V 7HD
Tel: 0171 734 2987

Seating capacity: 756. A turn-of-the-century theatre, the Apollo specialised in musicals in its early days. However, its most famous production was the comedy, *Boeing Boeing*, which ran for $3^{1}/_{2}$ years from 1962. At the time of going to press Ben Elton's *Popcorn*, directed by Laurence Boswell, was enjoying a long run. Part of Stoll Moss Theatres Ltd. *Funding*: self-financing.

Apollo Victoria Theatre
17 Wilton Road, London SW1V 1LG
Tel: 0171 834 6318
Fax: 0171 630 7716

Seating capacity: 1,574 (current); original seating capacity prior to *Starlight Express*: 2,860. Opened as a cinema in 1930. In 1964 the stage facilities were brought into fuller use and the building closed as a cinema in 1975. Since 1980, the theatre has been part of the Apollo Leisure Group initially presenting international artists and major musicals. For the last 14 years the theatre has housed Andrew Lloyd Webber's *Starlight Express*. *Funding*: self-financing.

BAC (Battersea Arts Centre)
– *see* Fringe and Alternative Theatre, page 197

Bloomsbury Theatre
15 Gordon Street, London WC1H 0AH
Tel: 0171 383 5976
Fax: 0171 383 4080
E-mail: blooms.theatre@uu.ac.uk

Seating capacity: 558. Opened in 1968 and operated by University College, London as a student theatre until 1974 when, to help finances, visiting professional companies were encouraged to present shows. Now operates as a professional receiving house for 42 weeks a year, with the remaining 10 still being used by students of the college, with a diverse programme of opera, dance, drama and music theatre. *Funding*: University College, London grant.

Cambridge Theatre
Earlham Street, London WC2H 9HU
Tel: 0171 240 7664

Seating capacity: approximately 1,000. Reopened in 1987 with the American musical version of *Peter Pan* and in

1988 staged the musical *Budgie* starring Adam Faith and Anita Dobson. Other productions include *Return to the Forbidden Planet* and, more recently, *Grease*, directed by David Gilmore. Part of Stoll Moss Theatres Ltd. *Funding*: self-funding.

Cochrane Theatre

Southampton Row,
London WC1B 4AP
Tel: 0171 430 2500
Fax: 0171 831 5476

Seating capacity: 314. Owned by the London Institute of Higher Education Corporation and used for educational and exhibition purposes, the theatre also hosts touring professional companies.

Comedy Theatre

Panton Street, London SW1Y 4DN
Tel: 0171 973 0018
Fax: 0171 839 3663

Seating capacity: 796. Opened in 1881, designed by Thomas Verity. In the fifties, the theatre was an important centre for strong contemporary drama and became the base for the New Watergate Club which presented American works banned by the Lord Chamberlain. With plays by Arthur Miller and Tennessee Williams on offer – *A View from the Bridge* (world première) and *Cat on a Hot Tin Roof* – the club's membership rocketed to 68,000, making it an important force in weakening the power of the censor. Recent productions have included plays written and directed by Harold Pinter and *Talking Heads* by Alan Bennett. Part of Mayfair Theatre & Cinemas Ltd. *Funding*: self-financing.

Criterion Theatre

2 Jermyn Street, London SW1Y 4XA
Tel: 0171 839 8811
Fax: 0171 925 0596

Seating capacity: 584. Opened in 1874 with the Criterion Restaurant and reopened in 1992 after major refurbishment. One of the most important surviving mid-Victorian theatres. Everything, except the entrance and foyer, is below street level and one of the most distinctive features is the Victorian tilework, added by Charles Wyndham when he took over the theatre in 1884. Recent productions have included: *Taking Sides, My Night with Reg* and the Reduced Shakespeare Co.'s *The Complete Works of William Shakespeare (Abridged)*. Part of Mayfair Theatre & Cinemas Ltd. *Funding*: self-financing.

Dominion Theatre

268–269 Tottenham Court Road,
London W1H 0AQ
Tel: 0171 580 1889
Fax: 0171 580 0246

Seating capacity: 2,082 (+ 100 standing). Originally built in 1928 and converted to a cinema in 1930. Although live shows were presented, the theatre was primarily used as a cinema until 1940 when, during the height of the Blitz, it closed temporarily, reopening in 1941. The first major live performance came in 1957 with the Judy Garland Show. The theatre continued as a mixed venue, presenting films, pop shows and opera seasons until 1991 since when it has been a live venue only for such shows as *Grease, Scrooge* and *Beauty and the Beast*. Partially owned by Apollo Leisure (UK) Ltd. *Funding*: self-financing.

Duchess Theatre

Catherine Street,
London WC2B 5LA
Tel: 0171 839 1134

Seating capacity: 484. One of the smallest West End theatres, the Duchess was built to an original design by the architect Ewen Barr in 1929. The theatre is on two different levels; the circle is narrower than the stalls and is supported by steel girders from the roof, giving it some of the best sight lines of any London theatre. The theatre really became established in 1932 with Frank Vosper's performance as Henry VIII in *The Rose Without a Thorn*. J. B. Priestley began a long association with the theatre in 1933, and a number of his plays were seen here. 1935 saw Emlyn Williams in his own play, *Night Must Fall*, which ran for over a year; T. S. Eliot's *Murder in the Cathedral* followed and prior to the theatre's closure at the outbreak of the war, Emlyn Williams and Sybil Thorndike starred in *The Corn is Green*. Coward's *Blithe Spirit* transferred from the Piccadilly Theatre in 1942 and ran for 1,997 performances. After the war, one of the big hits was Terence Rattigan's *The Deep Blue Sea*, starring Kenneth More and Peggy Ashcroft. Harold Pinter's *The Caretaker* ran for 450 performances in 1960. *Oh! Calcutta* occasioned some raised eyebrows in 1974, even though it had already run for 4 years at the Royalty. The theatre was acquired by Stoll Moss Theatres in 1986. Productions since then have included: *A Month of Sundays*, *No Sex Please – We're British!*, *Run for Your Wife*, *An Evening with Gary Lineker*, *Don't Dress for Dinner*, *Live and Kidding*, the RSC production of *The Herbal Bed* by Peter Whelan and *Scissor Happy*. *Funding*: self-financing.

Duke of York's Theatre

St Martin's Lane, London WC2N 4BG
Tel: 0171 565 5050
Fax: 0171 565 5001

Seating capacity: 600. Currently the home of the Royal Court Theatre Downstairs.

Fortune Theatre

Russell Street, Covent Garden,
London WC2B 5HH
Tel: 0171 836 6260
Fax: 0171 379 7493

Seating capacity: 440. This tiny theatre, opened in 1924, was the first to be built after the First World War and was named after the original of Shakespeare's time. Its intimacy is ideally suited to revue and straight plays and distinguished productions such as *At the Drop of a Hat*, *Beyond the Fringe* and *Joyce Grenfell* originated here. Recent years have produced the musical *Mr Cinders*, John Godber's *Up 'n' Under*, Maureen Lipman in *Re-Joyce* and *The Woman in Black*, now in its ninth year. *Funding*: self-financing.

Garrick Theatre

Charing Cross Road,
London WC2H 0HH
Tel: 0171 836 8271

Seating capacity: 700. Opened in 1889 with Pinero's play *The Profligate*. Among its successes were *Love on the Dole* in 1935, which introduced Wendy Hiller to the West End, Theatre Workshop's *Fings Ain't Wot They Used to Be*, *No Sex Please – We're British!* and more recently, Coward's *The Vortex* and Priestley's *An Inspector Calls*. Part of Stoll Moss Theatres Ltd. *Funding*: self-financing.

Gielgud Theatre
Shaftesbury Avenue,
London WC1V 8AR
Tel: 0171 439 1912

Seating capacity: 897. Formerly known as the Globe Theatre, the theatre was designed in Louis XVI style and built in 1906 as a pair to the Queen's Theatre. It has seen successful productions by Maugham, Coward, Novello, Rattigan, Fry, Bolt and, more recently, Ayckbourn and Frayn. 1997 productions included: *Romance Romance*, *The Bible – The Complete Word of God* with the Reduced Shakespeare Co. and the Peter Hall Company's production of *An Ideal Husband*. Owned by Stoll Moss Theatres Ltd. *Funding*: self-financing.

Hackney Empire
291 Mare Street, London E8 1EJ
Tel: 0181 986 0171
Fax: 0181 985 4781
E-mail: office@hackemp.demon.co.uk

Seating capacity: 1,227. Designed by Frank Matcham, the Empire opened in 1901 as a No. 1 circuit variety theatre. Its large but friendly auditorium and splendid Edwardian decor were the setting for Marie Lloyd's famous song, *The Boy I Love Is Up in the Gallery*. Reopened in 1986 after 25 years as a bingo hall, the theatre was acquired by the Hackney Empire Preservation Trust in 1988 and is now undergoing a complete restoration to its former glory. Presents a full programme of comedy, Black theatre, opera, drama, pantomime, children's shows, dance, music, clowning and new variety. *Funding*: local council and other sources.

Her Majesty's
Haymarket, London SW1Y 6ST
Tel: 0171 930 5337

Seating capacity: 1,210. The history of Her Majesty's is long and illustrious. The original theatre – designed by the architect and playwright, Sir John Vanbrugh – opened in 1705. Two further theatres, both with established reputations for fashionable opera, occupied the site until the present theatre opened in 1897. One of the larger London theatres, this final version was built by the famous actor-manager, Max Beerbohm Tree. In his day, there were spectacular revivals of Shakespeare, the first production of Shaw's *Pygmalion* and the musical *Chu Chin Chow*. Musicals have proved popular fare in recent years: *West Side Story*, *Fiddler on the Roof*, *Ain't Misbehavin'* and currently *Phantom of the Opera*. Owned by Stoll Moss Theatres Ltd. *Funding*: self-financing.

ICA Theatre
Nash House, Carlton Terrace,
The Mall, London SW1Y 5AH
Tel: 0171 930 0493

Seating capacity: 220. The Institute of Contemporary Arts theatre opened in 1973. It has a large acting space that lends itself well to free-ranging experimental theatre. No in-house productions; this is a centre for British and foreign touring companies offering highly visual new works.

London Coliseum
St Martin's Lane, London WC2N 4ES
Tel: 0171 836 0111
Fax: 0171 836 8379

Seating capacity: 2,356. The Coliseum is

London's largest theatre. It was built on a grand scale in 1904 by Oswald Stoll, and had a special escalator to take royal parties to their boxes, lifts to conduct patrons to the upper levels and foyer facilities for typing and sending telegrams. Moreover, the theatre was equipped with the first revolving stage in Britain. In the early days, spectaculars of all kinds were staged here. Musicals took over in the 1930s and the English National Opera moved here from Sadler's Wells in 1968.

London Palladium
Argyll Street, London W1A 3AB
Tel: 0171 437 6678

Seating capacity: 2,317. The Palladium started life in the 1880s as the home of Hengler's Circus, so it is entirely fitting that *Barnum*, the story of the nineteenth-century circus impresario, should have had a run of several years here. After Hengler's death in 1887, a skating rink replaced the circus, until the new music hall opened in 1900. One of its unique features was a box-to-box telephone system that enabled patrons to talk to their friends! The Palladium still provides spectacular entertainment, most recently, *Joseph and the Amazing Technicolor Dreamcoat* and a successful revival of *Oliver!*. Owned by Stoll Moss Theatres Ltd. *Funding*: self-financing.

The Lyceum Theatre
21 Wellington Street,
London WC2E 7DA
Tel: 0171 420 8100
Fax: 0171 240 4155

Seating capacity: 1,899. The original Lyceum was built in 1771. The home of operas and pantomimes for its first half-century, the theatre was rebuilt in 1816 (leading the way in introducing gas lighting) to become the venue for the vastly popular dramatic monologues of Charles Mathews. After a devastating fire, a bigger and better Lyceum emerged from the ashes. Opened in 1834, the theatre played host to a mix of drama and burlesque until 1871 when a melodrama called *The Bells* brought Henry Irving, the great Victorian actor and first actor-knight, to the London stage. The Lyceum remained Irving's theatre until the turn of the century, a period in which it was managed by Bram Stoker, the creator of *Dracula*. But with fashion turning against melodrama the Lyceum was sold in 1904 and turned into a music hall. With mixed fortunes, the theatre reached its lowest point after the Second World War when it became a dance hall before closing down to await demolition. But after remaining derelict for over 10 years, the theatre was bought and lavishly restored by the Apollo Leisure Group. Reopened in 1996 with *Jesus Christ Superstar*. *Funding*: self-financing.

Lyric Theatre
Shaftesbury Avenue,
London W1V 7HA
Tel: 0171 437 3694

Seating capacity: 967. Opened in 1888 with a long-forgotten, but then highly popular, operetta. It was the second theatre in the Victorian grand design for Shaftesbury Avenue. Completely redecorated in 1933, it still retains its thirties style. In 1997, staged *Marlene* with Siân Phillips. Owned by Stoll Moss Theatres Ltd. *Funding*: self-financing.

Mermaid Theatre

Puddle Dock, Blackfriars,
London EC4V 3DB
Tel: 0171 236 1919
Fax: 0171 236 1819

Seating capacity: 610 (main house), 90 (studio). Opened in 1959 and quickly became a centre for exciting and original work. Founded and run by Bernard Miles until the early eighties when he sold it to the present owners. Since 1983 it has been a receiving house for new work, classics and international theatre. Recent productions have included: *Coriolanus* with Steven Berkoff, the Ninagawa Company's *A Midsummer Night's Dream*, *Le Cercle Invisible* with Victoria Chaplin and Jean-Baptiste Thienné. *Funding*: self-financing.

New London Theatre

Drury Lane/Parker Street,
London WC2B 5PW
Tel: 0171 242 9802
Fax: 0171 831 5487

Seating capacity: 900. Opened in 1973. A highly versatile theatre: stage, seats and even walls move at the flick of a switch. *Cats* has been a sensational hit here, having passed the record for London's longest-ever-running musical.

The Old Vic

Waterloo Road, London SE1 8NB
Tel: 0171 928 2651

Seating capacity: 1,000. Opened as the Royal Coburg in 1818 and renamed the Royal Victoria Theatre in 1833. In 1912, Lilian Baylis became theatre manager and founded The Old Vic Shakespeare Company in 1914. The legendary productions starring actors such as Sybil Thorndike, Edith Evans, Peggy Ashcroft, John Gielgud, Laurence Olivier and Ralph Richardson carried on until 1941 (Tyrone Guthrie took over from Lilian Baylis in 1937), when the war forced the theatre to close. It reopened in 1950 and The Old Vic Company played 49 seasons until the advent of the National Theatre in 1963. The Prospect Theatre Company made The Old Vic its London base until 1981 and in 1982 the theatre was bought by Canadian businessman Ed Mirvish. A nine-month, £32-million facelift followed and the theatre reopened in 1983. Jonathan Miller was artistic director of a season of plays from 1988 to 1990, and the Peter Hall Company made its home at The Old Vic in 1997 for an ambitious season of plays including: *Waste, Waiting for Godot, King Lear, Hurlyburly, The Seagull and The Provok'd Wife*. At the time of going to press, The Old Vic had been put up for sale by Ed Mirvish at an asking price of £7.5 million.

Palace Theatre

Shaftesbury Avenue, London W1V 8AY
Tel: 0171 434 0088
Fax: 0171 734 6157

Seating capacity: 1,400. This extraordinary red-brick and terracotta theatre took two years to build and was opened by Richard D'Oyly Carte in January 1891 as the Royal English Opera House. D'Oyly Carte's hopes for English grand opera were short-lived, however, and in 1892 until 1914 it was a variety theatre known as the Palace Theatre of Varieties. The theatre hosted the first Royal Variety Performance in 1912. The greatest successes here have been musicals: *The Sound of Music* played for 6 years and *Jesus Christ Superstar* for 8. *Les Misérables*, the Royal Shakespeare Company production of the musical by Alain Boublil and Claude-Michel Shonberg, is now in its 12th year. The Palace Theatre is part of the Really Useful Group. *Funding*: self-financing.

Peacock Theatre

Portugal Street, off Kingsway,
London WC2A 2HT
Tel: 0171 278 6563

Seating capacity: 1,000. Formerly the Royalty Theatre which opened with *The Visit*, directed by Peter Brook in 1958. Currently home to Sadler's Wells Theatre, which is in the process of being rebuilt.

Phoenix Theatre

110 Charing Cross Road,
London WC2H 0JP
Tel: 0171 465 0211
Fax: 0171 465 0212

Seating capacity: 1,045. Opened in 1930 with Noël Coward's *Private Lives* with Laurence Olivier and Gertrude Lawrence. *The Canterbury Tales*, which opened in 1968, played for over 2,000 performances and Kenneth Branagh's Renaissance Theatre Company subsequently staged a season of classic plays. Other recent productions include: *The Merchant of Venice*, starring Dustin Hoffman, *Into the Woods*, *Richard II* and *Richard III*, starring Derek Jacobi. Since 1992, the theatre has been the home of Willy Russell's musical, *Blood Brothers*. The theatre is owned by Mayfair Theatres & Cinemas Ltd. *Funding*: self-financing.

Piccadilly Theatre

Denman Street, London W1V 8DY
Tel: 0171 867 1128

Seating capacity: 1,232. Built in 1928 and then taken over by Warner Bros. to become a screening venue for the country's first talkies. Live entertainment returned in the thirties when Noël Coward scored a hit with *Blithe Spirit*. Gielgud's *Macbeth* and the musical *Panama Hattie* played to wartime audiences until the theatre was damaged by flying bombs in 1944. Donald Albery took over in 1960 and under his management, links were formed between commercial and subsidised theatre. A number of transfers, mainly from the Royal Shakespeare Company, have been housed here: *Wild Oats*, *Privates on Parade*, *Piaf*, *Once in a Lifetime*, *Educating Rita*. Other productions include: *The Rocky Horror Show*, *Elvis – The Musical* and *Cinderella*. Part of Mayfair Theatres & Cinemas Ltd. *Funding*: self-financing.

Prince Edward Theatre

Old Compton Street,
London W1V 6HS
Tel: 0171 437 2024

Seating capacity: 1,647. The theatre has had a chequered career since it was opened in 1930. Designed as a musical and revue venue, it was converted into a cabaret restaurant in 1936 and renamed the London Casino. In 1954 it housed the spectacular Cinerama, and in 1974, it became a dual-purpose theatre offering both films and shows. In 1977, live entertainment had its revenge when the musical *Evita* moved in. Recently housed *Martin Guerre*. Owned by Delfont Mackintosh Theatres Ltd. *Funding*: self-financing.

Prince of Wales

31 Coventry Street, London W1V 8AS
Tel: 0171 930 1867
Fax: 0171 930 5018

Seating capacity: 1,133. Actor-manager Edward Bruce opened the first theatre on this site in 1884. Gracie Fields laid the foundation stone of the present theatre which was redesigned and rebuilt in 1937. An ideal venue for musicals, recent productions have included: *Aspects of Love, Annie Get Your Gun, Copacabana, Elvis – The Musical* and *Smokey Joe's Café*. Owned by Delfont Mackintosh Theatres Ltd. *Funding*: self-financing.

Queen's Theatre

Shaftesbury Avenue,
London W1V 8BA
Tel: 0171 734 1348

Seating capacity: 979. The Queen's Theatre was originally built in 1907 as the twin to the Globe. After bomb damage, it was almost completely restored in 1958, when Hugh Casson and Bryan Westwood designed the present glass frontage (preserving the Edwardian interior). In recent years, the theatre has been associated with a string of prestigious productions – *Otherwise Engaged, Saturday, Sunday, Monday, Another Country, Beyond Reasonable Doubt* and, more recently, *Masterclass* and *Hurlyburly*. Owned by Stoll Moss Theatres Ltd. *Funding*: self-financing.

Sadler's Wells Theatre

Rosebery Avenue, London EC1R 4TN

Closed for rebuilding. Due to reopen in autumn 1998.

St Martin's Theatre

West Street, London WC2H 9NH
Tel: 0171 497 0578
Fax: 0171 379 8699

Seating capacity: 554. Since 1974, home of Agatha Christie's *The Mousetrap*, which has now been running in London for 46 years. *Funding*: self-financing.

Savoy Theatre

Savoy Court, Strand,
London WC2R 0ET
Tel: 0171 836 8117
Fax: 0171 379 7322

Seating capacity: 1,158. Opened in 1881 by Richard D'Oyly Carte as the home for Gilbert and Sullivan operettas, the Savoy was the first theatre to have electric light. In 1902, it became a general West End venue, and the entrance was switched from the Embankment to its present position in the front courtyard of the Savoy Hotel. Complete rebuilding took place in 1929 when the interior was swept away to be replaced by the present striking art deco design. Following considerable damage caused by fire, the theatre reopened in 1992 with the interior carefully restored. Recently presented Chichester Festival Theatre's production of Pinero's *The Magistrate*. *Funding*: self-financing.

Shaftesbury Theatre

210 Shaftesbury Avenue,
London WC2H 8DP
Tel: 0171 379 3345
Fax: 0171 836 0466

Seating capacity: 1,400 (variable). Opened on Boxing Day, 1911 with a production of *The Three Musketeers*. At that time, the theatre was known as the Princes Theatre, the name it retained until 1963. The musical *Hair* played from September 1968 (the month when censorship was abolished) until July 1973 when it was forced to close as a result of the roof collapsing during the run. A fire in 1985 led to a full refurbishment and the theatre is now listed as a building of special interest. Owned by the Theatre of Comedy Company Ltd since 1984, recent productions have included *Sinderella, Tommy, Return to the Forbidden Planet, Kiss of the Spiderwoman, Carousel, Follies, The Three Lives of Lucie Cabrol* and *M. Butterfly*. One of the venues used by the Royal Opera House while Covent Garden undergoes refurbishment. *Funding*: self-financing.

Strand Theatre
Aldwych, London WC2B 5LD
Tel: 0171 836 4144
Fax: 0171 836 4992

Seating capacity: 923. Opened May 1905, the theatre was designed, like its twin the Aldwych, by W. G. R. Sprague. It has had a history of long-running comedies: *Arsenic and Old Lace* played 1,337 performances to wartime audiences, while *No Sex Please – We're British!* played here for over a decade before moving to the Garrick. More recently, housed the musical *Buddy*. *Funding*: self-financing.

Theatre Royal Drury Lane
Catherine Street, London WC2B 5JF
Tel: 0171 836 3687
Fax: 0171 836 6465

Seating capacity: 2,196. This theatre – now a Grade I listed building – has the longest continuous theatrical tradition in the UK. The first theatre on the site was opened in 1663, and was rebuilt in 1674 (by Sir Christopher Wren) and 1794 (commissioned by Sheridan).

Destroyed by fire in 1809, a fourth theatre was opened in 1812 with financial help from Samuel Whitbread and Lord Byron. The 1880s were famous for Augustus Harris's great spectaculars – sea battles and chariot races were re-enacted with no expense spared. Then followed a move towards romantic musicals which reached its peak in the thirties with a series of Ivor Novello successes. ENSA made the theatre their wartime headquarters which remained open despite severe bomb damage. The post-war period has been devoted almost entirely to musicals; productions have included: *A Chorus Line, Billy, Pirates of Penzance, 42nd Street, Miss Saigon* and *My Fair Lady*. Part of Stoll Moss Theatres Ltd. *Funding*: self-financing.

Theatre Royal Haymarket
18 Suffolk Street, London SW1Y 4HT
Tel: 0171 930 8890
Fax: 0171 321 0139

Seating capacity: 894. Although this theatre dates back to 1720, it was not granted the essential 'Royal' patent until 1766. Even then, it was only allowed to open in the summer months when the two grand houses – Drury Lane and Covent Garden – were closed. The present Grade I listed theatre, with its splendid portico, was designed by John Nash and opened in 1821 with a production of *The Rivals*. It has a long and distinguished history as an upmarket venue, and this tradition is continued today with its starry programme of classics. Recent productions have included: *Lady Windermere's Fan, A Streetcar Named Desire* and Lynn Redgrave in *Shakespeare for my Father*. Owned by Louis I. Michaels Ltd. *Funding*: self-financing.

Vaudeville Theatre
Strand, London WC2R 0NH
Tel: 0171 836 1820
Fax: 0171 836 1820

Seating capacity: 690. This small theatre was built in 1870 and redesigned in 1891. In 1969, the new owner, Sir Peter Saunders, gave it a complete decorative overhaul. The Vaudeville has presented a wide range of shows, its most memorable productions include: *Salad Days*, which ran for over 2,000 performances from 1954, *The Man Most Likely To*, *Move Over Mrs Markham*, *Present Laughter*, *An Evening with Gary Lineker* and David Hare's *Skylight*. Owned by Sir Stephen Waley-Cohen. *Funding*: self-financing.

Victoria Palace
Victoria Street, London SW1E 5EA
Tel: 0171 834 2781
Fax: 0171 931 7163

Seating capacity: 1,564. Designed as a music hall, the Victoria Palace has been associated with variety and musical productions throughout its history. The Crazy Gang installed themselves here in 1949 and remained until 1962, when *The Black and White Minstrel Show* began its 8-year run. *Annie*, *The Sound of Music* and *Buddy* have proved lucrative in recent years. *Funding*: self-financing.

Whitehall Theatre
14 Whitehall, London SW1A 2DY
Tel: 0171 925 2107
Fax: 0171 839 3462

Seating capacity: 646 (variable). The Whitehall was one of a rash of theatres to open in 1930 and is best known as the post-war home of British farce, most notably with Brian Rix as actor-manager. During the seventies the theatre was taken over by impresario Paul Raymond for his sex revues but there was a return to the good old days in 1981 when the political farce, *Anyone for Denis?* swept in. Recent productions have included: *Run for Your Wife*, *Absurd Person Singular*, *A Tribute to the Blues Brothers*, *Travels with My Aunt* and *Trainspotting*. Part of Mayfair Theatres & Cinemas Ltd. *Funding*: self-financing.

Wimbledon Theatre
The Broadway, London SW19 1QG
Tel: 0181 543 4549
Fax: 0181 543 6637

Seating capacity: 1,502. A community theatre on a large scale. Built in 1910 by J. B. Mulholland, an Edwardian entrepreneur who firmly believed that every community should have its own theatre. It was purchased by the local council in 1965 and completely renovated before reopening in 1968. The theatre is now on the circuit for the big touring companies and offers a wide range of entertainment, including an annual pantomime. *Funding*: self-financing.

Wyndham's Theatre
Charing Cross Road, London WC2H 0DA
Tel: 0171 867 1125
Fax: 0171 240 3492

Seating capacity: 757 + 41 standing. One of London's most romantic theatres, Wyndham's was built in 1899 by the actor-manager Charles Wyndham. The auditorium is decorated in cream, gold and blue, and the bust above the proscenium is said to be of Mary Moore, Wyndham's leading lady and later his wife. Recent successes have included *Medea, Three Tall Women, Skylight* and *Art*. Part of Mayfair Theatres & Cinemas Ltd. *Funding*: self-financing.

UK (Excluding London)

Aberdeen
His Majesty's Theatre
Rosemount Viaduct,
Aberdeen AB25 1GL
Tel: 01224 637788
Fax: 01224 632519

Seating capacity: 1,450. Built in 1906 and restored and modernised in the early eighties, His Majesty's Theatre is a premier venue for large touring companies presenting opera, ballet, concerts and drama.

Bath
Theatre Royal Bath
Sawclose, Bath BA1 1ET
Tel: 01225 448815
Fax: 01225 444080

Seating capacity: 987. One of the oldest theatres in the country, it was opened originally just before the Battle of Trafalgar in 1805. A fire in 1862 left only the outside walls standing; a completely new interior was built to the specifications of C. J. Phipps, who went on to become the leading theatre architect of his time. Refurbished in 1982, with its elegant interior and excellent technical and catering facilities, the theatre is one of the finest in the country. Has recently presented productions by the Royal National Theatre and the Royal Shakespeare Companies, also *Dracula, Mrs Warren's Profession* and *Carmen on Ice. Funding*: self-financing.

Belfast
Grand Opera House
Great Victoria Street, Belfast BT2 7HR
Tel: 01232 240411
Fax: 01232 236842

Seating capacity: 1,001. A splendidly ornate Victorian theatre which was used as a cinema from 1960 to 1972. The Arts Council of Northern Ireland bought the building in 1976 and restored the auditorium and modernised the facilities, finally reopening in 1980. Now a No. 1 touring venue for a wide range of shows: drama, musicals, ballet, opera, concerts, variety and pantomime.

Billingham
The Forum Theatre
Town Centre, Billingham,
Cleveland TS23 2LJ
Tel: 01642 551389
Fax: 01642 360656

Seating capacity: 619. Founded in 1968; part of a large, multi-purpose centre. Offers a mixed programme of all types of touring productions, concerts and pantomimes plus some local-based productions and an annual international folklore festival. Recent productions: *Elvis – The Musical, Once a Catholic, Stagestruck* and *Three Steps to Heaven. Funding*: local authority.

Birmingham
Alexandra Theatre
Station Street, Birmingham B5 4DS
Tel: 0121 643 5536
Fax: 0121 632 6841

Seating capacity: 1,347. Built in 1901 by William Coutts for £10,000 and originally known as the Lyceum. Renamed (after Queen Alexandra) in 1902.

Extensively refurbished in the early nineties at a cost of £2.5 million. In 1990, the theatre was chosen as the new home of the D'Oyly Carte Opera Company and their operettas were premièred before national and international tours. The theatre was taken over by E & B Productions in 1994 and then by Apollo Leisure Group in 1995. It is now a major touring venue for musicals such as *Scrooge*, *Great Expectations*, *Copacabana*, *Grease* and, in 1997/8, *Summer Holiday* and *West Side Story*. *Funding*: self-financing.

Birmingham Hippodrome

Hurst Street, Birmingham B5 4TB
Tel: 0121 662 7437
Fax: 0121 622 5518

Seating capacity: 1,887. Restored and renovated in the eighties, this huge theatre is a No. 1 touring venue for opera, ballet and variety shows.

MAC (Midlands Arts Centre)

Cannon Hill Park,
Birmingham B12 9QH
Tel: 0121 440 4221
Fax: 0121 446 4372

Seating capacity: 202 (Theatre 1); 86 (Theatre 2); 470 (Theatre 3 – outdoor). One of Britain's most exciting arts centres. It was one of the first when it opened in 1963 as a centre for young people. Now with a vast programme of performances, exhibitions, film screenings and educational workshops, it attracts over half a million people a year. Productions have included *Susannah*, an opera by Carlisle Floyd, *Arabian Nights* and *Beauty and the Beast*, both adapted by John Ginman, and *Singing Rock* by Jon Trevor and Lorna Laidlaw. *Funding*: Birmingham City Council, West Midland Arts Board,

Arts Council of England and Crafts Council.

Blackpool

Blackpool Grand Theatre

Church Street, Blackpool FY1 1HT
Tel: 01253 28309
Fax: 01253 752036

Seating capacity: 1,192. Originally built in 1894, designed by the great theatre architect Frank Matcham. The theatre was owned by EMI until the mid-seventies and saved from demolition by Friends of the Grand. It reopened in 1981 as a major touring venue, offering a wide range of entertainment, most recently, *A Chorus Line*, *Lettice and Lovage*, the English Shakespeare Company, Lindsay Kemp, DV8, Siobhan Davies. *Funding*: self-financing.

Bournemouth

Pavilion Theatre

Westover Road, Bournemouth, Dorset
Tel: 01202 456400
Fax: 01202 456500

Seating capacity: 1,518. Newly refurbished touring venue for opera, musicals, concerts, ballet, drama, summer seasons and pantomime.

Bradford

Alhambra Theatre

Morley Street, Bradford,
West Yorkshire BD7 1AJ
Tel: 01274 752375
Fax: 01274 752185

Seating capacity: 1,464. Major touring venue for drama, musicals, opera, concerts, ballet and pantomime. Underwent a £6-million refurbishment in 1986. The exterior, with towers and cupolas, was completely restored with the addition of some ultra-modern design features, including a glass-fronted staircase inside the main rotunda which unites all the interior levels. *Funding*: Bradford Metropolitan District Council.

Brighton

Dome Complex

29 New Road, Brighton, East Sussex
BN1 1UG
Tel: 01273 700747
Fax: 01273 707505

Seating capacity: 1,832 (Dome Concert Hall); 1,200 (Corn Exchange); 350 (Pavilion Theatre). Originally built as the stables for the Royal Pavilion, the Dome complex was last refurbished in 1935. There is currently an application with the National Lottery to invest in a £30-million refit to bring the buildings up to date. Recent productions: Victoria Wood, Van Morrison, City of Birmingham Orchestra, *Turandot*, *Playdays* and *Beauty and the Beast*. *Funding*: local authority.

Gardner Centre Theatre

University of Sussex, Falmer,
Brighton, East Sussex BN1 9RA
Tel: 01273 685447
Fax: 01273 678551

Seating capacity: 482. Set in the campus of the University of Sussex, the theatre hosts tours of concerts, drama, dance and visual arts.

Theatre Royal

New Road, Brighton, East Sussex
BN1 1SD
Tel: 01273 327480
Fax: 01273 777156

Seating capacity: 951. Established in 1774 on a site on Duke Street. In 1807 it was transferred, under the patronage of HRH The Prince Regent, to its present position in New Road. A top touring venue, with many of the productions going on to the West End. Productions: *Marlene*, *Reduced Shakespeare Co.*, *Blues Brothers*, Shared Experience's *The Tempest*, *Forty Years On*, *Prisoner of Cell Block H* and *Tap Dogs*. *Funding*: self-financing.

Bristol

Bristol Hippodrome

St Augustine's Parade,
Bristol BS1 4UZ
Tel: 0117 926 5524
Fax: 0117 925 1661

Seating capacity: 1,097. Opened in December 1912 by impresario Oswald Stoll, the Hippodrome was one of the last theatres to be built to Frank Matcham's designs and was a major variety venue up until 1930. Noël Coward's *Sail Away* was premièred at the Hippodrome in 1962, introducing Elaine Stritch to British audiences. A leading touring venue for ballet and opera companies and acclaimed musicals such as *Singin' in the Rain* with Tommy Steele, *Evita*, *Oliver!* and *Jesus Christ Superstar*. Owned by Apollo Leisure (UK) Ltd. *Funding*: self-financing.

Bury St Edmunds

Theatre Royal

Westgate Street, Bury St Edmunds,
Suffolk IP33 1QR
Tel: 01284 755127
Fax: 01284 706035

Seating capacity: 352. A small period
theatre owned, since 1975, by the
National Trust. Built in 1819, the
theatre was closed from 1925 until 1962
and only the foresight of a specially
formed trust saved it from its fate as a
barrel store for the neighbouring
brewery. Touring venue for concerts,
ballet and opera; also pantomime and
amateur shows.

Buxton

Buxton Opera House

Water Street, Buxton,
Derbyshire SK17 6XN
Tel: 01298 72190
Fax: 01298 27563
E-mail: admin@buxton-opera.co.uk

Seating capacity: 937. Designed by
Frank Matcham in 1903. Refurbished
and reopened for the first Buxton
Festival in July 1979 and now also
holds an annual Gilbert and Sullivan
Festival in August. Receiving house for
classical drama, opera, comedy, ballet,
children's shows and pantomime.
Funding: charity – High Peak Theatre
Trust Ltd and local-authority grant.

Cambridge

Cambridge Arts Theatre

6 St Edward's Passage,
Cambridge CB2 3PJ
Tel: 01223 578933
Fax: 01223 578929
E-mail: theatre@cambarts.co.uk

Seating capacity: 670 (variable). Found-

ed by John Maynard Keynes in 1936.
Closed for rebuilding in 1993 and
reopened December 1996. Traditional
home of the Cambridge Footlights;
launched the careers of, among others,
Peter Hall, Derek Jacobi and Jonathan
Miller. Recent productions: Robert
Lepage's *Elsinore*, English Touring
Theatre's *Henry IV*, *Design for Living*
and *The Seagull*, DV8 and Rambert
Dance Companies, Out of Joint's *The
Positive Hour*, Royal National Theatre's
Skylight and Gesher Theatre of Israel's
The Village. Run by the Cambridge Arts
Trust. *Funding*: Eastern Arts Board,
South Cambridgeshire District Council,
Cambridge City Council, FGA and self-
financing.

Canterbury

Gulbenkian Theatre

University of Kent, Canterbury,
Kent CT2 7NB
Tel: 01227 827861
Fax: 01227 827861

Seating capacity: 343. Built in 1969 with
a thrust stage. Provides the focus for
middle-scale performance arts in Kent.
The programme is a broad mix of
professional drama (Red Shift, ATC,
Compass Theatre Co., Trestle Theatre
Co.), dance (Cwmni Ballet) and music
(Humphrey Lyttelton, The Albion
Band), combined with student,
amateur and community productions.
Funding: University of Kent; South-
East Arts.

The Marlowe Theatre

The Friars, Canterbury, Kent CT1 2AS
Tel: 01227 763262
Fax: 01227 781802

Seating capacity: 993. Touring venue,
mostly one-night stands. Annual

pantomime. *Funding*: Canterbury City Council.

Crawley

The Hawth
Hawth Avenue, Crawley,
East Sussex RH10 6YZ
Tel: 01293 552941
Fax: 01293 533362
E-mail: hawth@enterprise.net

Seating capacity: 855 (main theatre); 146 (studio). Opened in 1988, The Hawth presents a wide range of touring theatre, dance, music and entertainment all year round in both houses. The resident company, Shaker Productions, was founded in 1993 and stages 2 productions annually. Recent production: *The Sleeper* by writer-in-residence, Louise Warren. *Funding*: Crawley Borough Council.

Crewe

Lyceum Theatre
Heath Street, Crewe,
Cheshire CW1 2DA
Tel: 01270 537321
Fax: 01270 537322

Seating capacity: 693. Originally opened in 1887 and operated until it was destroyed by fire in 1910. The existing theatre opened in 1911. The theatre was run as a repertory venue by a trust from 1964 until its collapse in 1982. Refurbished in 1994, it now operates as a presenting venue with a diverse programming policy ranging from opera to ballet, children's shows to drama, variety, amateur shows and an annual pantomime. *Funding*: Crewe and Nantwich Borough Council.

Croydon

Ashcroft Theatre
Park Lane, Croydon, Surrey CR9 1DG
Tel: 0181 681 0821
Fax: 0181 760 0835

Seating capacity: 763. Hosts a mixed programme such as drama, ballet, opera, one-nighters and variety.

Darlington

Darlington Civic Theatre
Parkgate, Darlington,
Co. Durham DL1 1RR
Tel: 01325 468006
Fax: 01325 368278

Seating capacity: 909. Built in 1907 as the New Hippodrome and Palace of Varieties. Renamed the Civic Theatre in 1958. Presents major tours of plays, ballet, opera, musicals, concerts, variety and pantomime. *Funding*: Darlington Civic Council.

Douglas

Gaiety Theatre
Harris Promenade, Douglas, Isle of Man IM1 2HH
Tel: 01624 620046
Fax: 01624 629028

Seating capacity: 869. Built by Frank Matcham in 1900, the theatre has recently undergone a complete restoration with the recreation of original carpets and wallpapers. Touring venue for a wide range of entertainment – *Phantom of the Opera on Ice*, *Me and My Girl*, *Singing in the Rain*, *Hobson's Choice*, Syd Lawrence Orchestra, *Stillgoe and Skellern*. *Funding*: local authority.

Eastbourne

Devonshire Park Theatre

Compton Street, Eastbourne,
East Sussex BN21 4BS
Tel: 01323 415500
Fax: 01323 727369

Seating capacity: 936. One of the 4 theatres run by Eastbourne Borough Council, the Devonshire Park houses major touring plays. Its sister theatres, the Congress, Winter Gardens and Royal Hippodrome, come into their own in the summer when tourism at this seaside resort is at its height.

Royal Hippodrome Theatre

Seaside Road, Eastbourne,
East Sussex BN21 4BP
Tel: 01323 412000

Seating capacity: 643. Originally known as the New Theatre and Opera House, the theatre, designed by C. J. Phipps, first opened its doors in August 1883. Renamed the Royal Hippodrome in 1904. Saved from closure in 1991, the theatre has undergone major refurbishment to restore it to its former Victorian glory. Recent shows: *The Show of Shows, The Return of the Minstrels*. Also owns Babbacombe Theatre, Torquay. *Funding*: self-financing.

Edinburgh

King's Theatre

2 Leven Street, Edinburgh EH3 9LQ
Tel: 0131 229 4840

Seating capacity: 1,340. Built in 1905, the King's Theatre has a splendid auditorium and an imposing lobby with a wide marble staircase leading to the first-floor foyer. No. 1 venue which hosts all types of large-scale productions: ballet, opera, mainstream drama, comedy. *Funding*: City of Edinburgh District Council.

Playhouse Theatre

18–22 Greenside Place,
Edinburgh EH1 3AA
Tel: 0131 557 2692
Fax: 0131 557 6520

Seating capacity: 3,056. Vast touring venue which attracts a wide range of productions: musicals, opera, ballet, pop concerts, cinema screenings. Part of Apollo Leisure (UK) Ltd. *Funding*: self-financing.

Glasgow

King's Theatre

294 Bath Street, Glasgow G2 3AX
Tel: 0141 332 7579
Fax: 0141 331 2745

Seating capacity: 1,449. No. 1 touring theatre venue which offers a full range of entertainment: drama, ballet, music, opera and one-night stands. Splendidly grand and ornate theatre, it was built in 1904 and is now run by Glasgow City Council.

Theatre Royal

Hope Street, Glasgow G2 3QA
Tel: 0141 332 3321
Fax: 0141 332 4477

Seating capacity: 1,547. This beautifully restored ornate Victorian theatre is home to the Scottish Opera for its season from September through to June each year. For the remaining months, the theatre takes in top touring companies. *Funding*: self-financing.

Tramway

25 Albert Drive, Glasgow G41 2PE
Tel: 0141 422 2023
Fax: 0141 422 2021

Seating capacity: 600 (Tramway 1); 1,000 (Tramway 2); 125 (Tramway 4 – studio theatre); (Tramway 3 is an exhibition space). Began life in 1893 as the Coplawhill tramshed. In 1964, it opened as the Museum of Transport but the collection was moved when it became too large for the venue. Demolition was prevented and the Tramway was saved for the staging of Peter Brook's only British performances of the epic *Mahabharata* in 1988. Last December, Peter Brook returned to Tramway with his production of Samuel Beckett's *Oh Les Beaux Jours* (*Happy Days*). Now one of Europe's most prestigious multi-purpose performance and exhibition spaces, Tramway is owned and managed by the city's Department of Performing Arts.

Grays

Thameside Theatre

Orsett Road, Grays, Essex RM17 5DX
Tel: 01375 382555
Fax: 01375 392666

Seating capacity: 303. This intimate theatre opened in 1971 as part of the Thameside Complex which comprises theatre, library and museum. Hosts 13 weeks of amateur shows annually plus a wide variety of touring shows – Chas and Dave, Joe Brown, Alan Price, Snap People's Theatre Trust. *Funding*: Thurrock Council.

Harlow

Harlow Playhouse

Playhouse Square, Harlow,
Essex CM20 1LS
Tel: 01279 446760
Fax: 01279 424391
E-mail: jon.harris@harlow.gov.uk

Seating capacity: 400 (main house); 120 (studio). A municipal theatre built in 1971 and run until 1994 as a pre-/post-West End weekly touring house. Reopened in 1996 as a multi-purpose community arts venue under council control, hosting theatre companies such as Hull Truck and Red Shift, and light entertainers such as Max Bygraves and Paul Daniels. *Funding*: local council.

Hastings

White Rock Theatre

White Rock, Hastings,
East Sussex TN34 1JX
Tel: 01424 781010
Fax: 01424 781170

Seating capacity: 1,165 (seated); 1,470 (seated and standing). Built originally in 1927 as a concert hall but over the years has developed into a No. 1 touring venue. Refurbished in 1985, recent shows have included Birmingham Stage Production's *Woof, Three Steps to Heaven, Me and My Girl, Playdays,* Hank Marvin and comics, Jack Dee and Ben Elton. *Funding*: local council.

Hayes

The Beck Theatre

Grange Road, Hayes,
Middlesex UB3 2UE
Tel: 0181 561 7506
Fax: 0181 569 1072

Seating capacity: 600. Hosts major tours

plus local amateur shows. Owned by Apollo Leisure (UK) Ltd. *Funding*: self-financing.

Hereford
The Courtyard
Edgar Street, Hereford,
Herefordshire HR4 9JR
Tel: 01432 268785
Fax: 01432 274895

Seating capacity: 400 (main house); 140 (studio). New arts centre due to open in 1998 under the artistic directorship of Jonathan Stone. The Courtyard will be the focus for the arts in the City of Hereford, the region and beyond, promoting a wide-ranging programme of performances, films, exhibitions and participant events. *Funding*: National Lottery, Hereford Civic Council and West Midland Arts.

High Wycombe
Wycombe Swan Theatre and Town Hall
St Mary Street, High Wycombe,
Buckinghamshire HP11 2XE
Tel: 01494 514444
Fax: 01494 538080

Seating capacity: 1,076 (theatre); 400 (town hall). The newly built theatre and refurbished town hall were opened in 1992. Owned by Wycombe District Council and leased to Hetherington Seelig Theatres Ltd for 10 years, a mixed programme of tours is presented – plays, musicals, opera, ballet, contemporary dance, children's theatre and concerts. Committed to community theatre through an in-house youth theatre and presentations of local productions. *Funding*: combination of local-authority subsidy and private commercial enterprise.

Hull
Hull New Theatre
Kingston Square, Jarratt Street,
Kingston upon Hull,
East Yorkshire HU1 3HA
Tel: 01482 320244
Fax: 01482 613961

Seating capacity: 1,189. Built in 1830, the building's original purpose was that of an assembly room. Converted to the New Theatre in 1939 and refurbished in 1985, the theatre houses large touring productions, opera, ballet and musicals. *Funding*: Kingston upon Hull City Council.

Ilford
Kenneth More Theatre
Oakfield Road, Ilford, Essex IG1 1BT
Tel: 0181 553 4464
Fax: 0181 553 5476
E-mail: kmtheatre@aol.com

Seating capacity: 365. Opened 1976. A community oriented theatre presenting local amateur companies with the occasional children's show. Annual in-house professional pantomime. 'The theatre has a policy of encouraging young actors early in their careers.' *Funding*: self-financing.

Inverness
Eden Court Theatre
Bishops Road, Inverness IV3 5SA
Tel: 01463 239841
Fax: 01463 713810

Seating capacity: 800. Touring venue for drama, opera, dance, ballet and concerts. Also an annual pantomime. *Funding*: Scottish Arts Council and local authorities.

Ipswich

Sir John Mills Theatre

Gateacre Road, Ipswich,
Suffolk IP1 2LQ
Tel: 01473 218101
Fax: 01473 250954

Seating capacity: up to 120. Converted school which, since 1988, has been run by Eastern Angles Theatre Company (*see* Touring Theatre Companies, page 165) for their use.

Leeds

Leeds Grand Theatre and Opera House

46 New Briggate, Leeds,
West Yorkshire LS1 6NZ
Tel: 0113 245 6014
Fax: 0113 246 5906

Seating capacity: 1,550. Designed by local architect George Corson, this magnificent Victorian theatre, with its richly ornate auditorium, was opened in 1878. In addition to being home to Opera North, it offers a varied programme of opera, one-night stands, touring ballet and drama. *Funding*: local authority.

Leicester

Phoenix Arts Centre

Newarke Street, Leicester LE1 5SS
Tel: 0116 255 5627
Fax: 0116 255 8805

Seating capacity: 270. Reopened in 1988, after extensive refurbishment, as an arts centre run in conjunction with De Montfort University. Visiting companies plus films.

Lincoln

Theatre Royal

Clasketgate, Lincoln LN2 1JJ
Tel: 01522 523303
Fax: 01522 545490

Seating capacity: 482. This tiny Victorian theatre is excellently preserved and hosts touring companies as well as films and amateur productions. *Funding*: Lincoln City Council.

Liverpool

Empire Theatre

Lime Street, Liverpool L1 1JE
Tel: 0151 709 3514
Fax: 0151 709 6757

Seating capacity: 2,348. One of the major touring houses in the North-West, attracting top drama, opera and ballet companies. Part of Apollo Leisure (UK) Ltd. *Funding*: self-financing.

The Neptune Theatre

Hanover Street, Liverpool L1 3DY
Tel: 0151 709 7844
Fax: 0151 225 4455

Seating capacity: 445. Built in 1913 by the Crane Brothers. The theatre only fully began to function as an arts venue in 1938 when it was named the Crane Theatre. It became known as the theatre for amateur drama but today with its successful comedy club, pantomimes and drama, it is recognised as an important and dynamic element in the professional Liverpool arts scene. With its Grade II listing, the theatre is rated as one of the 50 most architecturally significant theatres in the UK. Tours have included the Reduced Shakespeare Co., The

Cholmondeleys, Rory Bremner, *She Knows You Know – The Life of Hylda Baker* and *Gulp Fiction*. *Funding*: Liverpool City Council.

Lowestoft

The Marina Theatre

The Marina, Lowestoft,
Suffolk NR32 1HH
Tel: 01502 523443
Fax: 01502 538179

Seating capacity: 751. Built in 1897 and operated as a live-theatre venue until 1929. Saved from demolition in 1985, the theatre was renovated extensively and reopened in 1988. Hosts a wide-ranging programme of concerts, comedy, drama, opera, ballet and children's shows. *Funding*: local-authority grant.

Malvern

Malvern Festival Theatre

Grange Road, Malvern,
Worcestershire WR14 3HB
Tel: 01684 569256
Fax: 01684 893300

Seating capacity: 880. The Malvern Assembly Rooms opened in 1885 to which a cinema was added in 1923. Major alterations to the Assembly Rooms in 1927 created the Festival Theatre as it is today. The Winter Gardens complex closed in 1997 for a £7-million Lottery-funded refurbishment which will upgrade facilities and transform the building into a more unified centre for theatre and the arts. Companies appearing at the theatre have included the Chichester Festival Theatre, Opera Factory, Shared Experience and the Richard Alston Dance Company. *Funding*: local authority.

Manchester

Labatt's Apollo Manchester

Ardwick Green, Manchester M12 6AP
Tel: 0161 273 6921
Fax: 0161 273 3033

Seating capacity: 2,641. Mostly a venue for rock concerts and pantomime. Part of Apollo Leisure (UK) Ltd. *Funding*: self-financing.

The Opera House

Quay Street, Manchester M3 3HP
Tel: 0161 834 1787
Fax: 0161 834 5934

Seating capacity: 2,000. Although the history of The Opera House dates back to the eighteenth century, the present building was opened in 1912 as the New Theatre and was renamed the New Queens Theatre in 1915. Following the successful opera seasons of Sir Thomas Beecham's company, the theatre changed its name once more to become The Opera House in 1920. The theatre is now a No. 1 touring house for major musicals, dance and ballet companies and opera. Owned by Apollo Leisure (UK) Ltd. *Funding*: self-financing.

The Palace Theatre

Oxford Street, Manchester M1 6FT
Tel: 0161 228 6255
Fax: 0161 237 5746

Seating capacity: 2,000. Opened in May 1891 with *Cleopatra*, a grand ballet from the London Empire. The theatre was extensively refurbished and reopened in 1981 following a fight against closure, led by comedian Ken Dodd, in the late seventies. Hosts major touring shows, including a 13-month run of *Les Misérables*. Owned by Apollo Leisure (UK) Ltd. *Funding*: self-financing.

Newcastle upon Tyne

Theatre Royal

Grey Street, Newcastle upon Tyne
NE1 5BR
Tel: 0191 232 0997
Fax: 0191 261 1906

Seating capacity: 1,294. Refurbished in the late eighties at a cost of £8 million, with the superb Matcham interior faithfully restored. No. 1 touring venue, including an annual Royal Shakespeare Company season.

Norwich

Theatre Royal

Theatre Street, Norwich,
Norfolk NR2 1RL
Tel: 01603 623562
Fax: 01603 762904

Seating capacity: 1,314 (main house); 150 (studio). Touring venue for a wide range of touring companies. Stages an annual in-house pantomime. *Funding*: local authority.

Nottingham

Theatre Royal

Theatre Square,
Nottingham NG1 5ND
Tel: 0115 948 3505
Fax: 0115 947 4218

Seating capacity: 1,186. The Theatre Royal is the work of two distinguished architects: the original design was conceived by C. J. Phipps in 1865 and then part-reconstructed in 1897 by Frank Matcham. Beautifully restored, the theatre is a No. 1 touring venue for leading theatre, ballet and opera companies, also concerts and pantomime. *Funding*: Nottingham City Council.

Oxford

Apollo Theatre

George Street, Oxford OX1 2AG
Tel: 01865 243041
Fax: 01865 791976

Seating capacity: 1,826. Touring venue for a wide range of companies. Part of Apollo Leisure (UK) Ltd. *Funding*: self-financing.

Peterborough

Key Theatre

Embankment Road, Peterborough,
Cambridgeshire PE1 1EF
Tel: 01733 52437
Fax: 01733 67025

Seating capacity: 399. Plays, musicals, jazz, amateur shows – entertainment of all kinds. *Funding*: Peterborough City Council.

Richmond (N. Yorks)

Georgian Theatre Royal

Richmond, North Yorkshire DL10 4DW
Tel: 01748 823710

Seating capacity: 200. This remarkable theatre, built in 1788, reopened in 1963 after being used as a wine store and an auction house. Offers an interesting programme of touring professional drama and concerts as well as hosting amateur dramatic societies. *Funding*: self-financing.

Richmond (Surrey)

Richmond Theatre

The Green, Richmond,
Surrey TW9 1QJ
Tel: 0181 940 0220
Fax: 0181 948 3601

Seating capacity: 840. An attractive

Victorian theatre which attracts many pre-West End productions. *Funding*: self-financing.

St Albans

Maltings Arts Theatre

The Maltings, St Albans,
Hertfordshire AL1 3HL
Tel: 01727 844222

Following a Lottery award, the auditorium has been newly designed. *Seating capacity*: 146. Reopened September 1997. Receiving house for a wide range of professional companies – drama, children's theatre, concerts and dance. Recent tours have included: *Beauty and the Beast* (Image Theatre Company), *Les Misérables* (Red Shift Theatre Company), *The Manylegged Musicians of Bremley Town* (Little Angel Puppet Theatre), *The Rivals* (ReCreation Theatre Company), *Uncle Vanya* (Vivid Theatre Company), *The Life of Edward the Second of England* (The Cherub Company).

Sheffield

Lyceum Theatre

55 Norfolk Street, Sheffield S1 1DA
Tel: 0114 276 0621
Fax: 0114 270 1532

Seating capacity: 1,100. No. 1 touring theatre for ballet, opera, drama, musicals and pantomime.

Southampton

Mayflower Theatre

Commercial Road, Southampton,
Hampshire SO15 1GE
Tel: 01703 711800
Fax: 01703 711801

Seating capacity: 2,289. No. 1 venue for a wide range of companies.

Stevenage

Gordon Craig Theatre

Stevenage Arts and Leisure Centre,
Lytton Way, Stevenage,
Hertfordshire SG1 1LZ
Tel: 01438 317956

Seating capacity: 506. This venue provides a wide programme of light touring drama, music, films, children's shows and an annual panto, aiming to suit all tastes and ages. *Funding*: Stevenage Borough Council.

Stirling

MacRobert Arts Centre

University of Stirling, Scotland
Tel: 01786 467155
Fax: 01786 451369

Seating capacity: 497. Scotland's first purpose-built arts complex was opened in 1971. Attracts a good range of touring drama. The whole spectrum of arts is accommodated – ballet, modern dance, opera, musicals, concerts, visual arts, and the centre is the home of Stirling Film Theatre. Stages an annual in-house pantomime. *Funding*: Scottish Arts Council; University of Stirling; local authorities.

Sunderland

Empire Theatre

High Street West,
Sunderland SR1 3EX
Tel: 0191 510 0545
Fax: 0191 553 7427

Seating capacity: 1,900. Touring venue for opera, ballet (Birmingham Royal Ballet), musicals (*Blood Brothers, Tommy*), comedy (Eddie Izzard, Frank Skinner) and concerts. Also, annual pantomime – *Cinderella* in 1997/8. Owned by Sunderland Empire Theatre Trust.

Swindon

Wyvern Theatre and Arts Centre

Theatre Square, Swindon,
Wiltshire SN1 1QN
Tel: 01793 535534

Seating capacity: 617. Hosts touring drama, dance and opera companies as well as children's theatre, concerts and exhibitions. Part of Apollo Leisure (UK) Ltd.

Taunton

The Brewhouse Theatre and Arts Centre

Coal Orchard, Taunton,
Somerset TA1 4JL
Tel: 01823 274608
Fax: 01823 323116

Seating capacity: 352. This delightful little theatre takes its name from an early Georgian house, once the home of a brewery manager, which is now incorporated into the theatre building. Opened in 1977, it is a popular touring venue for middle-scale companies. Hosts a wide range of productions, including drama, both professional and amateur, opera and dance.

Torquay

Babbacombe Theatre

Babbacome Downs Road, Torquay,
Devon TQ1 3LU
Tel: 01803 328385
Fax: 01803 296710
E-mail: matpro@btinternet.com

Seating capacity: 600. Built in 1938, one summer season was presented before the theatre was taken over by the RAF for lectures. Many well-known names started their careers at this theatre, including Bruce Forsyth who was discovered in 1959. The theatre was taken over by Matpro Ltd in 1986 who have now developed the longest summer season in the country. Recent productions: *The Golden Years, Alive with Laughter* and *The Time of Your Life*. Also owns Royal Hippodrome Theatre, Eastbourne. *Funding*: self-financing.

Wakefield

Theatre Royal and Opera House

Drury Lane, Wakefield,
West Yorkshire WF1 2TE
Tel: 01924 215531
Fax: 01924 215525

Seating capacity: 504. All forms of touring productions – music, dance and drama.

Windsor

Theatre Royal

Thames Street, Windsor,
Berkshire SL4 1PS
Tel: 01753 863444

Seating capacity: 633. No longer producing in-house shows, this splendid Regency theatre is a receiving house for No.1 tours. Owned by Bill Kenwright.

Woking

New Victoria Theatre

The Peacocks, Woking,
Surrey GU21 1GQ
Tel: 01483 770477
Fax: 01483 740477

Seating capacity: 1,308. Situated in the modern shopping complex, the New Victoria Theatre attracts large-scale tours of musicals, drama, opera, ballet and concerts.

Wolverhampton

Grand Theatre

Lichfield Street, Wolverhampton,
West Midlands WV1 1DE
Tel: 01902 28165
Fax: 01902 21447

Seating capacity: 1,200. No. 1 touring venue for drama, opera, musicals, ballet, light entertainment, concerts. Annual pantomime. *Funding*: Wolverhampton Borough Council.

Worthing

Connaught Theatre

Union Place, Worthing,
West Sussex BN11 1LG
Tel: 01903 231799
Fax: 01903 215337

Seating capacity: 514. Formerly a repertory theatre, now a receiving house for a mixed programme of professional and amateur companies.

York

The Grand Opera House

Cumberland Street,
York YO1 1SW
Tel: 01904 655441
Fax: 01904 671858

Seating capacity: 1,032. Touring venue for a wide range of shows: musicals, drama, opera, dance, comedy. Part of Apollo Leisure (UK) Ltd. *Funding*: self-financing.

Television

An ever-increasing percentage of television output, both for the BBC and ITV networks, is produced by independent production companies. Series such as *The Bill* and *Brookside* have their own production offices (at Pearson Television and Mersey Television Company respectively – see Film, Video and Independent Production Companies, pages 300 and 299). A large turnover of actors is required and, in the case of *The Bill*, as well as two more or less permanent casting directors, around four freelancers are employed, some on a frequent basis.

Casting is usually conducted via agents with script breakdowns being made available to them – something the individual actor is unlikely to obtain. However, some television casting departments do keep actors' details on file.

BBC

BBC Television
Television Centre, Wood Lane, London W12 7RJ
Tel: 0181 743 8000
Chief Executive, BBC Broadcast
Will Wyatt
Chief Executive, BBC Production
Ronald Neil
Controller, BBC1 *Peter Salmon*
Controller, BBC2 *Mark Thompson*

Major restructuring at the BBC resulted in two new directorates, BBC Production and BBC Broadcast, being formed in October 1996. For the first time, both network television and radio were brought together as bi-media departments. BBC Production includes all the BBC drama producers (television, radio and the World Service) in England as well as Entertainment, Music, Arts and Factual areas. BBC Broadcast is responsible for Television, Radio, Regional Broadcasting and Education.

Department addresses given if different from above.

BBC DRAMA
Head of Drama *Colin Adams*
Head of Serials *Michael Wearing*
Head of Series *Mal Young*
Head of Films and Single Drama
David Thompson
**Executive Producer, Films and
Single Drama** *Jane Tranter*
**In-house casting directors
Drama:**
Julia Crampsie
Jane Deitch
Jonathan McLeish
Thalia Reynolds
Entertainment/Comedy:
Tracey Gillham

The casting of actors in BBC television programmes is the responsibility of individual producers and directors. In-house casting directors are used – see list above – with occasional freelance casting directors engaged for special projects. Contact specific casting directors for information. General auditions are not held. Fees and contracts are negotiated by the BBC's Artists Contracts Department.

BBC ARTS
Room EM07, East Tower, Television Centre, Wood Lane, London W12 9RJ
Tel: 0181 895 6770/6500
Head of BBC Arts *Kim Evans*
Editor, Arts Features *Keith Alexander*

BBC CHILDREN'S PROGRAMMES
**Head of BBC Children's
Programmes** *Lorraine Heggessey*
Executive Producer, Drama *Richard Langridge*
Producer, Grange Hill *Stephen Andrew*

BBC CONSUMER AND LEISURE
**Head of BBC Consumer and
Leisure** *Anne Morrison*

BBC DOCUMENTARIES AND HISTORY
White City, 201 Wood Lane,
London W12 7TS
Tel: 0181 752 5252
Head of Documentaries *Paul Hamann*

BBC EDUCATION PRODUCTION
Head of BBC Education Production
Marilyn Wheatcroft

BBC ENTERTAINMENT
Head of BBC Entertainment *Paul Jackson*
Head of Comedy *Geoffrey Perkins*
Head of Light Entertainment
Michael Leggo
Head of Comedy Entertainment *Jon Plowman*

BBC EVENTS
Head of BBC Events *Philip Gilbert*

BBC MUSIC
Head of Classical Music *Roger Wright*
Head of Music Entertainment *Trevor Dann*

BBC NEWS AND CURRENT AFFAIRS
**Chief Executive, News and Current
Affairs** *Tony Hall*

Head of Weekly News & Current Affairs *Mark Damazer*
Head of News Programmes *Peter Bell*
Head of News Gathering *Richard Sambrook*

BBC SCIENCE
201 Wood Lane, London W12 7TS
Tel: 0181 752 6178
Head of BBC Science *Glenwyn Benson*

BBC SPORT
Controller, TV Sport *Jonathan Martin*
Head of BBC Sport *Brian Barwick*

BBC TOPICAL FEATURES
Broadcasting House,
London W1A 1AA
Tel: 0171 580 4468
Head of BBC Topical Features *Anne Winder*

BBC REGIONS

BBC Northern Ireland
Broadcasting House, 25–27 Ormeau Avenue, Belfast BT2 8HQ
Tel: 01232 338000
Controller *Patrick Loughrey*
Head of Broadcasting *Anna Carragher*
Head of Production *Paul Evans*
Head of Drama *Robert Cooper*

Very little drama is produced in-house, with the main body of work being supplied by independent production companies. Employs freelance casting directors as and when required and advertises for actors in SBS and PCR. CVs and photographs sent to the department are kept on file for future reference. Recent independent productions for BBC Northern Ireland include the series *Ballykissangel* and *The Ambassador*; the serials *Amongst Women* and *Falling for Dancer*; and a film by Scala Productions, *Divorcing Jack*.

BBC Scotland
Broadcasting House, Queen Margaret Drive, Glasgow G12 8DG
Tel: 0141 338 2517 (Television Drama Dept)
Controller *John McCormick*
Head of Broadcasting *Ken MacQuarrie*
Head of Production *Colin Cameron*
Head of Drama *To be appointed*
Development Executive *Barbara McKissack*
Production Executive *Cristine MacLean*

Headquarters of BBC Scotland with centres in Aberdeen, Dundee, Edinburgh and Inverness. Drama output has included: *Hamish Macbeth, Cardiac Arrest, The Crow Road, The Missing Postman, Truth or Dare* and feature films *Small Faces* and *Mrs Brown*. Welcomes casting queries from actors, either by telephone or letter. Does not hold general auditions.

Aberdeen
Broadcasting House, Beechgrove Terrace, Aberdeen AB9 2ZT
Tel: 01224 625233
Mainly news output.
Dundee
Nethergate Centre, 66 Nethergate, Dundee DD1 4ER
Tel: 01382 202481
News output only.

Edinburgh
Broadcasting House, Queen Street,
Edinburgh EH2 1JF
Tel: 0131 225 3131
Religious, arts and science program-
ming. Bi-media news.

Inverness
7 Culduthel Road, Inverness IV2 4AD
Tel: 01463 720720
News output only.

BBC Wales
Broadcasting House, Llandaff,
Cardiff CF5 2YQ
Tel: 01222 322000
Controller *Geraint Talfan Davies*
**Head of Broadcast (Welsh
Language)** *Gwynn Pritchard*
**Head of Broadcast (English
Language)** *Dai Smith*
Head of Production *John Geraint*
Head of Drama *Pedr James*
Casting Coordinator *Gary Howe*
Series Producer, Pobol y Cwm
Glenda Jones

Headquarters of BBC Wales with
regional television centres in Bangor
and Swansea. All Welsh-language
programmes are transmitted by S4C
and produced in Cardiff or Swansea.
Drama output includes *Pobol y Cwm*
(Welsh-language series). Actors should
send cvs and photographs to: the
casting coordinator, Gary Howe, at
Broadcasting House in Cardiff.

Bangor
Broadcasting House,
Meirion Road,
Bangor,
Gwynedd LL57 2BY
Tel: 01248 370880
News output only.

Swansea
Broadcasting House,
32 Alexandra Road,
Swansea SA1 5DZ
Tel: 01792 654986

BBC Midlands and East
Broadcasting Centre, Pebble Mill
Road, Birmingham B5 7QQ
Tel: 0121 414 8888
Head of Network Production *Rod
Natkiel*
Head of Local Programmes *Laura
Dalgleish*

Home of the Pebble Mill Studio. No in-
house drama. Output is mainly light-
entertainment programmes such as *The
Clothes Show, Telly Addicts, Call My
Bluff, Kilroy* and *Gardener's World.*

BBC East Midlands (Nottingham)
East Midlands Broadcasting Centre,
York House, Mansfield Road,
Nottingham NG1 3JA
Tel: 0115 955 0500
News output only.

BBC East (Norwich)
St Catherine's Close, All Saint's
Green, Norwich, Norfolk NR1 3ND
Tel: 01603 619331
Regional news/magazine
programmes.

BBC North
New Broadcasting House, Oxford
Road, Manchester M60 1SJ
Tel: 0161 200 2020
**Head of Youth and Entertainment
Features** *To be appointed*

Headquarters of BBC North, incorporating the former North-East and
North-West divisions. Leeds and

Newcastle continue to make their own programmes, each having its own head of centre. Output includes *Red Dwarf* (produced by Grant Naylor Productions, associates of Noel Gay Television) and the travel programmes *Rough Guides* and *The Travel Show*.

Leeds

Broadcasting Centre, Woodhouse Lane, Leeds, West Yorkshire LS2 9PX
Tel: 0113 244 1188
Head of Centre *Martin Brooks*

Newcastle upon Tyne

Broadcasting Centre, Barrack Road, Newcastle upon Tyne NE99 2NE
Tel: 0191 232 1313
Head of Centre *Olwyn Hocking*

BBC South/BBC West/BBC South-West/BBC South-East

The four regional television stations, BBC South, BBC West, BBC South-West and BBC South-East produce more than 1,100 hours of television each year, mainly news magazine and current affairs programmes.

BBC South (Southampton)

Broadcasting House, Havelock Road, Southampton, Hampshire SO14 7PU
Tel: 01703 226201

BBC West (Bristol)

Whiteladies Road, Bristol BS9 2LR
Tel: 0117 973 2211
Head of Development (Natural History Unit) *Michael Bright*
Home of the BBC Natural History Unit. 'Actors are mainly sought for voiceovers, both for radio and television, although there are occasional drama-documentary productions. A library of voiceover artists is maintained; audition audio cassettes, to

include straight narrative readings, should be sent to the above.'

BBC South-West (Plymouth)

Broadcasting House, Seymour Road, Mannamead, Plymouth, Devon PL3 5BD
Tel: 01752 229201

BBC South-East (Elstree)

Elstree Centre, Clarendon Road, Borehamwood, Hertfordshire WD6 1JF
Tel: 0181 953 6100

INDEPENDENT TELEVISION

Anglia Television

Anglia House, Norwich, Norfolk NR1 3JG
Tel: 01603 615151
Fax: 01603 631032
Managing Director *Graham Creelman*

All drama productions for Anglia Television are supplied by United Film and Television Productions (*see entry under* Film, Video and Independent Production Companies, page 304).

Border Television plc

Television Centre, Durranhill, Carlisle, Cumbria CA1 3NT
Tel: 01228 25101
Fax: 01228 41384
Chairman and Chief Executive *James Graham OBE*
Head of Programmes *Neil Robinson*

Very little drama output, apart from a one-off regional drama showcase aimed at encouraging new writing talent. No in-house casting directors.

Carlton Television

101 St Martin's Lane,
London WC2N 4AZ
Tel: 0171 240 4000
Fax: 0171 240 4171
Chairman *Nigel Walmsley*
Chief Executive *Clive Jones*
Director of Programmes *Andy Allan*
Casting Director *Sally Fincher (at Carlton Productions)*

Carlton Television includes Carlton Broadcasting, which is responsible for the ITV licence for London and the South-East, plus Central Broadcasting and Westcountry (*see entries*). Programmes are made by Carlton Productions – formerly Central Films – *see entry under* Film, Video and Independent Production Companies, page 290

Central Broadcasting

Central House, Broad Street,
Birmingham B1 2JP
Tel: 0121 643 9898
Fax: 0121 643 4897
Managing Director *Ian Squires*

Part of Carlton Television – responsible for the ITV licence for East, West and South Midlands. Output is chiefly documentary programmes.

Channel 4

124 Horseferry Road, London SW1P 2TX
Tel: 0171 396 4444
Fax: 0171 306 8356
Chief Executive *Michael Jackson*
Director of Programmes *John Willis*

Head of Drama *Gub Neal*
Controller, Arts and Entertainment *Stuart Cosgrove*
Independent Film and Video *Robin Gutch*
Arts *Janey Walker*
Entertainment *Kevin Lygo*
Comedy *Seamus Cassidy*

Started broadcasting in November 1982 – the first new television service to be launched in Britain for 18 years. Channel 4 does not make any of its own programmes; they are commissioned from independent production companies, from the ITV sector, or co-produced with other organisations.

Channel 5

22 Long Acre, London WC2E 9LY
Tel: 0171 550 5555
Fax: 0171 421 7260
Chairman *Greg Dyke*
Chief Executive *David Elstein*
Head of Programmes *Dawn Airey*
Controller of Drama *Corinne Hollingworth*
Controller of Children's Programmes *Nick Wilson*
Controller of Features and Arts *Michael Attwell*

Channel 5 Broadcasting Ltd won the franchise for Britain's third commercial terrestrial television station in 1995. Describing itself as 'intelligent and stylish and a force for change in popular contemporary culture', it came on air in March 1997. During its first months of broadcasting, audiences did not prove as large as expected with many areas of Britain having difficulty receiving the station. Regular programmes include the soap opera (Monday to Friday) *Family*

Affairs, produced by the independent production company, Reg Grundy Productions (Casting Director: Val Farron, tel: 0181 797 2236).

Channel Television

The Television Centre, La Pouquelaye, St Helier, Jersey, Channel Islands JE1 3ZD
Tel: 01534 816816
Fax: 01534 816817
Also at: The Television Centre, St George's Place, St Peter Port, Guernsey
Tel: 01481 723451
Managing Director *John Henwood*
Director of Television *Michael Lucas*
Controller of Production and Development *Philippe Bassett*

After its successful debut on ITV, *Island*, Channel Television's teen drama went to a second series in 1997 and it looks likely that Channel will have other drama commissions in the future. Uses freelance casting directors.

GMTV

The London Television Centre, Upper Ground, London SE1 9TT
Tel: 0171 827 7000
Fax: 0171 827 7001
Managing Director *Christopher Stoddart*
Director of Programmes *Peter McHugh*

Winner of the national breakfast franchise, GMTV took over from TV-AM in January 1993. Output is chiefly current affairs, topical features, showbiz, lifestyle, sport, quizzes and competitions.

Grampian Television Ltd

Queen's Cross, Aberdeen AB15 4XJ
Tel: 01224 846846
Fax: 01224 846800
Director of Programmes/Head of Documentaries and Features
George W. Mitchell, MA
Head of Gaelic *Robert Kenyon*

Output covers regional news, farming and fishing, sport, light entertainment, Gaelic programmes and live coverage of the Scottish political and industrial scene. No drama programmes. Serves the area stretching from Fife to Shetland.

Granada Television

Granada TV Centre, Quay Street, Manchester M60 9EA
Tel: 0161 832 7211
Fax: 0161 953 0283
Granada Film *see entry under* Film, Video and Independent Production Companies, page 295
Director of Programmes *To be appointed*
Director of Production *Max Graesser*
Controller of Drama *Simon Lewis*
Controller of Drama Serials *Carolyn Reynolds*
Controller of Comedy *Andy Harries*
Casting Directors *James Bain and Judi Hayfield (Manchester); Lin Cordoray (casting assistant, Granada Films, London)*

A large drama output of series, films and plays. Programmes include *Prime Suspect, Cracker, Reckless, The Grand* and *Coronation Street* (which is cast by Judi Hayfield). Approach the Manchester office in writing in the first instance; welcomes performance notices.

HTV

Television Centre,
Culverhouse Cross,
Cardiff CF5 6XJ
Tel: 01222 590590
Fax: 01222 597183
Managing Director *Menna Richards*
HTV (Wales)
(address/telephone number as above)
HTV (West)
Television Centre, Bath Road,
Bristol BS5 3HG
Tel: 0117 9722722
Fax: 0117 9722400
Managing Director *Jeremy Payne*
Controller of Children's
Programmes *Dan Maddicott*

HTV produces drama, children's, factual and natural history programmes, including *Wycliffe*, *The Famous Five* and *The Slow Norris*. The Welsh-language drama series for children, *Pamdan Fi Duw? (Why Me God?)* is produced by Brian Roberts for S4C. Welsh-speaking actors can contact him at the Television Centre in Cardiff (address above).

ITN (Independent Television News Ltd)

200 Gray's Inn Road,
London WC1X 8XZ
Tel: 0171 833 3000
Editor-in-Chief *Richard Tait*
Editor, ITN Programmes for ITV
Nigel Dacre

Provider of the main national and international news for ITV, Channel 4 and Channel 5, and radio news for IRN.

LWT (London Weekend Television)

The London Television Centre,
Upper Ground, London SE1 9LT
Tel: 0171 620 1620
Chief Operating Officer *Charles Allen*
Managing Director *Eileen Gallagher*
Director of Programmes *Marcus Plantin*
Controller of Arts *Melvyn Bragg*
Controller of Drama *Jo Wright*
Controller of Entertainment *Nigel Lythgoe*
Casting Directors (Entertainment)
Nikki Finch, Janie Frazer

Produces a significant amount of drama with series such as *The Knock* (produced by Bronson Knight) and *London's Burning*. Recent output has included *Wuthering Heights* and *Tess of the D'Urbervilles*. NB uses freelance casting directors for all drama productions.

Meridian Broadcasting

Television Centre, Southampton,
Hampshire SO14 0PZ
Tel: 01703 222555
Fax: 01703 335050
Managing Director *Mary McAnally*
Controller of Programmes *Richard Simons*
Controller of Drama *Michele Buck*
Controller of Children's
Programmes *Richard Morss*

All drama productions for Meridian Broadcasting are supplied by United Film and Television Productions (*see entry under* Film, Video and Independent Production Companies, page 304).

S4C

Parc Ty Glas, Llanishen,
Cardiff CF4 5DU
Tel: 01222 747444
Fax: 01222 754444
Director of Broadcasting *Dafydd Rhys*
Director of Production *Huw Eirug*

The Welsh 4th Channel is responsible for a schedule of Welsh and English programmes on the Fourth Channel in Wales. Broadcasts about 30 hours per week of Welsh-language programmes and more than 85 hours of English-language output from Channel 4. Ten hours a week of the Welsh programmes are provided by the BBC, the remainder are purchased from HTV and independent producers.

Scottish Television

Cowcaddens, Glasgow G2 3PR
Tel: 0141 300 3000
Fax: 0141 300 3030
London office: 20 Lincoln's Inn Fields, London WC2A 3ED
Tel: 0171 446 7000
Fax: 0171 446 7010
Director of Broadcasting *Blair Jenkins*
Controller of Drama *Robert Love*
Controller of Entertainment *Sandy Ross*

Scottish Television's networked drama continues to draw high viewing figures, particularly the Glasgow detective series *Taggart* starring James Macpherson and Blythe Duff (3-part series and TV movies are screened annually). Another success has been the London-based series *McCallum*, starring John Hannah as a Scottish forensic pathologist working in an East End hospital. The networked soap, *High Road*, which is mainly filmed on location at Loch Lomond, consists of 52 weekly episodes each year. Apart from this regular output, STV also produces occasional one-off dramas and mini-series. No in-house casting directors. Freelance casting directors have been increasingly employed.

Tyne Tees Television

The Television Centre, City Road,
Newcastle upon Tyne NE1 2AL
Tel: 0191 261 0181
Fax: 0191 261 2302
London office: 15 Bloomsbury Square, London WC1A 2LJ
Tel: 0171 405 8474
Fax: 0171 242 2441
Managing Director *Margaret Fry*
Director of Programmes *Peter Mitchell*
Head of Young People's Programmes *Lesley Oakden*
Head of Entertainment *Christine Williams*

Continued drama success on the ITV Network with the Catherine Cookson adaptations, including *The Wingless Bird, The Moth* and *The Rag Nymph*. ITV commissioned a further 12 hours of Cookson drama for production in 1997/8 to include *The Round Tower* and *Colour Blind*, shot entirely in the North-East. Also produces various children's programmes, including the Saturday morning magazine *Mashed* for CITV. Tyne Tees does not have a drama department; the Catherine Cookson productions are made by Festival Film and Television Ltd (*see* Film, Video and Independent Production Companies, page 294).

UTV (Ulster Television)
Havelock House, Ormeau Road,
Belfast BT7 1EB
Tel: 01232 328122
Fax: 01232 246695
Controller of Programming
A. Bremner

No drama output. Regular news and current affairs, sport and documentary programmes.

Westcountry
Langage Science Park, Western Wood Way, Plymouth, Devon PL7 5BG
Tel: 01752 333333
Fax: 01752 333444
Director of Programmes *Jane McClosky*

Part of Carlton Television. News, current affairs, documentary and religious programmes. No drama output.

Yorkshire Television
The Television Centre, Leeds,
West Yorkshire LS3 1JS
Tel: 0113 243 8283
Fax: 0113 244 5107
London office: 15 Bloomsbury Square, London WC1A 2LJ
Tel: 0171 312 3700
Fax: 0171 2422 2441
Chief Executive *Bruce Gyngell*
Managing Director (Broadcasting)
Richard Gregory
Managing Director (Production)
David Holdgate
Group Controller, Drama *Keith Richardson*
Group Controller, Entertainment
David Reynolds
Head of Children's and Education
Patrick Titley
Casting Director *Sue Jackson (Leeds office)*

The long-running series *Emmerdale* and *Heartbeat* are cast by Sue Jackson. Virtually all other drama output by Yorkshire is supplied by independent production companies.

SATELLITE AND CABLE TELEVISION

Asianet
Elliott House, Victoria Road, London NW10 6NY
Tel: 0181 930 0930
Fax: 0181 930 0546
Chief Executive *Dr Banad Viswanath*
Managing Director *Deepak Viswanath*

Transmits to the Asian community 24 hours a day in English, Hindi, Gujarati, Punjabi, Bengali and Urdu.

British Sky Broadcasting (BSkyB)
Grant Way, Isleworth, Middlesex TW7 5QD
Tel: 0171 705 3000
Fax: 0171 705 3030
Chief Executive and Managing Director *Mark Booth*
General Manager, Broadcasting
Elisabeth Murdoch
Head of Programming *James Baker*
Director of Broadcasting *Tim Riordan*
Director of Programme Acquisitions *Jeremy Boulton*

Sky programmes are distributed by cable and satellite, offering a choice of more than 40 channels to the UK and Eire, plus 15 independent channels in its multi-channel package in addition to the Disney Channel.

Sky One
Family entertainment such as *The Simpsons* and *The X-Files*.
Sky Two
'Hottest youth entertainment' from home and abroad.
Sky News
Twenty-four-hour news service.
Sky Sports 1/ Sky Sports 2/ Sky Sports 3
Over 1,000 hours of sport a month.
Sky Movies/The Movie Channel
Twenty-four-hour channels showing over 400 movies every month including around 30 British television premières.
Sky Movies Gold
Classic movies from 70 years of cinema.

Channel One Television Ltd
60 Charlotte Street,
London W1P 2AX
Tel: 0171 209 1234
Fax: 0171 209 1235
Also at: The Television Centre, Bath Road, Bristol BS4 3HG
Tel: 0117 9722551
Fax: 0117 9722492
Managing Director *Julian Aston*

Twenty-four-hour, news-led channel owned by the *Daily Mail* and General Trust Plc.

Cable News Network International (CNNI)
CNN House,
19–22 Rathbone Place,
London W1P 1DF
Tel: 0171 637 6800
Fax: 0171 637 6868
Bureau Chief *Charles Hoff*

Wholly-owned subsidiary of Time Warner Inc., CNNI is the international sister network to CNN. Distributes 24-hour news to more than 210 countries.

L!VE TV
24th Floor, One Canada Square,
Canary Wharf, London E14 5AP
Tel: 0171 293 3900
Fax: 0171 293 3820
Managing Director *Mark Cullen*
Director of Programming *Nick Ferrari*

Twenty-four-hour cable channel with an emphasis on upbeat and lively entertainment and information programming.

MTV Networks Europe Inc
Hawley Crescent, London NW1 8TT
Tel: 0171 284 7777
Fax: 0171 284 7788

Europe's 24-hour music and youth entertainment channel.

UK Living/UK Gold
The Quadrangle, 180 Wardour Street,
London W1V 4AE
Tel: 0171 306 6100
Fax: 0171 306 6101
Chief Executive *Bruce Steinberg*
Programme Director, UK Living *Liz Howell*
Programme Director, UK Gold *Andrew Keyte*

UK Living broadcasts women's magazine programmes, gameshows, soaps and films from 6 a.m. to midnight daily. UK Gold broadcasts vintage drama and light entertainment from 6 a.m. to 2 a.m. daily.

Radio

BBC AND INDEPENDENT RADIO

BBC Radio

Broadcasting House, London W1A 1AA
Tel: 0171 580 4468
Fax: 0171 636 9786
Director, BBC Radio/Controller, Radio 1 *Matthew Bannister*
Controller, Radio 2 *James Moir*
Controller, Radio 3 *Nicholas Kenyon*
Controller, Radio 4 *James Boyle*
Controller, Radio 5 Live *Roger Mosey*

Major restructuring at the BBC resulted in two new directorates being formed in October 1996: BBC Production and BBC Broadcast. For the first time, both network television and radio were brought together as bi-media departments. BBC Production includes all the BBC drama producers (television, radio and the World Service) in England as well as Entertainment, Music, Arts and Factual areas. BBC Broadcast is responsible for Television, Radio, Regional Broadcasting and Education.

BBC RADIO DRAMA
Head of BBC Radio Drama *Kate Rowland*

BBC Radio Drama is produced by the Radio Drama Department (with production centres in London, Birmingham – home of *The Archers* – and Manchester, and includes World Service Drama) and by production teams in Edinburgh, Belfast and Cardiff. The Department is part of the Bi-media BBC Drama Department within the BBC Production Directorate and produces drama, readings and features for broadcast across BBC Radio networks including the World Service. Drama output on Radios 3 and 4 remains high. In 1996/7, out of a total of 8,611 hours of broadcasting on Radio 3, 114 hours of drama were produced; Radio 4 broadcast 1,087 hours out of a total of 7,652 hours of broadcasting.

The Radio Drama Company was founded in 1940 to provide a pool of actors for BBC Radio work during the war. Originally known as the BBC Repertory Company, the Rep (as it is still often called) grew in stature and became the RDC, winning a special Sony award (the radio equivalent of an Oscar) in 1990 in recognition of 50 years' outstanding contribution to radio. Many actors, while in the company, have had their share of individual success: most recently, while a member of the RDC, Siriol Jenkins (who was runner-up in the Carleton Hobbs Competition in 1990) won a *Radio Times* award for Best Actress for her performance in a radio play.

At present, the RDC carries 17 1-year places and 2 6-month contracts for the student winners. The company mix is rich and varied, covering a range of voices and ages that contribute to the drama output recorded each year. At any one time, the RDC will include among its number actors new to radio (recruited via regular RDC workshops) along-side established members of the profession with considerable theatre and radio experience. In recent years, members have included Stephen Tompkinson, Michael Tudor Barnes, Liz Kelly, John Moffat, Rachel Gurney, Polly James, Edward de Souza, Margaret Courtnay, John Turner, Denys Hawthorne, Adjoa Andoh, Alex Jennings, Ben Onwukwe, Joanna Monro, Ann Beach and Janet Maw.

Members of the RDC take part in the many hours of plays, series, dramatisations and readings that Radio Drama records for Radios 2, 3, 4 (and even 5) each year. There will be a mix of contemporary and classic drama, comedies (often for the Light Entertainment Department), thrillers and challenging new plays written around contemporary issues.

The RDC are booked for readings too, not just sequences like *Book at Bedtime* and the *Afternoon Story* slot, but for strands like *Kaleidoscope*, *Woman's Hour*, *Treasure Islands*, Radio 3 Concert Interval programmes and the World Service Arts magazine, *Meridian*.

Actors are invited on to the company either through direct approach – because their work is already known – or more usually through attending a workshop. These are held throughout the year, and participation is by invitation. Actors are nominated by producers who have worked with them on radio or in the theatre, or who believe, having seen their work firsthand, that they have the qualities and range the RDC looks for in its members.

BBC ARTS (based at Television Centre)
Head of BBC Arts *Kim Evans*
Editor, Arts Features *Keith Alexander*
Editor, Kaleidoscope, Nightwaves
John Boundy
Editor, World Service Arts Radio
Jenny Bowen

BBC LIGHT ENTERTAINMENT
Head of Light Entertainment Radio
Jonathan James-Moore

Output includes topical comedy weeklies such as Radio 4's *Week Ending* and Radio 2's *The News Huddlines*. Also *King Street Junior* (comedy drama), *I'm Sorry I Haven't a Clue* and *Just a Minute*.

BBC TOPICAL FEATURES
Head of BBC Topical Features *Anne Winder*

A new bi-media department with regular radio programmes such as *Woman's Hour*, *Desert Island Discs* and *Does He Take Sugar?*.

BBC World Service

PO Box 76, Bush House,
Strand,
London WC2B 4PH
Tel: 0171 240 3456
Fax: 0171 379 6729
Managing Director Sam Younger
**Director World Service News and
Programme Commissioning** Bob
Jobbins
**Executive Producer, World Service
Drama** Gordon House (based at
Broadcasting House)
**Senior Producer, World Service
Drama** David Hitchinson
Producer, World Service Drama
Anne Edyvean

The World Service broadcasts in English and 44 other languages to an audience of 143 million listeners (excluding those countries where listener research is not possible). The English service is round-the-clock, with news and current affairs as the main component.

World Service Drama produces *Play of the Week* (52 per year), usually 1 hour in length and a soap opera, *Westway* which is produced by David Hitchinson and Anne Edyvean. Draws actors from the Radio Drama Company but occasionally uses OAs (outside actors). Unable to deal with general casting queries but welcomes voice tapes from actors. The Department recommends a tape of 5 minutes' duration which demonstrates vocal versatility: accents, different ages, poetry, prose, humour, drama, etc. Contact the individual producers as information is not normally pooled. Notification of performances in London which can be covered by the Department is welcome.

BBC Northern Ireland

Broadcasting House,
25–27 Ormeau Avenue,
Belfast BT2 8HQ
Tel: 01232 338000
Fax: 01232 338800
Controller, Northern Ireland Patrick
Loughrey
Head of Broadcasting Anna
Carragher
Head of Production Paul Evans
Senior Producer Roland Jaquarello

Although English actors are occasionally used, the Drama Department usually casts from a pool of actors based in Ireland, with additions from the Radio Drama Company. Also interested in hearing from actors either living in Ireland (Northern Ireland and the Republic) or from actors who are going to be working there in the future (give at least 2 months' notice).

BBC Radio Scotland

5 Queen Street, Edinburgh EH2 1JF
Tel: 0131 225 3131/Drama Dept: 0131
248 4240
Controller, Scotland John
McCormick
Contact Patrick Rayner (Editor), Joan
Raffan (Production Assistant)

Also at: Broadcasting House,
Queen Margaret Drive,
Glasgow G12 8DG
Tel: 0141 339 8844

Broadcasting House, Beechgrove
Terrace, Aberdeen AB9 2ZT
Tel: 01224 625233

Broadcasting House, 7 Culduthel
Road, Inverness IV2 4AD
Tel: 01463 720720

The Drama Department is a substantial employer of actors and is always looking to extend its casting possibilities. Seven producers and 3 production assistants provide many hours of plays, serials, dramatisations, short stories, serial readings, features and documentaries for the BBC's UK Networks and for BBC Radio Scotland. 'The work is wide-ranging and we don't cast Scottish actors or for Scottish parts exclusively; but for both public service and practical reasons most of our actors tend to be locally based. We hold general auditions for professional actors usually twice a year, for which we ask actors or their agents to apply formally in writing, with full cv and photograph. Auditionees are given advice beforehand on how best to prepare. But in order that they do themselves justice in what is a highly demanding field of acting, and make the most of their time at the microphone, we prefer to discourage younger actors from applying for an audition before they can demonstrate a solid professional grounding in the craft. We welcome advance notice from actors based elsewhere who are touring or otherwise coming temporarily to work in Scotland. And we are happy to receive general queries from actors or their agents, either by telephone or letter.'

Radio Drama Producers *Alison Hindell, Tanya Nash*

Also at: Broadcasting House, 32 Alexandra Road, Swansea West Glamorgan SA1 5DZ Tel: 01792 654986

Broadcasting House, Meirion Road, Bangor, Gwynedd LL57 2BY Tel: 01248 370880

The Drama Department produces about 30 hours a year of output for Radio 3, Radio 4, and Radio Wales. 'The broad brief of the Department is to represent contemporary Wales on the radio. CV and voice tapes are welcome but please note, the majority of the work is set in Wales and therefore preference will be given to actors who are native or who have genuine accents.' In 1997, the Department won the Gold Medal at the New York Radio Festival, the BT Innovations award at the British Radio Academy and a Sony award for Best Dramatic Performance.

BBC Wales

Drama Dept: Room 3007, Broadcasting House, Llandaf, Cardiff CF5 2YQ Tel: 01222 572888/Drama Dept: 01222 322448 (fax: 01222 322668) **Controller, Wales** *Geraint Talfan Davies* **Senior Bi-media Producer, Drama** *Foz Allan*

REGIONAL RADIO STATIONS

Opportunities for actors are few and far between with the local radio stations. Virtually no drama is produced and the outlet for work is likely to be limited to voiceovers, particularly for adverts with the commercial radio stations. In all instances, it is unlikely that a local station will use anyone other than a locally based actor.

BBC

BBC Asian Network

BBC Pebble Mill, Birmingham B5 7SH
Tel: 0121 414 8558
Fax: 0121 472 3174
Also at: Epic House, Charles Street,
Leicester LE1 3SH
Tel: 0116 251 6688
Fax: 0116 251 1463
Managing Editor *Vijay Sharma*

Commenced broadcasting in November 1996 to a Midlands audience with programmes in English, Bengali, Gujarati, Hindi, Punjabi and Urdu.

BBC Radio Berkshire

– see **Thames Valley FM**, page 281

BBC Radio Bristol

PO Box 194, Bristol BS99 7QT
Tel: 0117 974 1111
Fax: 0117 973 2549
Managing Editor *Michael Hapgood*

BBC Radio Cambridgeshire

PO Box 96, 104 Hills Road,
Cambridge CB2 1LD
Tel: 01223 259696
Fax: 01223 460832
Managing Editor *Nigel Dyson*

Occasionally broadcasts short stories.

BBC Radio Cleveland

Broadcasting House, PO Box 95FM,
Middlesbrough, Cleveland TS1 5DG
Tel: 01642 225211
Fax: 01642 211356
Managing Editor *David Peel*

Occasionally broadcasts short stories.

BBC Radio Cornwall

Phoenix Wharf, Truro,
Cornwall TR1 1UA
Tel: 01872 275436
Fax: 01872 240679
Managing Editor *Leo Devine*

Speech-based programming with a mix of news, current affairs and magazine-type programmes. Does not use actors.

BBC GLR 94.9

PO Box 94.9, 35C Marylebone High
Street, London W1A 4LG
Tel: 0171 224 2424
Fax: 0171 224 4772
Managing Editor *Steve Panton*

Speech-based and music programmes with a strong emphasis on London issues. Does not use actors.

BBC Radio Lancashire

Darwen Street, Blackburn,
Lancashire BB2 2EA
Tel: 01254 262411
Fax: 01254 680821
Managing Editor *Steve Taylor*

News and speech-based programming. Does not use actors but will consider demo tapes 'if the actor is ambitious to become a radio presenter'.

BBC Radio Merseyside

55 Paradise Street, Liverpool L1 3BP
Tel: 0171 794 0910
Fax: 0151 794 0988
E-mail: 100011.17@compuserve.com
Managing Editor *Mick Ord*

Local speech-based and music programmes. Will consider demo

tapes. 'Little demand for acting work but always looking for good presenters with thorough local knowledge.'

BBC Radio Newcastle

Broadcasting Centre, Newcastle upon Tyne NE99 1RN
Tel: 0191 232 4141
Managing Editor *Tony Fish*

News-talk programming. Does not use actors.

BBC Radio Norfolk

Norfolk Tower, Surrey Street, Norwich, Norfolk NR1 3PA
Tel: 01603 617411
Fax: 01603 633692
E-mail: norfolk@bbc.co.uk
Managing Editor *Tim Bishop*

Predominantly speech-based programming: news, information and entertainment about Norfolk. Does not use actors.

BBC Radio Northampton

Broadcasting House, Abington Street, Northampton NN1 2BH
Tel: 01604 239100
Fax: 01604 230709
Managing Editor *Claire Paul*

Programmes reflecting Northamptonshire life. 'We only use actors very, very occasionally.'

BBC Radio Nottingham

York House, Mansfield Road, Nottingham NG1 3JB
Tel: 0115 955 0500
Fax: 01155 955 0501
Managing Editor *Antony Bellekom*

Speech-based programmes with some music. Rarely uses actors.

BBC Southern Counties Radio

Broadcasting Centre, Guildford, Surrey GU2 5AP
Tel: 01483 306306
Fax: 01483 304952
Managing Editor *Chris Van Schaick*

Topical news and current affairs programmes. Does not use actors.

BBC Radio Stoke

Cheapside, Hanley, Stoke-on-Trent, Staffordshire ST1 1JJ
Tel: 01782 208080
Fax: 01782 285115
Managing Editor *Phil Ashworth*

Mainly speech-based programming: news, information, sport and conversation. Rarely uses actors, and then only locally based actors.

BBC Radio Suffolk

Broadcasting House, St Matthew's Street, Ipswich, Suffolk IP1 3EP
Tel: 01473 250000
Fax: 01473 210887
Managing Editor *Ivan Howlett*

Speech-based programming: news, information and entertainment for Suffolk. Rarely uses actors.

BBC Thames Valley FM

PO Box 952, Oxford OX2 7YL
Tel: 0645 311444
Fax: 0645 311555
Managing Editor *David Clargo*

Speech-led programmes, covering a wide range of subjects across Oxfordshire and Berkshire. Does not use actors.

BBC 3 Counties Radio

PO Box 3CR, Hastings Street, Luton,
Bedfordshire LU1 5XL
Tel: 01582 441000
Fax: 01582 401467
Managing Editor *Frances Reid*

Speech-based programming: news, talk and entertainment. Very few work opportunities for actors. 'Uses actors exceedingly rarely and then only for voiceovers, and local actors only.' Will consider demo tapes, 'if appropriate (i.e. examples of voiceover work).'

BBC Wiltshire Sound

Prospect Place, Old Town, Swindon,
Wiltshire SN1 3RW
Tel: 01793 513626
Fax: 01793 512718
Managing Editor *Sandy Milne*

News magazine programmes with a distinct local flavour. Does not use actors.

INDEPENDENT

Radio Borders

Tweedside Park, Galashiels TD1 3TD
Tel: 01896 759444
Fax: 01896 759494
Managing Editor *Rob Webster*

Sixties to nineties music aimed at a 25–55 audience. 'Plenty of local output. Very few opportunities for actors.'

The Breeze

– see **Essex FM**, page 282

CFM

Durran Hill Estate, Carlisle, Cumbria
CA1 3NG
Tel: 01228 818964
Fax: 01228 819444
E-mail: simongrundy@msn.com
Managing Editor *Simon Grundy*

Music radio. Commercials are made in-house for which voiceover artists are required. Will consider demo tapes.

Cheltenham Radio

Regent Arcade, High Street,
Cheltenham,
Gloucestershire GL50 1JZ
Tel: 01242 699555
Fax: 01242 699666
Managing Editor *Peter MacFarlane*

Classic hits and general entertainment; local and national news and features. Does not use actors.

Radio Clyde Ltd (Clyde 1 FM/ Clyde 2 AM)

Clydebank Business Park,
Clydebank G81 2RX
Tel: 0141 565 2200
Fax: 0141 565 2265
E-mail: clyde1srh.co.uk
Contact *Dan McCurdy (Head of Creative Services – Commercial Production)*

Clyde 1 broadcasts contemporary hit music; Clyde 2 is a speech and music station for a middle-of-the-road audience. Uses actors for voiceovers in commercials. Contact Dan McCurdy by fax, e-mail or letter. Will consider demo tapes.

Coast FM

– see **MFM**, page 283

Essex FM/The Breeze/Ten 17/Oasis FM/Vibe FM

Essex Radio Group, Radio House,
19–20 Clifftown Road, Southend-on-
Sea, Essex SS1 1SX
Tel: 01702 333711
Fax: 01702 345224
E-mail: essexfm@netforce.net
Creative Director *Mr Chris Slack*
Contact *Claire Fields (Creative Team,
PA to Commercial Production Dept)*

Mainly music-based programming.
Uses actors for commercials. Will
consider demo tapes which should
consist of 5 commercials, each approximately 30 seconds in length, showing
variety of style.

Radio Forth Ltd

Forth House, Forth Street,
Edinburgh EH1 3LF
Tel: 0131 556 9255
Fax: 0131 557 2941
E-mail: forth@srh.co.uk
Managing Editor *Tom Steele*
Contact *Derek Murray (Head of
Creative Services)*

Forth FM broadcasts contemporary hit
music while Forth AM broadcasts
classic hit records. Uses actors for
commercial voiceovers. Will consider
demo tapes.

Galaxy 101

Millennium House, 26 Baldwin Street,
Bristol BS1 1SE
Tel: 0117 901 0101
Fax: 0117 901 4555
E-mail: address*see*@galaxy101.co.uk
Managing Editor *Steve Parkinson*
Contact *Kenny Dillon (Creative
Services)*

Twenty-four-hour contemporary and

classic dance music. Uses actors for
commercial voiceovers. Will consider
demo tapes; send to Kenny Dillon as
above.

GNR

Longrigg, Swalwell, Newcastle upon
Tyne NE99 1BB
Tel: 0191 420 3040
Fax: 0191 496 0174
Managing Editor *Harry Dunne*

Music-based programming. Does not
use actors.

FM103 Horizon

The Broadcast Centre, 14 Vincent
Avenue, Crownhill, Milton Keynes,
Buckinghamshire MK8 0AB
Tel: 01908 269111
Fax: 01908 564893
Contact *Paul Kenton*

Uses actors for voiceover work. Will
consider demo tapes.

100.7 Heart FM

1 The Square, 111 Broad Street,
Birmingham B15 1AS
Tel: 0121 626 1007
Fax: 0121 696 1007
E-mail: pfairburn@heartfm.co.uk
Programme Director *Paul Fairburn*

Adult contemporary music. Uses
actors for commercial voiceovers and
comedy characters for programming
('we may need impersonators
occasionally'). Send demo tape and
brief cv.

Key 103/Piccadilly 1152

Castlequay, Castlefield,
Manchester M15 4NJ
Tel: 0161 288 5000
Fax: 0161 288 5001
Programme Director John Dash

Key 103 broadcasts contemporary music and Piccadilly 1152 plays classic hit records from the sixties up to today, with phone-ins and sport. Uses actors for commercial voiceovers. No demo tapes.

LBC 1152 AM

200 Gray's Inn Road,
London WC1X 8XZ
Tel: 0171 973 1152
Fax: 0171 312 8565
Programme Controller *Charles Golding*

News, views and interviews relating to London. Does not use actors but suggests they should contact the producer of drama for independent radio: Tim Crook at Independent Radio Productions, PO Box 518, Manningtree, Essex CO11 1XD.

Marcher Gold

– see **MFM**, *below*

MFM/Marcher Gold/Coast FM

The Studios,
Mold Road, Gwersyllt,
Wrexham LL11 4AF
Tel: 01978 752202
Fax: 01978 759701
E-mail: www.mfmradio.co.uk
Managing Editor/Programme Director *Terry Underhill*

MFM plays current hits and classics; Marcher Gold and Coast FM broadcast classic hits. Uses actors for voiceovers. Will consider demo tapes.

Moray Firth Radio

PO Box 271, Inverness IV3 6SF
Tel: 01463 224433
Fax: 01463 227714
E-mail: moray firth radio@cali.co.uk
Managing Editor *Thomas Prag*

Locally produced and presented programmes and local news. Occasionally uses actors. No casting queries and no demo tapes, please.

News Direct 97.3 FM

200 Gray's Inn Road,
London WC1X 8XZ
Tel: 0171 973 1152
Fax: 0171 312 8740
Programme Controller *Chris Mann*

Twenty-four-hour rolling news station. Does not use actors.

Oasis FM

– see **Essex FM**, page 282

Orchard FM

Haygrove House, Shoreditch Road,
Taunton TA3 7BT
Tel: 01823 338448
Fax: 01823 321611
Programme Controller *Bob McCreadie*
Contact *Ian Gill (Head of Commercial Production)*

Broadcasts a mixture of classic hits and contemporary music, international and local news, entertainment news and general features. Uses actors for voiceovers. Will consider demo tapes.

Piccadilly 1152
– see **Key 103**, page 283

Premier Radio
Glen House, Stag Place,
London SW1E 5AG
Tel: 0171 233 6705
Fax: 0171 233 6706
E-mail: premier@premier.co.uk
Contact *Peter Kerridge (Station Director), Charmaine Noble*

News, current affairs and lifestyle issues reflecting the values and beliefs of the Christian faith. Music features contemporary Christian artists. Uses actors 'on occasions'. Welcomes casting queries by fax or letter. Will consider demo tapes.

100.3 and 101.1 Scot FM
1 Albert Quay, Leith,
Edimburgh EH6 7DN
Tel: 0131 554 6677
Fax: 0131 554 2266
Managing Editor *Harriet Jones*

A mix of conversation and adult contemporary music for central Scotland. Uses actors for voiceovers. Does not welcome casting queries or unsolicited demo tapes.

Signal 105
Regent House, Heaton Lane,
Stockport, Cheshire SK4 1BX
Tel: 0161 285 4545
Fax: 0161 285 1010
Contact *Paul Allen (Managing Editor)*

Mainstream eighties and nineties music with a mix of local news and information. Uses actors for voiceovers. Send letter and demo tape.

Sunrise Radio (Yorkshire)
Sunrise House, 30 Chapel Street,
Little Germany, Bradford, West
Yorkshire BD1 5DN
Tel: 01274 735043
Fax: 01274 728534
Contact *Ms Usha Parmar (Managing Editor)*

Broadcasts to the Asian community across West Yorkshire, 24 hours a day. Uses actors for voiceovers. Does not welcome casting queries but will consider demo tapes.

Swansea Sound Ltd
Victoria Road, Gowerton, Swansea.
West Glamorgan SA4 3AB
Tel: 01792 511170
Fax: 01792 511171
Managing Director *Terry Mann*
Contact *Luke Whittacker (Commercial Producer)*

Contemporary hit music, headline news, sport, travel, weather and local information. Uses actors for voiceovers. Welcomes casting queries and will consider demo tapes.

Radio Tay Ltd (Radio Tay AM/ Tay FM)
6 North Isla Street, Dundee DD3 7JQ
Tel: 01382 200800
Fax: 01382 593252
E-mail: rtay@srh.co.uk
Managing Editor *A. J. Wilkie*

Radio Tay AM broadcasts classic hits; Tay FM plays popular chart music. Welcomes casting queries; approach in writing. Will consider demo tapes.

Ten 17
– see **Essex FM**, page 282

2CRFM

5–7 Southcote Road, Bournemouth,
Dorset BH1 3LR
Tel: 01202 259259
Fax: 01202 255244
Programme Controller *Tom Hardy*

Broadcasts contemporary music. Does not welcome casting queries. Will consider demo tapes.

Vibe FM

– see **Essex FM**, page 282

Viking FM

Commercial Road, Hull HU1 2SG
Tel: 01482 325141
Fax: 01482 587067
Managing Editor *Mark Matthews*
Contact *Graham Elliott (Commercial Production Manager)*

Broadcasts contemporary music. Uses actors for commercial voiceovers. Does not welcome casting queries. 'We use established commercial voices or agents.' Will consider demo tapes but only if examples of commercial work are included. 'Versatility is the key.'

West Sound/West FM

Radio House,
54A Holmston Road,
Ayr KA7 3BE
Tel: 01292 283662
Fax: 01292 283665
E-mail: wsradio@aol.com
Managing Editor *Gordon McArthur*
Contact *Julie Love (Traffic Manager)*

News, information and popular music. Uses actors for voiceovers. Does not welcome casting queries. Will consider demo tapes.

Film, Video and Independent Production Companies

The feature film has never been an easy genre to break into. This is true for both actors and agents. Many film companies and casting directors rely on a small coterie of top agents when casting a major movie. These agents represent not only leading actors but directors and screenwriters, and can offer a 'package' to the film company. Big money is involved and, sadly, many who cast films are unwilling to take a chance with untried actors.

So where does the average actor gain experience of acting to camera? For the beginner, film-school graduation shorts can prove a valuable learning environment. You may get to play the lead but ensure the script is worth working on. It is likely that the only payment will be expenses but you will be given a copy of the film on video once it has been edited and, if you are happy with the result, you may want to use it as a demo video tape. Some graduate films appear at film festivals and, occasionally, are bought by television companies.

Corporate videos and training films are a steady source of income for many actors although it has to be said that the market has never returned to the heady times of the mid-/late eighties when the demand for actors boomed.

Voiceovers for commercials is a skilled specialist field, requiring the actor to sight-read, often with little direction or rehearsal, a script which must be read precisely within strict time limits. As with dubbing for films, much of this work is done by a small band of actors who are constantly in demand because of their expertise. To break into this lucrative market, a specialist agent is essential and to attract representation you will need a demo voice tape. Ensure that it is produced professionally by people who know their business. Not the cheapest option but money well spent.

Alomo Productions

1 Stephen Street, London W1P 1PJ
Tel: 0171 691 6531
Fax: 0171 691 6081

Major producers of television comedy such as *Birds of a Feather* and *Goodnight Sweetheart*. Always uses a casting director who works in conjunction with agents. No casting queries or video showreels.

Antelope (UK) Ltd

29B Montague Street,
London WC1B 5BH
Tel: 0171 209 0099
Fax: 0171 209 0098
Contact *Justin Johnson (Production Manager)*

Producers of television drama, documentary and entertainment programmes. Output has included: *Cyberspace* (ITV), *Brunch* (Channel 5), *The Pier* (Meridian), *Omnibus, South Bank Show, Secret Lives* and *Timewatch*. Prefers to work through agents as only uses actors on rare occasions. No casting queries or video showreels.

Apex Television Production and Facilities Ltd

Button End Studios, Harston,
Cambridge CB2 5NX
Tel: 01223 872900
Fax: 01223 873092
Contact *Bernard Mulhern*

Producers of commercials and corporate videos – drama-based training programmes for the financial sector. Uses actors and voiceover artists but prefers to work through agents. Will consider demo tapes and video showreels.

Arlington Productions Limited

Pinewood Studios, Iver Heath,
Buckinghamshire SL0 0NH
Tel: 01753 651700
Fax: 01753 656050

Producers of television drama. Output includes: *The Masks of Death, Murder Elite, A One-way Ticket to Hollywood*. Always uses freelance casting directors.

Michael Barratt Ltd

Profile House, 5–7 Forlease Road,
Maidenhead, Berkshire SL6 1RP
Tel: 01628 770800
Fax: 01628 770800
E-mail:
11100540.121@compuserve.com
Contact *Michael Barratt*

Television, video and audio material – documentary and corporate programmes such as Inns of Court dramatised legal training. Uses actors and voiceover artists. Welcomes casting queries by letter or fax and will consider demo tapes and video showreels. 'Make sure you will be available before agreeing to audition for productions with set dates.'

BFI Production

29 Rathbone Street,
London W1P 1AG
Tel: 0171 636 5587
Fax: 0171 580 9456
Head of Production *Roger Shannon*

Part of the British Film Institute. Produces a range of programmes from short films and videos to feature-length films, acting as executive producer and co-investor. Output includes: *Gallivant, Stella Does Tricks, Smalltime*. Runs a New Directors

Scheme (advertised annually). Does not welcome casting queries.

or video showreels apart from agents' voice compilations on CD-ROM.

Black Coral Productions
Unit 130, Lea Valley Techno Park, Ashley Road, London N17 9LN
Tel: 0181 880 4860
Fax: 0181 880 4113
Contact *Lazell Daley, Isabelle Tracy*

Producers of film and television drama and documentary programmes. Prefers to work through casting directors and agents. No casting queries, demo tapes or video showreels.

Blue Heaven Productions Ltd
45 Leather Lane, London EC1N 7TJ
Tel: 0171 404 4222
Fax: 0171 404 4266
Contact *Graham Benson, Christine Benson, Neil Zeiger*

Producers of film and television dramas such as *The Ruth Rendell Mysteries* for ITV/Meridian and *Crime Story* for ITV/LWT. Always employs casting directors and works through agents; no casting queries, demo tapes or video showreels.

Bond Clarkson Russell Ltd
16 Trinity Churchyard, Guildford, Surrey GU1 3RR
Tel: 01483 562888
Fax: 01483 307237
E-mail: bondclarksonrussell@ compuserve.com
Contact *Peter Bond, Simon Kozak*

Video and audio corporate programmes. Projects have included material for Natwest Bank, South-West Trains, the Tea Council and IBM. Occasionally uses actors but prefers to work through agents. No demo tapes

Boxclever Productions
The Maples Centre, 144 Liverpool Road, London N1 1LA
Tel: 0171 619 0606
Fax: 0171 700 2248
E-mail: information@boxclever.co.uk
Contact *Elisabeth Hannah*

Producers of television documentary programmes. Occasionally uses actors but does not welcome casting queries. No demo tapes or video showreels.

British Lion Screen Entertainment Ltd
Pinewood Studios, Iver, Buckinghamshire SL0 0NH
Tel: 01753 651700
Fax: 01753 656391

Major film producers. Output has included: *A Man for All Seasons, Treasure Island, A Prayer for the Dying, Lady Jane, The Crucifer of Blood, Death Train.*

Caravel Film Techniques Limited
The Great Barn Studio, Cippenham Lane, Slough, Berkshire SL1 5AU
Tel: 01753 534828
Fax: 01753 571383
E-mail: 101637.20233@compuserve.com
Contact *N. C. J. See (Production Director)*

Television, video and audio producers – documentary, commercials and corporate programmes. Always employs casting directors and works through agents. Will consider demo audio tapes for voiceovers.

Carlton Productions

35–38 Portman Square,
London W1H 9FH
Tel: 0171 486 6688
Fax: 0171 486 1132
**Director of Drama and
Co-production** *Jonathan Powell*

Makers of independently produced TV drama for ITV. Output includes: *She's Out, Kavanagh QC, Morse, Boon, Gone to the Dogs, The Guilty, Tanamera, Soldier Soldier, Seekers, Sharpe, Peak Practice, Cadfael.* The Drama Department does not welcome casting queries from actors; always employs freelance casting directors.

Carnival (Films & Theatre) Ltd

12 Raddington Road, Ladbroke Grove,
London W10 5TG
Tel: 0181 968 0968
Fax: 0181 968 0155

Film, television and theatre producers. Film output includes: *The Mill on the Floss* (BBC), *Firelight* (Hollywood Pictures/Wind Dancer Productions), *Shadowlands* (Savoy/Spelling), *In Hitler's Shadow* (Home Box Office), *Under Suspicion* (Columbia/Rank/LWT), *Wilt* (Rank/LWT), *Whoops Apocalypse* (ITC). Television: *The Fragile Heart* (Channel 4), *Crime Traveller* (BBC), *Poirot* (LWT), *Bugs* (BBC), *All or Nothing at All* (LWT), *Head Over Heels* (Carlton), *The Big Battalions* (Channel 4), *Jeeves and Wooster I–IV* (Granada), *Traffik* (Channel 4), *Porterhouse Blue* (Channel 4), *Blott on the Landscape* (BBC). Theatre: *What a Performance, Juno and the Paycock, Murder is Easy, Misery, Ghost Train, Map of the Heart, Shadowlands, Up on the Roof.* Always uses casting directors. Call for details.

CCC Wadlow

3rd Floor, South Harling House, 47–51
Great Suffolk Street, London SE1 0BL
Tel: 0171 450 4720
Fax: 0171 450 4734

Film and video corporate programmes. Usually employs casting directors as and when required. No casting queries.

Central Office of Information Film and Video

Hercules Road, London SE1 7DU
Tel: 0171 261 8667
Fax: 0171 261 8776
Head of Production *Geoff Raison*

Film, video and television: drama, documentary, commercials, corporate and public information films. Does not welcome casting queries as they prefer to deal with agents.

Chatsworth Television

97–9 Dean Street, London W1V 5RA
Tel: 0171 734 4302
Fax: 0171 437 3301

Producers of film and television drama and entertainment. Output has included series, serials and single dramas for UK television. Always works through casting directors – all queries to be referred to them and *not* to Chatsworth. No demo tapes or video showreels.

Cinema Verity Productions Ltd

4 Parkside, Ravenscourt Park,
London W6 0UU
Tel: 0181 741 1515
Fax: 0181 741 1616

Leading independent producer of television drama. Output includes: Lynda La Plante's *Comics* (Channel 4) and *She's Out* (Carlton), *Class Act*

(Carlton), Simon Gray's *Running Late*. No casting queries; always uses casting directors and works through agents.

Circus Films
– see **Elstree (Production) Co. Ltd**, page 293

Creative Film Makers Ltd
Pottery Lane House, Pottery Lane, London W11 4LZ
Tel: 0171 229 5131
Fax: 0171 229 4999
Contact *Gaby Seligman*

Film, television and video producers of documentary, commercials and corporate programmes. Uses actors and voiceover artists but prefers to work through agents. No casting queries but will consider demo tapes and video showreels.

Cricket Limited
14–22 Ganton Street, London W1V 1LB
Tel: 0171 287 4848
Fax: 0171 413 0654
E-mail: john@cricket-Ltd.co.uk
Contact *Jonathan Freer*

Producers of film, video and audio corporate programmes. Uses actors and voiceover artists. Welcomes casting queries and will consider demo tapes and video showreels.

Croft Television & Graphics Ltd
Croft House, Whittle Parkway, Slough, Berkshire SL1 6DQ
Tel: 01628 66873
Fax: 01628 668791
E-mail: crofttv@compuserve.com
Contact *Keith Jones, Terry Adam*

Producers of television, video and audio corporate programmes, including training, promotional and factual material. Uses actors and voiceover artists; welcomes *written* casting queries. Will consider demo tapes and video showreels. 'Be honest. Don't lie and remember who is paying who.'

Cromdale Films Limited
12 St Paul's Road, London N1 2QN
Tel: 0171 226 0178
Contact *Ian Lloyd*

Film, television and video drama and documentary programmes. Output has included: *The Face of Darkness* (feature film), *Drift to Dawn* (music/science fiction) and *The Last Red Summer* (documentary on Russia). Uses actors but prefers to work through agents. No casting queries and no demo tapes or video showreels unless requested.

Dan Films Ltd
37 Percy Street, London W1P 9FG
Tel: 0171 916 4771
Fax: 0171 916 4773
E-mail: danfilmsltd@clara.net.

Film and television drama and documentary programmes. Output: *Butterfly Kiss*, *Madagascar Skin* (both feature films), *Everywhere* (short film). Always uses a casting director, working through agents. No casting queries and no demo tapes or video showreels.

Dareks Production House
58 Wickham Road, Beckenham, Kent BR3 6RQ
Tel: 0181 658 2012
Fax: 0181 325 0629
E-mail: dareks@dircon.co.uk
Contact *David Crossman*

Television and corporate work. Output has included: *The Final Frontier*, a corporate documentary for Forte Welcome Break. Always uses a casting director, working through agents. No casting queries and no unsolicited demo tapes or video showreels. 'Get a good agent and get yourself known to casting directors.'

Drake AV Video Ltd
89 St Fagans Road, Fairwater,
Cardiff CF5 3AE
Tel: 01222 560333
Fax: 01222 554909
E-mail: drakegroup@btinternet.com
Contact *Ian Lewis*

Audio and video corporate and educational programmes such as training for pre-school teachers and a south Wales tourism promotion. Uses voiceover artists; will consider demo tapes.

The Drama House Ltd
1 Hertford Place, London W1P 5RS
Tel: 0171 388 9140
Fax: 0171 388 3511

Film and television producers. Output includes: *Breaking the Code* (BBC), *Witness Against Hitler* (BBC), *Suffer the Little Children* (BBC2 'Stages'), *A Curse on the House of Windsor* (Channel 4 'Without Walls' drama-documentary). Always uses casting directors; no casting queries, please.

Eagle & Eagle
15 Marlborough Road,
London W4 4EU
Tel: 0181 995 1884
Fax: 0181 995 5648
E-mail:
producer@eagletv.demon.co.uk
Contact *Robert Eagle, Catharine Alen-Buckley*

Producers of television drama, documentary and children's programmes.

Output: *Grandpa Chatterji* (children's drama for Channel 4) and *Guru Busters* (documentary for Channel 4). Uses actors but always employs a casting director working in conjunction with agents. No casting queries, demo tapes or video showreels.

East Anglian Productions
Studio House, 21–3 Walton Road,
Frinton-on-Sea, Essex CO13 0AA
Tel: 01255 676252
Fax: 01255 850528
E-mail: eap@compuserve.com
Contact *Ray Anderson*

Producers of television commercials, corporate videos and audio documentary programmes. Uses actors and voiceover artists. Works with casting directors and agents but happy to receive cvs and photographs and will consider demo tapes and video showreels.

Eclipse Presentations Ltd
Walters Farm Road, Tonbridge,
Kent TN9 1QT
Tel: 01732 365107
Fax: 01732 362600
Contact *Wendy Honey, Tammy Christopher*

Producers of corporate and drama training videos. Uses voiceover artists and actors occasionally. Prefers to work through agents but welcomes cvs with covering letter; will consider demo tapes and video showreels.

Edinburgh Film & Video Productions
Nine Mile Burn, by Penicuik,
Midlothian EH26 9LT
Tel: 01968 672131
Fax: 01968 672685

Film and television drama. Output

includes: *Sara, Moonacre, Torch, Silent Mouse, The Curious Case of Santa Claus, The Stamp of Greatness*.

Edit 123

123 Blythswood Street,
Glasgow G2 4EN
Tel: 0141 248 3123
Fax: 0141 248 3423
Contact *Sharon Fullarton*

A facilities company dealing with a wide variety of work – film, television video, commercials and corporate programmes. Uses actors and voiceover artists. Does not welcome casting queries as prefers to work through agents but will consider demo tapes and video showreels.

Elstree (Production) Co. Ltd

Shepperton Studios, Studios Road,
Shepperton, Middlesex TW17 0QD
Tel: 01932 572680
Fax: 01932 572682

Producers of feature films and television drama and situation comedy. Co-owner of Circus Films with Trevor Nunn for feature-film projects. Output includes: *Othello* (BBC), *Great Expectations* (Disney Channel), *Porgy and Bess* (with Trevor Nunn), *Old Curiosity Shop* (Disney Channel/RHI), *London Suite* (NBC/Hallmark). Always employs casting directors; does not welcome casting queries.

Enigma Productions Ltd

13–15 Queen's Gate Place Mews,
London SW7 5BG
Tel: 0171 581 0238
Fax: 0171 584 1799

Major feature-film producers, backed by Warner Bros. Output includes: *Memphis Belle, Meeting Venus, Being Human, War of the Buttons, Le Confessional* by Robert Lepage. In development: *Fade Out* (drama set in Prague in the forties), *Shackleton* (true story of the Antarctic explorer), *Serenade* (musical romantic comedy), *The Scarlet Pimpernel, Lorna Doone, A Very Long Engagement, The Ginger Boy*. Always employs casting directors. Despite its impressive output, Enigma is a small company and does not welcome casting queries.

Essential Film & Television Productions Ltd

5 Anglers Lane, London NW5 3DG
Tel: 0171 482 1992
Fax: 0171 485 4287
Contact *Sarah Bryant*

Producers of film and television drama and sitcom programmes. Output: *Surgical Spirit, The Desmonds, Pork Pie, Behaving Badly*. Works with casting directors and agents but happy to receive casting queries by letter or fax; no telephone calls. Will consider demo tapes and video showreels.

The Farnham Film Company Ltd

34 Burnt Hill Road, Lower Bourne,
Farnham, Surrey GU10 3LZ
Tel: 01252 710313
Fax: 01252 725855
E-mail: info@farnfilm.demon.co.uk
Contact *Ian Lewis*

Television and video – drama, documentary and corporate programmes. Uses voiceover artists and actors occasionally. Welcomes enquiries, responding to casting needs published on their website: www.farnfilm.demon.co.uk

The Farrant Partnership

91 Knatchbull Road, London SE5 9QU
Tel: 0171 733 0711
Fax: 0171 738 5224
E-mail: farrant.stern@dial.pipex.com
Contact J. Stern

Producers of corporate videos. Uses voiceover artists; welcomes casting queries by letter and will consider demo tapes.

Festival Film and Television Ltd

Festival House, Tranquil Passage, Blackheath Village, London SE3 0BJ
Tel: 0181 297 9999
Fax: 0181 297 1155
Managing Director Ray Marshall

Producers of popular television drama, particularly the Catherine Cookson adaptations for Tyne Tees Television. Always employs freelance casting directors; no casting queries.

Fitting Images Ltd

Alfred House, 127A Oatlands Drive, Weybridge, Surrey KT13 9LB
Tel: 01932 840056
Fax: 01932 858075
Contact Rebecca Jones

Producers of corporate videos. Uses voiceover artists and actors on occasion but prefers to work direct with agents. No casting queries and no unsolicited demo tapes or video showreels.

Flashback Communications Ltd

25 Greenhead Street, Glasgow G40 1ES
Tel: 0141 554 6868
Fax: 0141 554 6869

Video and television producers: drama, documentary, corporate training and education. Occasionally uses actors but prefers to deal direct with agents.

Focus Films Ltd

The Rotunda Studios,
Rear of 116–118 Finchley Road,
London NW3 5HT
Tel: 0171 435 9004
Fax: 0171 431 3562

Film and television producers. Output includes: *Crime Time* (medium-budget feature thriller), *Diary of a Sane Man* (experimental feature for Channel 4). Always employs casting directors; no casting queries.

Freeway Films

67 George Street,
Edinburgh EH2 2JG
Tel: 0131 225 3200
Fax: 0131 225 3667
Contact John McGrath, Susie Brown, Joshua Barker

Producers of film and television drama. Output has included: *Carrington* and *Ma Vie En Rose* (both feature films). Employs casting directors and works with agents but will consider demo tapes and video showreels. No phone calls. 'Send cards before a screening or transmission so that we can see you in action, please.'

Friday Productions Ltd

23A St Leonard's Terrace,
London SW3 4QG
Tel: 0171 730 0608
Fax: 0171 730 0608

Film and television drama. Output includes: *Goggle Eyes, Harnessing Peacocks, The December Rose.* Uses casting directors and prefers to deal with agents. 'Unfortunately, we are not in a position to respond to casting queries from actors.'

Noel Gay Television

1 Albion Court, Albion Place,
Hammersmith, London W6 0QT
Tel: 0181 600 5200
Fax: 0181 600 5222

One of the most securely financed independent television production companies in the business. Output includes: *Red Dwarf* (BBC), *10%ers* (Carlton/ITV), *I-Camcorder* (Channel 4), *Les Bubb* (BBC Scotland), *Dave Allen* (ITV). Joint ventures and new companies include a partnership with Odyssey, a leading Indian commercials, film and TV producer, and international networks; a joint venture with Reed Consumer Books to develop book and magazine ideas for film, video and television, and the Noel Gay Motion Picture Company, whose 1996 credits include: *Trainspotting* (with Channel 4 and Figment Films) and *Killer Tongue*, a co-production with Iberoamericana. Other associate NGTV companies are Grant Naylor Productions, Rose Bay Film Productions and Pepper Productions. All casting is handled by Associate Casting Director Jane Davies (address and telephone number in Casting Directors, page 109).

Goldcrest Films International Ltd

65–6 Dean Street, London W1V 6PL
Tel: 0171 437 8696
Fax: 0171 437 4448

Founded in the late seventies. Formerly part of the Brent Walker Leisure Group but independent since 1990 following a management buyout.

Major producer of feature films and a worldwide distributor.

Granada Film

The London Television Centre,
Upper Ground, London SE1 9LT
Tel: 0171 737 8681
Fax: 0171 737 8682

Major film producers. Output has included: *My Left Foot, Jack and Sarah* and *Up on the Roof* (feature films); *Girls' Night* and *Heart* (TV films). 'We use casting directors for our films. Once these have been appointed all actors/agents deal with them. Any cvs/photos we receive here we try to pass on but it is wasting your time and money to do "mailshots" to us without a specific project in mind. Ideally, you should send direct to the casting director once you have found out their details.'

Grant Naylor Productions

– *see* **Noel Gay Television**, page 294

Howard Hall

6 Foster Road, Abingdon,
Oxfordshire OX14 1YN
Tel: 01235 533981
Fax: 01235 533981
E-mail: howardhall@compuserve.com
Contact *Howard Hall*

Film and video producers of commercials, drama, documentary and corporate programmes. Uses actors and voiceover artists – employs casting directors but will respond to queries by telephone. Will consider demo tapes and video showreels.

Hammer Film Productions Ltd

Millennium Studios, Elstree Way,
Boreham Wood,
Hertfordshire WD6 1SF
Tel: 0181 207 4011
Fax: 0181 905 1127

Feature-film producers. Employs casting directors. No casting queries.

Hammerwood Film Productions Pan European Films

110 Trafalgar Road, Portslade,
East Sussex BN41 1GS
Tel: 01273 277333
Fax: 01273 705451
Contact *Ralph Harry, Petra Ginman, Sara Currie*

Producers of film and television drama and comedy. Welcomes casting queries 'but please put name and telephone number on the back of photographs and date taken. Phone enquiries are not encouraged, nor follow-up calls.' Will consider video showreels – 'they are better than photographs'.

HandMade Films Ltd

19 Beak Street, London W1R 3LB
Tel: 0171 434 3132
Fax: 0171 434 3143
E-mail: handmadefilms.co.uk
President *Gareth Jones*

Major feature-film producers with a back catalogue of 23 titles. Six new titles have been completed in the last 2 years and 3 or 4 projects are in pre-production. Recent output has included: *Dinner at Fred's, The James Gang, The Assistant, The Wrong Guy, Intimate Relations, Sweet Angel Mine.* Earlier titles include *Nuns on the Run, A Private Function, The Long Good Friday,* *Withnail and I, The Missionary, Time Bandits* and *The Life of Brian.* Does not deal with direct queries from actors; always uses casting directors. 'In the light of our system, it is best to be represented by an agent who can approach companies on your behalf. We look for "names", or up-and-coming names, and go on the recommendations of the producer/director/casting director and then review their work.'

Hartswood Films Ltd

Twickenham Film Studios,
The Barons, St Margaret's,
Middlesex TW1 2AW
Tel: 0181 607 8736
Fax: 0181 607 8744

Film and television producers for drama and light entertainment. Output includes: *Men Behaving Badly* (BBC, previously Thames), *Is it Legal?* (Carlton), *The English Wife* (Meridian), *A Woman's Guide to Adultery* (Carlton), *My Good Friend* (ITV), *Code Name Kyril* (HTV). Always employs casting directors and is unable to deal with direct casting queries from actors.

Hat Trick Productions Ltd

10 Livonia Street,
London W1V 3PH
Tel: 0171 434 2451
Fax: 0171 287 9791

Television programme makers. Output includes: *A Very Open Prison, Drop the Dead Donkey, Eleven Men Against Eleven, Father Ted, Have I Got News for You, The Peter Principle.* Employs freelance casting directors; Hat Trick does not welcome casting queries from actors.

Head to Head Communication

The Hook, Plane Tree Crescent,
Feltham, Middlesex TW13 7AQ
Tel: 0181 893 7766
Fax: 0181 893 2777
E-mail: headtohead@atlas.co.uk
Contact *Harry McNicol, Anthony Chilton*

Producers of corporate videos. Uses voiceover artists and actors on occasion. No casting queries; employs casting directors and works through agents. Will consider demo tapes and video showreels.

Hourglass Pictures Ltd

117 Merton Road,
Wimbledon,
London SW19 1ED
Tel: 0181 540 8786
Fax: 0181 542 6598

Film and video documentaries, drama and commercials. Prefers to deal with agents rather than receive direct casting queries from actors.

Hourglass Productions Limited

4 The Heights,
London SE7 8JH
Tel: 0181 858 6870
Fax: 0181 858 6870
Contact *John Walsh (Producer/Director)*

Film and television producers of drama and documentary programmes. Output has included *Monarch*, a major historical feature-film drama on the death of Henry VIII played by T. P. McKenna and with Jean Marsh. Always deals with agents only; will consider demo tapes and video showreels.

Alan Hydes Associates

East Royd House, Woodlands Drive,
Apperley Bridge,
West Yorkshire BD10 0PA
Tel: 0113 250 3467
Fax: 0113 250 3467

Film, video and television: drama and corporate work, including children's television programmes. Employs casting directors and does not welcome direct casting queries from actors.

Ideal Image Ltd

Cherrywood House, Crawley Down Road, Felbridge, Surrey RH19 2PP
Tel: 01342 300566
Fax: 01342 312566

Producers of documentary and drama for film, video, television and corporate clients. Output includes: *The Devils' Year* (documentary on the Red Devils), *Just Another Friday* (corporate drama). Uses freelance casting directors.

Illuminations Films

19–20 Rheidol Mews, Rheidol Terrace,
London N1 8NU
Tel: 0171 226 0266
Fax: 0171 359 1151
E-mail: griff@illumin.co.uk
Contact *Keith Griffiths*

Producers of documentary films. Output has included: *London, Robinson in Space, Secret Joy of Falling Angels, Institute Benjamenta* and Jan Svankmajer's *Conspirators of Pleasure*. Uses actors but always employs casting directors; welcomes written queries related to production information in *Screen International*. Will consider demo tapes and video showreels.

Lagan Pictures Ltd

7 Rugby Court, Agincourt Avenue,
Belfast BT7 1PN
Tel: 01232 326125
Fax: 01232 326125
Contact *Stephen Butcher*

Previously concentrated on documentary and corporate work but now developing television drama and feature films. Always uses casting directors; 'we do not have the resources to deal with general enquiries' but welcomes cvs and (small) photographs from actors based in or originating from Northern Ireland for reference in casting future productions.

Maverick Television

The Custard Factory, Gibb Street,
Birmingham B9 4AA
Tel: 0121 771 1812
Fax: 0121 771 1550

Founded 1994. Documentary and drama programmes. Output includes: *Blazed* (Channel 4 drama), *Trade Secrets* (BBC2), *Wingnut and the Sprog* (Channel 4 drama), *Michelle's Story* (Comic Relief special for BBC1). Occasionally uses actors and voiceover artists. Prefers to deal with agents rather than with actors direct.

Maya Vision Ltd

43 New Oxford Street,
London WC1A 1BH
Tel: 0171 836 1113
Fax: 0171 836 5169
E-mail:
maya@mayavision.demon.co.uk
Contact *John Cranmer*

Producers of film and television drama and documentary programmes.

Output has included *A Bit of Scarlet* (feature documentary with voiceover by Sir Ian McKellen), *Headcase* (15-minute experimental drama) and *In the Footsteps of Alexander the Great* (4 x 1 hour documentaries for BBC1). No casting queries; always uses casting directors and works through agents. No demo tapes or video showreels.

Mentorn Barraclough Carey

Mentorn House, 140 Wardour Street,
London W1V 4LJ
Tel: 0171 287 4545
Fax: 0171 287 3728
E-mail: mfadmin@mentorn.co.uk
Contact *George Carey (Director of Programmes), John Needham (Controller of Drama)*

Producers of television drama, documentary and children's programmes, as well as radio drama and entertainment for the BBC. Television output has included: *Space Precinct* (BBC), *Exclusive* (Channel 5) and *Scratchy & Co.* (ITV). No casting queries; always uses casting directors and works through agents. No demo tapes or video showreels.

Merchant Ivory Productions

46 Lexington Street,
London W1R 3LH
Tel: 0171 437 1200
Fax: 0171 734 1579

Makers of quality literate cinema for an international audience. Producer Ismail Merchant and director James Ivory's list of credits includes: *Heat and Dust, The Bostonians, A Room with a View, Howard's End, Maurice, The Remains of the Day, Jefferson in Paris, Surviving Picasso.* Usually employs casting director Celestia Fox; no casting queries.

Mersey Television Company Ltd

Campus Manor, Abbey Road,
Liverpool L16 0JP
Tel: 0151 722 9122
Fax: 0151 722 1969
Casting Director *Dorothy Andrew*

The best known of the independents in the north of England. Makers of television programmes such as *Brookside* and *Hollyoaks* for Channel 4. Approach in writing; send cv and photograph and performance notices. 'We try to cover shows in Liverpool and Manchester.' Will consider showreels if accompanied by sae.

The Morrison Company

302 Clive Court, Maida Vale,
London W9 1SF
Tel: 0171 289 7976
Fax: 0171 681 1031
E-mail:
donmorrisonUK@compuserve.com
Contact *Don Morrison*

Film and video producers of drama, documentary and corporate material, plus multimedia and training. Always uses casting directors but will consider audio tapes and video showreels.

MW Entertainments

– *see* Producing Theatres and Independent Managements, page 151

Newgate Company

13 Dafford Street, Larkhall, Bath,
Somerset BA1 6SW
Tel: 01225 318335
Contact *Jo Anderson*

A commonwealth of established actors,

directors and playwrights, Newgate originally concerned itself solely with theatre writing (at the Bush, Stratford, Roundhouse, etc.). However, in the course of development, several productions have fed into a list of ongoing drama for the BBC and Channel 4. Now looking to develop this co-production strand for television and film projects with other 'indies'.

Ovation Productions

1 Prince of Wales Passage,
London NW1 3EF
Tel: 0171 387 2342
Fax: 0171 380 0404
E-mail: ovationgb@aol.com
Contact *John Plews*

Producers of corporate videos. Uses actors and voiceover artists. Welcomes casting queries although prefers to work through agents. 'A biography and photograph through the post is fine but don't send a showreel unless asked. When you do send a showreel, make sure it is a decent-quality tape and properly labelled.'

Barry Palin Associates Ltd

143 Charing Cross Road,
London WC2H 0EE
Tel: 0171 478 4680
Fax: 0171 494 1305

Some television drama, but corporate videos in the main. Sometimes uses casting directors but, otherwise, prefers to deal direct with agents.

Parallax Pictures Ltd

7 Denmark Street, London WC2H 9LS
Tel: 0171 836 1478
Fax: 0171 497 8062

Feature film and television drama

producers. Output includes: *Riff-Raff, Bad Behaviour, Raining Stones, Ladybird, Ladybird, ID, Land and Freedom, The Englishman Who Went up a Hill but Came Down a Mountain, Bliss, Jump the Gun, Carla's Song.* Employs casting directors and prefers to deal with agents.

Pearson Television Ltd
1 Stephen Street, London W1P 1PJ
Tel: 0171 691 6000

UK's largest independent production and distribution company. Output includes: *Birds of a Feather, Goodnight Sweetheart, This is Your Life, Strike it Lucky, Mosley.* Casting directors are employed for each production. Also produces *The Bill* for which all casting is dealt with by the Casting Department at the production office: 1 Deer Park Road, Merton, London SW19 3TL (tel: 0181 540 0600).

Penumbra Productions Ltd
80 Brondesbury Road,
London NW6 6RX
Tel: 0171 328 4550
Fax: 0171 328 3844
E-mail: 101621.3135@compuserve. com
Contact *H. O. Nazareth (Film and TV), Roger Elsgood (Radio)*

Producers of film, television, video and audio drama and documentary programmes. Output has included *To the Wedding* (adaptation of a John Berger novel for Radio 3), *Mother* – provisional title (Channel 4 drama based on a true story) and *Sold* – provisional title (feature film). No casting queries; always uses casting directors and works through agents. No demo tapes or video showreels.

Pepper Productions
– see **Noel Gay Television**, page 295

Picture Palace Films Ltd
19 Edis Street,
London NW1 8LE
Tel: 0171 586 8763
Fax: 0171 586 9048

Founded 1971. Leading independent producer of television drama. Output includes: *Sharpe's Rifles* (Carlton), *Little Napoleons* (Channel 4), *The Orchid House* (Channel 4). Employs freelance casting directors and does not welcome casting queries.

Pola Jones Associates Ltd
– see Producing Theatres and Independent Managements, page 152

Portman Productions
167 Wardour Street,
London W1V 3TA
Tel: 0171 468 3400
Fax: 0171 468 3499

Producers of television drama. Output includes: *Rebecca* (Carlton), *Coming Home* (ITV). Always uses casting directors. Does not welcome casting queries from actors.

Premiere Productions
3 Colville Place,
London W1P 1HN
Tel: 0171 255 1650

Corporate training videos and some feature films. Always uses casting directors. Does not welcome casting queries.

Sarah Radclyffe Productions

5th Floor, 83–84 Berwick Street,
London W1V 3PJ
Tel: 0171 437 3128
Fax: 0171 437 3129

Feature-film producers. Founded in 1993 by Sarah Radclyffe who previously founded and co-owned Working Title Films. Output includes: *Second Best* directed by Chris Menges, *Sirens* directed by John Duigan. Always employs freelance casting directors and does not welcome casting queries.

Red Rooster Film & Television Entertainment Ltd

29 Floral Street, London WC2E 9DP
Tel: 0171 379 7727
Fax: 0171 379 5756
Contact *Jill Green (Managing Director)*

Producers of film and television drama. Red Rooster works entirely through casting directors and so does not encourage direct correspondence from actors. No demo tapes or video showreels.

Richmond Films & Television Ltd

5 Dean Street, London W1V 5RN
Tel: 0171 734 9313
Fax: 0171 287 2058

Film and television, drama and comedy. Output includes: *Press Gang, The Lodge, The Office, Wavelength.* No casting queries; always uses casting directors and works through agents.

Rose Bay Film Productions

– *see* **Noel Gay Television**, page 295

Sands Films

119 Rotherhithe Street,
London SE16 4NF
Tel: 0171 231 2209
Fax: 0171 231 2119

Film and television drama. Output includes: *Little Dorrit, The Fool, As You Like It, A Dangerous Man, The Long Day Closes, A Passage to India, The Nutcracker.*

Scala Productions

39–43 Brewer Street,
London W1R 3FD
Tel: 0171 734 7060
Fax: 0171 437 3248

Production company set up by ex-Palace Productions Nik Powell and Stephen Woolley. An impressive list of credits includes: *Company of Wolves, Absolute Beginners, Mona Lisa, Scandal, Crying Game, Backbeat, Hollow Reed, Neon Bible.* No casting queries; always uses casting directors and works through agents.

Sianco Cyf

7 Ffordd Segontiwm, Caernafon,
Gwynedd LL55 2LL
Tel: 01286 673436
Fax: 01286 673436
Contact *Siân Teifi*

Producers of television and audio-visual drama, corporate, children's and educational programmes. Welcomes casting queries; approach in writing with cv and follow up with a telephone call. 'Enthusiasm is welcomed, pestering is *not.*' Will consider demo tapes and video showreels.

Smith & Watson

The Gothic House, Fore Street,
Totnes, Devon TW9 5EH
Tel: 01803 863033
Fax: 01803 864219
Contact *Chris Watson, Nick Smith*

Television and video – commercials, documentary, corporate and light entertainment. Rarely uses actors. Does not welcome casting queries, prefers to work through agents. Will consider demo tapes and video showreels.

Spellbound Productions Limited

90 Cowdenbeath Path, Islington,
London N1 0LG
Tel: 0171 278 0052
Fax: 0171 278 0052
Contact *Paul Harris*

Film, television and video drama producers who are currently expanding into audio, documentary, commercials, corporate and animation programmes. Output has included: *Leave to Remain* (Film on 4) and *Ink* (theatrical feature film). 'We are happy to look at an actor's cv and showreel but generally use casting directors and work through agents. Get yourself known to casting directors; have an agent who is keen to promote you and your work; have high-quality publicity material, photographs, showreels, audio tapes, etc.; keep in touch with producers and production companies.'

'Spoken' Image Ltd

The Design Centre, 44 Canal Street,
Manchester M1 3WD
Tel: 0161 236 7522
Fax: 0161 236 0020
Contact *Stephen Foster*

Television, video and audio – drama, documentary and corporate programmes. No casting queries; always uses casting directors and works through agents. Will consider demo tapes and video showreels.

Stagescreen Productions

12 Upper St Martin's Lane,
London WC2H 9DL
Tel: 0171 497 2510
Fax: 0171 497 2208
E-mail: stgescreen@aol.com
Contact *Jeffrey Taylor*

Producers of film and television drama. Output has included: *A Handful of Dust* and *Foreign Affairs*. Always employs casting directors. Welcomes *written* casting queries and will consider demo tapes and video showreels.

Strawberry Productions

36 Priory Avenue, London W4 1TY
Tel: 0181 994 4494
Fax: 0181 742 7675
Contact *John Black*

Film, television and audio – drama, documentary and corporate programmes. No casting queries; always uses casting directors and works through agents. No demo tapes or video showreels.

Table Top Productions

1 The Orchard, Chiswick,
London W4 1JZ
Tel: 0181 742 0507
Fax: 0181 742 0507
Contact *Alvin Rakoff*

Producers of film and television drama. Output has included: *Dance to the Music of Time* (Channel 4). No casting queries; always uses casting directors and works through agents.

Talisman Films Ltd

5 Addison Place, London W11 4RJ
Tel: 0171 603 7474
Fax: 0171 602 7422
E-mail: talisman films@dial.pipex.com

Drama for film and television: developing the full range of drama – TV series, serials and single films. Feature films: *Rob Roy, Remember Me*; television: *Just William, The Rector's Wife*. No casting queries; always uses casting directors and works through agents.

TalkBack Productions

36 Percy Street, London W1P 0LN
Tel: 0171 323 9777
Fax: 0171 637 5105

Independent television production company set up in 1981 by Mel Smith and Griff Rhys Jones. Specialises in comedy, comedy dramas and drama; also corporate and training films. Output includes: *Smith and Jones, Murder Most Horrid, Bonjour la Classe, Demob, The Day Today, Paris, Knowing Me Knowing You with Alan Partridge, Milner, Loose Talk, In Search of Happiness, They Think It's All Over*. Always employs freelance casting directors, as required; does not welcome casting queries.

Televideo Ltd

The Riverside, Furnival Road,
Sheffield S4 7YA
Tel: 0114 249 1500
Fax: 0114 249 1505
E-mail: telvid.demon.co.uk
Contact *Graham King*

Television and corporate video programmes and sports presentation. Output has included a video for 11 leading football clubs and clients include Midland Bank and the Department of Education and Employment. Rarely uses actors. No casting queries. Will consider audio tapes but not video showreels. 'Budgets mean that we only ever use people based in the north.'

Teliesyn

Helwick House, 19 David Street,
Cardiff CF1 2EH
Tel: 01222 667556
Fax: 01222 667546

Film and video: drama, documentary, music and social action in English and Welsh. Celtic Film Festival, BAFTA Cymru, Grierson and Indie award winner. Output includes: *Branwen* (feature film for S4C), *Reel Truth* (drama-documentary series on the history of early film for S4C and Channel 4), *Subway Cops and the Mole Kings* (Channel 4), *Codi Clawr Hanes II* (a second drama-documentary series on women's history for S4C). No telephone calls but happy to receive cvs and photographs which are kept on file.

Tern Television Productions Ltd

73 Crown Street, Aberdeen AB11 6EX
Tel: 01224 211123
Fax: 01224 211199
E-mail: office@terntv.u-net.com
Contact *Gwyneth Hardy, David Strachan, Evelyn Paterson*

Television, video and audio – documentary, corporate and religious features. Output has included: *The Beechgrove Garden* (BBC Scotland), *Growing Spaces* (Radio 4) and *Scotland on Location* (CD-ROM). Uses actors and voiceover artists. No casting queries; 'prefer to trawl when required'. Will consider demo tapes and video showreels.

Thames Television Ltd
– see **Pearson Television Ltd**, page 300

Tiger Aspect Productions
5 Soho Square, London W1V 5DE
Tel: 0171 434 0672
Fax: 0171 287 1448

Television producers for documentary programmes, dramas and comedy – variety, sitcom and comedy drama. Output includes: *Mr Bean*, *The Thin Blue Line*, *The Vicar of Dibley*, *Howard Goodall's Organ Works*, *Deacon Brodie*, *Hospital*. Always employs freelance casting directors. Does not welcome casting queries.

Turning Point Productions
Pinewood Studios,
Pinewood Road, Iver Heath,
Buckinghamshire SL0 0NH
Tel: 01753 630666
Fax: 01753 650855

Television drama producers. Output includes: *Red Fox* (LWT mini-series), *Cider with Rosie* (ITV). Always employs freelance casting directors. Does not welcome casting queries.

Two Four Productions Ltd
Quay West Studios,
Old Newnham, Plymouth,
South Devon PL7 5BH
Tel: 01752 345424
Fax: 01752 344224
E-mail: enq@twofour.co.uk
Contact *Jinx Mattinson*

Television, video and audio – documentary and corporate programmes. Output has included documentary dramas for the Department of Health and Social Security, training videos for the British Heart Foundation and Barnardos and television programmes for BBC1, ITV and Channel 4. Uses actors and voiceover artists; welcomes casting queries – 'send a letter with a photograph for our files'. Will consider demo tapes and video showreels.

United Film and Television Productions
48 Leicester Square,
London WC2H 7FB
Tel: 0171 389 8555
Fax: 0171 930 8499
Managing Director *Vernon Lawrence*
Controller of Drama *Simon Lewis*

Producers of drama programmes for Anglia Television and Meridian Broadcasting. Output includes: *Touching Evil II, A Certain Justice, Where the Heart Is II, Hornblower*. Uses freelance casting directors. Contact the production company for details.

United Media Ltd
68 Berwick Street, London W1V 3PE
Tel: 0171 287 2396
Fax: 0171 287 2398

Film, video and television drama. Output includes: *To the Lighthouse, Jamaica Inn, The Krays, The Inside Man, In a Shallow Grave*. Usually employs freelance casting directors.

Vera Media – Productions & Training
30–38 Dock Street, Leeds,
West Yorkshire LS10 1JF
Tel: 0113 242 8646
Fax: 0113 245 1238
E-mail: vera@vera-media.demon.co.uk
Contact *Al Garthwaite*

Producers of television and video

documentary, corporate and participatory educational programmes. Output has included: *Choosing to Foster – The Challenge to Care, The Waltz* (production by West Yorkshire Playhouse Schools' Company), *Street Children* (Leeds Development Education Centre) and *There's More to Drugs than Dying.* Rarely uses actors. Welcomes casting queries regarding voiceovers but employs *local* voiceover artists only. Will consider demo tapes if you come within this category.

Video Enterprises

12 Barbers Wood Road,
High Wycombe,
Hertfordshire HP12 4EP
Tel: 01494 534144
Fax: 01494 535144
E-mail: maurice@vident.u-net.com
Contact *Maurice R. Fleisher*

Producers of corporate videos. Uses voiceover artists. Prefers to work through agents but will consider demo tapes.

Video Presentations

PO Box 281,
Wimbledon,
London SW19 3DD
Tel: 0181 542 7721
Fax: 0181 543 0855
Contact *John Holloway*

Producers of corporate and documentary videos. Does not welcome casting queries; prefers to work through agents. No unsolicited demo tapes or video showreels. 'Keep trying; we never know when something may turn up that requires actors.'

Visible Productions Limited

3 The Flag Store, Jubilee Yard,
Queen Elizabeth Street,
London SE1 2LP
Tel: 0171 403 9333
Fax: 0171 403 5225
E-mail: 10303.675@compuserve.com
Contact *Mike Raggett*

Video and audio material – drama, documentary, corporate and multimedia programmes. Uses actors and voiceover artists. Sometimes uses casting directors and prefers to work through agents but 'a head shot and cv are acceptable'. No unsolicited demo tapes or video showreels.

Wall to Wall Television

8–9 Spring Place,
London NW5 3ER
Tel: 0171 485 7424
Fax: 0171 267 5292

Producers of documentary, features and drama. Output includes: *Plotlands, It's Not Unusual, Nightmare: The Birth of Horror, Baby It's You, A Taste of the Times.* Employs casting directors.

The Walnut Partnership

Crown House, Armley Road, Leeds,
West Yorkshire LS12 2EJ
Tel: 0113 245 6913
Fax: 0113 243 9614
Contact *Gary Nutland*

Producers of corporate videos – dramas and documentaries for a range of blue-chip companies. The main area of programmes is in training and internal communications departments. Employs actors and voiceover artists but casting queries should be from local actors only. Will consider demo tapes and video showreels if you come within this category.

Warner Sisters Film & TV Ltd
Canalot Studios, 222 Kensal Road,
London W10 5BN
Tel: 0181 960 3550
Fax: 0181 960 3880
Chief Executives *Lavinia Warner,*
Jane Wellesley, Anne-Marie Casey,
Dorothy Viljoen

Founded 1984. Drama and comedy; television and feature films. Output includes: *Selling Hitler, Rides, Dangerous Lady, Life's a Gas, She-Play, A Village Affair, Dressing for Breakfast, The Spy that Caught a Cold, The Bite.* Employs casting directors; does not particularly welcome direct casting queries from actors.

Watershed Television
11th Floor, Clifton Heights,
Bristol BS8 1EJ
Tel: 0117 909 0909
Fax: 0117 973 3722

Film and video producers – corporate and commercials. Usually employs a freelance casting director when required and does not particularly welcome casting queries.

Workhouse Television
Granville House, St Peter Street,
Winchester, Hampshire SO23 8BP
Tel: 01962 626400
Fax: 01962 626401
E-mail: carol@workhouse.ltd.uk
Contact *Carol Wade, Mary Lou Warren*

Producers of television, video and multi-media documentary and corporate programmes. Output has included: *Birdwatch with Chris Packham* (Meridian), *Out and About* (BBC South), *Wizadora* (ITV) and numerous blue-chip corporate clients. Uses actors and voiceover agents but prefers to work through agents. No demo tapes or video showreels.

Working Title Films
Oxford House, 5th Floor, 76 Oxford Street, London W1N 9FD
Tel: 0171 307 3000
Fax: 0171 307 3001/2/3
Contact *Tim Bevan, Eric Fellner*

Producers of film and television drama and light entertainment. Output has included feature films: *Four Weddings and a Funeral, Dead Man Walking* and *The Borrowers* (second TV series and feature film) and *Tales of the City* (TV series). No casting queries; always uses casting directors and works through agents. Will consider demo tapes and video showreels but only if sent by agents.

Wortman Productions UK
48 Chiswick Staithe, London W4 3TP
Tel: 0181 994 8886
Contact *Neville Wortman*

Film, television, video, audio – drama, documentary and corporate programmes. Output has included *English Country Houses* (ITV), *Ellington* (BSkyB), *Jimmy Young* and corporate clients Boots Plc, St Ivel, Powergen and Eurofighter. No casting queries; sometimes uses casting directors and prefers to work through agents. 'We look for specialist appeal every time and therefore deal through agencies.' No unsolicited demo tapes or video showreels.

Zenith Productions Ltd

43–45 Dorset Street,
London W1H 4AB
Tel: 0171 224 2440
Fax: 0171 224 3194
E-mail: zenith@easynet.co.uk

Part of the Zenith Group. Producers of feature films and television prog-rammes. Output includes: *Inspector Morse, Hamish Macbeth, Rhodes, Bodyguards*. Always employs casting directors; no direct casting queries.

Zenith North

11th Floor, Cale Cross House,
156 Pilgrim Street,
Newcastle upon Tyne NE1 6SU
Tel: 0191 261 0077
Fax: 0191 222 0271
E-mail: zenithnorth@dial.pipex.com

Part of the Zenith Group. Producers of television programmes such as *Byker Grove* (BBC), *Blues and Twos* (Carlton), *The Famous Five* (ITV). Uses casting directors and is happy to hear from actors based in the region.

Audiobooks

BBC Worldwide Publishing Ltd (BBC Radio Collection)

Woodlands, (Room AA3132), 80 Wood Lane, London W12 0TT
Tel: 0181 576 2230
Fax: 0181 576 3851
E-mail: jan.paterson@bbc.co.uk
Managing Director Bob Phillis
Contact Jan Paterson, Piera Johnson

Audio collections of BBC Radio 4 comedy programmes such as *Round the Horne, News Quiz, I'm Sorry I Haven't a Clue* and full-cast dramatisations of classic and modern fiction. No casting queries; actors are contacted through agents only. 'Although BBC Radio Collection is a commercial publisher, almost everything we produce has been/will be broadcast on BBC Radio. If we are investing in the making of a programme, we have a limited say in who we would like to use for a reading.'

Chivers Press Limited

Windsor Bridge Road, Bath, Somerset BA2 3AX
Tel: 01225 335336
Fax: 01225 310771
Audio Editor Sarah Hadaway

Produces mainstream and literary fiction plus some non-fiction, mostly consisting of travel and autobiography. Deals with agents and also with actors direct. Will consider demo audio tapes. 'With two studios fully operational at our offices, we welcome approaches from actors based in the Bath area.'

CSA Telltapes Ltd

101 Chamberlayne Road, London NW10 3ND
Tel: 0181 960 8466
Fax: 0181 968 0804
Managing Director Clive Stanhope

Produces audiobooks of short stories and classic and modern literature. Prefers to deal with agents. 'Only actors with a "name" can be considered.'

CYP Limited/Audiosport Limited

The Fairway, Bush Fair, Harlow, Essex CM18 6LY
Tel: 01279 444707
Fax: 01279 445570
E-mail: cyp@btinternet.com
Joint Managing Directors Mike Kitson, John Bassett

Children's and sporting audio tapes. Does not welcome casting queries but will consider demo audio tapes.

HarperCollins Publishers Ltd (Adult Division)
77–85 Fulham Palace Road,
London W6 8JB
Tel: 0181 741 7070
Fax: 0181 307 4440
Publisher *Rosalie George*

Produces fiction, non-fiction and poetry audio cassettes, mostly in abridged form. Does not welcome casting queries; prefers to work through agents. No unsolicited demo audio tapes.

HarperCollins Publishers Ltd (Children's Division)
Address/tel/fax as above.
Senior Editor Stella Paskins

Produces picture-book and tape packs, unabridged younger fiction, abridged older fiction and dramatisations. Does not welcome casting queries; usually works through agents. No unsolicited demo audio tapes.

Isis Publishing Limited
7 Centremead, Osney Mead,
Oxford OX2 0ES
Tel: 01865 250333
Fax: 01865 790358
E-mail:
audiobooks@isis-publishing.co.uk
Managing Director *John Durrant*
Contact *Sarah Haywood (Studio Manager)*

Produces mainly adult unabridged modern fiction, autobiographical works and some classics. Uses actors with reading experience or with an extensive BBC Radio background. Welcomes casting queries, 'though we are very selective due to the sheer number of queries'. Send letter, cv and demo tape of a 5-minute reading of a classic and 5 minutes of modern fiction, including narration and characterisation. Sarah Haywood says, 'Most tapes sent by actors/agents are unsuitable because they contain commercials only, little of the actor's "natural" narrative voice and often have no reading extracts at all. It takes a lot of concentration. Playing one part isn't the same as narrating a book. I think it's important to try and create some intimacy in the delivery, drawing the listener in. It sounds obvious but very few actually achieve or maintain this. Experience of using microphones is useful.'

Naxos Audiobooks
16 Wolsey Mews, London NW5 2DX
Tel: 0171 482 4110
Fax: 0171 482 4101
Contact *Nicolas Soanes (Managing Director), Anna Britten*

Produces classic literature with classical music on CD and tape – novels, biography, Shakespeare plays, poetry, children's, etc. Prefers to work through agents but will consider demo audio tape and cv.

Penguin Audiobooks
27 Wrights Lane, London W8 5TZ
Tel: 0171 416 3000
Fax: 0171 416 3099
Contact *Anna Hopkins*

Produces classic and contemporary fiction and non-fiction, children's titles, plus poetry and drama. Some books are read by authors. Prefers to deal with actors via agents. No casting queries or demo audio tapes.

PolyGram Spoken Word

1 Sussex Place,
London W6 9XS
Tel: 0181 910 5000
Fax: 0181 910 5900
Managing Director *Brian Berg*
Contact *Alex Mitchison, Peter Ballard*

Produces comedy, abridged fiction, science fiction, autobiography and poetry. Welcomes casting queries; approach in writing. Will consider demo audio tapes.

Random House Audiobooks

20 Vauxhall Bridge Road,
London SW1V 2SA
Tel: 0171 840 8557
Fax: 0171 233 6127
Managing Director *Simon King*

Produces commercial and literary fiction and non-fiction. Does not welcome casting queries; prefers to deal with agents only. No demo audio tapes.

Reardon Publishing

56 Upper Norwood Street,
Leckhampton, Cheltenham,
Gloucestershire GL53 0DU
Contact *Mr N. Reardon (Managing Director)*

Produces walking and travel-guide audio packs and videos. Will consider demo audio tapes.

RNIB Talking Book Service

RNIB, 206 Great Portland Street,
London W1N 5HG

Uses professional actors and broadcasters to read books for the visually impaired. Does not welcome casting queries although, occasionally, readers are required with an *authentic* regional accent.

Simon & Schuster Ltd

West Garden Place,
Kendal Street,
London W2 2AQ
Tel: 0171 316 1900
Fax: 0171 262 3102
Managing Director *Nick Webb*

Produces business/self-help, quality fiction and *Star Trek* tapes. Does not welcome casting queries; prefers to deal with agents. 'Very few audios are originated in the UK – we usually take masters from our US parent company.'

Organisations

Equity

British Actors' Equity Association (incorporating Variety Artistes' Federation)

Guild House, Upper St Martin's Lane,
London WC2H 9EG
Tel: 0171 379 6000
Fax: 0171 379 7001
E-mail:infor@equity.org.uk
General Secretary *Ian McGarry*

North-West
Conavon Court, 12 Blackfriars Street,
Salford M3 5BQ
Tel: 0161 832 3183
Fax: 0161 839 3133

North-East
PO Box 1254, Sheffield S10 3XY
Tel: 01142 305294

Scotland
114 Union Street, Glasgow G1 3QQ
Tel: 0141 248 2472
Fax: 0141 248 2473

Wales, South-West and Midlands
Transport House, 1 Cathedral Road,
Cardiff CF1 9SD
Tel: 01222 397971
Fax: 01222 230754

Founded in 1930. Membership open to actors, club and circus performers, stage management, theatre designers and directors, choreographers, dancers, singers and many others in the entertainment industry. Deputies elected in each theatre company, TV production and film unit, etc. collect subscriptions and maintain contact between members and the Equity office.

Equity's principal functions are 'to secure the best possible terms and conditions for its members through collective bargaining, and to make representations to Government and other bodies on matters of policy relating to the performing arts'. Standard contracts laying down minimum terms and conditions have been negotiated in virtually every section of entertainment. Free legal advice is available for any case of dispute in connection with professional engagements, and advice can be given on National Insurance, Income Tax and VAT. *Equity Journal* is issued free to members.

A number of registers are maintained for the benefit of members and are circulated or made available to employers. The list includes: Afro-Asian artists, performers with disabilities,

315

foreign-language speakers, stunt performers, fight directors, theatre directors and designers, puppeteers, choreographers, twins/ triplets, walk-ons, Welsh speakers.

Entrance fee £35

Subscription rates per annum

GROSS
EARNINGS SUBSCRIPTION

GROSS EARNINGS	SUBSCRIPTION
Less than £3,000	£36
Between £3,001 and £4,000	£50
Between £4,001 and £5,000	£60
Between £5,001 and £6,000	£70
Between £6,001 and £7,000	£80
Between £7,001 and £8,000	£90
Between £8,001 and £9,000	£100
Between £9,001 and £10,000	£110
More than £10,000	1% of gross earnings but not exceeding £1600

Equity Guide to Membership

Equity provides the following guidelines for potential members:

Membership of Equity is open to anyone currently exercising professional skills in the entertainment industry.

To be eligible to apply, it is essential that you furnish proof of a current Equity contract (and details of previous engagements, if any). Upon receipt of acceptable evidence, an application form will be sent to you to complete and return, together with the specified entrance fee and annual subscription. Your completed application form will then be placed before the Equity Council who shall, in such matters, be the final arbiter.

In most areas of work, casting agreements have been made with employers in theatre, TV, film, radio and commercials, which stipulate that insofar as it is reasonable and practicable, engagements should be offered to experienced professional performers. In the event that performers with no previous experience are engaged, Equity is informed and the performer concerned is recruited into membership. An exception to the above arrangement applies to Walk-ons and Supporting Artists in TV and TV commercials. These artists are entitled to membership if they can provide evidence of at least six days' work, over a period of 12 consecutive months, undertaken in accordance with the appropriate Equity agreement.

Variety and Circus

Variety and circus artists need to provide contractual evidence of four engagements, within the last 12 months, and one pending engagement. Membership is also open to artists working as professional entertainers on long-term engagements who can provide contractual evidence of work in, for example, circuses, cruise ships, holiday centres and in clubs overseas.

Other Categories

Artists engaged as 'professional broadcasters' in TV or radio are entitled to join as are concert and session singers, who need to show evidence of at least one professional engagement.

Work Overseas

If you have worked professionally overseas and can provide proof of your employment, together with the details of membership of the relevant union in that country, you will be entitled to membership. This arrangement is available to UK or other EU citizens, or people from abroad who do not require work permits to work in this country.

Student Membership

Graduates from drama courses accredited by NCDT, and dance courses accredited by CDET are entitled to membership on graduating, without the necessity to obtain an engagement.

Equity also has a Student Membership scheme open to students on a full-time course lasting one year or more, preparing them for work in areas Equity covers in the entertainment industry.

Full details on membership and application forms are available from Equity's offices. Please enclose sae.

Selected extracts from Equity Agreements

TELEVISION

ITV Agreement

(Dated 1 May 1993; fees effective from 1 June 1996)

Minimum rehearsal day fee:	£38.25
Minimum production day fee:	£45.25
Minimum programme fee:	£81.25

Payment of a negotiated programme fee entitles a company to transmit a programme once simultaneously or non-simultaneously in any combination of transmission areas totalling up to 25% of National Television Households (NTH).

The proportion of NTH in each area covered by an ITV licence-holder is as follows:

Anglia	7
HTV	8
Border	1
Meridian	9
LWT/Carlton	19
Scottish	6
Central	15
Tyne Tees	5
Channel	1
Ulster	2
Grampian	2
West Country	3
Granada	12
Yorkshire	10

Where a programme is transmitted in areas totalling more than 25% of NTH the actor is paid proportionately as follows:

% of NTH in areas to which programmes are transmitted	Payment
26% to 50%	twice programme fee
51% to 75%	three times programme fee
76% to 100%	four times programme fee

Channel 4 (including S4C) is regarded as 100% of NTH.

Minimum Guaranteed Rate (per week of network engagement)

When an actor is engaged in a network production, the total earnings are calculated and then the total is divided by the total number of weeks of the engagement to give an average weekly earnings figure. If this average is less than the minimum weekly rate, then the difference for the number of weeks is paid. Total earnings include production day and rehearsal day payments, the programme fee, any overtime payments and any payments for location work and the commencement of the rehearsal period of up to six weeks. One week consists of five out of seven consecutive days.

Scripts should be sent to an actor at least three days before the first rehearsal and there should be a read-through by all the cast who have speaking parts prior to any rehearsal or performance.

A production day in the *studio* consists of up to nine hours, during which time rehearsal and/or recording can take place and two meal breaks of one hour each. Overtime is paid for each full or part hour at £7.25 per quarter hour.

A production day on *location* consists of up to ten hours during which time eight hours of rehearsal and/or recording may take place. In addition to the eight hours of work, one meal break of one hour and up to one hour travelling is allowed. Overtime is paid for each full or part hour at £7.25 per quarter hour.

Night work is work in the studio or on location scheduled to extend beyond midnight or to commence between midnight and 7a.m. Payment is $1^1/_2$ times the production day payment, with overtime at $^1/_2$ times the daytime overtime rate.

Repeat Fees

Programmes may not be transmitted more than twice in any one area within three years from the date of first transmission in the UK without the prior consent of Equity. A repeat within two years will result in the payment of 100% of the programme fee for each area, and a repeat between two and three years from the date of first transmission in the UK will result in the payment of 150% of the programme fee for each area. Four years – 175%, with an increase of 25% for each subsequent year from date of first transmission.

One Day Engagements – For Series, Serials and Similar Programmes

An actor may be engaged for a single day for an inclusive payment of £470.35. This entitles the company to rehearse and/or record the actor's performance for inclusion in not more than six episodes. Adequate opportunity should be afforded for rehearsals to take place on that day.

Travel Payments

Actors are paid the cost of travel by public transport between the centre of the standard radius (set out below) and the place of engagement. If an actor is asked by the company to use his own vehicle, reimbursement is made based on mileage rates applied by the company.

Town	*Centre*	*Radius*
London	Charing Cross	10 miles
Birmingham	Town Hall	7 miles
Manchester	Public Library	7 miles
Glasgow	George Square	7 miles
Belfast	City Hall	7 miles
Cardiff	Town Hall	7 miles
Southampton	Civic Centre	7 miles
Plymouth	City Centre Building	7 miles
Carlisle	Town Hall	7 miles
Aberdeen	Town Hall	7 miles
Newcastle upon Tyne	White Cross	7 miles
Norwich	City Hall	7 miles
Bristol	St James Barton Roundabout	7 miles
Leeds	Town Hall	7 miles
Nottingham	Council House	7 miles
Maidstone	Town Hall	7 miles

BBC Agreement
(dated 1 July 1996)

Fees

Weekly fees (known as *Engagement Fees*) are negotiated for each engagement, bearing in mind the nature and weight of the actor's contribution, the number of programmes to be recorded, the length of the engagement and the actor's status and earning power in television and elsewhere.

The minimum one-week engagement fee is £396.50; engagements of two, three and four weeks attract the following fees:

Duration of Engagement:	*Two Weeks*	*Three Weeks*	*Four Weeks*
Duration of Programme:			
Up to 35 minutes	£625	£855	£1083
36–60 minutes	£793	£1022	£1250
61–90 minutes	£793	£1189	£1418
Over 90 minutes	£793	£1189	£1585

Engagements of five weeks or more: as above plus minimum of £229 for each of the fifth and subsequent weeks.

For engagements of one week's duration, the Work Day entitlement is six days; for a two-week engagement, the entitlement is five Work Days per week (including the first week). Work Days can be used for rehearsals or recording or travel, singly or in combination. Additional Work Days in any one week attract a fee of £61.00 per day (£40.50 per travel only day). Apart from exceptional circumstances, actors are not required to work on more than six days in any consecutive seven-day period.

Serials that are rehearsed and performed within seven days are subject to a special rate of weekly fees.

Payment of the Engagement Fee entitles the BBC to transmit or permit the transmission of the actor's performance in the relevant programme, whether live or recorded, once only from every transmitter of the relevant BBC channel either simultaneously or at different times in different BBC regions.

Hours of work

Studio: for principal (or nominated) performance day: a continuous period of 12 hours to include up to 10 hours' work. Overtime: £28.10 per 15 minutes or part. *Location:* a continuous period of nine hours, including up to eight hours' work and not less than one hour's meal break. *Overtime:* £25.90 per hour or part.

Time spent in costume and make-up preparation counts towards the overall work period. If the actor is required to attend a read-through, costume fitting or photographic session *prior* to the start of an engagement (subject to the actor's availability), a fee of £40.50 is paid for a full day (maximum eight hours); £20.50 for a half day (maximum four hours).

Expenses

When the actor is required to travel from his own region (where he lives or normally works), the BBC pay travel and subsistence.

Repeat Fees

The BBC can transmit two repeats

within three years from the date of the original transmission on both BBC1 and BBC2. 80% of the agreed Residual Basic Fee is paid, but if the programme is shown more than two years from the original transmission (but less than $2^1/_2$ years), the amount is 90% of the Residual Basic Fee*. For programmes repeated more than $2^1/_2$ years (but less than three years), the amount is 100%.

*The Residual Basic Fee for each engagement is not less than 80% and not more than 100% of the total Engagement Fee.

INDEPENDENT PRODUCTION COMPANIES

Television Production Agreement

(dated 15 September 1994)
between Equity and the Producers Alliance for Cinema and Television (PACT)

Fees
Payment of a *UK Network Fee* entitles transmission of the production, simultaneously or non-simultaneously on one channel, by a UK terrestrial broadcaster, i.e. ITV, BBC1, BBC2 and Channel 4.
Minimum Network Engagement Fee: £360 for the first day worked in each and every consecutive seven-day period while on first call to the producer. This is a negotiable fee.
Production Day Payment: in addition to the *Engagement Fee*(s), the actor is paid a non-negotiable production day payment of £40 for each subsequent

day worked beyond the first. If the actor works on a seventh consecutive day, he receives an enhanced production day payment of £60.
Example of work over a consecutive seven-day period:

Two days:
Engagement Fee plus a Production Day Payment of £40.

Six days:
Engagement Fee plus five Production Day Payments at £40.

Seven days:
Engagement Fee plus five Production Day Payments at £40 plus one Production Day Payment at £60.

Payment of an *ITV Regional Engagement Fee* entitles transmission of the production, once simultaneously or non-simultaneously, in any combination of transmissions areas totalling up to 25% of National Television Households (NTH) – *see* ITV Agreement.
ITV Regional Engagement Fee & Production Day Payment: not less than £90 for the first day worked in each and every consecutive seven-day period while on first call to the producer. *Production Day Payment*: as for UK Network above.

Working Hours
Normal Day or Night: 10 hours, inclusive of an unpaid one-hour meal break. Day Calls: commence between 7.00 a.m. and 12 noon.
Continuous Working Day/Night: continuous working periods consist of eight hours without a break for a meal. These periods normally take place between 7.00 a.m. and 7.00 p.m., or 8.00 p.m. and 8.00 a.m. Overtime applies if work continues beyond eight hours.

Time spent in costume and make-up preparation counts towards the overall work period.

RADIO

BBC Radio Agreement
(dated 1 October 1997)

Fees are negotiated taking into account the actor's professional status and value to broadcasting. Special fees may be negotiated for particular programmes to take into account the weight of the actor's contribution and other relevant factors.

Minimum Performance Fee (Full Day Engagements): £152.
Read-Through Half-Day Fee: £54.35.
Additional Days: £90.75.
Overtime Payments: £5.05 for each 15 minutes.
Payment of the actor's fee entitles the BBC to broadcast the programme or recording twice in the Domestic Services of the BBC. One broadcasting covers transmission once in each UK region; where the transmissions are not simultaneous, Equity prefers the transmissions take place within 24 hours of each other. The fee also covers the simultaneous transmission, once, overseas. Variations occur with World Service transmissions.

Hours of Work
A full day consists of a continuous period of nine hours which must include not less than two hours of meal and/or rest breaks. A half day consists of a period of four hours.

Radio Independent Production Companies

In November 1996, Equity negotiated an agreement with the Radio Independents Organisation (formerly IARP) for the recording of productions for BBC Radio. The negotiable fees are in line with the BBC rates listed above. The BBC is responsible for secondary payments for overseas sales, further repeats, etc.

TELEVISION COMMERCIALS

Television Commercials Agreement
(dated 1 November 1991)

between Equity and the Advertising Film and Videotape Producers Association, the Institute of Practitioners in Advertising and the Incorporated Society of British Advertisers.
NB: since September 1997, Equity has been in dispute with the TV Commercials employers and at the time of going to press, Equity members had been instructed not to accept any offer of engagement to work on any UK commercial in any capacity, and not to grant consent for the re-use of any TV commercial made under a contract which has expired.

Auditions
• No payment is made for a first call, nor for videotapes and/or photographs taken.
• For a recall, expenses are paid by the producer or advertiser for travel and out-of-pocket expenses (not less than £20). This also applies if the recall is on the same day as the first call.
• For videotape at a recall, the actor is paid not less than £29 to cover reasonable travel and out-of-pocket expenses (not in addition to the recall expenses above).
• If, for an audition, a voiceover artist is called in to record a script, not less than £20 must be paid. This sum is in

addition to travel and out-of-pocket expenses claimed above.

Wig/Wardrobe Fittings

If the actor is required to attend a wig/wardrobe fitting outside the period of engagement, a payment of £33 is paid for a half day (up to $4^{1}/_{2}$ hours) and £60 for a full day (up to 10 hours, including an hour break).

Studio or Session Fees

The basic studio fee (BSF) is the fee for each working day. The minimum rate for featured actors is £115.

Rehearsal Call

A half-day rehearsal (up to $4^{1}/_{2}$ hours) entitles the actor to 50% of his BSF. For a call of more than $4^{1}/_{2}$ hours, he receives his full BSF plus meal allowances.

Additional Voice Work

If the actor is required on a day other than the visual recording day(s) to do additional voice work (e.g. post-synching), the actor must receive 50% of his BSF for each two-hour session. This does not qualify for use fees.

Working Hours

A working day or night is normally no more than nine hours, excluding an hour's meal break.

(Time spent in make-up, hairdressing and wardrobe is included in working hours.) Day calls commence between 7.30 a.m. and 12 noon. Dawn calls are for services rendered between 4.00 a.m. and 7.30 a.m. For these calls, overtime at the rate of one-fifth of the BSF for each hour or part hour up to 7.30 a.m. is paid in addition to the BSF. Night calls are those scheduled to extend beyond midnight or to commence between midnight and 4.00 a.m. A fee of 50% of the BSF is paid in

addition to the BSF in respect of each session of night work. This night fee does not qualify for use fees.

Overtime

One-fifth of the BSF is paid for each hour or part hour (but a producer may use the actor for up to 15 minutes over the normal day to complete a take). Overtime (other than a night call) after midnight is paid at one-third of the BSF for each hour or part hour. No overtime payment qualifies for use fees.

Breaks Between Calls

Not less than 12 hours between the end of any period of work and the time of the next call must be allowed. Additional payments are made if, for unavoidable reasons, this break is reduced.

Sunday and Public Holidays

Not less than 50% of the BSF (in addition to the BSF) is paid for work on these days. This does not qualify for use fees.

Travelling Time

Where transport is not provided, time spent in travelling to and from a studio or location, within a 20-mile radius of Charing Cross, London, is not included in working hours. If more than 20 miles, it is included in the working hours, excluding 30 minutes each way. Where transport is provided from a central London rendezvous, the working hours are calculated from 30 minutes after the time of call to the rendezvous until 30 minutes before the time the actor is returned to the rendezvous.

Where transport is provided from the performer's home, and when he is required to travel to and from a studio or location more than 30 miles from Charing Cross, travelling time is included in the working hours, excluding 30 minutes each way.

Meal and Rest Breaks
The performer is not required to work for more than five consecutive hours without a break (of not less than one hour) for rest and refreshment. If, for any reason, a main meal break is curtailed or delayed for more than 30 minutes, the actor is paid one-fifth of the BSF in compensation.

Use Fees
Repeat/use fees are based on the BSF. The life of a commercial is three years from the date of the first transmission of the commercial. Use fees are calculated by the number of viewers in the UK, aged four and over, reported to have viewed transmission of the commercial by the audience measurement service operated by the Broadcasters' Audience Research Board (BARB). The total arrived at is expressed as a percentage (TVR-TV Rating) of these UK viewers and the payments are calculated according to a scale which provides for four separate rates as the commercial gains a larger cumulative audience. For example, where the studio fee is £200 and the commercial achieves 550 Network TVRs, the actor receives use fees of £5162.

Ancillary Use
The use of a commercial is limited to TV transmission in the UK. Any extension to other media in the UK or elsewhere, such as cinema, radio or press advertising or inclusion in a film or television documentary, is subject to agreed terms between the performer and the producer/advertiser.

Stills
The producer/advertiser has no right to use still photographs of the actor without his consent. This consent is subject to agreement and payment of a negotiated fee.

Overseas Use
Subject to the consent of the performer.

Payment
Remuneration is due not later than the end of the same month when work-sheets/invoices are received by the 15th, or not later than the 15th of the month following when work-sheets/invoices have been received between the 15th and the end of the month. (It seems to be common practice for the majority of advertisers not to pay before a month has elapsed.) The advertising agency is responsible for having Performer's Work Record forms at the shoot. These should be completed and signed in duplicate at the end of the day's shoot.

WEST END THEATRES

West End Agreement
(dated 12 January 1998)

between Equity and the Society of London Theatres (SOLT)

Wages
Minimum weekly: £275 once nightly (eight performances per week); £322 twice nightly (12 performances per week).

Holiday Pay
Subject to the production having run at least 12 weeks (13 weeks for musicals) and the artist having worked for at least 10 of these weeks, he is entitled to one-half day's holiday for each week (maximum annual entitlement of 24

days) having elapsed since the first rehearsal of the production.

Hours of Work

Not less than three weeks' rehearsal (four weeks for musicals) for every new production. In the event of 75% or more of the cast being replaced at any one time, there must be an adequate rehearsal period of not less than two weeks. A rehearsal period must not exceed six weeks for straight plays (eight for musicals) without Equity's consent.

Performance Time

Defined as beginning 35 minutes (50 for full body make-up) before rise of curtain and running continuously until 15 minutes after curtain down (30 for heavy or full body make-up).

Performances

Maximum of eight performances (Monday to Saturday inclusive) per week (once nightly) or 12 per week (twice nightly/daily) and a maximum of two performances on any one day. Any performances additional to these attract an additional payment of one-eighth of the artist's salary. If, after the production has opened, the manager wishes to give occasional additional performances, the cast must be given not less than two weeks' prior notice, and such performances are included in the weekly hours of work.

Understudies

The manager is obliged to provide adequate and suitable understudy cover for every character in the production except for one-person shows.

No walking understudy should be required to cover more than one leading role or two non-leading roles for the minimum salary.

Minimum performance salary for each performance as an understudy is £22.75 for a leading role; £13.64 for non-leading roles.

Understudy responsibility payment is £24.63 per week for each leading role; £18.48 for non-leading roles.

Programme Notes

The artist has the right of approving all biographical material to be included in the programme.

If there are any errors in the programme, it must be slipped as soon as reasonably practical and the programme must be corrected at the next reprint.

Insurance

Where the performer is required to undertake business of a hazardous nature, including any fight sequences, management are obliged to arrange personal accident insurance for the actor.

Flying

Unless specially engaged for the purpose, the actor has the right to refuse to be lifted for flying.

Stage Management

For a straight play, a team of not less than one stage manager (SM) or company and stage manager (CSM), one deputy stage manager (DSM), none of whom shall act or understudy, and either an assistant stage manager (ASM, who shall neither act nor understudy in any production), or an understudy with stage management duties shall be employed.

Wages

ASM: £275 (once nightly); £322 (twice nightly)

DSM: £344 (once nightly); £402 (twice nightly)
SM: £386 (once nightly); £451 (twice nightly)
CSM: £413 (once nightly); £505 (twice nightly)

PROVINCIAL THEATRES

Provincial Theatres Agreement
(dated 4 April 1994)

between Equity and the Theatrical Management Association (TMA).
NB: In September 1997, Equity launched a campaign for a substantial increase in salaries. At the time of going to press, members of Equity had been instructed not to enter into new contracts with the TMA which would require them to work on or after 6 April 1998.

This agreement covers most provincial theatres not covered by the subsidised rep agreement (*see below*) – i.e. tours, pantomimes, summer seasons, non-subsidised rep and sessional work.

Wages
Two-tier system of payments – a higher minimum of £212.50 once nightly (eight performances per week); £232.00 twice nightly (twelve performances per week), and a lower minimum of £180.00 (once nightly); £191.00 (twice nightly). The higher minimum weekly wage generally applies unless most of the following conditions apply:

• None of the actors is a West End or national name.

• The production is not advertised as pre- or post-West End.
• The production is non-subsidised rep or uses the sessional contract.
• The number in the cast is less than 12.
• The theatre seating capacity is generally under 650.
• The population within a 25-mile radius is not more than one million.

Subsistence
£60 per week for the first 12 weeks if the actor's home address is 25 miles or more from the place of employment.

Touring Allowance
£110 per week.

Holiday Pay
Half a day's holiday pay per week. A broken week counts as a complete one for holiday purposes.

Hours of Work
All calls made by the manager count as working time, as will all travel time in connection with the production, irrespective of whether a call for travel has been made (excluding Sunday travel). In the case of a tour, this is assessed as the most practical train journey between venues, as advised by British Rail. A week of six days (Monday to Saturday inclusive) consisting of 48 hours (including costume fittings) and not more than eight hours out of ten in any one day between 8.30a.m. and 11.00p.m. No actor is required to work in excess of 12 hours a day. After the first performance, rehearsals are normally limited to nine hours a week. 15 minutes (to count as working time) is allowed for at the end of the last performance on any day for removal of make-up and/or changing (30 minutes where complete body make-

up is required and where no showers are provided).

Understudies

The manager is obliged to provide adequate and suitable understudy cover for every character in the production except for one-person shows. The actor may be required to cover up to two major or three minor roles. No actor can be expected to cover an 'unreasonable number of roles'. Minimum performance salary for each performance as an understudy is £21.34 for leading role; £12.82 for non-leading roles. Understudy responsibility payment is £15.90 per week; £8.52 for each additional role.

Stage Management

Minimum staff of not less than one senior stage manager (SM), or company and stage manager (CSM), one deputy stage manager (DSM) and one assistant stage manager (ASM).

Wages

Two-tier system, as for actors.

Higher minimum:
ASM: £204.00 (once nightly); £222.50 (twice nightly)
DSM: £255.00 (once nightly); £278.12 (twice nightly)
SM: £285.60 (once nightly); £311.50 (twice nightly)
CSM: £306.00 (once nightly); £333.75 (twice nightly)

Lower minimum:
ASM: £175.21 (once nightly); £185.58 (twice nightly)
DSM: £219.01 (once nightly); £231.97 (twice nightly)
SM: £245.29 (once nightly); £259.81 (twice nightly)
CSM: £262.81 (once nightly); £278.37 (twice nightly)

SUBSIDISED REPERTORY

Subsidised Repertory Agreement

(dated 4 April 1994; rates of pay as at April 1998)

between Equity and the Theatrical Management Association (TMA)

Wages

Each theatre has a 'middle-range salary level' (MRSL). This is worked out by dividing the 'total basic salaries' paid by the total number of 'actor weeks' in the year, the minimum salary being £250 per week. Negotiation of salaries in rep is generally fairly restricted.

Subsistence

Payable for the first 13 weeks of a contract or for the whole of the engagement on fixed term contracts of more than 13 weeks to an actor whose home address is 25 miles or more from the theatre or place of rehearsal. From April 1998, the rate is £75 per week.

Touring Allowance

£105.60 per week, but currently under review.

Holiday Pay

Two days' holiday pay for every four weeks worked and pro rata.

Hours of Work

From April 1988, the hours have been reduced substantially to 44 per week (43 from April 1999).

Performances

Eight performances per week but not more than two on any one day.

Stage Management

Minimum staffing: Repertory: not less

than one stage manager (SM), one deputy stage manager (DSM) and one assistant stage manager (ASM), none of whom shall act or understudy. Repertoire: not less than two teams consisting of one stage manager, one deputy stage manager and one assistant stage manager.

Wages
Minimum: ASM – £215; DSM – £252.62; SM – £274.12 (Grade 1 MRSL theatres).

SMALL-SCALE THEATRE COMPANIES

Agreement for Performers and Stage Managers (Small-Scale Theatre Companies)
(dated April 1996)

between Equity and the Independent Theatre Council (ITC)

This contract generally applies to those that are not TMA, Subsidised Rep, West End or a No. 1 tour.

Wages
Minimum of £245 per week (from 6 April 1998).
Hours
No more than 45 hours (excluding meal breaks) worked over no more than six days, the working day being 10 hours (excluding meal breaks) and those hours to fall between 8.00a.m. and 12.00 midnight. A minimum period of at least 11 hours must elapse after the conclusion of a day's work and the next call.

Performances
No more than eight performances per week.

Overtime
Paid for anything over the 45 hours per week. For work up to 12 hours over the 45 hours per week, overtime is calculated as one-fortyfifth of the weekly salary in half-hour segments.

Touring Conditions
Companies touring distances requiring more than two hours' travelling time must have at least two drivers per vehicle. On a performance day, no driver must drive for more than two hours without a beak or for more than four hours in total.

Relocation Costs
If a company member's home address is 25 miles or more from the company base, he may claim costs in living away from home. This is paid for the first 16 weeks at a maximum rate of: £48.84 per week (out of London); £59.22 (in London).

Holiday Pay
One-half day's pay for each week of the engagement.

Organisations, Associations and Societies

Actors' Benevolent Fund

6 Adam Street,
London WC2N 6AA
Tel: 0171 836 6378
President *Penelope Keith OBE*
General Secretary *Mrs Rosemary Stevens*
Minimum Subscription £5 p.a.

Founded 1882. The foremost representative charity of the theatrical profession in the UK. The objectives of the fund are to help, by allowances, grants and loans, elderly or distressed actors and actresses, managers, stage managers, business managers and their wives; also choristers whose efforts are entirely devoted to theatrical work. Those connected with the theatrical profession, coming within the fund's scope, can become members on payment of the minimum subscription; they will then be entitled to participate in all matters affecting the welfare of the fund.

The Actors Centre

1A Tower Street, Covent Garden,
London WC2H 9NP
Tel: 0171 240 3940
Fax: 0171 240 3896
Full Membership £38 p.a./£22 half-year (for Equity members); **Social Membership** £25 p.a. (Open to all for use of facilities, excluding classes.)

Founded in 1979 by a group of actors led by Sheila Hancock, Clive Swift and John Alderton for the benefit of the acting profession. As well as enabling members to develop their professional skills and acquire fresh ones, it also offers the opportunity for the exploration of new ideas and methods of work away from commercial pressures for both the experienced actor as well as the novice. The centre's extensive premises provide excellent club facilities: fully-licensed bar and green room, fully-equipped gymnasium, fax and message service, noticeboards, trade journals and information on current theatrical events; a vocal and singing studio with piano, a media studio with video camera and monitor, the John Curry Room with full-length mirrors and sprung floor and a meeting/ audition room. The Tristan Bates Theatre is available for members' showcase work (*see* Fringe and Alternative Theatre, page 197). Schedules detailing times, tutors and directors, etc. are mailed 4 times a year. Workshops are available in acting, camera technique, singing, voice and dialect, verse, fencing, tap, movement and radio technique. All classes and workshops are at subsidised prices.

The Actors' Centre (Manchester)

see **The Northern Actors Centre**, page 343

The Actors' Centre North-East

1st Floor, 1 Black Swan Court, Westgate Road, Newcastle upon Tyne NE1 1SH Tel: 0191 221 0158 **Administrator** *Allan Blakey* **Membership** £15 p.a.

Founded 1994. Self-funding, non-profit-making organisation providing support for, and seeking to further the interests of, all professional actors and performers living or working in the north-east of England. Provides classes in which professionals can share existing skills and learn new ones while offering a meeting place and information exchange. Schedules of classes are mailed 3 times a year.

The Actors' Charitable Trust

Suite 255–256, Africa House, 64–78 Kingsway, London WC2B 6BD Tel: 0171 242 0111 Fax: 0171 242 0234 **Contact** *General Secretary* **Membership** £10 p.a.

Founded 1896. Formerly the Actors' Orphanage Fund. Assists the children of members of the theatrical profession in need of support during family crises with one-off grants or regular payments. Holds a small education fund for students over 18 in full-time arts education. The trust also administers Denville Hall in Northwood, Middlesex, the residential and nursing home for elderly members of the theatrical profession (the original house was donated by Alfred Denville, the actor-manager).

Actors' Church Union

St Paul's Church, Bedford Street, London WC2E 9ED Tel: 0171 836 5221 **Contact** *Canon Bill Hall* **Subscription** £10

Founded in 1898 to serve the profession. The present members and associates continue this work through their interest and action and by their prayers and worship together. Often works in association with other related bodies. Additionally, more than 200 honorary chaplains seek to serve everyone in theatres, studios and schools at home and overseas. As well as spiritual counsel and practical advice, material help is given when possible: through the Children's Charity, for example, funds are available for theatrical parents facing difficulties with the costs of their children's education.

The Agents' Association (Great Britain)

54 Keyes House, Dolphin Square,
London SW1V 3NA
Tel: 0171 834 0515
Fax: 0171 821 0261
E-mail: gensec@agents-uk.com
Contact *Ivan Birchall*

Founded in 1927 to 'represent and enhance the interests of entertainment agents in the UK who were willing to be bound by a strict code of conduct and professional ethics'. Frequently consulted by government departments, the association plays an active role in current legislation. A constituent member of the Variety and Allied Entertainments' Council of Great Britain.

APT (Association of Professional Theatre for Children and Young People – incorporating ASSITEJ GB)

Unicorn Arts Theatre, Great Newport Street, London WC2H 7JB
Tel: 0171 836 3623
Fax: 0171 836 5366
Contact *Paula Van Hagen, Ann Cross*
Subscription Company membership: £1 per £1,000 of turnover (min. £50, max. £250); individual membership: £25 p.a.; group associates £50 p.a.; individual associates £25 p.a.

Founded 1994. The aims of the APT are to ensure that funders, politicians, the media, the theatre profession, educationalists and the general public are aware of the value, needs and concerns of theatre for children and young people. Publishes the APT magazine 3 times a year, an annual Directory of Theatre Companies for Children and Young People, and an international festivals guide. Organises training events where members meet and exchange ideas, see each other's work and work from overseas, share ideas about ways of working and acquire new skills. Operates a resource library and 2 helplines linked to databases. By joining APT you become a member of ASSITEJ (the International Association of Theatre for Children and Young People) – a worldwide organisation.

Arts Club

40 Dover Street, London W1X 3RB
Tel: 0171 499 8581
Membership Secretary *Mrs J. Downing*
Subscription £500 p.a. (town)

Founded 1863. Some connection with the arts, literature or science necessary for membership which is only available by application with 2 sponsors who must be current members.

Artsline

54 Chalton Street, London NW1 1HS
Tel: 0171 388 2227
Fax: 0171 383 2653
E-mail: artsline@dircon.co.uk
Contact *Pauline Guthrie, Roger Robinson*

Founded 1981. London's only information and advice service for disabled people on access to the arts and entertainment – a helpline on accessibility to such venues by phone and letter. Also produces access guides in print and on tape; a mobile library of videos in major ethnic languages for delivery to and collection from the homes of disabled people from ethnic minority communities; a Disability Equality training service for venue front-of-house staff; and a consultancy to arts and entertainment venues on access. Organises a comedy benefit annually.

ASSITEJ
– see **APT**, page 331

Association for Business Sponsorship of the Arts

Nutmeg Wharf, 60 Gainsford Street,
Butlers Wharf, London SE1 2NY
Tel: 0171 378 8143
Fax: 0171 407 7527

ABSA is the independent national association that exists to promote and encourage partnerships between the private sector and the arts to their mutual benefit and to that of the community at large. ABSA represents the interests of the business sponsor, in particular those of its business members, and also advises and trains the arts community both individually and corporately on the development of private-sector support. A major initiative of ABSA is Business in the Arts which encourages businessmen and women to share their management skills with the arts to their mutual benefit. The National Heritage Arts Sponsorship Scheme (commonly known as the 'Pairing Scheme') is designed to increase the level of sponsorship of the arts.

Association of British Theatre Technicians

47 Bermondsey Street,
London SE1 3XT
Tel: 0171 403 3778
Fax: 0171 378 6170
Administrator *Jenny Straker*
Subscription £35 (associate membership); £10 (student membership); £100 (organisations)

Founded in 1961 to provide a forum for discussion among technicians in the presentation industry, to collect and disseminate information of a technical nature, to arrange in-service training, to influence draft standards and regulations affecting the industry and to advise and assist all those involved in the planning and construction or reconstruction of new and existing theatres. Arranges visits for members to various theatres and productions of technical interest. Publishes Codes of Practice on various subjects. Publication list available from the address above. The association is a member of the Theatres Advisory Council and acts as technical advisor to the council. Associate Membership is open to all those who are interested in the technical aspects of the presentation industry; Full Membership is awarded to experienced professional technicians.

Association of Professional Theatre for Children and Young People
– see **APT**, page 331

BECTU
– see **Broadcasting Entertainment Cinematograph & Theatre Union**, page 334

British Academy of Film and Television Arts (BAFTA)

195 Piccadilly, London W1V 0LN
Tel: 0171 734 0022
Fax: 0171 734 1792
Chief Executive *Harry Manley*
Subscription £155 p.a.

Founded 1947. Membership limited to 'those who have contributed to the industry' over a minimum period of 3 years. Provides facilities for screening and discussions, encourages research and experimentation and makes annual awards.

British Actors' Equity Association
– see **Equity**, page 315

British American Arts Association

118 Commercial Street,
London E1 6NF
Tel: 0171 247 5385
Fax: 0171 247 5256
E-mail: baa@easynet.co.uk
Executive Director *Jennifer Williams*
Projects Officer *Sam Perkins*
Subscription (for newsletter) £10 p.a.
(UK); £13 p.a. (EU); £15/$23 (US)

Founded in 1978 to 'support and advocate the role of the arts and of artists in society'. A non-profit organisation working in the field of arts and education. Conducts research, organises conferences, produces a quarterly newsletter and is part of an international network of arts and education organisations. As well as a specialised arts and education library, BAAA has a more general library holding information on opportunities for artists and performers both in the UK and abroad. It is not a grant-giving organisation.

British Council

11 Portland Place, London W1N 4EJ
Tel: 0171 389 3097
Fax: 0171 389 3088
Director General *Dr David Drewry*
Director of Drama and Dance *Simon Gammell*

Founded 1934. The British Council exists to promote a wider knowledge of Britain and the English language abroad and to develop closer cultural relations between Britain and other countries. It maintains staff in 109 countries, and from 30 offices in Britain advises and assists visitors and students from overseas. The council organises tours overseas by British theatre, dance and opera companies and individual recitalists and by orchestras and individual musicians, enabling them to perform in most parts of the world, including Africa, the Indian subcontinent and the Far East, where opportunities for British artists would otherwise be rare.

British Film Commission

70 Baker Street, London W1M 1DJ
Tel: 0171 224 5000
Fax: 0171 224 1013
E-mail: info@britfilmcom.co.uk
Contact *Joanna Dewar Gibb*

Founded in 1991 to promote the British production sector – its production personnel, facilities, locations – to international film, television and commercial producers considering basing productions in the UK. Works within the network of 25 commissions located in the UK.

British Film Institute

21 Stephen Street, London W1P 2LN
Tel: 0171 255 1444
Fax: 0171 436 7950
Membership from £11.95

Founded 1933. Exists to encourage the development of film, television and video in the UK. Its divisions include: the National Film and Television Archive; BFI on the South Bank (National Film Theatre, London Film Festival and Museum of the Moving Image); BFI Production; BFI National Film Library; and BFI Information and Education (including Publishing, *Sight and Sound*). It also provides programming support to a regional network of film theatres.

British Library National Sound Archive

96 Euston Road, London NW1 2DB
Tel: 0171 412 7440
Fax: 0171 412 7441

Open from 9.30 a.m. to 8 p.m. Monday to Friday (Saturday till 5.30 p.m.), the National Sound Archive holds over 1,000,000 discs and more than 170,000 tape recordings, including all types of music, oral history, drama, wildlife, selected BBC broadcasts and BBC Sound Archive material. Produces a thrice-yearly newsletter, *Playback*.

A Listening Service is available, by appointment only, same hours as above, Monday to Friday. Also: Northern Listening Service at the British Library Document Supply Centre, Boston Spa, West Yorkshire, 9.15 a.m. to 4.30 p.m. Monday to Friday.

British Music Hall Society

Brodie & Middleton Ltd,
68 Drury Lane,
London WC2B 5SP
Tel: 0171 836 3289/80
Fax: 0171 497 8425
Chairman *John Roscoe*
Secretary *Daphne Masterton*
Subscription £13 (UK); £15 (overseas); £19 (couples at same address)

Founded 1963. An influential, world-wide group of British music-hall and variety enthusiasts, including many professionals from the world of entertainment – artistes, agents and managers. The central aims of the society are to preserve the history of music hall and variety, to recall the artistes who created it and to encourage and support the entertainers of today. Holds regular monthly entertainments on the first Tuesday of every month (except December and January),

publishes a quarterly journal, *The Call Boy*, giving news, views and information on music hall and variety, which is issued free to members. Contributes to theatrical and various charities out of the proceeds of its variety shows and exhibitions. Membership application forms are available from the secretary.

British Screen Development

14–17 Wells Mews, London W1P 3FL
Tel: 0171 323 9080
Fax: 0171 323 0092
E-mail: bs@cd-online.co.uk

Founded 1985. Formerly the National Film Development Fund. Supports writers, directors and producers through various loan schemes: screenplay loans to encourage first-time cinema writers and development loans to enable producers to commission writers and also cover some of the producer's ancillary costs. Also has 3 short-film schemes in operation across Britain to identify and develop new film-makers.

Broadcasting Entertainment Cinematograph & Theatre Union (BECTU)

111 Wardour Street, London W1V 4AY
Tel: 0171 437 8506
Fax: 0171 287 8984
General Secretary *Roger Bolton*
Subscription 1% of earnings; minimum freelance fee £96 p.a.

Founded 1991. An amalgamation of the Association of Cinematograph Television and Allied Technicians (ACTT) and the Broadcasting & Entertainment Trades Alliance (BETA). TUC-affiliated trade union covering all areas of non-performing categories in theatre, broadcasting, film and other sectors of the media and entertainment industries. Negotiates minimum rates and conditions with West End (SOLT) and regional theatre managements (TMA) as well as individual theatre employers, cinema owners, television and film companies. All theatre staff, both full- and part-time, are eligible for membership.

Campaign for Press and Broadcasting Freedom (CPBF)

8 Cynthia Street, London N1 9JF
Tel: 0171 278 4430
Fax: 0171 837 8868
E-mail: cpbf@architechs.com
Director Granville Williams
Subscription £12 (waged); £6 (unwaged)

Founded 1979. The CPBF campaigns for a democratic, diverse and accountable media, accessible to all. It opposes monopoly ownership of the press and seeks a Freedom of Information Act. Organises events and publishes *Free Press* 6 times per year, occasional pamphlets and the Media Catalogue of mail-order books, videos and postcards.

Commercial Radio Companies Association

77 Shaftesbury Avenue,
London W1V 7AD
Tel: 0171 306 2603
Fax: 0171 470 0062
Chief Executive Paul Brown

Founded 1973. The Commercial Radio Companies Association (formerly the Association of Independent Radio Companies) is the trade body for commercial radio in the UK. All but a handful of commercial radio companies are members and the CRCA has been an influential force in British broadcasting throughout its existence.

It represents commercial radio to Government, the Radio Authority, copyright societies and other organisations concerned with radio. It provides a forum for industry discussion, is a source of advice to members and acts as a clearing house for radio information.

Conference of Drama Schools

Central School of Speech and Drama, Embassy Theatre, Eton Avenue, London NW3 3HY
Tel: 0171 722 8183
Fax: 0171 722 4132
Contact George Kitson

Founded in 1969 to strengthen the voice of member drama schools and encourage the highest standards of training. Produces an annual official guide to UK drama schools for careers officers, teachers and applicants to drama school. Associated with the National Council for Drama Training.

Critics' Circle

c/o *The Stage (incorporating Television Today)*, 47 Bermondsey Street, London SE1 3XT
Tel: 0171 403 1818 ext 106 (Catherine Cooper)
Fax: 0171 357 9287
President Allen Robertson
Honorary General Secretary Charles Hedges
Administrator Catherine Cooper
Subscription £18 p.a.

Membership by invitation only. Aims to uphold and promote the art of criticism (and the commercial rates of pay thereof) and preserve the interests of its members: professionals involved in criticism of film, drama, music, dance, art and architecture.

Department for Culture, Media and Sport

2–4 Cockspur Street, London SW1Y 5DH
Tel: 0171 211 6000
Fax: 0171 211 6032

The Department for Culture, Media and Sport has responsibilities for government policies relating to the arts, museums and galleries, public libraries, sport, broadcasting, press standards, film, the built heritage, tourism and the National Lottery. It funds the Arts Council, national museums and galleries and the British Library.

Directors Guild of Great Britain

15–19 Great Titchfield Street, London W1P 7FB
Tel: 0171 436 8626
Fax: 0171 436 8646
E-mail: dggb.co.uk
Membership Secretary Kate Hillman
Subscription 1% of directing income (max. £800; min. £80); £50 p.a. (associate membership)

Founded 1982. Representing 1,000 directors in film, television, radio and theatre, the Directors Guild is a trade union offering help with contracts, a campaigning voice and a policy to influence the future of the industry. Gives advice to members in dispute and offers a wide programme of events, from small-scale workshops to large events open to the general public with unrivalled opportunities for members to meet and share their skills. Publishes a directory of members, contract advice guides and rates cards. 'The Observer Scheme', exclusive to Guild members, allows directors to expand their understanding and skills by observing senior colleagues at work. A theatre director can observe film, or a television documentary director can observe drama.

Drama Association of Wales

The Library, Singleton Road, Splott, Cardiff CF2 2ET
Tel: 01222 452200
Director Aled Rhys-Jones
Contact Kirsty Foster (Administrator), Gary Thomas (Member Services Officer)
Subscription Variable rates

Founded 1934. The association's aim is to increase opportunities for people in the community to be creatively involved in drama which is fun and of a high standard. Its main activities are an extensive mail-order library service and training courses in all aspects of theatre, including a 7-day summer school and a winter school in the Mediterranean. New writing schemes include a script-reading service, annual playwriting competition, workshops of work in progress and support for first productions. Organises the Welsh National Drama Festival from January to June, culminating in the Wales One-Act Final, and encourages cooperation between the professional and amateur theatre worlds.

English Folk Dance and Song Society

Cecil Sharp House, 2 Regent's Park Road, London NW1 7AY
Tel: 0171 485 2206
Fax: 0171 284 0523
Contact Hannah Booth
Subscription £21 p.a.

Founded 1932. The English Folk Dance and Song Society promotes English folk dance, song and music, custom and drama, and stimulates its practice and enjoyment. Cecil Sharp House is used as a venue for rehearsals by theatre and television companies, etc., and is home of the Vaughan Williams Memorial Library which contains over 20,000 items of literature, records and video tapes.

ETmA (Educational Television and Media Association)

37 Monksgate, York YO3 7PB
Tel: 01904 639212
Fax: 01904 639212
Administrator *Josie Key*

The ETmA comprises a wide variety of users of television and other electronic media in education. Annual awards scheme (video competition) and annual conferences. New members always welcome.

Federation of Entertainment Unions

1 Highfield, Twyford, Nr Winchester, Hampshire SO21 1GR
Tel: 01962 713134
Fax: 01962 713288
E-mail: harris@interalpha.co.uk
Contact *Steve Harris*

Founded 1990. The FEU is a collective body of trade unions representing the interests of 140,000 members in the arts, entertainment and broadcasting industries. The affiliated unions are British Actors' Equity Association, BECTU, Musicians' Union, National Union of Journalists, The Writers' Guild and the AEEU. Provides liaison between these unions and lobbying representation and coordinated campaigning on a range of issues of common concern.

FIA (International Federation of Actors)

Guild House, Upper St Martin's Lane, London WC2H 9EG
Tel: 0171 379 0900
Fax: 0171 379 8260
Secretary *Marie-José Albertini-Dassa*

Western European members of FIA:

Austria:
KMFB Artisten und Bühne, Maria Theresien Strasse 11, A-1090 Vienna (tel: 00 43 1 31316 83840; fax: 00 43 1 31316 7700)

Belgium:
SACV Cultuur, Pastorijstraat 23, B-2060-Antwerp (tel: 00 32 3 271 0026; fax: 00 32 3235 2921)
SCC, Galerie Agora, Rue du Marché aux Herbes 105, Bte 38–40, B-1000 Brussels (tel: 00 32 2 549 0760; fax: 00 32 2 512 8591)
ACOD Cultuur, Fontainasplein 9–11, B-1000 Brussels (tel: 00 32 2 508 5886; fax: 00 32 2 508 5840)
CGSP, Place Fonainas 9–11, B-1000 Brussels (tel: 00 32 2 508 5811; fax: 00 32 2 508 5902)

Denmark:
DSF, Sankt Knuds Vej 26, DK-1903 Frederiksberg C (tel: 00 45 33 24 2200; fax: 00 45 33 24 8159)
DAF, Vendersgade 24, DK-1363 Copenhagen K (tel: 00 45 33 32 6677; fax: 00 45 33 33 7330)

Finland:
STL – Dance Artists, Teatterikulma, Meritullinkatu 33, SF-00170 Helsinki 17 (tel: 00 358 9 135 7295; fax: 00 358 9 135 6658)
FSSkadelpelarforbund, Johannesbrinken 2 C 24, SF-00120

Helsingfors (tel: 00 358 9 664 323; fax: 00 358 9 448 501)
SN, Suomen Nayttelijalitto, Arkadiankatu 12 A 18, SF-00100 Helsinki (tel: 00 358 9 495 355; fax: 00 358 9 448 501)

France:
SFA 21 bis Rue Victor Masse, F-75009 Paris (tel: 00 33 1 42 85 8811; fax: 00 33 1 45 26 4721)

Germany:
IG Medien, Friedrichstrasse 15, D-70174 Stuttgart (tel: 00 49 711 2018 102; fax: 00 49 711 2018 300)
GDBA, Feldbrunnenstrasse 74, D-20148 Hamburg (tel: 00 49 40 44 51 85; fax: 00 49 40 45 93 52)

Greece:
UGS, Union of Greek Singers, 10 Sapfous Street, GR-105 53 Athens (tel: 00 30 1 364 5837; fax: 00 30 1 321 1614)
GAU, Greek Actors' Union, 33 Kaniggos Street, GR-106 82 Athens (tel: 00 30 1 383 3742; fax: 00 30 1 380 8651)

Iceland:
FIL, Lindargotu 6, IS-101 Reykjavik (tel: 00 354 552 6040; fax: 00 354 562 7706)

Ireland:
SIPTU, Liberty Hall, Dublin 1 (tel: 00 353 1 874 0081; fax: 00 353 1 874 3691)

Italy:
SAI, Via Ofanto 18, 1–00198 Rome (tel: 00 39 6 841 7303; fax: 00 39 6 854 6780)

Luxembourg:
OAGL, 3 Rue de la Foret, L-3354 Leu de Lange (tel: 00 352 46 15 14 23; fax: 00 352 49 67 98)

Netherlands:
Kunstenbond FNV, Postbus 63107, NL-1005 LC Amsterdam (tel: 00 31 20 683 7176; fax: 00 31 20 683 6821)

Norway:
NSF, Wesselsgate 8, N-0165 Oslo (tel: 00 47 22 41 1874; fax: 00 47 22 41 7044)
NBF, Wesselsgate 8, N-0165 Oslo (tel: 00 47 22 41 3304; fax: 00 47 22 36 0602)

Portugal:
STE, Rue de Fe 23, 2do Piso, P-1100 Lisbon (tel: 00 351 1 885 2728; fax: 00 351 1 885 3787)

Spain:
FUAEE, C/Montera 34, Iro Piso, E-28013 Madrid (tel: 00 34 1 522 2804; fax: 00 34 1 522 6055)
FeS/UGT, Avenida de America 25, E-28002 Madrid (tel: 00 34 1 589 7594; fax: 00 34 1 589 7587)
FESPACE, Cristino Martos 4, 5a Planta, E-28015 Madrid (tel: 00 34 1 548 2636; fax: 00 34 1 548 1897)

Sweden:
STF, Box 12710, S-11294 Stockholm (tel: 00 46 8 441 1300; fax: 00 46 8 653 9507)

Switzerland:
SSRS, 6 Rue Vuillermet, CH-1005 Lausanne (tel: 00 41 21 320 3695; fax: 00 41 21 320 3695)
SBKV, Leonhardsstrasse 38, CH-4051 Basel (tel: 00 41 61 274 1520; fax: 00 41 61 274 1522).

Independent Television Commission

33 Foley Street, London W1P 7LB
Tel: 0171 255 3000
Fax: 0171 306 7800
E-mail: 100731.3515@compuserve.com

Founded 1991. The Independent Television Commission is the public body responsible for licensing and regulating commercially funded television services provided in and from the UK. These include Channel 3 (ITV), Channel 4, Channel 5, public teletext, digital terrestrial television and a range of cable, local delivery and satellite services. They do not include services provided by the BBC, or by S4C, the fourth channel in Wales.

Independent Theatre Council

12 The Leathermarket,
Weston Street,
London SE1 3ER
Tel: 0171 403 1727
Fax: 0171 403 1745
E-mail: itc@dircon.co.uk
Contact *Annabel Arndt, Nicola Thorold, Charlotte Jones, Joanna Yates (Training)*
Subscription Company and venue membership: £115–£540 (+VAT); individual membership: £45 (+VAT)

Founded 1974. The management association and representative body for small-middle-scale performing-arts companies and venues (up to 350 seats). Negotiates contracts and has established standard agreements with Equity on behalf of all professionals working in theatre. Provides legal and management advice, lobbying and networking and a training programme of short courses on various aspects of running a theatre company. New companies to ITC are offered 1 free place on the 'Starting a Performing Arts Company' one-day course. ITC produces publications on Equal Opportunities and 'Policy into Practice' booklets. Also supplies an information pack which contains application forms for ITC membership and a reference sheet of sources of

information and legal requirements for starting a theatre company. Regular membership mailings provide news, information and a noticeboard service.

Institute for Creativity
– see Additional Skills, page 374

International Association of Theatre for Children and Young People
– see **APT**, page 331

International Federation of Actors
– see **FIA**, page 337

International Theatre Institute (British Centre)

ITI at Goldsmiths' College,
University of London,
Lewisham Way, New Cross,
London SE14 6NW
Tel: 0171 919 7276
Fax: 0171 919 7277
E-mail: iti@gold-ac.uk
Chairman and Director *Neville Shulman OBE*
Administrator *Lynne Kendrick*
Subscription Variable rate, max. £85 (company); £10 (students)

Founded in 1948 under the auspices of UNESCO to 'promote cultural exchange and deepen mutual understanding between nations and thereby participate in the promotion of peace'. There are 80 National Centres throughout Europe, Africa, the Middle East, the Far East, Asia, Australasia, North and South America and the Caribbean. The British Centre provides international contacts, research and networking for British theatre and dance practitioners and information and contacts for overseas professionals visiting the UK. Publishes a regular bulletin and presents 2 awards to celebrate World Theatre Day (27 March) and International Dance Day (29 April). Its archive contains publications from around the world, including magazines, scripts and reference books. Membership is open to all those with an interest in theatre and the performing arts.

ITV Network Centre

200 Gray's Inn Road,
London WC1X 8HF
Tel: 0171 843 8000
Fax: 0171 843 8158

The ITV Network Centre, wholly owned by the ITV companies, independently commissions and schedules the television programmes which are shown across the ITV network. As a successor to the Independent Television Association, it also provides a range of services to the ITV companies where a common approach is required.

IVCA (International Visual Communication Association)

Bolsover House, 5–6 Clipstone Street,
London W1P 8LD
Tel: 0171 580 0962
Fax: 0171 436 2606
Chief Executive *Wayne Drew*

The IVCA is a professional association representing the interests of the users and suppliers of visual communications. In particular, it pursues the interests of producers, commissioners and manufacturers involved in the non-broadcast and independent facilities industries and also business-event

companies. It represents all sizes of company and freelance individuals, offering information and advice services, publications, a professional network, special interest groups, a magazine and a variety of events including the UK's Film and Video Communications Festival.

London Screenwriters' Workshop

The Holborn Centre, Three Cups Yard,
Sandland Street, Holborn,
London WC1R 4PZ
Tel: 0171 242 2134
Contact *Paul Gallagher, Anji Loman Field*
Membership £25 p.a.

Established by writers in 1983 as a forum for contact, information and tuition. LSW helps new and developing writers in the film, TV and video industries. Organises a continuous programme of workshops, events with industry figures, seminars and courses. Free monthly events and magazine newsletter every 2 months.

Raymond Mander and Joe Mitchenson Theatre Collection

The Mansion, Beckenham Place Park,
Beckenham,
Kent BR3 2BP
Tel: 0181 658 7725
Fax: 0181 663 0131
Contact *Richard Mangan*

Founded 1938. Enormous collection of all aspects of the theatre: plays, actors, dramatists, music hall, theatres, singers, composers, etc. Not open to the public but to researchers, by appointment. Also functions as a picture library on a commercial basis.

Musicians' Union

National office: 60–62 Clapham Road,
London SW9 0JJ
Tel: 0171 582 5566
Fax: 0171 582 9805
General Secretary Dennis Scard
Subscription A Rate: Annual
earnings from music up to £5,000: £55
(£50 direct debit; reduced rate for
those aged under 21: £25); B Rate:
£5,000–£10,000: £89 (£84 direct
debit); C Rate: £10,000–£20,000:
£127 (£122); D Rate: earnings over
£20,000: £171 (£166)

The Musicians' Union caters for all
who make their living, or part of their
living, from performing music: bands,
groups, orchestral musicians, chamber
musicians, folk and jazz. The Union
negotiates basic rates of pay, recovers
unpaid fees, gives advice on contracts
and provides legal assistance and aid.

National Campaign for the Arts

Francis House, Francis Street,
London SW1P 1DE
Tel: 0171 828 4448
Fax: 0171 931 9959
E-mail: nca@ecna.org
Contact Jennifer Edwards, Laverne
Layland
Subscription Individual: £19.50 p.a.
(waged), £13.50 p.a. (unwaged);
organisation rates available

Founded 1985. The National
Campaign for the Arts is unique in
being an independent lobbying organisation which represents all areas of the
arts. Works in public and behind the
scenes to influence policy change. It
brings together people and organisations to work for common goals. The
NCA receives no public funding and is
sustained by the membership fees and
donations of both individuals and arts
organisations.

National Council for Drama Training

5 Tavistock Place,
London WC1H 9SS
Tel: 0171 387 3650
Executive Secretary Adele Bailey

Founded in 1976 following the publication of the Gulbenkian report into
professional training. The NCDT is an
independent body, composed of repre-
sentatives from the three main sections
of the theatrical profession: British
Actors' Equity Association (the union),
the Theatrical Management Association, the Society of London Theatre, the
BBC and Channel Four Television (the
employers/management) and the
Conference of Drama Schools (the
training providers).

The purpose of the council is encour-
agement of the highest possible
standards of vocational training and
education for the professional actor
and stage manager/technician and the
provision of a forum within which the
different sides of the profession can
discuss matters of common interest in
relation to training. It is particularly
concerned to promote the possible
links between those engaged in training and those working in the profession.

Since its establishment, the council
has perceived the accreditation of
courses in drama schools as its first
priority. There are two accreditation
boards – one for Acting courses and
one for Stage Management and
Technical Theatre courses.

The following is a list of those
schools with NCDT-accredited
courses. It is the course which receives
accreditation, not the drama school,
and it should not be assumed that
because one course in a school is
accredited other courses provided by
the same school are also accredited:

Academy of Live and Recorded Arts; Arts Educational Schools London; Birmingham School of Speech and Drama; Bristol Old Vic Theatre School; Central School for Speech and Drama; Drama Centre London; Guildford School of Acting; Guildhall School of Music and Drama; London Academy of Music and Dramatic Art; London Academy of Performing Arts; Manchester Metropolitan University School of Theatre; Mountview Theatre School; Oxford School of Drama; Queen Margaret College; Rose Bruford College of Speech and Drama; Royal Academy of Dramatic Art; Royal Scottish Academy of Music and Drama; The Webber Douglas Academy of Dramatic Art; The Welsh College of Music and Drama.

National Entertainment Agents Council

PO Box 112, Seaford, East Sussex
BN25 2DQ
Tel: 01323 492266
Fax: 01323 492234
Contact Chris Bray

Founded in 1976 to provide a medium through which members can trade, communicate, be kept updated in current matters via newsletter and other circulations, complain, confer and lobby for the mutual benefit of members.

National Lottery

PO Box 1010, Liverpool L70 1NL
Tel: 0645 100000
Fax: 0151 478 5551

Following the passing of the National Lottery Act in 1993, the National Lottery run by Camelot was launched in November 1994. Twenty-eight pence in every pound goes to 5 'good causes' – the Arts Councils, the Sports Councils, the National Lotteries Charities Board, the National Heritage Memorial Fund and the Millennium Commission. In the first $2^{1}/_{2}$ years since the launch of the Lottery, the 5 have received over £3.2 billion. Enquiries regarding funding for specific arts projects should be directed to the Arts Councils (England, Northern Ireland, Scotland or Wales – see Arts Councils and Regional Arts Associations, pages 353–8) and not to the National Lottery.

National Operatic and Dramatic Association (NODA)

Noda House, 1 Crestfield Street,
London WC1H 8AU
Tel: 0171 837 5655
Fax: 0171 833 0609
Chief Executive Mark Thorburn
Subscription £16 (individual)

Founded in 1899 'to protect and advance the interests of operatic and dramatic art and of societies engaged therein'. Support is given to producing societies by 150 volunteers on 11 area committees. NODA has 2,300 amateur societies affiliated nationwide, plus 2,500 individuals. Publishes a quarterly National Magazine, plus less frequent Area Magazines. Holds an Area and National Conference each year, workshops and an annual summer school in August. Sells discounted production insurance, pantomimes, make-up, scripts, vocal scores, etc. to members.

NETWORKING for women in film, video and television

Vera Media, 30–38 Dock Street,
Leeds, West Yorkshire LS10 1JF
Tel: 0113 242 8646
Fax: 0113 245 1238
E-mail: networking@vera-media.demon.co.uk
Contact *Jane Howarth, Al Garthwaite*
Subscription £15 p.a.

Founded 1990. A membership organisation for women working, seeking work or in any way involved in film, video and television. Benefits include a 20-page quarterly newsletter, members' index and individual advice and information.

New Playwrights Trust

Interchange Studios, Dalby Street,
London NW5 3NQ
Tel: 0171 284 2818
Fax: 0171 482 5292
E-mail: npt@easynet.co.uk
Contact *Jonathan Meth*
Subscription London membership:
£26 p.a. (waged), £16 p.a. (part-waged), £8 p.a. (unwaged); non-London membership: £22 p.a. (waged), £14 p.a. (part-waged), £8 p.a. (unwaged)

Founded in 1985, New Playwrights Trust is the only national support and research network for new writing for all forms of live and recorded performance. Writers are supported in 3 ways: 'by advocating new writing; by researching and disseminating information about new writing; and by improving representation within new writing'. Publishes a range of information leaflets and a 6-weekly journal.

New Producers Alliance

9 Bourlet Close, London W1P 7PJ
Tel: 0171 580 2480
Fax: 0171 580 2484
E-mail: npa@npa.org.uk
Contact *Harriet Bass, Victoria Lorkin-Lange*

Founded 1992; current membership of over 1,000. Aims to encourage the production of commercial feature films for an international audience and to educate and inform feature-film producers, writers and directors. The NPA is an independent networking organisation providing members with access to contacts, information, free legal advice and general help regarding film production. Publishes a monthly newsletter and organises meetings, workshops and seminars.

The Northern Actors Centre

30 St Margaret's Chambers, 5 Newton Street, Manchester M20 4PH
Tel: 0161 236 0041
E-mail: nac manchester@geocities.com

Membership £25 p.a./£14 half-year; £20 p.a./£10 half-year (graduate membership); £5 (1-month temporary membership for professionals working in the region); other rates on request

Founded 1996. Provides classes and workshops for actors and other professionals working in theatre and the mechanical media, allowing them to maintain, develop and extend their skills. Is a source of information on theatre, the mechanical media and related activities in the region. Caters for those living or working in the north-west of England, South and West Yorkshire, north Wales and the north Midlands. Membership is open to Equity members, graduates and current students of recognised drama courses and to those who can demonstrate a professional commitment to performing in theatre and related media. Also offers classes in a variety of theatre-related techniques which are open to the general public and those attempting to embark on an acting career.

NWP (North-West Playwrights)
Contact Theatre, Oxford Road, Manchester M15 6JA
Tel: 0161 274 4418
Fax: 0161 274 4418

Founded 1982. Award-winning organisation whose aim is to develop and promote new theatre writing. Operates a script-reading service, Commission and Residency Award Scheme, *The Lowdown* newsletter and the Summer Workshops – an annual showing of 6 workshopped plays by local writers.

PACT (Producers Alliance for Cinema and Television)
45 Mortimer Street, London W1N 7TD
Tel: 0171 331 6000
Fax: 0171 331 6700
Chief Executive *Shaun Williams*
Membership Officer *David Alan Mills*

Founded 1991. PACT is the trade association of the UK independent television and feature-film production sector and is a key contact point for foreign producers seeking British co-production, co-finance partners and distributors. Works for producers in the industry at every level and operates a members' regional network throughout the UK with a divisional office in Scotland. Membership services include: a dedicated industrial relations unit; discounted legal advice; a varied calendar of events; business advice; representation at international

film and television markets; a comprehensive research programme; various publications; a monthly magazine; an annual members' directory; affiliation with European and international producers' organisations; extensive information and production advice. Lobbies actively with broadcasters, financiers and governments to ensure that the producer's voice is heard and understood in Britain and Europe on all matters affecting the film and television industry.

The Performing Right Society Ltd (PRS)
29–33 Berners Street, London W1P 4AA
Tel: 0171 580 5544
Fax: 0171 306 4050
E-mail: pubrel@prs.co.uk

Founded 1914. The PRS is the UK association of composers, songwriters and music publishers with a membership of 30,000. Collects and distributes royalties arising from the performance and broadcast of copyright music on behalf of its members and members of affiliated societies worldwide.

The Personal Managers' Association Limited
Rivercroft, 1 Summer Road, East Molesey, Surrey KT8 9LX
Tel: 0181 398 9796
Fax: 0181 398 9796
Contact *Angela Adler*
Subscription £250 p.a.; £125 p.a. (out of town)

Founded 1950. An association of artists' and dramatists' agents (membership not open to individuals). Applicants are screened. Monthly meetings for exchange of information and discussion. Maintains a code of conduct and acts as a lobby when necessary.

Player-Playwrights
9 Hillfield Park, Muswell Hill, London N10 3QT
Tel: 0181 883 0371
Fax: 0181 883 0371
Secretary *Peter Thompson*
Subscription £10 p.a. plus £1 per every meeting attended

Founded 1947. A cooperative of writers and actors who meet every Monday evening, except holidays, to read/ perform and criticise new scripts submitted by members. Has a membership of approximately 100. The venue for meetings is a hall-with-stage at St Augustine's in Queen's Gate, South Kensington in south-west London. Average attendances are between 25 and 30 with established writers and professional actors among the regulars, as well as novices.

Radio Authority
Holbrook House, 14 Great Queen Street, London WC2B 5DG
Tel: 0171 430 2724

The Radio Authority authorises independent radio licences and acts as a regulator of services. The number of independent radio stations continues to increase with new licences being advertised on a regular basis.

Royal Television Society
Holborn Hall, 100 Gray's Inn Road, London WC1X 8AL
Tel: 0171 430 1000
Fax: 0171 430 0924
Subscription £57 p.a.

Founded 1927. Covers all disciplines involved in the television industry.

Provides a forum for debate and conferences on technical, social and cultural aspects of the medium. Presents various awards, including journalism, programmes, technology, design and commercials. Publishes *Television Magazine* 8 times a year for members and subscribers.

Royal Theatrical Fund
11 Garrick Street, London WC2E 9AR
Tel: 0171 836 3322
Fax: 0171 379 8273
Contact *Mrs Roslyn Oliver*

Founded in 1839 by Charles Dickens and his friends to provide pensions for actors. The fund was granted its royal charter by Queen Victoria in 1853. In 1974, it became a general charity for people in the entertainment profession who cannot practise their craft through illness, adversity or infirmity, giving such help as contributions to a shortfall in nursing-home fees for elderly actors or cash grants for people who are ill or convalescing. All donations are gratefully received.

Save London's Theatres Campaign
Guild House, Upper St Martin's Lane, London WC2H 9EG
Tel: 0171 379 6000
Fax: 0171 379 7001
Chairman *John Levitt*
Secretary *Sheila Collings*

Founded in 1972 in response to the threat to many London theatres from redevelopment and road-widening schemes, the Save London's Theatres Campaign has been active ever since. The campaign's many victories include securing the future for the Shaftesbury, Whitehall, Criterion and Dominion Theatres. It is a voluntary organisation with no formal membership but supporters drawn from all sections of the theatrical profession and theatre lovers from all walks of life.

The campaign relies on theatre lovers to keep them informed. If a theatre in the London area is being threatened, be it in the West End or the outlying suburbs, the campaign needs to be notified so that appropriate action can be organised.

Scottish Actors Studio

60 Candleriggs,
Glasgow G1 1NQ
Tel: 07000 229 288
Fax: 07000 229 288
Artistic Director *Andrew Byatt*

Founded in 1994 after a successful feasibility study for the Scottish Arts Council and Glasgow City Council. The idea for the studio was developed by actor Andrew Byatt with his late playwright father George and actress Mairi Wallace after working together in George Byatt's Theatre PKF (Peace Keeping Force), an actor-oriented company which worked on purely equal contributory lines. There was no director and actors were encouraged to work in collaboration with George, the writer, on his plays. The result was stunning work of great depth, especially the Prix Italia award-winning *The Clyde is Red* and *The Brus*.

The non-competitive environment of PKF and its open rehearsals and discussions with audiences after every performance is the mainstay of the Scottish Actors Studio. There is no feeling of competition or judgement on any participating actor in the full-day, practical workshops. Another key element is that of other professional actors observing each workshop. There have been sessions with as many as 120 observers. Each workshop finishes with a feedback period involving all participants, observers and finally the workshop leader. This empowers the actors and makes it their workshop. SAS is an actors organisation run by and for actors. Workshop Seasons have been on both theatre and film acting and have been led by such people as Tom Conti, Alison Peebles, Alison Steadman, Gerry Mulgrew, Giles Havergal, Philip Howard, Bill Bryden, Peter McDougal, Jonathan Pryce, Brian Cox, Janet Suzman, Pauline Collins, Robbie Coltrane and Billy Connolly.

Film workshops (using full crew in a BBC Scotland studio) have been led by Rutger Hauer, Ken Russell, David Hayman, Simon Callow, Danny Boyle, Mike Newell, David Drury and Mickey Rooney.

SAS is a registered charity. Membership, open to any Equity person, is £15. Full-day sessions cost £10 to participate and £5 to observe, regardless of workshop leader.

Society of Authors

84 Drayton Gardens, London SW10 9SB
Tel: 0171 373 6642
Fax: 0171 373 5768
E-mail: authorsoc@writers.org.uk
Subscription £70 p.a.

Founded 1884. The Society of Authors is an independent trade union with some 6,000 members. It promotes the interests and defends the rights of authors and offers advice to individual members on contractual and business-related issues. Benefits of membership include: advice on negotiations and contracts with publishers and broadcasters; assistance with problems/ disputes; free quarterly journal; free *Quick Guide to*

Publishing Contracts, Copyright and Moral Rights, Authors' Agents and other professional issues; books at a discount; meetings, seminars and social gatherings.

Society for Theatrical Research

c/o Theatre Museum, 1E Tavistock Street, London WC2E 7PA
E-mail: e.cottis@unl.ac.uk
Contact *Eileen Cottis*
Subscription £20 (UK individual); other rates on request

Founded 1948. The Society for Theatre Research aims to promote the public knowledge and appreciation of the history and technique of British theatre by fostering research into historical and current theatre practice through annual programmes of publications and lectures and annually awarding grants towards the costs of such research. Publishes at least 1 book per year and the 3 issues of each annual volume of the journal, *Theatre Notebook*, are sent free to members. Monthly lectures are held in London from October to May, open to the public, admission free. Other events are arranged from time to time in the north of England and in Scotland by the Society's Northern Group.

Society of London Theatre (SOLT)

Bedford Chambers, The Piazza, Covent Garden, London WC2E 8HQ
Tel: 0171 836 0971
Fax: 0171 497 2543
Chief Executive *Rupert Rhymes*

Founded 1908. SOLT is the trade association acting on behalf of West End theatre owners, managers and producers. It provides industrial

relations and legal services, and collective marketing and advocacy for the industry. SOLT publishes the London Theatre Guide, the Theatre List, the Complete Guide to London's West End Theatres, the Disabled Access Guide, administers the Laurence Olivier awards, runs the nationwide Theatre Tokens scheme and manages the Half-price Ticket Booth in Leicester Square.

Sussex Playwrights Club

2 Princes Avenue, Hove, East Sussex BN3 4GD
Secretary *Mrs Constance Cox*
Subscription £5 p.a.

Founded in 1935 to encourage the writing of plays, not only by local Sussex people but by writers from all over the country. Staged readings of plays written by members are given monthly at the New Venture Theatre in Brighton.

Stage Management Association

South Bank House, Black Prince Road, London SE1 7SJ
Tel: 0171 587 1514
Administrator *Joy Cruickshank*
Subscription £42 p.a.

Founded in 1954 to promote the interests of stage management, to provide a forum for debate on the issues that concern them, to try to upgrade the training and professional status of stage management and to act as a pressure group on other organisations. Prints a monthly list of members available for work which is posted out on request. Membership is open to anyone working professionally in stage management in the UK.

Theatre Investment Fund

The Palace Theatre, Shaftesbury
Avenue, London W1V 8AY
Tel: 0171 287 2144
Fax: 0171 287 0565
Chief Executive *Nick Salmon*
Administrator *Liz Clift*

The Theatre Investment Fund is a registered charity (Charity Reg No. 271349) which was established 20 years ago to encourage and assist commercial theatre producers. It runs seminars and workshops on all aspects of presenting commercial productions, as well as publishing a starter pack for new producers and giving them individual advice. Occasionally, the fund invests modestly in productions, provided they meet its rigorous commercial guidelines.

Theatre Museum

1E Tavistock Street,
London WC2E 7PA
Tel: 0171 836 7891
Fax: 0171 836 5148
Head of Press and Marketing *Sue Rolfe*
Education Manager *Sophie Ward*

Founded as a separate department of the Victoria & Albert Museum in 1974 and moved to its own building in Covent Garden in 1987. Houses the world's largest collection of material relating to the British stage. Permanent collections include exhibitions on the development of the British stage from Shakespeare to the present day. Various temporary exhibitions, such as 'Dressing the Part' featuring costumes from the English National Ballet's production of *Alice in Wonderland*, and Somerset Maugham's collection of theatrical paintings on loan from the Royal National Theatre. The Education and Marketing departments run workshops twice daily for the public, using costumes, props and lighting, as well as three guided tours a day.

Theatre Writers' Union

Amalgamated with the Writers' Guild of Great Britain in 1997, *see* page 350

Theatregoers Club of Great Britain

Harling House,
47–51 Great Suffolk Street,
London SE1 0BS
Tel: 0171 450 4040
Fax: 0171 450 4041
President *Susan Hampshire OBE*

Founded in 1978, the club has over 70 branches in 24 countries. Each branch has its own programme of excursions to shows, including drama, opera or ballet. Membership offers coach travel to West End and regional shows; special discounts on ticket prices; theatre holidays in the UK and abroad. Members receive *Stagecoach* magazine.

Theatres Advisory Council

47 Bermondsey Street,
London SE1 3XT
Tel: 0171 403 3778
Fax: 0171 378 6170
Secretary *Jenny Straker*

A federation of theatre organisations, its membership consisting of 22 national bodies representative of all theatre interests. Founded in 1963 with the primary aim of ensuring the preservation of theatre buildings, its unique composition, including unions, managerial associations and advisory bodies, has enabled the council to act as spokesman for the whole theatre industry on issues which are of concern to all sides of the theatre.

Its main objectives now are to provide a forum for the discussion, examination and solution of problems affecting the performing arts, excluding those directly related to industrial relations; to make such representations on behalf of the theatre to Government and other bodies as members may collectively determine and to endeavour to keep the press and public informed; to give advice regarding new projects for places of performance and to cooperate with the Theatres Trust regarding places of performance which are thought to be endangered.

Theatres Trust

22 Charing Cross Road,
London WC2H 0HR
Tel: 0171 836 8591
Fax: 0171 836 3302
Director *Peter Longman*
Administrator *Paul Connolly*
Subscription £12 p.a.

Founded 1976. Set up by an act of parliament 'to promote the better protection of theatres for the benefit of the nation'. Local authorities are required by government order to consult the trust when considering planning applications affecting land on which there is a theatre. However, the trust's work extends far more widely and covers other planning issues, advice on theatre buildings to grant-making bodies and in relevant matters helping theatre managements and preservation bodies. The trust works closely with an associated charitable fund.

Membership as a Friend of the Theatres Trust gives access to a number of special events and offers, a quarterly newsletter and the annual report.

Theatrical Management Association (TMA)

Bedford Chambers, The Piazza,
Covent Garden, London WC2E 8HQ
Tel: 0171 836 0971
Fax: 0171 497 2543
Chief Executive *Rupert Rhymes*

Founded 1894. The TMA is the trade association for theatre managers, owners and producers, both grant-aided and commercial, in England, Scotland, Wales and Northern Ireland. Activities include industrial relations and legal advice, lobbying, training and events such as the Barclays Theatre awards, as well as publications such as *Prompt*, a quarterly magazine.

Variety Artistes' Federation

see Equity, page 315

Variety & Allied Entertainments' Council of Great Britain

54 Keyes House, Dolphin Square,
London SW1V 3NA
Tel: 0171 834 0515
Fax: 0171 821 0261
Guild House, Upper St Martin's Lane,
London WC2H 9EG
Tel: 0171 379 6000
Fax: 0171 379 7001
Joint Secretaries *Ivan Birchall, Ian McGarry*

'The VAEC exists to regulate the relations between managers, agents and artistes engaged in the variety and allied entertainment business. In particular the council maintains machinery for the adoption of certain minimum salaries, standard contracts for all live entertainment and the settlement of disputes arising therefrom.'

Voice of the Listener and Viewer (The Citizen's Voice in Broadcasting)

101 King's Drive, Gravesend,
Kent DA12 5BQ
Tel: 01474 352835
Fax: 01474 35112
Chairman *Mrs Jocelyn Hay*
Subscription £10 p.a. (single);
£15 p.a. (joint)

The Citizen's Voice in Broadcasting is an independent, non-profit-making society working to ensure high standards, diversity and independence in broadcasting and is the only consumer body speaking for listeners and viewers on the full range of broadcasting issues. Holds public lectures, seminars and conferences in London and elsewhere and arranges visits to broadcasting centres for its members throughout the UK. It is in frequent contact with Members of Parliament, civil servants, the BBC and independent broadcasters, regulators, academics and other consumer groups. VLV has responded to all parliamentary and public enquiries on broadcasting since 1984 and to all consultation documents issued by the ITC and Radio Authority since 1990. Produces a quarterly newsletter, reports and briefing papers on broadcasting developments; holds the archive of the former independent Broadcasting Research Unit (BRU) and of the former British Action for Children's Television (BACTV). VLV set up a Forum for Children's Broadcasting in 1995.

Westminster Reference Library

35 St Martin's Street,
London WC2H 7HP
Tel: 0171 641 4636 (General Media and Performing Arts)
Fax: 0171 641 4640

A general reference library with an emphasis on the performing arts – theatre, cinema, radio, television and dance. Open from 10 a.m. to 7 p.m. Monday to Friday and 10 a.m. to 5 p.m. on Saturday.

Writers' Guild of Great Britain

430 Edgware Road,
London W2 1EH
Tel: 0171 723 8074
Fax: 0171 706 2413
E-mail: postie@wggd.demon.uk
Website:
http:\\www.writers.org.uk/guild
Subscription £70 p.a. plus 1% of income from writing over £7,000; maximum £920

Founded 1959. The Writers' Guild is the writers' trade union, affiliated to the TUC. It represents writers in film, radio, television, theatre and publishing. The guild has negotiated agreements on which writers' contracts are based with the BBC, independent television companies and PACT. Those agreements are regularly renegotiated, both in terms of finance and conditions.

In 1979, together with the Theatre Writers' Union, the guild negotiated the first-ever industrial agreement for theatre writers, the TNC Agreement, which covers the Royal National Theatre, the Royal Shakespeare Company, and the English Stage Company. Further agreements have been negotiated with the Theatrical Management Association which covers regional theatre and the Independent Theatre Council, the organisation which covers small theatres and the Fringe.

The guild provides individual help and advice to members on contracts, conditions of work, and matters which affect a member's life as a professional writer. A new type of membership was launched in 1997 called Candidate Membership. This is open to all those who wish to be involved in writing but have not yet had work published. The subscription fee for this is £35.

Arts Councils and Regional Arts Associations

Arts Council of England

14 Great Peter Street, London SW1P 3NQ
Tel: 0171 333 0100
Fax: 0171 973 6590
Chairman *Gerry Robinson*
Acting Secretary General *Graham Devlin*

The 1996/7 grant dispensed by the Arts Council stands at £123 million. From it, the Arts Council supports arts organisations, artists, performers and others; grants can also be made for particular productions, exhibitions and projects. The total amount set aside for drama in 1997/8 is £27 million (a cut of approximately 0.8%). The Arts Council also provides grants to the 10 Regional Arts Boards.

Drama Director *Anna Stapleton*

The Drama Department directly assists funding of the Royal National Theatre, Royal Shakespeare Company and the Royal Court, as well as 23 national touring companies. It also looks at applications for separate new projects, often by emergent new companies. The Department also administers a number of training schemes designed to offer advanced in-service and further training to professional designers and directors. There are a number of schemes available to encourage new theatre writing. The council's Touring Department funds a number of projects which are suitable for presentation in large- and middle-scale mixed-programme theatres. However, these generally originate from established companies. Further information available from the free Arts Council leaflet, 'Development Funds'.

Arts Council of Northern Ireland

185 Stranmillis Road, Belfast BT9 5DU
Tel: 01232 381591
Fax: 01232 661715
Performing Arts Director *Philip Hammond*

Provides funding for locally based theatres and drama companies, individual awards for performers, and supports youth drama and youth dance. Further details can be obtained from the Performing Arts Director.

Scottish Arts Council

12 Manor Place,
Edinburgh EH3 7DD
Tel: 0131 226 6051
Fax: 0131 225 9833
Drama and Dance Director *David Taylor*
Contact *Annette Greenfield*

The council's bursaries scheme for theatre practitioners (actors, directors, technicians, administrators, etc.) is aimed at providing career refreshment and reinforcement by enabling candidates to extend their expertise in specific areas of work. Bursaries are generally provided to enable attendance at short-term training or to undertake a period of study or a special research project. Applicants should have a minimum of 3 years' professional experience in Scotland.

Arts Council of Wales

Museum Place,
Cardiff CF1 3NX
Tel: 01222 394711
Fax: 01222 221447
Director of Artform Development
Michael Baker

In the past 2 years, the main concern of the drama board has been the reorganisation of local government and the resultant cuts in funding to theatre companies in the region. For example, Theatr Clwyd faced a cutback of 51 per cent in local-government support and the Arts Council of Wales increased its grant to the theatre. Local-government funding for the Sherman Theatre in Cardiff is also under review. A new subcommittee, Delivering Drama Panel, has been briefed to design a strategy and policy basis for 'healthy' drama programming across Wales and the drama department played a key role in enabling the Royal Shakespeare Company to tour to Newport in 1997.

Regional Arts Boards (RABs)

5 City Road, Winchester,
Hampshire
SO23 8SD
Tel: 01962 851063
Fax: 01962 842033
E-mail: info.erab@artsfb.org.uk
Chief Executive *Christopher Gordon*
Assistant *Carolyn Nixson*

The representative body for the 10 English Regional Arts Boards. Scotland, Northern Ireland and Wales have their own Arts Councils. The three Welsh Regional Arts Associations are now absorbed into the Welsh Arts Council. RABs are support and development agencies for the arts in the regions.

The resources available to the RABs during 1997/8 total over £60 million. They provide financial support for professional companies, dance and mime companies, musical ensembles, etc. Some assistance is also given to support amateur work. A number of opportunities are available for individual artists, mostly aimed at helping them to reach a new and wider audience. A variety of commissions, bursaries, fellowships and residencies are available and information for specific schemes can be obtained on request from individual RABs. The Regional Arts Boards have a key role in advising and assessing applications to the National Lottery through the Arts Council of England.

Eastern Arts Board

Cherry Hinton Hall,
Cambridge CB1 4DW
Tel: 01223 215355
Fax: 01223 248075
Drama Officer *Alan Orme*
Performing Arts Assistant (Drama and Literature) *Lisa Canessa*

Covers Bedfordshire, Cambridgeshire, Essex, Hertfordshire, Lincolnshire, Norfolk and Suffolk. The Drama Unit budget will primarily be used to support theatres, small-scale venues, regional theatre companies, puppetry, theatre for young people and touring throughout the region.

London Arts Board

Elme House, 133 Long Acre, Covent Garden, London WC2E 9AF
Tel: 0171 240 1313
Fax: 0171 240 4580
Principal Drama Officer *Sue Timothy*

The arts funding and development agency for the capital, the London Arts Board serves the 32 boroughs and the Corporation of London. The Theatre Production Fund supports the production of 'challenging new work' throughout London in a variety of venues, taking into consideration the cultural diversity of the region. The Theatre for Young People Fund supports imaginative and original theatre for young people and/or family audiences in London, the money being given for research and development, and for production.

'Diverse Acts' supports 3 new plays which emerge from communities and individuals originating in the Caribbean, Indian subcontinent, China, Africa, the Pacific Rim and Latin America where there is a commitment to produce the work by an established company and/or theatre in London. Contact the Principal Drama Officer for more information.

East Midlands Arts Board

Mounfields House, Epinal Way,
Loughborough,
Leicestershire LE11 0QE
Tel: 01509 218292
Fax: 01509 262214
E-mail:
firstname.surname.ema@artsfb.org.uk
Head of Performing Arts *Helen Flach*
Arts Officer, Dance *Louise Sutton*
Arts Assistant, Drama *Suzy Smith*

Covers Leicestershire, Nottinghamshire, Derbyshire (excluding the High Peaks) and Northamptonshire. The bulk of the drama budget supports a network of 4 regional producing theatres: Derby Playhouse, Leicester Haymarket, Northampton Royal and Nottingham Playhouse, and 1 independent touring company, New Perspectives.

The Independent Theatre Companies scheme supports regional companies to produce new work. The Small Scale Promoters scheme supports promoters to initiate or extend an annual programme with a minimum of 4 events. The Artists at Your Service scheme supports workshops in schools and the community. The Write In scheme offers a script-reading service for playwrights as well as workshops and surgeries.

Training bursaries support individual artists' training and development. Details of these and other projects and schemes are available from the Information Officer.

North-West Arts Board
Manchester House, 22 Bridge Street, Manchester M3 3AB
Tel: 0161 834 6644
Fax: 0161 834 6969
E-mail: nwarts-info@mcrl.poptel.org.uk
Contact *Ian Tabbron (Performing Arts Officer – Drama)*

North-West Arts Board is the regional arts development agency for Cheshire, Greater Manchester, Lancashire, Merseyside and the High Peak of Derbyshire. Core activities are 'to support the arts in the region financially, to help develop the region's arts infrastructure and to increase the levels of skill, expertise and professionalism among the region's practitioners'.

Provides revenue funding to the Bolton Octagon Theatre, Chester Gateway, Duke's Lancaster, Liverpool Everyman, Liverpool Playhouse, Manchester Royal Exchange, Manchester Young People's Theatre (Contact), and Oldham Coliseum. Funding is given to 3 Theatre-in-Education companies and a number of smaller theatre companies and projects. NWAB offers a range of projects and schemes together with a service of support and advice on other sources of funding. Contact the Performing Arts Officer (Drama) for details of drama-related projects and schemes.

Northern Arts
9–10 Osborne Terrace, Jesmond, Newcastle upon Tyne NE2 1NZ
Tel: 0191 281 6334
Fax: 0191 281 3276
E-mail: nab@norab.demon.co.uk
Website: http://www.poptel.org.uk/arts/
Head of Performing Arts *Brian Debnam*
Administrator, Performing Arts *Ursula Horan*

Covers Cumbria, Durham, Northumberland, Teeside and Tyne and Wear, and was the first regional arts association in the country to be set up by local authorities. The Performing Arts team is responsible for dance, drama, mime, music, circus and cabaret, European arts programmes, touring support, training in the performing arts, venue and festival development, travel and training. The team can answer queries about grants for arts projects and deal with questions specifically related to performing-arts development.

South-East Arts
10 Mount Ephraim, Tunbridge Wells, Kent TN4 8AS
Tel: 01892 515210
Fax: 01892 549383
Drama Officer *Linda Lewis*

South-East Arts is the regional arts development agency for Kent, Surrey, East Sussex and West Sussex. It supports and develops the arts in the south-east through funding, advice, information and other services. The board also gives advice and guidance on Capital and A4E Lottery applications.

The Drama Department offers 4 funding schemes: a three-tier pilot system of Drama Production Funding: Tier 1 Research and Development –

grants of up to £5,000; Tier 2 The Production Phase – towards the production and touring of new work; Tier 3 Major Investment Phase – for major investment in high-profile and nationally significant projects based in the region; Presentation of New Work, grants of up to £2,000 for programming of new work in small- to mid-scale venues; Improving Viability, grants of up to £500 to strengthen the viability of organisations; Support for Individuals, bursaries of up to £300.

Applicants should contact the Drama Officer, in the first instance, to discuss their application.

South-West Arts

Bradninch Place, Gandy Street, Exeter, Devon EX4 3LS
Tel: 01392 218188
Fax: 01392 413554
E-mail: swarts@mail.zynet.co.uk
Director of Performing Arts Nick Capaldi

South-West Arts is the regional agency responsible for the funding and development of the arts in Cornwall, Devon, Dorset (except Christchurch, Poole and Bournemouth), Somerset, Gloucestershire and the Unitary Authorities of Bristol, South Gloucestershire, Bath and north-east Somerset. It is also the regional adviser to the Arts Council on all National Lottery matters. Financially supports the Everyman Theatre in Cheltenham, the Bristol Old Vic, Exeter Northcott Theatre and Plymouth Theatre Royal. In addition, funding is given to a number of regionally based touring theatre companies including Orchard Theatre Company and Theatre Alibi. South-West Arts also supports a network of venues and promoting organisations across the South-West.

Southern Arts

13 St Clement Street, Winchester, Hampshire SO23 9DQ
Tel: 01962 855099
Fax: 01962 861186
Theatre Officer Nicolas Young

Southern Arts covers Berkshire, Buckinghamshire, Hampshire, Isle of Wight, Oxfordshire and Wiltshire, with Bournemouth, Milton Keynes, Poole, Portsmouth, Southampton and Swindon and the borough of Christchurch in Dorset – a region of over 4 million people and 80 arts centres, theatres and concert halls. Funding is concentrated on a wide range of companies, developing audiences and supporting small- to mid-scale touring.

West Midlands Arts

82 Granville Street, Birmingham B1 2LH
Tel: 0121 631 3121
Fax: 0121 643 7239
Performing Arts Officer (Drama) Kate Organ
E-mail: kate.organ. wma@artsfb.org.uk
Performing Arts Officer (Dance and Mime) Anouk Perinpanayagam
E-mail: anouk.perinpanayagam.wma@artsfb.org.uk

Covers the metropolitan authorities of Birmingham, Sandwell, Dudley, Solihull, Wolverhampton and Coventry; the unitary authority of Stoke-on-Trent and the counties of Warwickshire, Staffordshire, Worcestershire and Herefordshire.

Most grant aid is available to regional organisations and companies rather than to individuals. Can offer information and advice about networks and other opportunities. Currently looking at puppetry, new circus, live art, physical theatre, projects involving new technology, new writing and combined arts/inter-disciplinary projects. Limited project and development funding. Lottery, information and resources advice.

Yorkshire and Humberside Arts

21 Bond Street, Dewsbury,
West Yorkshire WF13 1AY
Tel: 01924 455555
Fax: 01924 466522
E-mail: yharts-info@geo2.poptel.org.uk
Drama Officer *Shea Connolly*

Yorkshire and Humberside Arts offers advice, contact and support to theatre and drama projects through its Performing Arts Department. The Department includes a Drama Officer, Dance and Mime Officer and Music Officer working across all these areas. New companies can get advice about setting up tours, making contacts, establishing good working practices, Equal Opportunities policies and financial systems. Support can be given for fees to guest practitioners or rehearsal costs, but it cannot be given towards fees for full-time study.

Miscellaneous

Festivals

Arundel Festival

The Mary Gate, Arundel,
West Sussex BN18 9AT
Tel: 01903 883690
Fax: 01903 884243

Founded 1977. Annual, 10-day summer arts festival, held at the end of August, of which drama is an important element. Open-air theatre is staged in the grounds of Arundel Castle – the 1997 production being the Oxford Stage Company's *All's Well That Ends Well* directed by Irina Brook. Other companies which appeared in 1997 included: Ridiculusmus, Theatre Mélange Children's Theatre, Brouhaha and Midsommer Actors. Street theatre and a festival Fringe are regular features as well as concerts, exhibitions, fireworks and jazz.

Belfast Festival at Queen's

Festival House, 25 College Gardens,
Belfast BT9 6BS
Tel: 01232 667687
Fax: 01232 663733
E-mail: r.turner@qub.ac.uk

Founded 1963. Annual 3-week international arts festival held in November (13th–29th in 1998). The largest festival in Ireland, presenting music, opera and song, theatre and dance, jazz, comedy, folk and world music, literature, visual arts and film. The 1997 festival saw the only UK visit of the Merce Cunningham Dance Company from New York; the Royal Shakespeare Company's production of *Beckett Shorts* directed by Katie Mitchell; the Bristol Old Vic's production of *Macbeth*, with Pete Postlethwaite in the title role; Tricycle Theatre's *Srebrenica* directed by Nicolas Kent; Druid Theatre Company's *A Skull in Connemara* by Martin McDonagh.

Bradford Festival

The Windsor Baths,
11 Great Horton Road,
Bradford, West Yorkshire BD7 1AA
Tel: 01274 309199
Fax: 01274 724213
Director *Dusty Rhodes*

Founded 1987. Annual 2-week summer festival. Includes the Mela ('bazaar' or 'fair' in Urdu) which reflects the city's cultural mix. Music, dance, street theatre and the Black Literature Festival.

361

Brighton Festival

21–22 Old Steine, Brighton,
East Sussex BN1 1El
Tel: 01273 292950
Fax: 01273 622453
E-mail: info@brighton-festival.org.uk

Founded 1967. Annual 24-day international arts festival held in May (2nd–24th in 1998). Companies which have appeared include the Maly Theatre of St Petersburg and the Gesher Theatre from Israel.

Bury St Edmunds Festival

Festival Office, Borough Offices,
Angel Hill, Bury St Edmunds,
Suffolk IP33 1XB
Tel: 01284 757080
Fax: 01284 757091

Founded 1986. Annual 17-day festival held in May (8th–24th in 1998). Covers a wide range of events with a particular emphasis on classical music and jazz.

Buxton Festival

1 Crescent View, Hall Bank, Buxton,
Derbyshire SK17 6EN
Tel: 01298 70395
Fax: 01298 72289

Founded 1979. Annual 17-day classical music festival with the Buxton Opera House at its heart. Held in July (10th–26th in 1998). Although the main events are music-based, there is some drama and a festival fringe.

Canterbury Festival

Festival Office, Christchurch Gate,
The Precincts, Canterbury,
Kent CT1 2EE
Tel: 01227 452853
Fax: 01227 781830

Founded 1984. Annual 15-day mixed arts festival with over 200 events. Held in October (10th-24th in 1998). The main venues are the Marlowe Theatre, Gulbenkian Theatre and the Cathedral. Past festivals have seen productions by the Royal National Theatre, the Royal Shakespeare Company (*Henry V* in 1997), ATC, Moving Theatre, Millstream, Siobhan Davies Dance, Phoenix Dance and the Moscow State Circus.

2002 = 12th – 26th

Chichester Festival Theatre

– *see* Repertory and Regional Theatres, page 123

Contact Young Playwrights' Festival

Contact Theatre, Oxford Road,
Manchester M15 6JA
Tel: 0161 274 3434

Founded in 1986 and open to young people aged between 11 and 25 living in the north-west of England. The festival plays are staged by the Contact Theatre Company (*see entry under* Children's and Young People's Theatre Companies, page 212).

Festival of Dover

Dover District Council, White Cliffs Business Park, Dover, Kent CT16 3PD
Tel: 01304 872058
Fax: 01304 872062

Founded 1961. Annual 1- or 2-week combined arts festival held at the end of May (23rd–30th in 1998). Mainly focuses on community arts projects and activities which are low-cost and highly accessible. In 1997, there was a major street theatre project which actively involved over 300 schoolchildren and 1,000 members of the community. A torchlit procession was followed by an open-air production and fireworks. There are also story-telling and Theatre-in-Education activities.

Edinburgh Festival Fringe

180 High Street,
Edinburgh EH11 1QS
Tel: 0131 226 5257
Fax: 0131 220 4205
E-mail: admin@edfringe.com

Founded 1947. Huge open, non-programmed 3-week festival held each August (9th–31st in 1998). Offers theatre, comedy, music and dance in more than 150 different venues. Theatre companies such as Red Shift, Hull Truck, Volcano and Forkbeard Fantasy regularly perform at the Fringe. Excellent showcase opportunities for small-scale productions, and the Fringe Club regularly hosts workshops and masterclasses in which actors can participate.

Edinburgh International Festival

21 Market Street,
Edinburgh EH1 1BN
Tel: 0131 473 2001
Fax: 0131 473 2002
E-mail: www.90-edinburgh.co.uk

Founded 1947. Leading annual 3-week international festival (16th August–5th September in 1998) of music, theatre, film, jazz, dance and the tattoo held at the castle. 1997 drama productions included *Measure for Measure* directed and designed by Stéphane Braun-schweig, *The Cherry Orchard* directed by Peter Stein, *The Cocktail Party* directed by Philip Franks.

Exeter Festival

Room 4.44, Civic Centre, Paris Street,
Exeter, Devon EX1 1JN
Tel: 01392 265205
Fax: 01392 265366

Founded 1974. Annual 18-day arts festival held in July (2nd–19th in 1998). Broad range of performing arts – classical music, jazz, theatre, dance and comedy.

First Bite – BBC Young Writers' Festival

Room 6067, Broadcasting House,
London W1A 1AA

Founded in 1988 (formerly the Young Playwrights' Festival). Takes place every 2 to 3 years and open to writers aged 16–30 (inclusive) who are new to radio.

(Glasgow) West End Festival

4 Kirklee Circus, Glasgow G12 0TW
Tel: 0141 337 6177
Fax: 0141 357 1204

Founded 1996. Annual 2-week festival held in June of (mostly) free events, outdoor concerts, exhibitions, street theatre and community events. The main feature is a spectacular carnival parade from the Botanic Gardens in the centre of the West End, culminating in a free concert and party in the park.

Greenwich and Docklands International Festival

6 College Approach, Greenwich,
London SE10 9HY
Tel: 0181 305 1818
Fax: 0181 305 1188

Founded 1970 (as Greenwich Festival) 1996 (as Greenwich & Docklands International Festival). Annual 10-day multi-arts summer festival held in July (10th–19th July in 1998). Pub and fringe theatre; outdoor street theatre; productions at Greenwich Theatre and site-specific events. In 1997, theatre productions included G&J Productions and Boilerhouse Theatre's *Headstate* by Irvine Welsh, and a promenade production of *Longitude* in the grounds of the Royal Naval College.

Harrogate International Festival

Royal Baths, Harrogate,
North Yorkshire HG1 2RR
Tel: 01423 562303
Fax: 01423 521264
E-mail: info@harrogate-festival.org.uk

Founded 1966. Annual 16-day multi-arts summer festival (24th July–8th August in 1998). Concerts, ballet, contemporary dance, drama (usually 2 events, one of which is an open-air production), opera, street theatre, jazz, comedy, exhibitions, walks and talks. A Street Theatre Festival runs alongside the main festival every year.

International Playwriting Festival

Warehouse Theatre, Dingwall Road,
Croydon CR0 2NF
Tel: 0181 681 1257
Fax: 0181 688 6699

Founded 1986. The festival is in 2 parts: the competition has a script submission deadline in July and the November festival includes performed excerpts from the shortlisted plays, workshops and discussions, a performance from a partner festival in Italy, the Premio Candoni Arta Terme, and the staged reading of the winning play. Recent winners include: *YoYo* by Dino Mahoney (1994), *Iona Rain* by Peter

Moffat (1995; broadcast on BBC Radio 4/film rights acquired), *Fat Jane is Dead* by Simon Smith (1996). All winning plays are staged at the Premio Candoni Arta Terme. There are limited casting opportunities for the staged readings in November; apply with sae at the end of October.

Lichfield International Arts Festival

Tourist Information Centre, Donegal House, Bore Street, Lichfield, Staffordshire WS13 6NE
Tel: 01543 257557

Annual 10-day festival held in July. Highlights of the 1997 Festival included: *Julius Caesar* performed by the MDCC Theatre Company, the Endellion String Quartet, English Symphony Orchestra, the BBC Concert Orchestra.

London International Festival of Theatre (LIFT)

19–20 Great Sutton Street,
London EC1V 0DN
Tel: 0171 490 3964
Fax: 0171 490 3976
E-mail: lift@mail.easynet.co.uk

Founded 1981. Biennial festival bringing the best of international contemporary performance to London for a month-long season every other summer. Performances take place in large and small venues and outdoor locations all over London. Next festival will be in June/July 1999. LIFT commissions and produces new pieces of work for each festival and these events often bring together international directors and artists with UK performers. In addition, LIFT commissions work from UK artists. LIFT '97 saw several shows which required the spectators' input: *Oráculos* from Columbia, *La Feria de los Cinco Sentidos* from Spain and the home-grown *Now and Again*.

City of London Festival

Bishopsgate Hall, London EC2M 4QD
Tel: 0171 377 0540
Fax: 0171 377 1971

Founded 1962. Annual, 3-week arts festival (23rd June–16th July in 1998) staged in the unique venues of the City of London's square mile. Highlights of the 1997 festival included the Orchestra of the Age of Enlightenment in the Guildhall Great Hall and the Takacs Quartet performing Brahms in the City Livery Halls.

London New Play Festival

34 Osnabrook Street,
London NW1 3ND
Tel: 0171 209 2326
Artistic Director *Phil Setren*
Workshop Director *Christopher Preston*

Founded in 1989. Open to full-length and one-act plays which are assessed for originality, form, etc. by a reading committee. Deadline for scripts is the end of January; details can be obtained from the Writers' Guild (*see* Organisations, Associations and Societies, page 351).

Ludlow Festival

Castle Square, Ludlow,
Shropshire SY8 1AY
Tel: 01584 872150 (box office)

Annual summer festival – the dates for 1998, which is its 39th year, are 20th June – 5th July. Drama, music, exhibitions. During the 2 weeks of the festival, a Shakespeare play is performed in the grounds of Ludlow Castle.

Minack Theatre Summer Festival

Porthcurno, Penzance,
Cornwall TR19 6JU
Tel: 01736 810694
Fax: 01736 810779
E-mail: minack@dial.pipex.com

Founded 1932. Annual, 17-week summer season of plays, musicals, opera, etc. held at the unique open-air theatre carved into the Cornish cliffside. Created in 1929 by the enterprising Rowena Cade and her gardener Billy Rawlings, the Minack lends itself to large-cast plays. Most companies involved are amateur although approximately 3 each year are professional.

National Student Drama Festival

20 Lansdowne Road, Muswell Hill,
London N10 2AU
Tel: 0181 883 4586
Fax: 0181 883 7142
E-mail: lpaiormb@lipa.ac.uk

Founded 1956. Annual 7-day festival held in various venues (1st–8th April in 1998, in Scarborough) featuring the best of UK student productions. Also, a massive range of twice-daily professionally led workshops (mostly practical) plus daily discussion of plays seen. An average of 2 new productions a day, providing many useful professional contacts, for students and pros alike. Over 650 now established professionals, such as Alan Yentob, Rik Mayall, Sandi Toksvig and Terry Hands, participated when students. Outstanding foreign student companies have occasionally brought guest productions to the festival.

Pitlochry Festival Theatre
– *see* Repertory and Regional Theatres, page 136

Royal Court Young Writers' Festival
Royal Court Young People's Theatre,
309 Portobello Road,
London W10 5TD
Tel: 0181 960 4641
Fax: 0181 960 1434

Open to young people up to the age of 23 in targeted regions. Focuses on the process of playwriting: writers and directors from the Royal Court visit parts of Britain with 5 centres in each area, leading a workshop on playwriting. A second visit extends this process to the point at which young people attending are invited to submit work for the festival. Intensive work on the final drafts of plays precedes production at the Royal Court Theatre Upstairs, before going on tour in the participating areas.

Salisbury Festival
Festival Office, 75 New Street,
Salisbury, Wiltshire SP1 2PH
Tel: 01722 323883
Fax: 01722 410552

Founded 1972. Annual festival held at the end of May/beginning of June. The 1997 Festival included the Royal National Theatre production of David Hare's *Skylight*, the Reduced Shakespeare Company in *The Complete Works of William Shakespeare*, Jane Lapotaire in *Shakespeare As I Knew Her*, plus the Phoenix Dance Company and Cirque Baroque.

Scottish Young Playwrights Festival
Scottish Youth Theatre,
Old Athenaeum Theatre,
179 Buchanan Street,
Glasgow G1 2JZ
Tel: 0141 332 5127
Fax: 0141 333 1021
Artistic Director *Mary McCluskey*

The Scottish Young Playwrights project operates throughout Scotland. In every region an experienced theatre practitioner runs regular young writers' workshops aimed at developing the best possible scripts from initial ideas. A representative selection of scripts is then taken to form a showcase. The festival is mounted at the Old Athenaeum Theatre in December in conjunction with the Royal Scottish Academy of Music and Drama. Scripts are workshopped, revised and developed, culminating in an evening presentation.

Scripts are welcome throughout the year from young people aged 15–25 who are native Scots and/or resident in Scotland; synopses of unfinished scripts also considered. There is no restriction on style, content or intended media but work must be original and unperformed.

Stratford-upon-Avon Poetry Festival
The Shakespeare Centre,
Henley Street,
Stratford-upon-Avon, Warwickshire
CV37 6QW
Tel: 01789 204016
Fax: 01789 296083

Founded in 1953, an annual festival held on Sunday evenings during July and August. Readings by poets and professional actors.

The Sunday Times Hay Festival

Festival Office, Hay-on-Wye HR3 5BX
Tel: 01497 821217
Fax: 01497 821066

Founded 1988. Annual 10-day festival, held in May (22nd–31st in 1998). Literature, comedy, music and food, and workshops with major playwrights. Those appearing at the 1997 included: Arthur Miller, Richard Eyre, Adrian Noble, Bruce Robinson, David Hare, Ariel Dorfman and Alan Ayckbourn.

Warwick and Leamington Festival

Northgate, Warwick CV34 4JL
Tel: 01926 410747
Fax: 01926 407606

Founded 1980. Annual 12-day festival held in July (1st–12th in 1998). Principally a music festival, with an emphasis on chamber and early music, but also features 2 plays performed in the grounds of Warwick Castle.

Publications and Services

ACID Publications
Suite 247, 37 Store Street,
London WC1E 7BS
Tel: 07050 205 206
Contact *Frank Scantori*

Founded in 1990. Weekly noticeboard for actors, cooperative agencies and personal managers providing current casting. Provides a 'friendly and approachable service and up-to-date information on available work in anything from fringe to film. Classified ads can be inserted at a reasonable rate and casting information is accepted free of charge'. Deadline for casting adverts is Fridays 5.00 p.m. Actors can also ring the ACID office for 'support and advice'.

Amateur Stage
83 George Street, London W1H 5PL
Tel: 0171 486 1732
Fax: 0171 224 2215
Owner *Platform Publications Ltd*
Editor *Charles Vance*

Monthly publication covering amateur drama with reviews of latest productions and practical techniques.

Applause
*– see **Plays and Players Applause**,* page 371

British Alternative Theatre Directory
*– see **McGillivray's Theatre Guide**,* page 371

British Theatre Directory
Richmond Publishing Company Ltd,
Douglas House,
3 Richmond Buildings,
London W1V 5AE
Tel: 0171 437 9556
Fax: 0171 287 3463
Editor *Nicholas David Leigh*

Annual directory listing venues throughout the UK.

Broadcast

33–39 Bowling Green Lane, London
EC1R 0DA
Tel: 0171 505 8014
Fax: 0171 505 8050

Founded 1960. Weekly trade magazine of the broadcasting world.

Casting Couch/Casting Couch Video File

Casting Couch Productions Ltd,
Unit 011, Canalot Productions Studios,
222 Kensal Road,
London W10 5BN
Tel: 0181 964 4043
Fax: 0181 960 8907
Contact *Moira Townsend*

The Casting Couch was set up in 1991 to provide an arena in which performers of all ages and at different stages of their careers could show their work to casting people. 'Hundreds of actors from all over the UK have been seen. They've obtained work and been called in for castings while many more have been taken on by an agent.'

The Video File is a video directory of performers designed to let the casting industry see hundreds of new and established actors in performance. Entry is by audition. Either telephone, leaving name, address and telephone number and information will be sent, or send in a cv, photograph and sae.

Castcall Information Service

106 Wilsden Avenue, Luton,
Bedfordshire LU1 5HR
Tel: 01582 456213
Fax: 01582 826370
E-mail: ron@castcall.demon.co.uk
Contact *Ron O'Brien*

Established 1986. An information service for actors (also runs Castfax for agents) with casting news which is updated 3 times per week. Premium-rate telephone-line service or a subscription service whereby actors receive Castcall by post, fax or e-mail. Also offers an Internet service; for sample pages on the World Wide Web, contact http://www.castcall.demon.co.uk.

Castingdex

PO Box 100,
Broadstairs,
Kent CT10 1UJ
Tel: 01843 860885

A–Z of names and addresses of main advertising agencies, including creative directors and casting directors, voiceover specialists, production houses. Price: £18.

Contacts

– see **The Spotlight**, page 372

Film Log

Subscribers: PO Box 100,
Broadstairs, Kent CT10 1UJ
Editorial: PO Box 11, London N1 7JZ
Tel: 01843 860885 (Subscribers)/
0171 566 8282 (Editorial)
Fax: 0171 566 8284 (Editorial)
Subscription £10 (3 months); £20 (6 months); £35 (12 months)

Monthly. Listing of films in production and pre-production, giving details of studios, locations and key production people.

McGillivray's Theatre Guide (formerly The British Alternative Theatre Directory)

Rebecca Books, 7 Shrubland Road,
London E8 4NN
Tel: 0171 923 7166
Editor David McGillivray

Annual listings publication.

Plays International

33A Lurline Gardens,
London SW11 4DD
Tel: 0171 720 1950
Fax: 0171 720 1950
Editor Peter Roberts

Monthly magazine covering the theatre scene in the UK and abroad. News, reviews, interviews and a complete play text in each issue.

Plays and Players Applause

Northway House, 1379 High Road,
London N20 9LP
Tel: 0181 343 9977
Fax: 0181 343 7831
Editor Sandra Rennie

Monthly. A mixture of news, reviews, reports and features on all the performing arts. For professionals and the general public.

Professional Casting Report (PCR)

Subscribers: PO Box 100,
Broadstairs, Kent CT10 1UJ
Editorial: PO Box 11, London N1 7JZ
Tel: 01843 860885 (Subscribers)/
0171 566 8282 (Editorial)
Fax: 0171 566 8284 (Editorial)
Subscription £24 (5 weeks); £45 (10 weeks); £115 (26 weeks); £226 (52 weeks)

Weekly. Gives details of imminent TV, film and theatre casting.

Who's Where, an A–Z of contacts within the business, issued annually with addenda from time to time. Free to new subscribers of PCR and Film Log; further copies available for £7 to subscribers only.

Repertory REPORT

Subscribers: PO Box 100,
Broadstairs, Kent CT10 1UJ
Editorial: PO Box 11, London N1 7JZ
Tel: 01843 860885 (Subscribers)/
0171 566 8282 (Editorial)
Fax: 0171 566 8284 (Editorial)
Subscription £10 (3 months); £20 (6 months); £35 (12 months)

Monthly. Listing of regional repertory theatres and their production schedules and audition plans.

Screen International

33–9 Bowling Green Lane,
London EC1R 0DA
Tel: 0171 505 8080
Fax: 0171 505 8117
Editor Boyd Farrow

International trade paper of the film, video and television industries.

Script Breakdown Service (SBS)

Suite 1,
16 Sidmouth Road,
London NW2 5JX
Tel: 0181 459 2781
Fax: 0181 459 7442

Weekly. Available to agents only. A list of casting requirements for film, TV, theatre, light entertainment, commercials, videos and documentaries.

Sight and Sound
British Film Institute,
21 Stephen Street,
London W1P 1PL
Tel: 0171 255 1444
Fax: 0171 436 2327
Editor *Philip Dodd*

Founded 1932. Monthly. Topical and critical articles on international cinema, with regular columns from the USA and Europe.

The Spotlight
7 Leicester Place,
London WC2H 7BP
Tel: 0171 437 7631
Fax: 0171 437 5881

Annual. A photographic casting directory used throughout the business by agents, casting directors and directors. Essential for all actors. *Actresses* published in October; entries should be delivered in March/April. *Actors* published in April; entries should be delivered in September/October. *New Actors and Actresses* published in February, in association with the Conference of Drama Schools. All actors' information is also kept on CD-ROM and the Internet.

The Spotlight maintains computerised records of members of the profession, which are regularly updated and are referred to continuously. An advisory service is available to everyone who advertises in *The Spotlight* between 10 a.m. and 12.30 p.m. Monday to Thursday.

Other directories include *The Stunt Register* and *Children's Spotlight*. *The Spotlight* has now taken over *The Players Guide* in New York. Also publishes the listings handbook, *Contacts*.

The Stage (incorporating Television Today)
47 Bermondsey Street,
London SE1 3XT
Tel: 0171 403 1818
Fax: 0171 357 9287
Editor *Brian Attwood*

Founded 1880. Weekly newspaper for professionals in the entertainment industry, with reviews, comment and job advertisements.

Theatre
PO Box 7913,
London SE1 4EZ
Tel: 0171 378 1055
Fax: 0171 378 1069
Editor *Ann Shuttleworth*

Theatre magazine – 6 issues per year. Comprehensive UK theatre listings, reviews, news and interviews.

Theatre Record
305 Whitton Drive,
Isleworth,
Middlesex TW7 7NE
Tel: 0181 892 6087
Fax: 0181 893 9677
Editor/Publisher *Ian Herbert*

Started in 1981 as *London Theatre Record* and was renamed *Theatre Record* in 1990. Issued every fortnight. Publishes all reviews which appear in the national press and leading listings magazines for selected current plays.

Who's Where
– see **Professional Casting Report (PCR)**, page 371

Additional Skills

Actors should always try to extend their abilities so that the listing of skills on their cv makes them an attractive proposition to directors. The ability to dance, sing, play an instrument, ride a horse, juggle or offer a range of dialects are just a few of the possibilities. For the actor who intends to work in small-scale touring, a driving licence is almost essential. The Actors Centres in London, Newcastle upon Tyne and Manchester (see Organisations, Associations and Societies) have excellent workshops and classes available to members. Local-authority evening classes offer a wide range of options, and adverts in the trade press will point you in the right direction for specialist classes and tutors. Here are a few to give a flavour of what's available.

The Arts Educational Schools London

Cone Ripman House, 14 Bath Road, Chiswick, London W4 1LY
Tel: 0181 994 9366
Fax: 0181 994 9274
Principal *Peter Fowler*
Registrar *Brenda Gray*

Offers 1-year, post-experience vocational training for professional actors who 'seek to refocus their work' or for performers from other disciplines who wish to change the course of their careers.

Black Mime Theatre Co.

34–36 Colombo Street,
London SE1 8DP
Tel: 0171 928 1311
Fax: 0171 928 1740

Offers annual training projects. See entry under Touring Theatre Companies, page 159

Braithwaite's School of Acrobatics

8 Brookshill Avenue, Harrow Weald,
Middlesex HA3 6RZ
Tel: 0181 954 5638
Contact *Valerie Braithwaite*

Professional acrobatic and tumbling
classes; also BAGA gymnastics. Classes
held in the evenings and on Saturdays.
Contact the address above for details.

Constructive Teaching Centre

18 Lansdowne Road, Holland Park,
London W11 3LL
Tel: 0171 727 7222
Principal *Mr W.H.M. Carrington*
Contact *John Brown*

Founded 1960. Offers teacher training
in the F. Matthais Alexander Technique
and also individual private lessons.
The first training course was started in
London in 1930. The centre is recognised by the Society of Teachers of the
Alexander Technique to which students become eligible for admission as
Teaching Members on the satisfactory
completion of their training. Candidates must be between the ages of 18
and 35 and have a solid grounding in
the Alexander Technique from a course
of individual lessons. After graduation, students are encouraged to
remain for a postgraduate term, without fee, and for which they receive
nominal remuneration.

The Drill Hall

16 Chenies Street,
London WC1E 7EX
Tel: 0171 631 5107

Offers classes and workshops in a wide
variety of topics, including Mask
Theatre; Voice (women only); Acapella
Voices; Free Your Voice; Classical Yoga;
Acrobatics; BodyTalk (an intensive
physical theatre workshop).

East 15 Acting School

Offers a refresher 'Faststream Acting
Course' and also a course on directing.
See entry under Drama Schools,
page 21

Institute for Creativity (in association with FRACTALS)

PO Box 3206, Wokingham,
Berkshire RG41 3YH
Tel: 0118 977 6130
Fax: 0118 977 3224

Now in its twentieth year, 'The
Mastery' 3-day workshop 'puts you in
touch with your passion and enables
you to discover the joy that comes from
realising your unique ability to
communicate creatively and expres-
sively'.

London College of Printing and Distributive Trades (LCPDT)

Herbal House, 10 Back Hill,
Clerkenwell, London EC1R 5EN
Tel: 0171 514 6562/6770
Fax: 0171 514 6563

Offers 2-day courses in acting and
presenting to camera. Of particular
value to those with experience of
theatre work who wish to extend their
presentation skills or to gain practice
for auditions. Also holds 'tailor-made'
training in radio work, with specialisation in voice training and radio presentation.

Royal Academy of Dramatic Art

18–22 Chenies Street,
London
WC1E 7EX
Tel: 0171 636 7076
Fax: 0171 323 3865

Offers courses throughout the year for professional actors. A wide range of topics is covered and run for varying lengths from a single weekend to 2 weeks, full-time. Recent courses have included weekend workshops on Audition Preparation, Dialect and Accents, Voice, Movement and Text, Acting for Radio, full-week courses on Working in Television and Audition Preparation, and once-a-week evening sessions in Acting – Exploring Realism, Exploring Shakespeare, Exploring Character. Write to the Administrator, Short Courses for further details.

Directors

Maria Aitken

Theatre director and actress. Directing credits include: *Happy Family* (Duke of York's), *Private Lives* (Oxford Playhouse), *After the Ball is Over* (Compass tour), *The Rivals* (Court Theatre, Chicago), *Are You Sitting Comfortably?* (Palace Theatre, Watford), *The Mystery of Irma Vep* (Haymarket Theatre, Leicester/ Ambassadors Theatre, London), *As You Like It* (Regent's Park Open Air Theatre), *School for Scandal* (Theatr Clwyd).

Bill Alexander

Began his career as a director at the Bristol Old Vic before joining the Royal Shakespeare Company in 1977 with a special brief for new plays. Productions included: *Factory Birds, Shout Across the River, The Hang of the Gaol* and *Bastard Angel*. On becoming an Associate Director of the RSC in 1984, he directed the highly acclaimed *Richard III* with Antony Sher. His production of *The Merry Wives of Windsor* won the Olivier award for Best Director in 1986. Other credits include: *Entertaining Mr Sloane* (Nottingham Playhouse), *The Price of Cotton, Sex and Kinship in a Savage Society, Class Enemy, Sugar and Spice* (Royal Court), *Romeo*

and Juliet (Victory Theatre, New York), *Troilus and Cressida* (Shakespeare Theatre, Washington), *After Easter* (Lyric Theatre, Belfast). Became Artistic Director of Birmingham Rep in 1992 where he has directed *Othello, Volpone, Old Times, The Snowman, Awake and Sing!, The Tempest, The Servant, Macbeth, The Way of the World, Divine Right, Dr Jekyll and Mr Hyde* and *The Merchant of Venice.*

Mike Alfreds

Theatre director and writer. Trained as a director in the US where he began his career before moving back to Britain in the early sixties. Founded Shared Experience Theatre Company in 1975 (where his credits included: *Arabian Nights, Bleak House, La Ronde, A Handful of Dust* and *Three Sisters*). Was an Associate Director of the Royal National Theatre where he was voted Best Director by the London critics in 1986 for his production of *The Cherry Orchard* starring Ian McKellen at the Cottesloe. Became Artistic Director of the Cambridge Theatre Company in 1991. In their first year (1995) as the renamed Method & Madness company, he directed (and adapted) *Jude the Obscure, Private Lives* and

Philip Osment's *Flesh and Blood* and was awarded the British Regional Theatre award for Best Director.

Jon Amiel

Film and television director. Credits include: *Tandoori Nights* (Channel 4, 1985), *The Silent Twins* (BBC, 1985), *The Singing Detective* (BBC, 1986), *Queen of Hearts* (Enterprise Pictures, 1989), *Aunt Julia and the Scriptwriter* (Cinecom, 1990), *Sommersby* (Warner Bros, 1993), *Copycat* (1995).

Jeremy Ancock

Television drama and documentary and radio drama director. Credits include: *A Class of His Own* (BBC, 1984), *EastEnders* (BBC, 1985/8), *Kisses on the Bottom* (BBC, 1986), *Rockcliffe's Babies* (BBC, 1987), *Bergerac* (BBC, 1989), *The Bill* (Thames, 1990), *The Riff Raff Element* (BBC, 1992; BAFTA nomination), *Brookside* (Mersey TV/Channel 4, 1994).

Sarah Pia Anderson

Theatre, film and TV director. Theatre credits include: *Hello and Goodbye, Sorry, The Caucasian Chalk Circle* (all Crucible Theatre, Sheffield), *Last Resort* and *Crowning Glory* (Traverse, Edinburgh/Bush Theatre), *The Estuary, These Men, The Nest* (all Bush Theatre), *Waiting* (Lyric Studio), *Derek* (RSC tour), *Rosmersholm* (Royal National Theatre), *Indigo, Old Year's Eve, Across Oka* and *Mary and Lizzie* (all RSC), *Carthaginians* (Abbey Theatre, Dublin/Hampstead Theatre), *The Winter's Tale* (Santa Cruz Shakespeare Festival), *Mary Stuart* (Folgar Theatre, Washington), *Hedda Gabler* (Roundabout Theatre, New York), *Three Sisters* (University of California). TV credits: *A Silly Little Habit* (BBC), *Summer's Awakening* (Channel 4), *A Woman Calling* (BBC), *The Raving Beauties* (Channel 4), *This is History Gran* (BBC), *The Bill* (Thames), *The Alleyn Mysteries* (BBC), *Dr Finlay* (STV, 1993), *Prime Suspect V 'Inner Circles'* (Granada TV), *Profiler* (NBC), *Leaving LA* (ABC).

Michael Apted

TV and film director. Film credits include: *Triple Echo* (1972), *Stardust* (1974), *The Squeeze* (1977), *Agatha* (1979), *Coal Miner's Daughter* (1980), *Gorky Park* (1983), *First Born* (1984), *Gorillas in the Mist* (1988), *The Long Way Home* (1989), *Class Action* (1991), *Thunderheart* (1992), *Blink* (1994), *Nell* (1994), *Extreme Measures* (1996). TV credits include: *P'tang Yang Kipperbang* (1982).

Moira Armstrong

TV director. Credits include: *Testament of Youth* (1979), *How Many Miles to Babylon?* (1982), *Freud* (1984), *Bluebell* (1985), *Dunroamin' Rising* (1987), *Countess Alice* (1991 – all for BBC), *Body and Soul* (Red Rooster/Carlton, 1993), *A Village Affair* (Carlton, 1994).

Michael Attenborough

Theatre and television director. Son of Richard Attenborough. Artistic Director of the Turnstyle Group, 1989–90. Was Artistic Director of Hampstead Theatre from 1984 to 1989 where he directed *The War at Home, Particular Friendship, That Summer, Observe the Sons of Ulster Marching Towards the Somme* (Time Out award), *Separation* (also West End).

Previous posts included: Associate Director of the Mercury Theatre in Colchester (1974–79), Leeds Playhouse (now West Yorkshire Playhouse, 1974–79), and the Young Vic (1979–80),

Artistic Director of Watford Palace Theatre (1980–84). Set up Turnstyle. Executive producer of the RSC (1991–95) and appointed Principal Associate Director of the RSC in 1996. Directed *Amphibians, The Changeling, Les Liaisons Dangereuses, After Easter, Pentecost,* Peter Whelan's *The Herbal Bed* and *Romeo and Juliet.* Other theatre credits include: *1984* (Citadel Theatre, Edmonton, Canada), *Yerma* (Abbey Theatre, Dublin), *Home Front* (Broadway), *Fashion* (Tricycle Theatre), *My Mother Said I Never Should* (Royal Court). Directed *The Importance of Being Earnest* for Channel 4.

Lord Richard Attenborough

Film director. Began his career as an actor, undertaking an ambitious range of characterisations including Pinky in *Brighton Rock* (1947). Went on to produce and direct. Among his credits as a director are: *Oh! What a Lovely War* (1969), *Young Winston* (1972), *A Bridge Too Far* (1977), *Magic* (1978), *Gandhi* (1982), *A Chorus Line* (1985), *Cry Freedom* (1987), *Chaplin* (1992), *Shadowlands* (1993), *In Love and War* (1997). Made a life peer in 1993.

David Attwood

TV and film director. Credits include: *Flowers in the Rain* (written and directed for BBC, 1985), *Rockcliffe's Babies* (BBC), *Tales from Sherwood Forest* (Central, 1989), *Killing Time* (BBC, 1990), *Made in Heaven* (Granada TV, 1990), *Wild West* (Initial Films/Channel 4/British Screen, 1992), episodes of *The Bill* (Thames, 1989/94), *Saigon Baby* (BBC, 1995), *Moll Flanders* (Granada, 1996).

Sir Alan Ayckbourn, CBE

Theatre director and author of over 50 plays. Began directing at the age of 19 for the Stephen Joseph Studio Company in Scarborough. As a BBC radio drama producer in Leeds, he directed an average of two plays a month for six years, working mostly with new writers. He left the BBC in 1970 to become Artistic Director of Scarborough's Library Theatre, responsible for a summer repertoire of four or five plays, one of which traditionally was his own annual offering. He managed to establish the company on a permanent basis and, in 1976, masterminded the transfer of the company from the Library Theatre into a converted Victorian high school where it became the Stephen Joseph Theatre-in-the-Round. Ayckbourn usually re-directs the London productions of his own plays when they transfer from Scarborough. These have included: *Relatively Speaking, Absurd Person Singular, The Norman Conquests, Just Between Ourselves, Ten Times Table, Joking Apart, Season's Greetings, Way Upstream, Intimate Exhanges, A Chorus of Disapproval, Woman in Mind, Communicating Doors.* In 1979 he was nominated for a Broadway Tony award for his co-direction, with Peter Hall, of the National Theatre production of *Bedroom Farce.*

In 1986, Ayckbourn took a two-year sabbatical from Scarborough to work with his own group of actors at the National Theatre. He has directed the twenties farce *Tons of Money,* his own play, *A Small Family Business,* Arthur Miller's *A View from the Bridge* (for which he was nominated for Director of the Year in the Olivier awards, and won the Plays and Players award) and *'Tis Pity She's a Whore.* In 1988, he directed *Henceforward* in the West End and *Man of the Moment.* In 1992, directed *Invisible Friends* and *Mr A's Amazing Maze Plays* at the Royal National Theatre, followed by *Time of*

My Life at the Vaudeville Theatre in 1993. For the RSC, he directed *Wildest Dreams* in 1993/4. Other credits: *Two Weeks with the Queen, Conversations with my Father* and his latest play, *Things We Do For Love* at the Stephen Joseph in Scarborough in 1997 and Gielgud Theatre, London in 1998.

In 1996, the Stephen Joseph Theatre Company moved to its new home in a converted cinema where the opening production was *By Jeeves*, a musical written in collaboration with Andrew Lloyd Webber (British Regional Theatre award for Best Musical).

In 1987, Ayckbourn was made a Commander of the British Empire; in 1992, he was the Cameron Mackintosh Professor of Contemporary Theatre at Oxford and in 1997, he received a knighthood for services to theatre.

Roger Bamford

TV director. Credits include: *Blott on the Landscape* (BBC), *Auf Wiedersehen Pet* (Central/Witzend), *Rumpole of the Bailey* (Thames), *Pulaski* (BBC), *Stolen* (LWT), *Come Home Charlie and Face Them* (LWT), *Spender* (BBC), *Minder* (Euston Films), *Love Hurts I and II* (Alomo/BBC), *A Touch of Frost* (Yorkshire TV), *Moving Story* (Carlton/Paravision); *No Bananas* (BBC), *Hetty Wainthropp Investigates* (BBC), *Crocodile Shoes II* (BBC); *Roger, Roger* (BBC).

Celia Bannerman

Theatre and TV director and actress. Directing credits include: *My Mother Said I Never Should* (Derby Playhouse), *September Tide* (Comedy Theatre), *The Price, Translations, Enemy of the People, Quartermaine's Terms, La Ronde* and *The White Devil* (all at the Bristol Old Vic), *Beached* and *Sinners and Saints* (Croydon

Warehouse), *Bête Noir* (Young Vic), *Sleeping Beauty* and *Magni* (Theatre Royal Stratford East), *A Midsummer Night's Dream* (Regent's Park Open Air Theatre), *Lips and Making Love* (Royal National Theatre) and *Brookside* for Mersey TV/Channel 4.

John Barton, CBE

Theatre and TV director. Advisory Director of the Royal Shakespeare Company. Joined the RSC in 1960 and devised the anthology programmes: *The Hollow Crown, The Art of Seduction* and *The Vagaries of Love*. He co-directed the Stratford histories cycle with Peter Brook and edited *The Wars of the Roses*. Subsequent productions include: *Love's Labour's Lost, Henry IV (Parts I and II)* and *Henry V* (co-direction), *All's Well That Ends Well, Julius Caesar, Troilus and Cressida, The Tempest, Othello, When Thou Art King, Richard II, King John, Cymbeline, Much Ado About Nothing, The Winter's Tale* (with Trevor Nunn), *King Lear* (with Trevor Nunn and Barry Kyle), *A Midsummer Night's Dream, The Merchant of Venice, Hamlet*. Non-Shakespearean work includes: *Dr Faustus, Perkin Warbeck, The Greeks, La Ronde; The Rover, Pillars of the Community, The Way of the World, Three Sisters*. He has also directed *The School for Scandal* at the Haymarket Theatre and *Waste* at the Lyric Theatre, Hammersmith. For TV, he has directed *Morte d'Arthur*, and has devised and presented the series *Playing Shakespeare*. Made a Commander of the British Empire in 1981.

Stephen Bayly

Film and TV director. Worked with Tony Scott and Ridley Scott before going to the National Film and Television School in Beaconsfield.

Credits include: *Notman, Joni Jones, And Pigs Might Fly, The Dream Factory, The Works, Just Ask for Diamond, Coming Up Roses/Rhosyn A Rhith* (the first film to be both financed in Wales and made in the Welsh language), *The Falcon's Malteser, Letters from Patagonia, Richard III.*

Adrian Bean

Film, TV, theatre and radio director. Former Artistic Director of the Inner City Theatre Company (1988/9). Credits include: *The Secret of Beatrix Potter* (Redgrave Theatre, Farnham), *Salem's Lot* (BBC Radio), *EastEnders* (BBC), *Bomber* (BBC Radio).

Alan Bell

TV and film director and writer. Began as a trainee film cameraman with the BBC. Credits include: *Chinese Puzzle* (BBC), *Fallen Hero* (Granada), *Friend of the Family* (Granada), *Death on the Mountain* (BBC), *Gaskin* (BBC), *Cat's Eyes* (TVS), *King and Castle* (Thames), *One Way Ticket to Hollywood* (Tyburn Productions/Channel 4 biography of Peter Cushing), *Who Cares Wins* (Walberry Productions/Channel 4), *The Beiderbecke Connection* (Yorkshire TV), *Children's Ward* (Granada), *Stealing the Fire* (Yorkshire), *Ape About the House* (Yorkshire), *The Bill* (Thames), *Taggart − Death Benefits* (STV), *Blood and Honey* (CTVC for the BBC), *True Crimes: Hot Dog Wars* (Central), *Casualty* (BBC).

Rodney Bennett

TV director and writer. Credits include: *The Lost Boys* (BBC, 1978), *Hamlet* (BBC, 1980), *Dombey and Son* (BBC, 1982), *Monsignor Quixote* (Euston Films, 1985), *Rumpole of the Bailey*

(Thames), *The Darling Buds of May* (Yorkshire, 1990), *The House of Eliott* (BBC, 1991), *Soldier Soldier* (Central Films, 1994), *Dr Finlay* (BBC).

Bruce Beresford

Australian film, documentary and commercial director. Feature films include: *The Getting of Wisdom* (1977), *Breaker Morant* (1979), *The Club* (1980), *Puberty Blues* (1981), *Tender Mercies* (1982), *King David* (1984), *The Fringe Dwellers* (1985), *Crimes of the Heart* (1986), *Driving Miss Daisy* (1989), *Mister Johnson* (1990), *Black Robe* (1991), *Rich in Love* (1993), *Ataturk* (1997).

Steven Berkoff

Theatre director, actor, writer and designer. Studied mime with Jacques Lecoq in the sixties and founded the London Theatre Group for whom he adapted and directed two works by Kafka − *In the Penal Colony* (1968) and *Metamorphosis* (1969). Credits include: *The Trial, Agamemnon* (1971), *The Fall of the House of Usher* (1974), *East* (1975), *Greek* (1979), *Decadence* (1981), *West* (1983), *Kvetch* (1986), *Sink the Belgrano!* (1986), *Salome* (1988), *Massage* (premièred at the 1997 Edinburgh Festival). Most of these have been produced several times, on the Fringe and in the West End. He also directed *Coriolanus* at Joseph Popp's Public Theatre in New York.

Kevin Billington

TV, theatre and film director. Theatre credits include. *The Deliberate Death of a Polish Priest* (Almeida Theatre and film for Channel 4), *Veterans Day* (Haymarket), *Old Times* (The Gate, Dublin). Film credits include: *Interlude* (Columbia, 1986), *The Rise and Rise of*

Michael Rimmer (Warner Bros, 1969), *The Light at the Edge of the World* (1970). TV credits include: *Henry VIII* (BBC, 1979), *The Jail Diary of Albie Sachs* (BBC, 1980), *The Good Soldier* (Granada, 1981), *Outside Edge* (LWT, 1981), *Reflections* (Court House Films/ Channel 4, 1984), *Heartland* (BBC, 1989), *A Time to Dance* (BBC, 1991).

Michael Blakemore

Theatre and film director, actor and writer. Born in Australia and came to England in 1950. Studied at RADA and in 1996, joined the Glasgow Citizens' Theatre as an actor and co-Artistic Director. Here he directed Peter Nichol's prize-winning play, *A Day in the Death of Joe Egg* (with Albert Finney), which transferred to London and New York. Other prize-winners he has directed include the British première of Brecht's *Arturo Ui*, Peter Nichol's *Forget-Me-Not Lane* and Michael Frayn's *Make and Break* and *Noises Off*. The latter two transferred to the West End from the Lyric Theatre, Hammersmith where Blakemore was resident Director from 1980. The Broadway production of Frayn's *Benefactors* (also a prize-winner) played on Broadway at the Brooks Atkinson, as did *Noises Off*. His successes at the National Theatre, where he was Associate Director (1971–76), included: *The National Health, Design for Living, Plunder, Long Day's Journey into Night* and *The Front Page* (the latter two winning the Plays and Players Best Director award) and *All My Sons*. Other West End credits include: *Knuckle, Candida, Separate Tables, Privates on Parade, Deathtrap* and *All My Sons, Made in Bangkok* by Anthony Minghella at the Aldwych Theatre; *Lettice and Lovage* by Peter Shaffer at the Globe Theatre; *After the Fall* at the Royal National Theatre;

The Sisters Rosenweig (Greenwich Theatre/The Old Vic); Arthur Miller's *The Ride Down Mount Morgan* (Wyndham's) and *Uncle Vanya* with Michael Gambon at the Vaudeville Theatre. His production of *City of Angels* played on Broadway and in London, and in 1995/6, he directed *Death Defying Acts* (three one-act plays by Woody Allen, David Mamet and Elaine May) off-Broadway. In 1997, he directed the hit musical *The Life*, for which he received a Tony nomination for Best Director of a Musical.

His first feature film was *Privates on Parade*, and he wrote, directed and acted in the film, *A Personal History of the Australian Surf*, for which he received the Peter Sellers award for comedy in the Evening Standard Film Awards. Other film credits include: *The Old Reliable* ('Tales of the Hollywood Hills'), *Country Life* (a film version of Uncle Vanya, starring Sam Neill and Greta Scacchi). Opera credits include: *Tosca* (Welsh National Opera); he has also written a novel about the theatre called *Next Season*.

Les Blair

Film: *Bad Behaviour* (1993); *Jump the Gun* (1997; also wrote); TV: *Number One* (1984); *Honest, Decent and True* (1985); *London's Burning* (1988); *Filipina Dreamgirls* (1991).

Michael Bogdanov

Theatre, TV and opera director. Associate Director, Tyneside Theatre Company (1971–73); Associate Director, Haymarket Theatre, Leicester; Artistic Director, Phoenix Theatre, Leicester (1973–77) and Young Vic (1978–80); Associate Director, Royal National Theatre, since 1980; Artistic Director Deutsches Schauspielhaus, Hamburg, 1989–91. Co-founder (1986) and joint Artistic Director of the English Shakespeare Company where he directed *The Wars of the Roses*. Work for the Royal National Theatre includes: *Sir Gawain and the Green Knight*, *The Hunchback of Notre Dame*, *The Romans in Britain*, *Hiawatha*, *One Woman Plays*, *The Mayor of Zalamea*, *The Hypochondriac*, *Uncle Vanya*, *The Caucasian Chalk Circle*, *The Spanish Tragedy*, *Macbeth*, *Lorenzaccio*, *You Can't Take it With You*, *Strider – The Story of a Horse*, *Orwell's England*, *The Ancient Mariner*. For the RSC, productions include: *The Taming of the Shrew* (Director of the Year SWET award), *The Shadow of a Gunman*, *The Knight of the Burning Pestle*, *Romeo and Juliet*, *The Venetian Twins*, *The Hostage*, *Faust Parts I and II*. In the West End he directed the musical *Mutiny*. Recently relaunched the English Shakespeare Company with a production of *A Midsummer Night's Dream*. For TV, he directed his own series *Broad and Narrow*, *Shakespeare Lives* and *Shakespeare on the Estate*. Opera credits include *Donnerstag aus Licht* (Royal Opera House) and *Montag aus Licht* (La Scala).

John Boorman

Film director. Began as a TV director, switching to films in the sixties. Has since moved to the US and has spent much time trying to keep the Irish film industry afloat. Credits include: *Point Blank* (1967), *Hell in the Pacific* (1969), *Leo the Last* (1970), *Deliverance* (1972), *Zardoz* (1974), *Exorcist II: The Heretic* (1977), *Excalibur* (1981), *The Emerald Forest* (1985), *Hope and Glory* (1987), *Where the Heart Is* (1990), *Beyond Rangoon* (1995), *I Once Had a Life*.

Laurence Boswell

Theatre director. Associate Director at The Gate Theatre, Notting Hill from 1990 to 1992 and Artistic Director from 1992 to 1995. Productions at that theatre include: *Punishment Without Revenge* (*Time Out* award and Charrington Fringe award), *Don Gil of the Green Britches*, *The Gentlemen from Olmedo*, *The Great Pretenders*, *Madness in Valencia* (Olivier award for Outstanding Achievement, 1992), *Hecuba*, *Agamemnon's Children*, *Electra*, *Orestes and Iphigenia in Taurus*, *The Cheating Hearts*, *Bohemian Lights* (LWT Plays on Stage award, 1993). Other credits include: *Bartholomew Fair* (Royal Shakespeare Company), *As You Like It* (Washington Shakespeare Theatre), *Beauty and the Beast* (Young Vic), Ben Elton's *Popcorn* (Nottingham Playhouse/West Yorkshire Playhouse/Apollo Theatre, London), *Long Day's Journey into Night* (Plymouth Theatre Royal), *The Painter of Dishonour* (Royal Shakespeare Company), *A Voyage Round My Father* (Nuffield Theatre, Southampton/Oxford Playhouse), *Long Day's Journey into Night* (Cambridge Theatre Company), *The Alchemist* and *A Doll's House* (Sheffield Crucible).

Michael Boyd

Former Artistic Director of the Tron Theatre in Glasgow; trainee director, Malaya Bronnaya Theatre, Moscow; Assistant and Associate Director, Coventry Belgrade Theatre (1979–82); Associate Director, Crucible Theatre, Sheffield (1982–84). Productions for the Tron Theatre include: *Macbeth*, *Good*, *The Real World* (also Stony Brook Festival, Long Island, New York), *Crow*, *Century's End*, *Salvation*, *The Baby*, *Clyde Nouveau*, *The Guid Sisters* (also Toronto and Montreal, Canada). Was Drama Director, New Beginnings Festival of Soviet Arts – productions include: *Losing Alec*, *The Funeral*, *Sleeping*

Beauty, Philadelphia Here I Come, Faustus, Mcgotty and Ludmilla, Muir, Macbeth. Other credits: *Commedia* and *Othello* (Lyric Theatre, Hammersmith), *A Passion in Six Days* (Royal Court), *Hard to Get* (Traverse Theatre, Edinburgh), *Hedda Gabler* (Haymarket Theatre, Leicester), *The Alchemist* (Cambridge Theatre Company), *The Broken Heart, Much Ado About Nothing, The Spanish Tragedy* and *Measure for Measure* (Royal Shakespeare Company).

Michael Brayshaw

TV director. Credits include: *Bergerac* (BBC), *Emmerdale* (Yorkshire TV), *All Creatures Great and Small* (BBC), *Hard Cases* (Central), *The Bill* (Thames), *Casualty* (BBC), *Take the High Road* (STV), *Soldier Soldier* (Central), *Wycliffe* (ITV).

Kenneth Branagh

Theatre and film director, actor and writer. Founded the Renaissance Theatre Company with fellow actor David Parfitt in 1986 and directed *Romeo and Juliet, Twelfth Night, Look Back in Anger, A Midsummer Night's Dream.* Directed and starred in the title roles of his films of *Henry V* (1989), *Dead Again* (1991), *Peter's Friends* (1992), *Much Ado About Nothing* (1993), *Mary Shelley's Frankenstein* (1994), *In the Bleak Midwinter* and *Hamlet* (1996).

Yvonne Brewster

Theatre, film and radio director. Artistic Director of Talawa Theatre Company. Credits include: *The Harder They Come* and *Smile Orange* (both films made in Jamaica), *The New Hardware Store* (Arts Theatre), *Raisin' in the Sun*

(Black Theatre Co-op), *Two Can Play* (Bristol Old Vic), *The Good Doctor* (Arts Theatre), *Black Jacobins* (Riverside Theatre), *School's Out* (Theatre Royal Stratford East), *Flash Trash* (Half Moon Theatre), *The Importance of Being Earnest* (Talawa), *The Dragon Can't Dance* (Stratford East), *Blood, Sweat and Fears* (Riverside).

Peter Brook, CBE

Theatre, film, TV and opera director. Author of *The Empty Space* on the art of directing. Directed his first theatre production, *Faustus*, at the Torch Theatre in 1943. Theatre credits include: *Hamlet* (with Paul Scofield – the Stratford Shakespeare Memorial Company's production which played at the Moscow Arts Theatre in 1955 and in London in 1956), *The Power and the Glory, A View from the Bridge, La chatte sur un toit brûlant* (*Cat on a Hot Tin Roof*) at the Théâtre Antoine, *Titus Andronicus* and *The Tempest* (1957 – also composed music and designed sets), *Eugene Onegin* (Metropolitan Opera, New York, 1958), *The Balcony* in Paris, *The Visit* (London, 1958 and New York, 1960). Directed and designed *King Lear* in 1962 and won the New York Drama Critics award for Best Director for his RSC production of *Marat/Sade* in 1964. Other RSC credits include: *US* (1966) and the internationally acclaimed production of *A Midsummer Night's Dream* in 1970. Directed a modern-dress production of Seneca's *Oedipus* for the National Theatre Company at The Old Vic in 1968.

Founded the Centre International de Créations Théâtrales in Paris in 1971. Activities with the Centre have included: *Orghast* for the Shiraz Festival at Persepolis in Iran (1971), a tour of central Africa in 1972 presenting mime plays, *Timon of Athens* (Paris,

1974), *The Ik*, tour 1975–76, including the Round House, London, *Ubu* (1977), *Antony and Cleopatra* (1978), *Conference of the Birds* (1979), *The Mahabharata* (theatre and film, 1985), *Woza Albert* (1985), *The Tempest* (1990), *Oh Les Beaux Jours* (*Happy Days* 1997).

Film credits include: *The Beggar's Opera* (1953), *Moderato Cantabile* (also co-wrote, 1960), *Lord of the Flies* (also screenplay, 1964), *Marat Sade* (1967), *Tell Me Lies* (film version of *US*, 1967), *King Lear* (starring Paul Scofield, 1969), *Meetings with Remarkable Men* (1977), *The Tragedy of Carmen* (1983). He was made a Commander of the British Empire in 1965.

Pip Broughton

Theatre and television director. Artistic Director of the Nottingham Playhouse (1990–94). Credits include: *She Stoops to Conquer* (Chester Gateway), *The Lady from the Sea* (Duke's, Lancaster), *Joking Apart* (Coventry Belgrade), *War of the Newts* (Liverpool Everyman), *A Midsummer Night's Dream* (KNS, Antwerp), *Paradise* (Nottingham Playhouse), *Germinal* and *The Art of Success* (Paines Plough), *Twelfth Night* (Birmingham Rep), *Having a Ball* (Comedy Theatre), *The Importance of Being Earnest*, *Thérèse Raquin* and *Two-way Mirror* (Nottingham Playhouse).

Ian Brown

Artistic Director of TAG Theatre Company in Glasgow for four years; Associate Director of Theatre Royal Stratford East. Artistic and Executive Director the Traverse Theatre, Edinburgh from 1988 to 1996. Productions during this period included: *Stones and Ashes* by Daniel Danis, *Reader* by Ariel Dorfman, *A*

Light in the Village by John Clifford, *Moscow Stations* by Venedict Yerofeev, translated by Stephen Mulrine (transferred to the Garrick Theatre, London and Union Square Theatre, New York; starred Tom Courtenay), *Buchanan* by Tom McGrath, *The House Among the Stars* by Michel Tremblay, *Hardie and Baird* by James Kelman, *Bondagers* by Sue Glover (also Donmar Warehouse, London). Was awarded a special Fringe First for services to new writing at the Edinburgh Festival in 1996. Directed the original production of *Trainspotting* for the Citizens' Theatre which transferred to the Bush Theatre in London. Other credits include: *An Inspector Calls* and *84 Charing Cross Road* (Perth Theatre), *The Caretaker* (Birmingham Rep), *Private Lives* and *Charley's Aunt* (Royal Lyceum Theatre, Edinburgh), *Endgame* (RAT Theatre Company), *Out on the Floor* and *Migrations* (Theatre Royal Stratford East), *Fool for Love* (Donmar Warehouse), *Babycakes* (Tron Theatre, Glasgow), *Widows* (Cambridge Arts Theatre/Oxford Playhouse/Traverse Theatre), *Steaming* (Piccadilly Theatre), *Of Mice and Men* (West Yorkshire Playhouse), *Goodnight Children Everywhere* (Royal Shakespeare Company); *Shining Souls* (Traverse Theatre).

Irina Brown

Theatre, TV and opera director. Credits include: *The Misunderstanding* (The Gate Theatre, London), *Boris Godunov* (Royal Opera House), *Our Country's Good* (Tabakov Theatre, Moscow), *Zinky Boys Go Underground* (BBC/BFI), *Hamlet* (Royal National Theatre Studio), *The Sound of Music* (West Yorkshire Playhouse). Since 1996, Director of the Tron Theatre, Glasgow where she directed and translated (with Iain Heggie) Alexei Shipenko's *Lavochkin-5 (La Funf in der Luft)*.

Bill Bryden

Theatre, TV, film and opera director and writer. Directed his first professional production, *Misalliance*, at the Belgrade Theatre, Coventry in 1965 and then worked as an assistant to William Gaskill at the Royal Court (1966–68). Productions for the Royal Court include: *Journey of the Fifth Horse, Backbone, Passion, Corunna* and *The Baby Elephant*. In 1971, Bryden was appointed Associate Director of the Royal Lyceum Theatre in Edinburgh where, with Clive Perry, he developed a company of mainly Scottish actors and a repertoire of new writing by Scottish playwrights. Productions included: *Benny Lynch* and *Willie Rough* (both written by Bryden), *The Iceman Cometh, The Flouers of Edinburgh, How Mad Tulloch Was Taken Away*. In 1975, he was appointed an Associate Director of the National Theatre, where he directed: *Spring Awakening, Romeo and Juliet, The Playboy of the Western World, Watch It Come Down, Il Campiello, Counting the Ways, The Passion* (co-director), *Old Movies* (also author), *The Plough and the Stars*. Appointed Director of the Cottesloe Theatre, where he directed *Lark Rise* (co-director), *American Buffalo, The World Turned Upside Down, Dispatches* (co-adaptor), *Candleford* (co-director), *The Long Voyage Home, Hughie, The Iceman Cometh, The York Mystery Plays, Glengarry, Glenross, A Midsummer Night's Dream, The Mysteries* (National/Lyceum Theatres). Other theatre credits include: *A Life in the Theatre* (starring Denholm Elliott, 1989), *The Ship* (written and directed for Glasgow's European City of Culture celebrations), *A Month in the Country* (starring Helen Mirren and John Hurt, 1994), *The Son of Man* (RSC), *Uncle Vanya* (Chichester Festival Theatre, 1996), *Whom Do I Have the Honour of Addressing?* (Chichester Festival Theatre, 1997).

In 1978, he was appointed a non-executive director of Scottish Television, heading the drama planning group. TV work has included: *Ill Fares the Land* (his own screenplay, Channel 4, 1982), *The Holy City* (BBC), *Six Characters in Search of an Author* (BBC, 1993), *The Big Picnic* (written and directed for BBC2), *Soho* (Promenade Productions/Channel 4). Was Head of Television Drama for BBC Scotland, 1985–88. Wrote the screenplay for the feature film *The Long Riders*.

Stuart Burge, CBE

Theatre, film and TV and opera director. Began his career as an actor and stage manager at The Old Vic and started directing in 1948 with a travelling repertory company. First London production: *Let's Make an Opera* at the Lyric Theatre, Hammersmith in 1949. Since then he has run the Queen's Theatre in Hornchurch, Nottingham Playhouse and the Royal Court. Notable theatre productions have included: the first performances of *The Ruling Class* by Peter Barnes and Wedekind's *Lulu* at Nottingham, *Uncle Vanya* with Laurence Olivier, Michael Redgrave and Joan Plowright. Co-directed *The Devil is an Ass* and *Measure for Measure* at the Edinburgh Festival with the Birmingham Repertory Theatre, which transferred to the National Theatre in 1977. Royal Court productions have included: *Fair Slaughter, The Eclipse, The London Cuckolds*. At the National Theatre he directed *The Prince of Hamburg*,

Antigone, Truth Dare Kiss, Command or Promise and *Neaptide.* Directed the première of *Another Country* (Queen's Theatre, with Rupert Everett, Kenneth Branagh, Daniel Day-Lewis and Colin Firth), *Curtains* by Stephen Bill (Hampstead Theatre Club), *The Black Prince* (Aldwych Theatre, with Ian McDiarmid), *Richard II* and *Henry IV Parts I and II* (Stratford, Ontario), *La Colombe* (Buxton Festival/Sadler's Wells), *Hobson's Choice* (West Yorkshire Playhouse), *The Father* (Churchill Theatre, Bromley, with Edward Fox and Stephanie Beacham). Work for BBC TV has included: *Sons and Lovers, The Old Men at the Zoo, Breaking Up, Naming the Names, Sons and Lovers, Under Western Eyes, The Power and the Glory, David Copperfield, School for Scandal, Much Ado About Nothing* (with Robert Lindsay and Cherie Lunghi), *The Importance of Being Earnest* (with Paul McGann and Joan Plowright), *Circles of Deceit, Talking Heads – A Chip in the Sugar* and *A Cream Cracker Under the Settee, The Rainbow* (with Imogen Stubbs), *After the Dance, Black Poppies* (which he originally directed at Theatre Royal, Stratford East in 1991), *The Wexford Trilogy.* Recently directed *The Writing Game* for Channel 4, *Maigret on the Defensive* and *Maigret and the Maid* (Granada TV, with Michael Gambon), *The House of Bernarda Alba* (Channel 4). Feature films include: *There Was a Crooked Man* (1960), *Othello* (1966, with Laurence Olivier), *The Mikado* (1967), *Julius Caesar* (1970, with Charlton Heston, John Gielgud, Jason Robards and Diana Rigg). He was made a Commander of the British Empire in 1974.

John Caird

Theatre, film and TV and opera director. Born in Canada, he worked there for a time before coming to England to train as an actor. He soon decided he preferred directing to acting and joined the Royal Shakespeare Company in 1977. Directed several successes at the Warehouse including: *Dance of Death, Savage Amusement* by Peter Flannery, *Look Out, Here Comes Trouble* by Mary O'Malley. In 1977, he began a series of productions co-directed with Trevor Nunn, starting with *The Merry Wives of Windsor* and *As You Like It*, continuing in 1979 with *The Life and Adventures of Nicholas Nickleby*, which went on to achieve enormous success with three seasons at the Aldwych, a transfer to Broadway and a TV film. This production won sixteen awards in the UK and US, including four for Best Director. Other collaborations with Trevor Nunn include *Les Misérables* and *Peter Pan.* Other work for the RSC includes the first production in The Pit – *Our Friends in the North* by Peter Flannery, *Twelfth Night, Red Star, Philistines, The New Inn, A Midsummer Night's Dream, Beggar's Opera* and *Antony and Cleopatra.* Outside the RSC, he has directed *Song and Dance* (the Andrew Lloyd Webber musical), *As You Like It* in Stockholm, which was filmed for Swedish TV, *Henry IV* for BBC TV, *Children of Eden, Trelawny of the Wells* and *The Seagull* and, most recently, *Peter Pan* for the Royal National Theatre.

Annie Castledine

Theatre director. Was Artistic Director of the Northern Studio Theatre, Associate Director of Theatr Clwyd in Mold and Artistic Director of Derby Playhouse. Credits include: *Hedda Gabler, Translations, Three Sisters* and *Maria Marten* (Theatr Clwyd), *The Children's Hour* and *Sunday's Children* (Derby), *Rosmersholm* (the Young Vic), *March for Fansa* (Royal Court Theatre

Upstairs), *Carrington* (Chichester Festival Theatre), *From the Mississippi Delta* (Talawa Theatre Company/Contact Theatre, Manchester), *Goliath* (Bush Theatre).

Michael Caton-Jones

Scottish-born film director. Graduate of the National Film and Television School, now based in Hollywood. Credits include: *Scandal* (1989), *Memphis Belle* (1990), *Doc Hollywood* (1991), *This Boy's Life* (1992), *Rob Roy* (1995), *Day of the Jackal* (1997).

James Cellan-Jones

TV, film and theatre director. Head of BBC Plays in the seventies. Film credits include: *Bequest to the Nation*, *Harnessing Peacocks*, *Vacillations of Poppy Carew*. TV credits include: *The Day Christ Died*, *A Fine Romance*, *Comedy of Errors*, *Oxbridge Blues*, *Fortunes of War*, *Arms and the Man*, *The Gravy Train Goes East*, *Maigret*, *I Love You Love Me Love*.

Penny Ciniewicz

Theatre director. Credits include: *Wallflowering* (West Yorkshire Playhouse, 1992), *Outside of Heaven* (Royal Court, 1992), *What the Butler Saw* (Salisbury Playhouse, 1993), *Weldon Rising* (Royal Court/Liverpool Playhouse, 1993), *Father's Day* (West Yorkshire Playhouse, 1993), *Sleuth* (Salisbury Playhouse, 1994), *Foreign Lands* (Wolsey Theatre, Ipswich, 1994). Since 1995, has been Artistic Director of Paines Plough.

Anthony Clark

Theatre director and writer. Directed at the Orange Tree Theatre, Richmond and served as a director to Tara Arts as the only white member of the company. Artistic Director of Contact Theatre, Manchester from 1984 to 1989. His Contact production of *To Kill a Mockingbird* won the Manchester Evening News Best Production award for 1987. Joined Birmingham Repertory Theatre as Associate Director in 1990 and productions directed for that company include: *The Seagull, Of Mice and Men, Cider with Rosie* (national tour), *My Mother Said I Never Should, The Atheist's Tragedy* (TMA/Martini award for Best Director), *The Red Balloon* (TMA/Martini award for Best Show for Children and Young People), *Playing by the Rules* (Mentorn First Night Production award), *Syme* (co-production with the Royal National Theatre Studio). Other credits include: *Dr Faustus* (Young Vic), *The Snowman* (Leicester Haymarket), *The Wood Demon* (Playhouse Theatre, London).

Jack Clayton

Film director and producer. Credits include. *The Bespoke Overcoat* (1955), *Room at the Top* (1958), *The Innocents* (1961), *The Pumpkin Eater* (1964), *Our Mother's House* (1967), *The Great Gatsby* (1974), *Something Wicked This Way Comes* (1983), *The Lonely Passion of Judith Hearne* (1987), *Momento Mori* (1992).

Ray Cooney

Theatre and TV director, actor, writer and manager. Has worked extensively as a director of West End comedy and farce, founding the Theatre of Comedy Company in 1983. Directing credits include: *Pygmalion, See How They Run, Run for Your Wife, Wife Begins at Forty, It Runs in the Family The Slow Drag.* Wrote, directed and played in *Two into*

One, Out of Order and *Funny Money*. TV production of *See How They Run*.

Tom Cotter

TV director. Following two years with STV, joined BBC Scotland in 1970 and during the following ten years, worked as both producer and director on a wide range of programmes covering drama, music and documentary. Credits include: *The Lost Tribe* (BBC, 1980), *Cloud Howe, Grey Granite, End of the Line, The House on Kirov Street* (all for BBC), *Bulman* (Granada), *Strike it Rich* (BBC), *Floodtide* (Granada, 1987/8), *Making Out* (BBC, 1991), *Casualty* (1992), *Just Us* (Yorkshire TV), *Frank Stubbs Promotes* (Carlton, 1993), *The Chief* (Anglia, 1994), *The Bill* (Thames), *Heartbeat* (Yorkshire TV, 1996/7), *Ballykissangel* (1997).

Malcolm Craddock

Film and TV director and producer. Originally a director but now, with his independent production company Picture Palace he has produced: *Tandoori Nights* (1985/7), *The Orchid House* (1991) and *Little Napoleons* (1994; all for Channel 4), *Sharpe's Rifles* (Central, 1992/7).

Ted Craig

Trained as a television director in Australia before working in Britain as an actor and director. Artistic Director of the Lyceum Theatre Crewe and then the Connaught Theatre Worthing before returning to Australia as Associate Director and then Director of Productions of the state theatre company at the Drama Theatre of the Sydney Opera House. Returned to Britain as a freelance director with productions at York, Sonning, Leatherhead, Watford, Southampton and the London Fringe. He was appointed Artistic Director at the Warehouse Theatre Croydon in 1986. His productions have included five new plays by David Allen, Anthony Davison's *Screamers*, Mark Bunyan's *Dinner*, the thirtieth anniversary revival of J. P. Donleavy's *Fairy Tales of New York*, Kevin Hood's *The Astronomer's Garden* (transferred to the Royal Court) and *Sugar Hill Blues* (transferred to the Hampstead Theatre), Bernard Kops's *Playing Sinatra* (transferred to the Greenwich Theatre), James Martin Charlton's *Fat Souls* (winner of the 1992 International Playwriting Festival), his own translation of Goldoni's *The Servant of Two Masters*, Peter Moffat's *The Blue Garden*. Has also directed two productions in Cyprus for Theatro Ena Nicosia of Arthur Miller's *The Last Yankee* and Joe Orton's *Entertaining Mr Sloane*.

Stephen Daldry

Artistic Director of the Royal Court from 1994 to April 1998. Associate Director, Crucible Theatre, Sheffield (1987–88); Artistic Director, The Gate Theatre, Notting Hill, London (1989–92) during which period he won the Olivier Observer award in 1992 and the Prudential award in 1991. Credits include: *The Ragged Trousered Philanthropists* (Stratford East/ Liverpool Playhouse, 1988), *Badlands* (Battersea Arts Centre), *Judgement Day* (Old Red Lion, London; Charrington Fringe Best Production, 1989, Time Out award, 1990), *An Inspector Calls* (York Theatre Royal, 1989), *Figaro Gets Divorced* (The Gate Theatre, 1990), *The Cutting Room* (Royal Court, 1990), *Rousseau's Tale* (RSC Fringe, 1990), *Manon Lescaut* (Dublin Opera Festival,

1991), *Pioneers in Ingolstadt* and *Purgatory in Ingolstadt* (The Gate Theatre, co-directed with Annie Castledine; Plays and Players award for Best Director), *Damned for Despair* (The Gate, 1992), *An Inspector Calls* (Royal National Theatre; Evening Standard award, 1992, transferred to Aldwych Theatre, 1993, Olivier award Best Revival, Best Set Design, Best Actress in a Supporting Role, tour to Broadway and Japan, 1994, 4 Tony awards and 7 Drama Desks, tour to Australia and Austria, 1995; now at the Garrick Theatre), *Search and Destroy* (Royal Court Theatre Upstairs), *Machinal* (Royal National Theatre; Olivier award Best Director and Best Actress for Fiona Shaw), *The Kitchen* and *The Editing Process* (Royal Court, 1994), *Rat in the Skull* (Royal Court Classic Season at the Duke of York's Theatre, 1995), *Body Talk* (Royal Court workshop, 1996), *This Is a Chair* (Royal Court at the Duke of York's, 1997).

Ron Daniels

Theatre director. Artistic Director of The Other Place in 1977 and Associate Director of the Royal Shakespeare Company (1979–91). Born in Brazil where he was a founder member of the Workshop Theatre of São Paolo. Came to England and worked as an actor before becoming an Assistant Director in 1969 at the Victoria Theatre, Stoke-on-Trent. Also directed for the Shaw Theatre, the Bristol Old Vic, Yale Repertory Theatre in Connecticut, RADA and the National Youth Theatre. On the London Fringe, he directed *Female Transport* (Half Moon Theatre) and *By Natural Causes* (Cockpit Theatre). His first production at The Other Place was *Afore Night Come* in 1974, and in 1976 David Edgar's *Destiny*, which transferred to the

Aldwych. Became Director of The Other Place in 1977 and directed *'Tis Pity She's a Whore, The Lorenzaccio Story, The Sons of Light, Hippolytus, Women Pirates* (at the Aldwych), *Pericles, The Suicide*. In 1980 at Stratford, he directed *Romeo and Juliet, Timon of Athens, Hansel and Gretel*, all of which transferred to London. Subsequent productions in Stratford which have transferred to London include: *The Tempest, A Midsummer Night's Dream, Peer Gynt, Hamlet, Camille*. Other RSC productions include: *Maydays, Breaking the Silence, Real Dreams, The Danton Affair, Much Ado About Nothing, The Plain Dealer, Hamlet* (with Mark Rylance), *A Clockwork Orange, E.A.R.W.I.G., Richard II*. In the 1997 season he directed *Henry V*. Other credits: *The Beastly Beatitudes of Balthazar B* with Simon Callow (Duke of York's Theatre), *Across from the Garden of Allah* (Comedy Theatre), *They Shoot Horses Don't They?* and *Breaking the Silence* (RSC/Mermaid Theatre), *Titus Andronicus* and *Hamlet* (Tokyo), *Afore Night Come* and *Camille* (USA), *Bingo, Ivanov, Puntilla and His Manservant Matti, Man is Man* (Yale University). As Associate Artistic Director of the American Repertory Theatre, Massachusetts he has directed *Hamlet* and *The Seagull* (both with Mark Rylance), *The Dream of the Red Spider, Silence, Cunning, Exile, Henry IV Parts I and II, The Cherry Orchard, The Threepenny Opera*.

Howard Davies

Theatre, television and opera director. Started work as Associate Director of the Bristol Old Vic, where credits included: *Narrow Road to the Deep North, Candida, Long Day's Journey into Night, Early Morning, Fear and Miseries of the Third Reich, Woyzeck, Spring Awakening*. He then worked in fringe and repertory theatre for three years before joining the Royal Shakespeare Company to direct *Man is Man, Schweyk in the Second World War, The Iceman Cometh.* A year later, he became an Associate Director of the RSC and established and ran the Warehouse Theatre in London for five years. Productions included: *Bandits, Bingo, The Fool, The Bundle, The Jail Diary of Albie Sachs, No Limits to Love, The Innocent, Outskirts, Good* and *Piaf* (which both transferred to the West End and Broadway). Other RSC productions have been: *The Time of Your Life, Macbeth, Henry VIII, Softcops, The Party, Troilus and Cressida, Flight, Les Liaisons Dangereuses, Penny for a Song, The General from America.* Productions for the Royal National Theatre, of which he is an Associate Director, include: *Mary Stuart* (with Isabelle Huppert and Anna Massey), *Children's Hour, Long Day's Journey into Night, Piano, The Crucible, Ma Rainey's Black Bottom, Hedda Gabler* (with Juliet Stevenson), *The Secret Rapture, The Shaughraun* (with Stephen Rea), *Cat on a Hot Tin Roof* (with Lindsay Duncan, Ian Charleson and Eric Porter), Mikhail Bulgakov's *Flight* and Wesker's *Chips with Everything.* For the Almeida Theatre, directed Diana Rigg and David Suchet in *Who's Afraid of Virginia Woolf?, The Iceman Cometh* (with Kevin Spacey) and Edward Albee's *The Play About the Baby.* Productions in the USA include: *Piaf* (with Jane Lapotaire and Zoe Wanamaker), *Good* (with Alan Howard), *Les Liaisons Dangereuses* (with Lindsay Duncan and Alan Rickman), *Cat on a Hot Tin Roof* (with Charles Durning and Kathleen Turner), *My Fair Lady* (with Richard Chamberlain), *Translations.* Opera credits: *Idomeneo* and *Eugene Onegin* for Welsh National Opera, *I Due Foscari*

(Scottish Opera), *The Italian Girl in Algiers* (ENO). Other credits: *Tales from Hollywood* (BBC), *The Secret Rapture* (Channel 4/British Screen).

Declan Donnellan

Joint Artistic Director of Cheek by Jowl and Associate Director of the Royal National Theatre. Productions for the Royal National Theatre include: *Fuente Ovejuna, Peer Gynt, Sweeney Todd* and *Angels in America.* Other credits: *Martin Guerre* (Prince Edward Theatre), *The Rise and Fall of the City of Mahagonny* (English National Opera).

Gregory Doran

Theatre director and actor. Associate Director, Nottingham Playhouse where productions included: *Long Day's Journey into Night, Waiting for Godot, The Norman Conquests, Hester, The Rose and the Ring.* Artistic Director of Century Theatre in Keswick. Assistant Director during the Royal Shakespeare Company 1988/9 season, productions included: *Cymbeline, Dr Faustus, Romeo and Juliet, Have.* Directed *Henry VIII* in the RSC's 1996/7 season and *Cyrano de Bergerac* (with Antony Sher) in the 1997/8 season. Other credits include: *September* (world première of Edward Bond play, Canterbury Cathedral), *Ispanka* (RSC Fringe), *Two Dogs and Freedom* (Sadler's Wells/Channel 4), *A Midsummer Night's Dream* (State University, New York), *Oakwell* (Interplay Community Theatre), *Titus Andronicus* (Market Theatre, Johannesburg/West Yorkshire Playhouse/Royal National Theatre).

Alan Dossor

Theatre, film and TV director. Artistic Director, Liverpool Everyman Theatre from 1970 to 1975. Theatre credits include: *John, Paul, George, Ringo and Bert* (Evening Standard award Best Musical), *Funny Peculiar, Breezeblock Park, Comings and Goings* (Hampstead Theatre), *Flying Blind* (Royal Court), *Liberty Hall* (Greenwich Theatre), *Having a Ball* (Lyric Hammersmith), *Rose* (Lyric Theatre), *Dracula* (Young Vic), *Harvest* (Ambassadors Theatre). Film and TV credits include: *Star Quality* and *Ice Dance* (BBC, 1989), *First and Last* (BBC, 1990, International EMMY award), *Broke* and *Flea Bites* (BBC, 1991), *Between the Lines* (Island World/BBC, 1992/4), *Fair Game* (BBC, 1993), *The Governor* (La Plante Productions, 1994), *No Bananas* (BBC, 1995), *The Locksmith* (BBC, 1996), *The Missing Postman* (BBC Scotland, 1996/7), *The Life and Crimes of William Palmer* (Yorkshire TV).

John Dove

Associate Director of Hampstead Theatre where his productions include: Anthony Minghella's *A Little Like Drowning*, Robert Holman's *Making Noise Quietly*, Stephen Bill's *Naked in the Bullring*, Shirley Gee's *Ask for the Moon, The Awakening, Hedda Gabler* (with Lindsay Duncan), *Flight into Egypt* and *Who Shall Return Us Our Children*. Other credits include: *Bingo* (Royal Court, co-directed with John Gielgud), *Henry IV Parts I and II, The National Health, The Widowing of Mrs Holroyd, Private Lives, The Importance of Being Earnest* (all for Nottingham Playhouse), *Drums in the Night, As You Like It, Shippel* (Birmingham Rep), *A Month in the Country, What the Butler Saw, All My Sons, The Philanderers, Cyril's Little Moment, Betrayal, Widowers, Houses, Duet for One* (Bristol Old Vic), *City Sugar* and *St Joan* (Prospect Theatre Company), *Cinderella* and *A Night in Old Peking* (Lyric Hammersmith), *A Perfect Retreat* and *Kate* (Bush Theatre), *Body and Soul* (Watford Palace), *The Prime of Miss Jean Brodie* (Royal Exchange, Manchester), *Rafts and Dreams* (Royal Court), *Someone Who'll Watch Over Me* (West Yorkshire Playhouse), *Back Stroke in a Crowded Pool, Crossing the Equator, Democracy* (all for the Bush Theatre), *A Soldier's Story* (Theatre Royal, Stratford East), *Night Must Fall* and *A Collier's Friday Night* (Greenwich Theatre), *Muse of Fire* (Edinburgh Festival, starring Alan Bates), *Prayers of Sherkin* (The Old Vic). Has directed a BBC Radio play, *The Airman Who Wouldn't Die*.

Tim Dowd

TV director. Credits include: *Supergran* (Tyne Tees), *Climbing Out* (Yorkshire TV), *Casualty* (BBC), *Emmerdale* (Yorkshire TV), *Yellowthread Street* (Yorkshire TV), *Families* (Granada), *Heartbeat* (Yorkshire TV), *Boon* (Central), *Ellington* (Yorkshire TV), *Famous Five* (Yorkshire TV).

Bill Douglas

Film director and screenwriter. Won a place at the London Film School with his drawings and went on to make an autobiographical trilogy of films: *My Childhood* (1971), *My Ain Folk* (1973) and *My Way Home* (1978). In 1986, made *Comrades* about the Tolpuddle Martyrs.

Dominic Dromgoole

Theatre director. At the age of 16, founded Cheapstreet Theatre Company which toured the south-west of England and performed at the Edinburgh Festival. Directed and translated Greek tragedy while at Cambridge University. Artistic

Director of the Bush Theatre for six years from 1990 during which period the company won 27 major theatre awards. While at the Bush, he directed new work for the Actors Theatre in Louisville, Kentucky, and raised the status of new writing in Romania. As director of new plays for The Peter Hall Company at The Old Vic, he directed *Grace Note* and *Snake in the Grass* in 1997.

Patrick Dromgoole

TV and film director/producer. Credits include: *Robin of Sherwood, Visage du passé, Eminent Domain, King of the Wind; Meurtres en douce, To Each His Own, Some Other Stories, Great Expectations.*

Han Duijvendak

Theatre director. Born and educated in Holland, he has worked in Britain since 1980. Associate Director of Liverpool Everyman 1983–87, where productions included *From a Jack to a King, Something Wicked This Way Comes, Two Can Play*. Artistic Director of the Keswick-based Century Theatre 1987–92, where he expanded the company's range of work and was instrumental in establishing a new base in Crewe in 1991. Artistic Director of the Duke's, Lancaster from 1993–97, where productions included *Romeo and Juliet, The Hobbit, Death and the Maiden* and *A Christmas Carol*. Other credits include *Sweet Charity* for Hand Stand Productions.

Sue Dunderdale

Theatre, TV and radio director. Artistic Director, Soho Poly (1984–88); Artistic Director, Greenwich Theatre (1988–89). Theatre credits include: *Coming Apart, Failsafe, Living with Your Enemies, Body Cell* and *The Last Waltz* (all for Soho Poly), *The Woman in White, Othello* and *Apocalyptic Butterflies* (all for Greenwich Theatre), *Deborah's Daughter* (Manchester Library), *Land of the Living* (Royal Court), *Killing the Cat* (Royal Court Theatre Upstairs). TV credits include: *The Blood that's in You* (BBC), *The Bill* (Thames), *Casualty* (BBC), *EastEnders* (BBC), *Brookside* (Mersey TV/Channel 4), *Cutting Loose* (LWT), *Good Time Girl* (BBC), *Emmerdale* (Yorkshire TV), *Coronation Street* (Granada).

Frank Dunlop

Theatre, film and opera director. Director of Nottingham Playhouse (1961–64). Credits include: *The Winter's Tale* (Pop Theatre); *Edward II; Home and Beauty; The White Devil* (all for the Royal National Theatre, 1967–69). Founded the Young Vic in 1970 and for this company directed: *Scapino; The Comedy of Errors; The Maids; Joseph and the Amazing Technicolour Dreamcoat; Childe Byron; Masquerade; The Duenna; King Lear*. Other credits include: *Sherlock Holmes* (RSC); *L'Elisir d'Amore* (Opera de Lyon); *Habeus Corpus* (New York); *The Winter's Tale* (film for Warner Bros). Director of the Edinburgh International Festival (1983–91).

Sir Richard Eyre, CBE

Theatre, film and TV director. Started as an actor, but moved into directing after a depressing stint in the chorus of *The Boyfriend* at Leicester. Directed his first production – *The Knack* – at Leicester Phoenix Theatre in 1965. Became Associate Director of the Royal Lyceum Theatre in Edinburgh in 1967 and Director of Productions from 1970 to 1972. Productions there included:

Three Sisters, Uncle Vanya, Trumpets and Drums, The White Devil, The Crucible, Juno and the Paycock, Othello, Macbeth, The Changeling, Random Happenings in the Hebrides, Confessions of a Justified Sinner. He won STV awards for Best Production in 1969, 1970 and 1971. As Artistic Director of the Nottingham Playhouse (1973–78), his productions included: *The Taming of the Shrew, The Plough and the Stars, The Government Inspector, The Churchill Play, Bendigo, The Comedians* (later also for the National Theatre and BBC TV), *The Alchemist, Deeds, Touched*. Work in London has included his own adaptation of *The Ha-Ha, The Great Exhibition* (Hampstead Theatre), *Hamlet, Edmond, Kafka's Dick* and *The Shawl* (all for the Royal Court), *High Society* (Leicester Haymarket/Victoria Palace, London). For the Royal Shakespeare Company, he has directed *Jingo*. Associate Director of the National Theatre (1980–86), becoming Director in 1988, handing over to Trevor Nunn in October 1997. Royal National Theatre productions: *The Beggar's Opera, Schweyk in the Second World War, Guys and Dolls* (SWET and Evening Standard awards for Best Director), *The Government Inspector, Futurists* (Time Out award), *The Changeling, Bartholomew Fair, Hamlet, The Voysey Inheritance, Richard III* (with Ian McKellen, European and US tour), *White Chameleon, Napoli Milionaria, The Night of the Iguana, Macbeth*, the David Hare trilogy: *Racing Demon, Murmuring Judges* and *The Absence of War, Johnny on a Spot, Sweet Bird of Youth, Skylight* (also West End and Broadway), *La Grande Magia, The Prince's Play, John Gabriel Borkman* (with Paul Scofield), *King Lear* (with Ian Holm), David Hare's *Amy's View* (with Judi Dench), Tom Stoppard's *The Invention of Love*.

From 1978 to 1981, he was Producer of the BBC Play for Today series and also directed: *Waterloo Sunset, The Cherry Orchard, The Imitation Game, Pasmore* (his own adaptation), *Country, The Insurance Man* (Tokyo Prize), *'v'* (RTS award), *Tumbledown* (Italia RAI prize 1988 and BAFTA award), *Suddenly Last Summer, The Absence of War*. Films include: *The Ploughman's Lunch* (Evening Standard award for Best Film), *Loose Connections, Laughterhouse* (Venice TV prize). His book, *Utopia and Other Places* was published by Bloomsbury in 1993. Was made a Commander of the British Empire in 1992, and knighted in 1997.

Bill Forsyth

Scottish film director and screenwriter. Formerly a maker of documentary films, whose first feature was made with boys from Glasgow Youth Theatre. Credits include: *That Sinking Feeling* (1980), *Gregory's Girl* (1981), *Local Hero* (1983), *Comfort and Joy* (1984), *Housekeeping* (1987), *Breaking In* (1989), *Being Human* (1994).

Giles Foster

Film and TV director. Credits include: *Northanger Abbey* (BBC), *Hotel Du Lac* (BBC; BAFTA awards), *Silas Marner* (BBC; BAFTA nomination), *Oliver's Travels* (World Wide TV), *Monster Maker* (Henson/NBC/ Channel 4), *The Aerodrome, Last Summer's Child, The Obelisk* (all for BBC), *Dutch Girls* (LWT), *Farmers Arms* (BBC), *The Aerodrome* (BBC), *Adam Bede* (BBC), *The Rector's Wife* (Talisman/ Channel 4). Feature films: *The Lilac Bus, Consuming Passion, Tree of Hands*. He has also directed three Alan Bennett films for LWT and the BBC – *A Woman of No Importance, A*

Lady of Letters (BAFTA nomination) and *Her Big Chance.*

Stephen Frears

Film and TV director. Worked as an assistant at the Royal Court Theatre on *Inadmissible Evidence* and *Waiting for Godot* in 1964, and then assisted Karel Reisz on *Morgan, a Suitable Case for Treatment*, Albert Finney on *Charlie Bubbles* and Lindsay Anderson on *If* . . . Film credits include: *The Burning* (1967), *Gumshoe* (1971), *The Hit* (1984), *My Beautiful Launderette* (1985), *Prick Up Your Ears* (1987), *Sammy and Rosie Get Laid* (1987), *The Grifters* (1990), *Accidental Hero* (1992), *Mary Reilly* (1996), *The Van* (1996). TV credits: *Walter* and *Walter and June* (Channel 4, 1982), *Saigon – Year of the Cat* (Thames, 1983), *Song of Experience* (BBC), *The Snapper* (1993). Directed Glenn Close and John Malkovich in *Les Liaisons Dangereuses* in Hollywood.

Martyn Friend

Film and TV director. Credits include: *Survival of the Fittest*, episodes of *Rumpole of the Bailey* and *Bergerac*, *All Passion Spent*, *The Daily Woman*, *The Daughter-in-Law*, *Anna of the Five Towns*, *Shackleton*, *Fair Stood the Wind for France*, *The Voyage of Charles Darwin* (BAFTA and BPG awards), *Sweet Nothings*, *Campion*, *All Passion Spent* (BAFTA nomination), *4.50 from Paddington*, *Summer's Lease* (BAFTA nomination), *Titmuss Regained*, *Inspector Alleyn*, *Love on a Branch Line*, *Seaforth*, *Wycliffe*, *Cuts*.

Patrick Garland

Theatre, opera and film director. Began career as an actor with the Bristol Old Vic. First directing credits include: *Brief Lives* (which he also wrote, and which was produced in London, on Broadway and for TV) and Alan Bennett's *Forty Years On* (1970). After directing *An Enemy of the People*, *The Apple Cart* and *Look after Lulu* at Chichester, he was made its Artistic Director in 1980. During his four-year stint, 8 productions transferred to London, including *Kipling*, a one-man show starring Ian McCowen. Opera credits include: *Don Giovanni* for Pavilion Opera, and two Royal Gala Performances: *Fanfare for Europe* (1976) and *Fanfare for Elizabeth* (1971). He directed the musicals *Billy* (with Michael Crawford), *Hair* (in Israel) and *My Fair Lady* (in the US), *The Secret of Sherlock Holmes* with Jeremy Brett and Edward Hardwicke at Wyndham's Theatre in London, *Brief Lives* (Bristol Old Vic; also adapted). Film credits include: *The Doll's House*, nominated at the Cannes Film Festival in 1974.

William Gaskill

Theatre director. One of the young directors brought on by George Devine in the early years of the English Stage Company at the Royal Court, where he directed plays by Osborne, Wesker, Arden and N. F. Simpson. Directed for the Royal Shakespeare Company for a short period – *Cymbeline*, *Richard III*, *The Caucasian Chalk Circle* – and then became one of Laurence Olivier's associates at the National Theatre (*The Recruiting Officer*, *Mother Courage*, *Armstrong's Last Goodnight*, *The Beaux' Stratagem*). From 1965 to 1972, he was Artistic Director at the Royal Court, where he directed the first productions of Edward Bond's *Saved*, *Early Morning*, *Lear* and *The Sea*, and a controversial version of *Macbeth* with Alec Guinness and Simone Signoret.

He was a founder-director of the Joint Stock Theatre Group in 1974, for whom he directed and co-directed *The Speakers, Fanshen, A Mad World, My Masters, Yesterday's News, The Ragged Trousered Philanthropists, An Optimistic Thrust* and *The Crimes of Vautrin*. Directed *The Beaux' Stratagem, A Fair Quarrel* and *Man, Beast and Virtue* for the National Theatre, his own translation of Marivaux's *Infidelities* at the Lyric Theatre, Hammersmith and *The Way of the World* at Chichester and the Theatre Royal, Haymarket.

David Giles

Theatre and television director. Directed *The Forsyte Saga* for the BBC in 1967. Other TV credits: *Resurrection, Vanity Fair, The Strauss Family, On Approval, The Mayor of Casterbridge, The Winslow Boy, Sense and Sensibility, Richard II, Henry IV Parts I and II, Henry V, King John, Fame is the Spur, The Barchester Chronicles, Mansfield Park, A Murder is Announced, The London Embassy, The Fools on the Hill, Forever Green, The Darling Buds of May, The Gospels*. Directed 6 episodes of *Just William* in 1995 and, most recently, has directed a number of episodes of *Hetty Wainthropp Investigates* for BBC TV. Theatre credits: *'Tis Pity She's a Whore* and *The Wood Demon* for the Actors Company, *Lies* and *Gigi* in the West End. Was appointed Director of Productions at the Lyric Hammersmith soon after it opened and for that theatre, directed *You Never Can Tell, Country Life, Hobson's Choice* and *The Potsdam Quartet*. *Twelfth Night* and *Measure for Measure* (Stratford, Ontario), *The Waltz of the Toreadors* (Niagara-on-the-Lake, Canada), *The Country Wife* (USA), Edward Bond's *Lear* (USA), *The Young Idea* (Guildford), *On Approval* (tour).

Peter Gill

Theatre and television director and writer. Was an actor from 1957 to 1964. Became an Assistant Director at the Royal Court in 1964 and an Associate Director in 1970. Directed many productions for the Royal Court during the sixties and seventies, including: *A Collier's Friday Night, The Local Stigmatic, The Ruffian on the Stair, A Provincial Life* (also adapted), *A Soldier's Fortune, The Daughter-in-Law, The Widowing of Mrs Holroyd, Life Price, The Duchess of Malfi*, his own plays *Over Gardens Out* and *The Sleeper's Den, Crete and Sergeant Pepper* by John Antrobus. Founding Director of the Riverside Studios in Hammersmith, London in 1976 and made an Associate Director in 1980. Productions at Riverside included: *Small Change* (which he also wrote), *The Changeling, The Cherry Orchard, Julius Caesar, Scrape Off the Black* by Tunde Ikoli. Associate Director of the Royal National Theatre since 1980 where productions include: *A Month in the Country, Don Juan, Much Ado About Nothing, Danton's Death, Fool for Love, Major Barbara, Tales from Hollywood, A Twist of Lemon, Bouncing, Up for None, Show Songs, Juno and the Paycock, Cardiff East* and his own *Kick for Touch* and *Small Change*. Founding Director of the National Theatre Studio in 1984, where he has directed the Festival of New Plays, including his own *Mean Tears* and *Mrs Klein*. Other theatre productions include: *Uncle Vanya* (Field Day Theatre Co.), *The Way of the World* (Lyric Theatre, Hammersmith), *New England* (Royal Shakespeare Company), *Down by the Greenwood Side* and *Bow Down* (Queen Elizabeth Hall), *Tongue of a Bird* (Almeida Theatre). TV credits include: *Grace* by James Joyce, *Girl* by James Robson, *A Matter of Taste* by Alex La Guma and *Fugitive* by Sean Walsh (all

BBC), *Hitting Town* by Stephen Poliakoff (Thames). In addition to those already mentioned, he has also adapted *The Merry-go-Round* and *Touch and Go* (from plays by D. H. Lawrence), *The Cherry Orchard* and *As I Lay Dying* (from the novel by William Faulkner).

David Gilmore

Theatre director. Started out in stage management before becoming an actor. Became Director of the Watermill Theatre for three years and was then appointed Artistic Director of the Nuffield Theatre, Southampton. During his five years at the Nuffield productions included: *The Tempest, The Resistable Rise of Arturo Ui, Uncle Vanya, Summer and Smoke*. West End productions include: *Daisy Pulls it Off* (Globe Theatre), *Lend Me a Tenor* (Globe), *Beyond Reasonable Doubt, The Hired Man, Nuts* (Whitehall Theatre), *A Swell Party* (Vaudeville Theatre), *Out of the Blue* (Shaftesbury), *Fatal Attraction* (Haymarket Theatre Royal), *Chapter Two* (Gielgud Theatre), *Grease* (Cambridge Theatre). Other credits: *Mandragola* (Royal National Theatre), *Dandy Dick* (Compass Theatre), *The Winter's Tale* (New Shakespeare Company), *Cavalcade* (Chichester Festival Theatre). Overseas productions include: *Glengarry, Glen Ross* (Royal Flemish Theatre, Brussels), *Song and Dance* (Sydney, Melbourne and Adelaide), *As You Like It* (Shakespeare Repertory Company, Chicago), *Alone Together* (Hong Kong/Peking), *Là-Haut* (Théâtre des Célestins, Lyons).

John Godber

Theatre and TV director, actor and writer. Artistic Director of Hull Truck Theatre Company since 1984. Credits include: *Up 'n' Under* (also film),

Bouncers, Teechers, Shakers, Blood, Sweat and Tears (also for BBC), *Cramp, Happy Jack, September in the Rain, Salt of the Earth, Happy Families, On the Piste, The Ritz* (also for BBC), *The Continental* (BBC Christmas Special), *April in Paris, Gym and Tonic, Weekend Break, The Office Party, Passion Killers, My Kingdom for a Horse* (BBC film, 1991), *Chalkface* (BBC series, 1991), *Bloomin' Marvellous* (BBC, 1997).

Jack Gold

TV, film and theatre director and writer. Started his career as a TV cameraman. Television credits include: *The Naked Civil Servant* (1975), *Charlie Muffin, The Sailor's Return* (1979), *The Last Romantics* (1990), *Praying Mantis* (1982), *Red Monarch* (1983), *Murrow* (1985), *Sakharov* (1984), *Escape from Sobibor* (1986), *Stones for Ibarra* (1988), *The Tenth Man* (1988), *Yiddish Documentary* (1990), *She Stood Alone* (1992), *The Last Romantics* (1992), *Spring Awakening* (1994), *Blandings* (1996). Film credits: *The Bofors Gun* (1968), *The Reckoning* (1969), *The National Health* (1973), *Who?* (1974), *Man Friday* (1975), *Aces High* (1976), *The Medusa Touch* (1977), *The Chain* (1985), *Ball Trap on the Côte Sauvage* (1989), *The Rose and the Jackal* (1990), *The War that Never Ends* (1991), *The Lucona Affair* (1993), *Return of the Native* (1994).

Peter Greenaway

Film director. Described by Derek Malcolm in the *Guardian* as 'a true original with an eccentric and bizarre sense of humour', Greenaway is an experimental film-maker whose *Draughtsman's Contract* (BFI/Channel 4, 1983) broke through to a wider audience while retaining his enigmatic style. Other credits include: *A Walk*

Through H (1978), *Vertical Features Remake* (1978), *The Falls* (1980), *Act of God* (1981), *A Zed and Two Noughts* (1985), *Drowning by Numbers* (1988), *The Cook, the Thief, His Wife and Her Lover* (1989), *Prospero's Books* (1991), *The Baby of Macon* (1993), *The Pillow Book* (1996).

Andrew Grieve

Film and TV director. Started directing with a short film, *Notice to Quit*, for which he received the French Prix de Qualité. Credits include: *Storybook International* series (HTV), *Young Sherlock Holmes* (Amblin Productions), *Suspicion* (Hemisphere, 1986), *On the Black Hill* (BFI/Channel 4, 1987, wrote and directed; Best Film at the San Sebastian Film Festival and Best Film at San Remo), *Agatha Christie's Poirot* (Carnival/LWT, 1989), *Lorna Doone* (Working Title, 1990, Best Film Monte Carlo Festival), *The ABC Murders* (Carnival/LWT, 1991), *The Big Battalions* (Carnival/Channel 4, 1992), *All or Nothing At All* (Carnival/LWT, 1993), *Moving Story* (Carlton/ABTV, 1993), *Hickory Dickory Dock* and *Murder on the Links* (Agatha Christie TV films, 1994), *Letters from the East* (feature film, 1994), *Kavanagh QC – True Commitment* and *A Stranger in the Family* (Central, 1995), *Original Sin* (P. D. James adaptation, 1996), *Hornblower* (TV films, 1997).

Piers Haggard

TV, theatre and film director. Started his career as an Assistant Director at the Royal Court Theatre, followed by the Brussels Ridea, Dundee Repertory Theatre, Glasgow Citizens' Theatre. Theatre credits include *The Ticket-of-Leave Man* (National Theatre, 1981). TV credits include: *Pennies from Heaven* (BBC; BAFTA award, 1979), *Mrs Reinhardt* (BBC, 1981), *Knockback* (BBC, 1984; US Ace award), *Return to Treasure Island* (Disney/HTV), *Visitors* (BBC, 1987), *The Fulfilment of Mary Green* (CBS, 1988), *Sam Found Out* (ABC, 1988), *Back Home* (Disney/TVS, 1989), *I'll Take Romance* (ABC, 1990), *Centre Point* (Channel 4, 1990), *Four Eyes and Six Guns* (TNT, 1991), *The Breakthrough* (US Cable 1993/4), *After Eskimo Day, Space Precinct, Heartstones* (Meridian/Blue Heaven 1995). Film credits: *The Blood of Satan's Claw* (AIP, 1970), *The Quatermass Conclusion* (Euston, 1979), *Venom* (Paramount, 1982), *A Summer Story* (ITC, 1988), *The Fiendish Plot of Dr Fu Manchu* (Orion, 1989).

Edward Hall

Theatre director. Credits include: *An Ideal Husband* (Theatre Royal, Windsor/tour); *Decadence* (Bratislava and Nye Theatre, Oslo), *Chambers of Glass* (Minerva Studio, Chichester), *Lysistrata* (redirected remounts at Wyndhams Theatre, Richmond Theatre and Epidaurus, Greece), *Bare Knuckle Selling* (Gilded Balloon, Edinburgh Festival), *The Hanuman* (National Theatre Studio), *Cain* (Minerva Studio, Chichester), *Richard III* (Tokyo Globe), *Othello* (Watermill Theatre, Newbury/Tokyo Globe), *That Good Night* (Yvonne Arnaud Theatre/tour), *Henry V* (Watermill Theatre), *The Two Gentlemen of Verona* (Royal Shakespeare Company).

Sir Peter Hall, CBE

After leaving Cambridge University, ran the Arts Theatre in London where he produced the world première of the English-language version of *Waiting for Godot*. First worked at Stratford-upon-Avon in 1956 and during the next three years directed *Cymbeline* (with Peggy Ashcroft), *Coriolanus* (with Laurence Olivier) and *A Midsummer Night's Dream* (with Charles Laughton). For the RSC he directed 18 plays at Stratford, including *The Wars of the Roses* and *Hamlet* (with David Warner in the title role). In addition, he directed the premières of *A Delicate Balance* and *All Over* by Edward Albee, *The Homecoming, Landscape, Silence, Old Times, No Man's Land, Betrayal* and *Other Places*, all by Harold Pinter, as well as premières of plays by Anouilh, Peter Shaffer, John Mortimer and John Whiting.

As Director of the Royal National Theatre from 1973 to 1988, he directed *John Gabriel Borkman, Happy Days, Hamlet, Tamburlaine the Great, Bedroom Farce, Amadeus, No Man's Land, Volpone, The Country Wife, The Cherry Orchard, Othello, The Oresteia, The Importance of Being Earnest, Antony and Cleopatra, Animal Farm* (his own adaptation), *Martine, Yonadab, Coming in to Land, The Tempest, Betrayal, Cymbeline, The Winter's Tale*. He has worked many times on Broadway, winning Tony awards for *The Homecoming* and *Amadeus*.

On leaving the National, he launched The Peter Hall Company with productions of *Orpheus Descending* with Vanessa Redgrave and *The Merchant of Venice* with Dustin Hoffman, both productions transferring to Broadway. Other productions for his own company include: *The Wild Duck, The Homecoming, Twelfth Night, The Rose Tattoo, Tartuffe, Born Again, Sienna Red, An Ideal Husband, Lysistrata, Separate Tables, She Stoops to Conquer, Piaf, An Absolute Turkey, Hamlet, The*

Master Builder, Mind Millie for Me. In 1997, The Peter Hall Company was based at The Old Vic for an ambitious season of plays, with Peter Hall directing *The Seagull, Waiting for Godot* and *King Lear*.

He has directed over 40 operas all over the world, at Glyndebourne Festival Opera (where he was Artistic Director from 1984 to 1990), the Royal Opera House Covent Garden, Geneva, Los Angeles, Houston, Chicago, the Metropolitan Opera in New York and Bayreuth, where he directed Wagner's *Ring Cycle*.

For television, he directed *The Camomile* Lawn (Channel 4), *Jacob* (Turner/Lux), *The Final Passage* (based on the book by Caryl Phillips). Films include: *A Midsummer Night's Dream, Three into Two Won't Go, The Homecoming, Akenfield, She's Been Away, Orpheus Descending*.

Terry Hands

Theatre and opera director. One of the founders of the Liverpool Everyman Theatre in 1964 and was Artistic Director there for two years. Joined the Royal Shakespeare Company in 1966 and was Artistic Director of the RSC's Theatregoround, presenting touring productions for schools and community centres between 1966 and 1968. Made an Associate Director of the RSC in 1967. Became Joint Artistic Director, with Trevor Nunn, in 1978; Artistic Director and Chief Executive of the RSC from 1987 until 1991. His work for the RSC has included: *The Criminals, The Merry Wives of Windsor, Pericles, Women Beware Women, Richard III, The Balcony, The Man of Mode, The Merchant of Venice, Murder in the Cathedral, Romeo and Juliet, The Bewitched*. In 1975, he directed all 4 productions in the centenary season at Stratford and the Aldwych: *Henry V, Henry IV Parts I and II* and *The Merry Wives of Windsor*. (*Henry V* was seen in New York as the official British Theatre offering for the US bicentennial celebrations.) For his direction of the three parts of *Henry VI* in 1977, he was joint winner of the *Plays and Players* award for Best Production and was also the Society of West End Theatres Director of the Year for 1978.

He was awarded the Meilleur Spectacle de l'Année by the Paris drama critics for his production of *Richard III* for the Comédie Française in 1973. The following year, he was appointed Consultant Director of the Comédie Française, and Chevalier of Arts and Letters by the French government. His Paris production of *Twelfth Night* in 1976 won another Meilleur Spectacle de l'Année, and he has also directed the plays *Le Cid* and *Murder in the Cathedral* and the opera *Otello* in Paris.

In 1979, he directed *Parsifal* at the Royal Opera House, and with productions of *Richard II* and *Richard III* in Stratford, he completed the whole of the Shakespeare history cycle, which he began in 1975. Among his other productions have been: *As You Like It, Troilus and Cressida, Much Ado About Nothing, Arden of Faversham,* the musical *Poppy* by Peter Nichols and Monty Norman at the Barbican (winner of SWET award for Musical of the Year). He also directed Derek Jacobi in *Cyrano de Bergerac* at the Barbican, which collected 9 awards including the SWET award for Best Director and the Drama awards' Best Director of a Classical Revival. *Much Ado About Nothing* and *Cyrano de Bergerac* played Los Angeles, Broadway and Washington where they won 11 awards including a New York Drama League award for Best Production together with 3 Tony nominations. *Cyrano* was televised on Channel 4 in 1985. In the same year, he directed Peter Barnes's *Red Noses* (Laurence Olivier award for Best New Play) and *Othello* (with Ben Kingsley and David Suchet). Directed the musical *Carrie* which opened in Stratford prior to Broadway. Other RSC credits include: *Julius Caesar, The Winter's Tale, The Balcony, Scenes from a Marriage, Romeo and Juliet, Singer, Coriolanus* (co-directed with John Barton), *Love's Labour's Lost, The Seagull*. Other productions include: *Arden of Faversham* (Zurich), *The Buffalo Bill Show* (Recklinghausen Festival, Germany), *Simon Boccanegra* (Bremen Opera House), *Tamburlaine the Great* (London Drama Critics award for Best Director, 1993), *Sag Mir Wo die Blumen Sind* (Berlin), *Hamlet* (Paris), *The Merry Wives of Windsor* (Royal National Theatre, 1995), *Hadrian the Seventh* and *The Visit* (Chichester Festival Theatre), *The Importance of Being Earnest* (Birmingham Rep/The Old Vic), *The Pretenders* (Ibsen Festival, Oslo, 1996), *The Royal Hunt of the Sun* (Tokyo, 1996), *The Importance of Being Earnest* (Theatr Clwyd/Birmingham Rep/ Toronto). Appointed Director of Theatr Clwyd in May 1997 where he directed *Equus* last November.

David Hare

Playwright and theatre, film and TV director. Plays he has written include: *Slag; The Great Exhibition; Brassneck* (co-wrote with Howard Brenton);

Knuckle; Fanshen (with Joint Stock Theatre Group); Teeth 'n' Smiles (at Royal Court and Wyndham's – also directed); Plenty (National Theatre and Broadway, also directed; won the New York Critics award for Best Director); A Map of the World (National Theatre and Adelaide Festival; also directed); Pravda (National Theatre, co-wrote with Howard Brenton; also directed); the trilogy, Racing Demon; Murmuring Judges and The Absence of War, Skylight, Amy's View. Directed Heartbreak House for the Almeida Theatre in 1997. Has directed many plays by his contemporaries, including Trevor Griffiths, Christopher Hampton and Howard Brenton. He co-founded Portable Theatre and Joint Stock Theatre Group and has been resident dramatist at the Royal Court and at Nottingham Playhouse. For TV, he wrote and directed Dreams of Leaving; Saigon – Year of the Cat; Paris by Night. He has written three screenplays: Wetherby (also directed; Golden Bear for Best Film at Berlin Film Festival); Plenty (adaptation of his own play); The Butter Mountain.

Frank Hauser, CBE

Theatre director. Started his career as a BBC Radio producer, working with Alec Guinness, Peter Ustinov, Pamela Brown, John Gielgud among others. In this capacity, he engaged the then unknown Richard Burton to play Henry V. A few years later, Burton returned the favour by funding the Oxford Playhouse Company, which Frank Hauser ran for 17 years, and where many new plays were pioneered, including the stage version of A Passage to India; Aruzov's The

Promise; Satre's Kean and Molnar's The Wolf (the last two were translated by Hauser). He has also written the book, lyrics and music for three pantomimes, including Cinderella, which was mounted in London and gave Twiggy her stage debut as Cinders. In 1987, he became a Commander of the British Empire. Other work has included: Captain Brassbound's Conversion (with Penelope Keith); A Village Wooing (Judi Dench and Michael Williams); The Assassin (Edward Woodward); Agnes of God (Susannah York); An Enemy of the People (his own translation; with Roy Dotrice at the Roundabout Theatre in New York); Thursday's Ladies (Apollo Theatre); A Man For All Seasons (with Charlton Heston, Savoy Theatre and tour); Getting Married (Chichester Festival Theatre). Among the many productions for the Glasgow Citizens': Hamlet, The Taming of the Shrew, The Caucasian Chalk Circle, The Mother, Blithe Spirit, Juno and the Paycock, Arms and the Man, Loot, No Man's Land, Death of a Salesman, A Streetcar Named Desire, The Balcony, Three Sisters, Early Morning, Sailor Beware, Arsenic and Old Lace, Dr Angelus, Travels with My Aunt (also Wyndham's Theatre, London – Olivier award; Minetta Lane Theatre, New York – Drama Desk award, ACT, San Francisco), Swing Hammer Swing! Other credits include: Pamela and The Heat of the Day (Shared Experience), The Way of the World (Greenwich Theatre), Marriage à la Mode (Folger Theatre, Washington), Men Should Weep (7:84 Scotland), Pygmalion (Stockholm's Stadtsteater), My Fair Lady (Minnesota Opera), The Barber of Seville, The Marriage of Figaro, The Seraglio and Ariadne (all for Welsh Opera), L'Elisir d'Amore and Die Fledermaus (Scottish Opera).

Mike Hodges

Film and TV director. Qualified as an accountant and served in the Royal Navy before starting his career in television as a writer in 1958. Writing and directing credits include: *Suspect* (1969), *Rumour* (1970), *Get Carter* (1971), *Pulp* (1972), *The Terminal Man* (1974, also produced), *Missing Pieces* (1982), *Black Rainbow* (1989). Directed *Flash Gordon* (1979–80), *Squaring the Circle* (TVS, 1984), *Morons from Outer Space* (1985), *Buried Alive* (1987), *Prayer for the Dying* (1988), *Dandelion Dead* (LWT, 1993), *The Healer* (1994), *The Croupier* (Channel 4, 1997).

Metin Huseyin

Graduate of the National Film and Television School where he initially wrote, animated and directed a short film, *Rockie, Sten et Pierre*. His graduation film, *Tight Trousers*, which he wrote and directed, was chosen as the British entry in the Student Film Oscars held in Los Angeles and was purchased by Channel 4. Credits include: *Teenage Health Freak* (Limelight Productions/Channel 4), *The All New Alexei Sayle* series (BBC; Bronze Rose at the Montreux TV Festival, 1994), *Common as Muck* (BBC), *Sorry About Last Night* (BBC), *Tom Jones* (BBC, 1997, six-hour adaptation of the Henry Fielding classic).

Jonathan Holloway

Theatre and radio director. Began directing at the Royal Court in 1977. Founder (1982) and Artistic Director of Red Shift Theatre. Directed all the company's productions including: *The Duchess of Malfi, The Mill on the Floss, Le Misanthrope, The Image of the Beast* (written and directed; Edinburgh Fringe First award), *Timon of Athens, Lulu, Fanny Hill, The Hammer, Orlando, Macbeth, Death in Venice, Crime and Punishment, George Dandin*. Other writing credits include a radio version of *The Hammer* for Radio 3, *Seaton's Aunt* and *The Lifted Veil* (both BBC Radio 4). Also directed *Le Misanthrope* (New Rep, Boston).

Hugh Hudson

Film director. Credits include: *Chariots of Fire* (1981), *Greystoke: The Legend of Tarzan, Lord of the Apes* (1984), *Revolution* (1986), *Lost Angels* (1989), *My Life So Far* (1997).

Nicholas Hytner

Theatre, film and opera director. Began directing at Cambridge University. His first theatre productions were at the Northcott Theatre, Exeter and Leeds Playhouse. Made an Associate Director of the Royal Exchange Theatre in Manchester in 1985 and his productions for that company included: *As You Like It, Edward II, The Country Wife, Mumbo Jumbo* and *Don Carlos*. Recent productions include: *Measure for Measure, The Tempest* and *King Lear* for the Royal Shakespeare Company; *Ghetto, The Wind in the Willows, The Madness of George III, The Recruiting Officer* and *Carousel* for the Royal National Theatre, *Volpone* (Almeida), *The Importance of Being Earnest* (Aldwych) and *Miss Saigon* (Theatre Royal Drury Lane). Opera credits include: *Rienzi, Xerxes, The Magic Flute, The Force of Destiny* (all ENO), *The King Goes Forth to France* and *The Knot Garden* (Royal Opera House), *Giulio Cesare* (Paris Opera). Film credits: *The*

Madness of King George, The Crucible, The Object of My Affection.

James Ivory

Film director. In partnership with producer Ismail Merchant and writer Ruth Prawer Jhabvala, he has made films touching on British colonial and expatriate experience, many of which are set in India. Credits include: *The Householder* (1962), *Shakespeare Wallah* (1964), *The Guru* (1969), *Bombay Talkie* (1970), *Savages* (1972), *Helen, Queen of the Nautch Girls* (1973), *Mahatma and the Mad Boy* (1974), *Autobiography of a Princess* (1975), *The Wild Party* (1975), *Roseland* (1977), *Hullabaloo Over Bonnie and George's Pictures* (1978), *The Europeans* (1979), *Jane Austen in Manhattan* (1979), *Quartet* (1981), *Heat and Dust* (1983), *The Bostonians* (1984), *A Room with a View* (1986), *Maurice* (1987), *Slaves of New York* (1989), *Mr and Mrs Bridge* (1990), *Howard's End* (1991), *The Remains of the Day* (1993), *Jefferson in Paris* (1995), *Surviving Picasso* (1996).

Alby James

Assistant Director at the Royal Court Theatre (1978–80), Assistant Director Royal Shakespeare Company (1982–83), Artistic Director of Temba Theatre Company (1984–93). Now working with own independent production company, Foundry Productions Ltd. Productions for Temba include: *Scrape off the Black, Woza Albert!, A Visitor to the Veldt, Mother Poem, Avé Afrika, Mamma Decemba & Streetwise.* Other credits include: *Jonas* (Westminster Theatre), *Meetings* (Hampstead Theatre), *Home* (tour of The Netherlands and Belgium); *Eden* (Riverside Studios), *Fences* (Liverpool Playhouse/Garrick

Theatre), *My Children, My Africa!* (Watermill Theatre, Newbury). BBC Radio credits include: *Mislike Me Not for My Complexion* (also wrote and presented); *Mamma Decemba, The Ramayana, The Words to Say It, Woza Afrika!, Death and the King's Horseman, The Man in the Trees, The Beatification of Area Boy, The Roads to Freedom, Song of a Bluefoot Man, Taking Sides* (also adapted), *Aman* (also dramatised).

Pedr James

TV and theatre director. Was Artistic Director of the Liverpool Everyman Theatre between 1979 and 1980. Head of Drama at BBC Wales since June 1997. TV credits include: *Our Flesh and Blood* (BBC), *Where the Heart Is* (Thames), *Daughters of Albion* (Yorkshire TV), *Whale Music* (Granada), *Coronation Street* (Granada), *Day to Remember* (Channel 4/TVS), *The Master of Marionettes* (BBC), *Aimée* (BBC; Prix SACD for Best Screenplay), *The Vision Thing* (BBC), *Martin Chuzzlewit* (BBC), *Our Friends in the North* (BBC; British Academy award for Best Drama Serial; The Broadcasting Press Guild Television award for Best Drama Serial).

Roland Joffe

Film and TV director and screenwriter. In his early career, became the youngest director at the National Theatre, under Laurence Olivier, in 1973. Film credits include: *The Scarlet Letter* (1995), *The Killing Fields* (1984), *The Mission* (1985), *The Shadowmakers* (1989), *City of Joy* (1992), *The Scarlet Letter* (1995). TV credits: *No, Mama, No* (1977), *The Spongers* (1978), *'Tis Pity She's a Whore* (1979), *United Kingdom* (BBC, 1980).

Sandy Johnson

Television and film director. Graduate of the National Film and Television School. Credits include: *The Magnificent One* (Channel 4/Rocking Horse Films, 1982), *The Comic Strip Presents – Summer School, Bad News, Slags, Eddie Monsoon – The Life, Dirty Movie* (Channel 4, 1983/4), *Coast to Coast* (BBC Screen Two, 1986), *Leaving* (BBC Screen Two, 1987), *Defrosting the Fridge* (BBC Screen Two, 1988), *The Wreck on the Highway* (BBC Play on One, 1989), *The Ruth Rendell Mysteries – Some Lie and Some Die* and *Put On By Cunning* (TVS, 1990), *The Weekenders* (Granada TV, 1991), *Gone to the Dogs* (Central Films, 1991), *The Ruth Rendell Mysteries – Achilles Heel* (TVS, 1992), *Gone to Seed* (Central Films, 1992), *A Pinch of Snuff – Dalziel and Pascoe* (Yorkshire TV, 1993), *Roughnecks* (BBC, 1994), *Soul Survivors* (BBC/Trisquare Productions, 1994), *Bugs* (Carnival Films, 1996), *The Ruth Rendell Mysteries – Front Seat* and *Dark Blue Perfume* (TVS, 1996), *A Touch of Frost* (Yorkshire TV, 1996), *Jonathan Creek* (BBC, 1996).

Richard Jones

Opera and theatre director. Initially worked as a jazz musician before being awarded an Arts Council trainee directorship bursary in 1982 to work with Scottish Opera. Opera credits include: *The Love for Three Oranges* (Opera North/ENO), *The Plumber's Gift* (ENO), *Rheingold* and *The Valkyrie* (Scottish Opera), *Die Fledermaus* (ENO), *Julius Caesar* (Munich, Openwelt Production of the Year, 1994), *Der Ring Des Nibelungen* (Royal Opera House; Evening Standard award for Outstanding Artistic Achievement). Theatre credits include: *Too Clever by Half* (The Old Vic; Olivier award), *A Flea in Her Ear* and *The Illusion* (The Old Vic), *Le Bourgeois Gentilhomme* (Royal National Theatre), *Into the Woods* (Phoenix Theatre; Olivier award and Evening Standard award), *La Bête* (Broadway; Tony nomination), *All's Well That Ends Well* (Public Theatre, New York), *Titanic* (Broadway).

Terry Jones

Film director, actor and screenwriter. Came to prominence as an actor with the TV series *Monty Python's Flying Circus*. Film credits include: *Monty Python and the Holy Grail* (co-directed with Terry Gilliam, 1974), *The Life of Brian* (1979), *The Meaning of Life* (1983), *Personal Services* (1987), *Erik the Viking* (1989).

Neil Jordan

Irish film director and screenwriter. Credits: *Angel* (1982), *Company of Wolves* (1984), *Mona Lisa* (1985), *High Spirits* (1988), *We're No Angels* (1989), *The Miracle* (1990), *The Crying Game* (1992), *Interview with the Vampire* (1994), *Michael Collins* (1996), *The Butcher Boy* (1997).

Ian Judge

Theatre and opera director. Studied at the Guildhall School of Music and Drama. Joined the Royal Shakespeare Company in 1985 as an Assistant Director, working on *Henry IV Parts I and II, Henry V, The Merry Wives of Windsor* and *Coriolanus*. Became an Associate Director on *Poppy* (Barbican and Adelphi Theatres). Other RSC productions include: *Showboat, The Comedy of Errors* (winner of three Olivier awards), *Love's Labour's Lost, A Christmas Carol, The Swan Down Gloves, Twelfth Night, Troilus and Cressida, The*

Merry Wives of Windsor. Other theatre credits include: *West Side Story* (Sydney), *The Rivals* and *King Lear* (The Old Vic), *The Orchestra* (King's Club Theatre Club), *Rookery Nook* (Barbican Centre), *Musical Chairs, Oh Kay!* and *Henry VIII* (Chichester Festival Theatre), *Peg* (Yvonne Arnaud Theatre, Guildford/Phoenix Theatre, London), *Friends of Dorothy* and *How Lucky You Can Get* (Donmar Warehouse Theatre), *Banana Ridge* (Shaw Festival, Canada). Opera credits: *Don Quixote* (ENO; Olivier awards nominee), *La Belle Hélène* (ENO), Ariodante (Buxton Festival), *Faust* (ENO/Opera North), *The Merry Widow* and *Cavalleria Rusticana/Pagliacci* (ENO), *Macbeth, Tosca* and *Acis and Galatea* (Opera North), *Ruddigore* and *Bitter Sweet* (New Sadler's Wells Opera), *Falstaff* (Bremer Theatre, Germany), *Lohengrin* (Staatstheater, Weisbaden), *Ruddigore* (New York), *Faust* (Lyric Opera, Queensland), *Falstaff* (Scottish Opera).

Helena Kaut-Howson

Theatre, TV, radio and opera director. Born in Poland and trained at the Polish State Theatre School before attending RADA. Former Artistic Director of Theatr Clwyd in Mold from 1992 to 1995, during which time she received the Peter Brook Open Space award for the outstanding body of work there. Productions included: *The Devils* (Liverpool *Daily Post and Echo* Arts award for Best Production, 1992), *All's Well That Ends Well* (also Playhouse Theatre, London), *Full Moon* (also the Young Vic and national/international tour). Other credits include: *The House of Bernarda Alba* (Lyric Theatre, Belfast), *The Beggar's Opera* (Belgrade Theatre, Coventry), *The Duenna* (Opera North), *Werewolves*

(Druid Theatre Co.), *Tess of the D'Urbervilles* (West Yorkshire Playhouse), *Maskerade* and *The Duenna* (Opera North), *The Keep* (BBC TV, Wales), *Goldfaden's Dream* (Israeli Theatre, Tel Aviv), *Hindle Wakes* (Royal Exchange Theatre, Manchester), *Sweet Bird of Youth* (Haifa Theatre, Israel), *King Lear* (Leicester Haymarket/Young Vic), *All's Well That Ends Well* (Regent's Park Open Air Theatre), *Much Ado About Nothing* (Royal Exchange, Manchester).

Jude Kelly

Artistic Director of West Yorkshire Playhouse. Productions include: *The Complete Guide to Sex* (National Theatre of Brent), *The Pink Briefcase* (Lyric, Hammersmith), *Accidental Death of an Anarchist* (Nuffield, Southampton), *Lynchville* (RSC, Stratford), *Sarcophagus* (RSC, The Pit and Mermaid), *Intimate Exchanges* (Bristol Old Vic), *The Tempest* (Roundabout Theatre, New York; *Othello* (Shakespeare Theatre, New York, the title role played by Patrick Stewart), *L'elisir d'amore* (English National Opera).

Jonathan Kent

Joint Artistic Director of the Almeida Theatre since 1990. Credits at the Almeida include: *When We Dead Awaken, All for Love, The Rules of the Game, Chatsky, The Showman, The School for Wives, Medea* (also West End and Broadway), *The Life of Galileo, Gangster, Tartuffe, Ivanov*. His production of Ranjit Bolt's new translation of Corneille's *Le Cid* appeared at the Cottesloe Theatre and in 1995, he directed Ralph Fiennes in *Hamlet* at the Hackney Empire and the Belasco Theatre on Broadway. Other credits include: *Mother Courage* (Olivier Theatre, with Diana Rigg).

Nicolas Kent

Theatre and TV director. Started out as an ABC TV trainee director at the Liverpool Playhouse. Was Artistic Director of the Watermill Theatre, Newbury and Associate Director of the Traverse Theatre in Edinburgh. Director of the Oxford Playhouse 1976–92; productions during that period included the premières of: *The Vegetable* by F. Scott Fitzgerald, *Ophelia* by C. P. Taylor, *The Man to Save Us* by Stephen Fagan, *Rain from Heaven* by S. N. Behrman, *The Bottom Drawer* by Stephen Bill. Artistic Director of the Tricycle Theatre in London since 1984 for whom productions have included: *Lonely Cowboy* by Alfred Fagon, *A Long Way Home* by Yemi Ajibade, *A Love Song for Ulster*, a six-hour trilogy by Bill Morrison, *Factory Girls* by Frank McGuinness, *Half the Picture* by Richard Norton-Taylor (*Time Out* award), *Nuremberg* by Richard Norton-Taylor, Keith Reddin and Goran Stefanovski, *Srebrenica* (also adapted), *The Mai* by Marina Carr. Other credits include: *Class Enemy* (Young Vic), *Love of a Good Man* and *No End of Blame* by Howard Barker (Royal Court), *The Great White Hope* (RSC; *Time Out* award), *The Workshop* (Hampstead Theatre), *The Trinidad Sisters* (Donmar Warehouse), *Ain't Misbehavin'* (Lyric Theatre), *Private Lives* (Court Theatre, Chicago), *The Workroom* (American Jewish Theatre, New York). TV credits include: *Oceans Apart* by Olwen Wymark, *Prodigal Grandfather* by Donald Churchill, *Playboy of the West Indies* by Mustapha Matura, *Pentecoste* by Stewart Parker – all for BBC TV. Film: *Half the Picture* (BBC2/Freeway Films).

Alex Kirby

TV director. Credits include: *Maneaters of Kumaon* (BBC), *Boon* (Central), *Robin of Sherwood* (HTV/Goldcrest), *Bergerac* (BBC), *Chronicles of Narnia* (BBC), *House of Elliot* (BBC), *The Bill* (Thames), *Harry's Mad II* (Central), *Lovejoy* (BBC/Witzend), *Harry's Mad III* (Central).

Robert Knights

Film, TV, theatre and opera director. Credits include: *The Glittering Prizes* (BBC, 1976, co-directed with Waris Hussein), *The History Man* (BBC, 1981), *The Ebony Tower* (Granada, 1984), *Tender is the Night* (BBC, 1986), *Porterhouse Blue* (Channel 4, 1987), *The Magic Flute* (Kent Opera), *The Dawning* (feature film, 1988), *The Man Who Made Husbands Jealous* (Anglia/Blue Heaven, 1996).

Ian Knox

TV and film director. Graduate of the National Film and Television School. Film credits include: *The Stronger* (National Film School, 1980), *The Privilege* (High Road Productions, 1982, BAFTA Best Short Film and Bilbao Film Festival Best Fiction Film award). TV credits: *Workhorses* (Scottish Radio and TV awards Best Play, 1983), *Sweet Nothings* (BBC, 1982), *Boon* (Central, 1985), *Shoot for the Sun* (BBC, 1986), *Down Where the Buffalo Go* (BBC, 1987), *Valentine Falls* (Channel 4, 1989), *The Police* (BBC, 1990; Berlin Film Festival Prix Futura Special Commendation), *Saracen* (Central, 1989), *Spender II and III* (BBC, 1991–93), *99–1* (Zenith/Carlton, 1993), *Between the Lines* (Island Pictures/BBC, 1994), *Hamish Macbeth* (Zenith/BBC, 1994), *Call Red* (Thames, 1995–96), *Silent Witness* (BBC, 1997).

Stanley Kubrick

American film director, producer and writer. Starting as a photographer on *Look* magazine, he made his first film – a short documentary called *Day of the Fight* – in 1950. Four years later, he set up his own production company to make *The Killing* with Sterling Hayden. He followed with *Paths of Glory* (1958), *Spartacus* (1960), *Lolita* (1962), *Dr Strangelove* (1963), *2001: A Space Odyssey* (1969), *A Clockwork Orange* (1971), *Barry Lyndon* (1975), *The Shining* (1979), *Full Metal Jacket* (1987).

Barry Kyle

Theatre director. Associate Director of the Royal Shakespeare Company. Gained a Thames TV director's bursary and went to the Liverpool Playhouse where he became Associate Director to Antony Tuckey and directed 21 productions, including: *Saved, In Celebration, Hadrian VII, The Knack, St Joan, King Lear*. In 1972, he went to the Theatre Royal, York as Associate Director, where *Forget-me-Not Lane* and *The Investigation* were among his credits.

In 1973, he joined the RSC as Assistant Director, directing *Sylvia Plath* at The Place and co-directing *Cymbeline* and *King John* with John Barton. In 1974, he was Director of The Place season in London, when he directed *Comrades* and co-directed several other productions. Work at The Other Place has included: *The Churchill Play, The Maid's Tragedy, The Witch of Edmonton* and Bond's *Lear*. Productions at the Warehouse have included: *Sore Throats* and *Thirteenth Night* by Howard Brenton, and *The Irish Play* by Ron Hutchinson. Other work for the RSC included: *Measure for Measure, The White Guard, The Taming of the Shrew, The Dillen, The Crucible, Golden Girls, Mary, After the Queen* (sequel to *The Dillen*), *Richard II, Two Noble Kinsmen, The Jew of Malta, Hyde Park, Moscow Gold, Dr Faustus, All's Well That Ends Well*.

Simon Langton

TV and film director. Film credits include: *The Whistle Blower* (with John Gielgud and Michael Caine), TV credits: *Thérèse Raquin, Rebecca* (BBC, 1979), *Anna Karenina* (CBS), *Lost Honour of Katherine Beck* (CBS), *Smiley's People* (BBC, 1982), *I Remember Nelson* (Central, 1982), *Mother Love* (BBC, 1990), *Jeeves and Wooster* (Carnival Films, 1991), *Headhunters* (BBC, 1992), *The Cinder Path* (Yorkshire TV, 1993), *Pride and Prejudice* (BBC, 1994).

Fiona Laird

Worked for two years as a staff director at the Royal National Theatre before embarking as a freelance in 1995. Assisted Declan Donnellan on the West End transfer and national tour of Cheek by Jowl's *As You Like It*. Restaged *Great Expectations* for an Apollo Leisure No. 1 tour. Other credits: *Penny Blue* by Vanessa Brooks (Greenwich Theatre), *Happy Families, Black Comedy* and *The Public Eye* (Palace Theatre, Watford), *Guys and Dolls* (with Richard Eyre), *Oh! What a Lovely War* (Royal National Theatre).

Brigid Larmour

Theatre and TV director. Graduate of the Granada TV Directors' Multi-Camera Course in 1995. Artistic Director of the Contact Theatre, Manchester (1990–94). Credits include: *Badger* (Granada; nominated for the Prix Danube in 1989), *Dr Faustus, The Carver Chair, Dracula* and *Strange*

Attractors (Contact Theatre, Manchester), *The Tempest* and *Henry V* (for the Royal National Theatre).

Mike Leigh, OBE

Playwright and theatre, TV and film director. Directed and designed the original production of *Little Malcolm and his Struggle Against the Eunuchs* at the Unity Theatre in 1965. Was Associate Director at the Midlands Arts Centre (1965–66) and Assistant Director at the Royal Shakespeare Company (1967–68). His first original piece for the stage was *The Box Play*, produced at the Midlands Arts Centre in 1966. All of his subsequent work, which he has scripted and directed, has evolved out of improvisation with actors. Theatre credits include: *Abigail's Party, Smelling a Rat, Greek Tragedy.* Film credits: *Bleak Moments* (1971), *High Hopes* (1989), *Life is Sweet* (1990), *Naked* (1993), *Secrets and Lies* (1996), *Career Girls* (1997).

Phyllida Lloyd

Theatre, opera and radio director. Associate Director of the Royal Exchange Theatre, Manchester and the Bristol Old Vic. Credits include: *Maneaters* (Man in the Moon Theatre, London), *The Virgin's Revenge* and *Glengarry, Glen Ross* (Soho Poly), *Letters Home* (Old Red Lion), *Educating Rita* (Wolsey Theatre, Ipswich), *Every Black Day, Accidental Death of An Anarchist, Insignificance, Much Ado About Nothing, A Midsummer Night's Dream, What the Butler Saw* and *Woyzeck* (all for Everyman Theatre, Cheltenham), *Inventing a New Colour* (Royal Court Theatre Upstairs), *Every Black Day* (Half Moon Theatre), *A Streetcar Named Desire, The Comedy of Errors, Dona Rosita the Spinster* and *Oliver Twist* (all

for Bristol Old Vic), *Medea* (Opera North), *The School for Scandal, Death of the King's Horsemen* (John Fernald award and the *Manchester Evening News* award) and *The Winter's Tale* (Royal Exchange, Manchester), *The Virtuoso* and *Artists and Admirers* (Royal Shakespeare Company), *Six Degrees of Separation* (Royal Court/Comedy Theatre), *Hysteria* (Royal Court), *L'Etoile* (Opera North), *Gloriana* (Opera North/Royal Opera House), *Pericles, What the Butler Saw* and *Way of the World* (Royal National Theatre), *The Threepenny Opera* (Donmar Warehouse, London; Olivier award Best Musical 1995), *La Bohème* and *Medea* (Opera North), *Hysteria* (Duke of York's Theatre), *Dona Rosita the Spinster* (Almeida Theatre), *Macbeth* (Royal Opera House). Radio credits include: *The Double Dealer* and *Scenes from Shakespeare* (BBC Radio 4).

Ken Loach

Film and TV director. Was an actor for two years before becoming Assistant Director at the Northampton Rep. In 1963, he joined the BBC as a trainee director in the Drama Department. TV credits include: *Diary of a Young Man* (1964), *Up the Junction* (1965), *Cathy Come Home* (1966), *In Two Minds* (1966), *Poor Cow* (1967), *The Big Flame* (1969), *The Rank and File* (1972), *Family Life* (1971), *Days of Hope* (1975), *The Price of Coal* (1977), *A Question of Leadership* (1981), *Questions of Leadership* (1983/4; four documentaries which were banned), *Which Side Are You On?* (1984; main prize at Florence Documentary Festival); *Dispatches* (Channel 4, 1991). Film credits: *Kes* (1970; Karlovy award), *In Black and White* (1970), *Family Life* (1972), *Black Jack* (1979; Cannes Critics award), *Looks and Smiles* (1981; Cannes Prize for Contemporary

Cinema), *Fatherland* (1986), *Hidden Agenda* (1990; Cannes Jury Prize), *Riff Raff* (1991), *Raining Stones* (1993; Cannes Jury Prize/Evening Standard Best Film and Best Screenplay awards), *Ladybird, Ladybird* (1994; Critics Prize and Best Actress award, Berlin Film Festival), *Land and Freedom* (1995; Cannes International Critics Prize/ Cannes Jury Prize/nominated for European Film Academy Film of the Year), *Carla's Song* (1996), *My Name is Joe* (1997).

Richard Loncraine

Film and TV director. Film credits include: *Flame* (1974), *Full Circle* (1976), *Bellman and True* (1987), *Brimstone and Treacle* (1982), *The Missionary* (1984), *Richard III* (1995). TV credits: *Vanishing Army* (BBC, 1978), *Secret Orchards* (Granada, 1979), *Blade on the Feather* (LWT, 1980), *The Wedding Gift* (1994).

Robert Love

TV director and producer. Currently Controller of Drama at Scottish Television. Credits include: *Van der Valk* (1973) and *Moody and Peg* (1975, both for Thames), *House on the Hill* (1980), *The Marriage Contract* (1984), *Extras* (1986), *Taggart* (1984/97), *Dr Finlay* (1992/97) – all for STV

Jonathan Lynn

Film and theatre director, actor and writer. Artistic Director of the Cambridge Theatre Company (1977–81), directing 19 productions, including: *The Deep Blue Sea, Macbeth, The Relapse* and 9 new plays and British premières. In London he has directed *The Plotters of Cabbage Patch Corner, The Glass Menagerie, The Gingerbread Man, The Unvarnished Truth, The Matchmaker,*

Arms and the Man, Pass the Butler, Loot (Theatre of Comedy), *Songbook* (Evening Standard and SWET awards, 1979). For the Royal Shakespeare Company, he directed *Anna Christie,* and for the National Theatre, *Three Men on a Horse* (Olivier award for Best Comedy), *Jacobowsky and the Colonel* and *A Little Hotel on the Side.* Has directed the TV films *Mick's People, Ferris Bueller* and *Smart Guys.* In addition to many theatre and TV appearances as an actor, has written two series of *My Brother's Keeper* and three series of *Yes Minister* (followed by *Yes Prime Minister*) with Anthony Jay. Film credits: *Clue, Nuns on the Run* (also wrote screenplay), *My Cousin Vinny, The Distinguished Gentleman, Greedy* (also screenplay), *Sergeant Bilko, Trial and Error.*

Ian McDiarmid

Joint Artistic Director of the Almeida Theatre in London where he has directed *Scenes from an Execution* (*Time Out* award), *The Rehearsal* (transfer to West End), *Lulu, A Hard Heart, Venice Preserved* and the opera *Siren Song.* Previously Associate Director at the Royal Exchange Theatre, Manchester where he directed *Don Juan,* and played the title role in *Edward II* and Phillip II in *Don Carlos.*

Robert David Macdonald

Co-director of the Citizens' Theatre Company since 1971. Originally trained as a musician then spent some years as a translator for UNESCO before becoming Assistant Director at Glyndebourne and Covent Garden opera houses. Has written 15 plays for the Citizens', including: *De Sade Show, Chinchilla, No Orchids for Miss Blandish, Summit Conference, Conundrum, Persons*

Unknown. Has directed over 40 plays at the Citizens', including: *The Last Days of Mankind, Maskerade, Niagra, Casanova Undone, The Ice House* and *Wittgenstein's Daughter.* His adaptation of the production of *War and Peace* ran for two seasons on Broadway and received an Emmy award when shown on US television. Has directed plays and operas in Amsterdam, Atlanta, Berlin, Boston, Brussels, Houston, Minneapolis and Vienna.

John Mackenzie

Film director. Feature films: *The Long Good Friday, The Fourth Protocol, Unman Wittering and Zigo, Made, The Honorary Consul, The Innocent, The Last of the Finest, Ruby, Voyage, Infiltrator.* TV films: *Act of Vengeance, Bangelstein's Boys, Black Dog, Just Another Saturday, Wild West Show, Passage to England, Double Dare, A Sense of Freedom, Looking after Jo Jo, Deadly Voyage.*

Mary McMurray

Film TV and theatre director. Credits include: *To Have and to Hold* (LWT), *Born in the RSA* (Channel 4), *Miss Marple* (1987), *The Ruth Rendell Mysteries* (Blue Heaven/TVS), *Family* (Channel 4), *Spender* (BBC), *Taggart: The Hit Man* (STV), *Degrees of Error* (BBC), *Buddy Breathing* (TVS), *New Brighton Rock* (Granada), *Kissing the Gunner's Daughter* (TVS), *Harry* (BBC), *The Mallens* (Granada), *Pigeon Summer* (Catalyst TV/Channel 4). Directed the film *The Assam Garden* (with Deborah Kerr and Madhur Jaffrey) and *Medea* at the Lyric Theatre, Hammersmith.

Bob Mahoney

TV, film and theatre director. Credits include: *Operation Julie* (Tyne Tees TV),

May We Borrow Your Husband, A Day in the Summer, Heartbeat and *Chillers* (all for Yorkshire TV), *The Wanderer* (Fingertip Productions), *The Governor* (Lynda La Plante Productions).

Andrew Manley

Theatre and radio director. Trained as an actor at the Central School of Speech and Drama. After nine years as an actor he was founder member of the touring company EMMA Theatre Company. Was Artistic Director of EMMA from 1974 until 1981. Artistic Director of the Torch Theatre, Milford Haven (1981–85), Artistic Director of Harrogate Theatre (1985–97). Currently, Artistic Director of the Wolsey Theatre, Ipswich. Writer of a number of plays, including adaptations of *A Christmas Carol* and *The Turn of the Screw.*

Sean Mathias

Theatre, film and radio director and writer. Credits include: *A Prayer for Wings* (Bush Theatre), *Infidelities* (Donmar Warehouse/Boulevard Theatre, US), *Exceptions* (New End), *Bent* (Royal National Theatre/Garrick; City Limits award for Revival of the Year), *Uncle Vanya* (Royal National Theatre; nominated for 5 Olivier awards, including Best Director and Best Revival), *Ghosts* (Sherman Theatre, Cardiff), *Les Parents Terribles* (Royal National Theatre; Evening Standard and Critics Circle awards for Best Director, nominated for 7 Olivier awards and on Broadway – as *Indiscretions* – nominated for 9 Tony awards), *Design for Living* (Donmar Warehouse/Gielgud Theatre; Evening Standard and Critics Circle awards for Best Director), *A Little Night Music* (Royal National Theatre, with Judi Dench), *Marlene* (Lyric, Shaftesbury

Avenue, with Siân Phillips). Has written several stage plays, including: *Cowardice, Infidelities, A Prayer for Wings, Swansea Boys*. His novel, *Manhattan Mourning* was published by Brilliance Books and his first feature film, *Bent*, was released in 1997. Most recent film: *Quadrille* for Initial Films.

Nancy Meckler

Artistic Director of Shared Experience Theatre Company. Productions for that company include: *Abingdon Square, True West, Heartbreak House, The Birthday Party, A Streetcar Named Desire, Sweet Sessions, Anna Karenina, The Danube, War and Peace*. Founder of Freehold Theatre Company (1968–72). Other theatre credits include: *Action* (Royal Court Theatre Upstairs, 1973), *Kiss Me Kate* (Oxford Playhouse, 1974), *Action and Killer's Head* (American Place Theatre, New York, 1975), *Susanne Adler* (Leicester Haymarket, 1975), *Dusa Fish Stas and Vi* (Hampstead Theatre/West End transfer, 1976), *Curse of the Starving Class* (Royal Court, 1977), *Penny Whistle* (Hampstead, 1978), *Twelfth Night* (Young Vic, 1978), *Daughters of Men* and *Uncle Vanya* (Hampstead, 1979), *The Tax Exile* (Bush Theatre, 1979), *Buried Child* (Hampstead, 1980), *Saint Joan* (Cambridge Theatre Company, 1981), *Who's Afraid of Virginia Woolf?* (National Theatre, 1981), *Drefus* and *The Hard Shoulder* (Hampstead, 1982), *The Communication Cord* (Hampstead, 1983), *Sufficient Carbohydrate* (Hampstead/West End transfer, 1982). Productions for Leicester Haymarket 1984–87) include: *The Cherry Orchard, A Midsummer Night's Dream, The People Show*, plus *Medea, The Bald Prima Donna, The Phoney Physician* all of which transferred from the Haymarket Studio to the Almeida Theatre in London. In 1987, she directed *My Sister in this House* for Monstrous Regiment and, in 1987, *Low Level Panic* for the Royal Court Theatre Upstairs and Lyric Hammersmith Studio. Film credits include: *Sister My Sister* (Channel 4/NFH), *Alive and Kicking* and *Indian Summer* (both for Channel 4).

Peter Medak

Hungarian film, TV and opera director. Film credits include: *A Day in the Death of Joe Egg* (1970), *The Ruling Class* (1971), *Ghost in the Noonday's Sun* (1974), *The Odd Job* (1978), *The Changeling* (1980), *Zorro, the Gay Blade* (1981), *The Men's Club* (1986), *The Krays* (1990), *Let Him Have It* (1991), *Romeo is Bleeding* (1993), *Pontiac Moon* (1994). Opera credits: *Salome, La Voix Humaine, Rigoletto*.

Sam Mendes

Began his theatrical career at the Chichester Festival Theatre, where he ran the Chichester Festival Theatre Tent, directing productions such as *Translations* and *Heartlands*. In the Minerva Studio at Chichester, he directed *Summerfolk* and *Love's Labour's Lost*. Other credits include: *London Assurance* (Theatre Royal, Haymarket, with Paul Eddington), *The Cherry Orchard* (Aldwych), *Kean* (The Old Vic, with Derek Jacobi), *The Plough and the Stars* (Young Vic), *The Sea, The Rise and Fall of Little Voice* and *The Birthday Party* (all for the Royal National Theatre), *Oliver!* (London Palladium), *Othello* (Cottesloe Theatre, 1997). For the Royal Shakespeare Company: *Troilus and Cressida, The Alchemist, Richard II* and *The Tempest*. Artistic Director of the Donmar Warehouse since 1992 where he has directed *Assassins* (Critics Circle award, 1993), *Translations, Cabaret* (with Alan Cumming, Jane Horrocks and Sara Kestleman), *Glengarry, Glen Ross, The Glass Menagerie* (transferred to the Comedy Theatre; Critics Circle award), *Company* (transferred to the Albery Theatre; 3 Olivier awards, including Best Director, and 2 Critics Circle awards), *Habeas Corpus* (with Jim Broadbent and Brenda Blethyn) and *The Fix*.

Roger Michell

Theatre and TV director. Won the Buzz Goodbody Prize in 1977 for his production of *Bingo* at the *Sunday Times* Student Drama Festival. Worked at the Royal Court for two years, where he assisted Beckett and Osborne and directed various plays in the Theatre Upstairs, including *The Key Tag* by Mike McGrath and *The Catch* by Nick Darke. Co-wrote and directed *The White Glove* with Richard Maher, which was performed at the Lyric, Hammersmith and in the West End. He then worked with the Cambridge Theatre Company. Joining the Royal Shakespeare Company in 1984, he worked as Assistant Director and then directed the première of Nick Darke's *The Dead Monkey* for The Pit in 1986. He has directed two RSC/ NatWest tour productions (*The Merchant of Venice* and *Hamlet*), the British première of Vaclav Havel's *Temptation* for The Other Place and The Pit, and *The Constant Couple, Restoration* and *Campesinos* for the 1988 Stratford season. Directed *My Night with Reg* for BBC TV in 1996.

Gavin Millar

Film and TV director. Film credits include: *Secrets: (First Love), Dreamchild, Danny, Champion of the World, The Most Dangerous Man in the World*. TV credits: *Young Indiana Jones Chronicles, Look at it This Way, The Dwelling Place, Pat and Margaret, A Case of Coincidence, Cream in My Coffee, Scoop, Tidy Endings*.

Jonathan Miller

Theatre, opera and film director, television producer and presenter, writer. Trained as a doctor of medicine but sprang to prominence in the Cambridge Footlights in *Out of the Blue* in 1954. Between 1961 and 1964 he co-wrote and appeared in *Beyond the Fringe* with Alan Bennett, Dudley Moore and Peter Cook. Theatre credits as director include: *The Merchant of Venice* (National Theatre, with Laurence Olivier), *Three Sisters, The Seagull* and *Long Day's Journey into Night* (London and Broadway, with Jack Lemmon), *The Emperor* (Royal Court), *The Taming of the Shrew* (Royal Shakespeare Company). As Artistic Director of The Old Vic between January 1988 and October 1990, he directed *Andromache, One-Way Pendulum* (also Royal Alexander Theatre, Toronto), *King Lear, The Liar, Bussy D'Ambois, The Tempest*. Opera credits include: *Arabella, Otello, Rigoletto, Don Giovanni, The Magic Flute, Tosca, The Barber of Seville* and *The Mikado* for the English National Opera, and productions for Scottish Opera, Vienna State Opera, Salzburg Festival, Los Angeles Opera, La Scala Milan, the Royal Opera House Covent Garden and many others. Work for TV includes *The Body in Question, Cosi Fan Tutte* and in 1980–82, 12 plays for the BBC Shakespeare series. He has written a number of books: *The Body in Question, States of Mind, The Human Body, Facts of Life, Subsequent Performances*.

Anthony Minghella

Film, TV and radio director and writer. Lecturer in Drama at Hull University until 1981. His first film as writer/director was *Truly, Madly, Deeply*, starring Juliet Stevenson, which won several prizes, including a BAFTA award. Other film credits include: *Mr Wonderful* (wrote and directed), *The English Patient* (wrote and directed; 2 Golden Globe awards, 9 Academy awards, including Best Picture and Best Director, Director's Guild of America award for Best Director and 3 BAFTA awards).

Katie Mitchell

Theatre and opera director. President of Oxford University Dramatic Society before going on to found Classics on a Shoestring Theatre Company. Credits include: *Vinegar Tom* (Old Fire Station), *The House of Bernarda Alba* and *The Good Person of Szechwan* (Oxford Playhouse), *Gobstopper* and *Hatikva – The Hope* (King's Head), *Vassa Zheleznova* and *The House of Bernarda Alba* (Gate Theatre), *Arden of Faversham* (Old Red Lion), *The Last* (Abbey Theatre, Dublin), *Live Like Pigs* (Royal Court), *Rutherford and Son* and *The Machine Wreckers* (Royal National Theatre), *End Game* (Donmar Warehouse), *Don Giovanni* (Welsh National Opera). For the Royal Shakespeare Company: *Easter, Henry VI, Ghosts, A Woman Killed with Kindness, The Dybbuk, The Mysteries, Beckett Shorts.*

Christopher Morahan

Theatre, TV and film director. Studied at The Old Vic Theatre School under Michel Saint-Denis and began directing at ATV, where his credits included: *Emergency Ward 10, Probation Officer* and *John Gabriel Borkman* (1958). From 1961 to 1971, he worked as a freelance TV director on such productions as *The Orwell Trilogy, Talking to a Stranger* (BBC, 1966), *The Ragged Trousered Philanthropists* (1967), *A Month in the Country, Uncle Vanya, The Gorge* (BBC,

1968), *Hearts and Flowers* (BBC, 1970), *Giants and Ogres, The Letter, The Chinese Prime Minister.* From 1972 to 1976, he was Head of Plays for BBC TV and directed *The Common* (Play of the Month, 1973) and *Old Times.* In 1983, he was co-director of *The Jewel in the Crown* for Granada, for which he received 2 British Academy awards and an International Emmy.

After theatre work in the late sixties and early seventies, which included *Little Murders, This Story of Yours, Flint* and *The Caretaker*, he joined the National Theatre and was deputy to the director (1979–80) and a full-time associate (1977–81). His productions with the National have included *State of Revolution, Brand, Strife, The Philanderer, Richard III, Sisterly Feelings, Man and Superman* and, in 1984, *Wild Honey* with Ian McKellen, which won the Olivier, Evening Standard, Drama and Plays and Players awards. He directed *In the Secret State* for the BBC; in 1986, the film *Clockwise*, starring John Cleese, Simon Gray's *After Pilkington* (BBC; Prix Italia award, 1987), *Troubles* (Channel 4), *Old Flames, Can You Hear Me Thinking*, the feature film *Paper Mask* (1990), Simon Gray's *Unnatural Pursuits* (BBC; International Emmy award, 1992), *The Bullion Boys* (Mentorn/BBC, 1993), *The Devil's Disciple* (Royal National Theatre, 1994), *Summer's Day Dream* (BBC, 1994, with John Gielgud), *It Might be You* (BBC, 1995), *The Peacock Spring* (BBC, 1995).

Braham Murray

Theatre director and writer. Sprang to prominence while still at Oxford University when *Hang Down Your Head and Die*, which he co-wrote and directed, transferred to the West End and then to Broadway. Currently Artistic Director of the Royal Exchange

Company in Manchester, he has been Artistic Director of the Century Theatre and of the 69 Theatre Company in Manchester, directing, among other plays, *She Stoops to Conquer, Charley's Aunt, Mary Rose* and the musicals *'Erb* and *Catch My Soul*, all of which transferred to London. Other West End productions include *The Good Companions* (with John Mills and Judi Dench) and *The Black Mikado*. Among his many productions at the Royal Exchange are: *The Rivals, What the Butler Saw, Leaping Ginger, The Dybbuk, Measure for Measure, Waiting for Godot, Have You Anything to Declare?, The Nerd* (European première), *Who's a Lucky Boy?* (musical conceived with Alan Price and Gerald Scarfe), *Riddley Walker* (adaptation of the cult novel by Russell Hoban), *Court in the Act, The Merchant of Venice* and the première of a new Woody Allen revue, *The Bluebird of Unhappiness*.

Adrian Noble

Artistic Director of the Royal Shakespeare Company. After graduating from Bristol University, worked for two years in Birmingham in community and young people's theatre at the Trinity Arts Centre. Went to the Bristol Old Vic in 1976 on a Thames TV Director's Bursary as a trainee director moving on to become an Associate Director; productions there included: *Ubu Rex, Man is Man, A View From the Bridge, Love for Love, Timon of Athens, Comedians, The Recruiting Officer*. In 1979, he joined the RSC as Assistant Director and worked on *As You Like It, Romeo and Juliet* and *Hamlet*. After a spell with the Royal Exchange in Manchester (*The Duchess of Malfi* with Helen Mirren and Bob Hoskins, Plays and Players London Drama Critics and Drama

awards) and *Dr Faustus* (with Ben Kingsley), he returned to Stratford, as an Associate Director, to direct his first RSC production, Ostrovsky's *The Forest*, which transferred to London and was named Best Revival in the 1981 Drama awards. In 1982, he directed *King Lear* (with Michael Gambon and Antony Sher) and *Antony and Cleopatra* (with Michael Gambon and Helen Mirren). Subsequent productions for the RSC have included: *A Doll's House, A New Way to Pay Old Debts* by Philip Massinger, *The Comedy of Errors, Measure for Measure, King Lear, Henry V, The Desert Air* by Nicholas Wright, *The Winter's Tale, As You Like It, Macbeth* (with Jonathan Pryce and Sinead Cusack), *Kiss Me Kate, The Art of Success* by Nick Dear, *Richard III, The Plantagenets, The Master Builder, Henry IV Parts I and II, The Thebans, Hamlet* (with Kenneth Branagh), *Travesties, King Lear* (with Robert Stephens), *A Midsummer Night's Dream, Romeo and Juliet, The Cherry Orchard* (with Alec McCowen and Penelope Wilton, transferred to the Albery Theatre in the West End), *Cymbeline, Little Eyolf, Twelfth Night, The Tempest*. Other directing credits include: *The Art of Success* (Manhattan Theatre Club, New York), the Cusack sisters in *Three Sisters* (The Gate Theatre, Dublin/Royal Court), *Don Giovanni* (Kent Opera), *The Duchess of Malfi* (Paris), *The Faerie Queen* (The Peter Hall Company).

Trevor Nunn

Won an ABC trainee director's scholarship to the Belgrade Theatre in Coventry in 1962 and later became resident director there. His productions there included *The Caucasian Chalk Circle, Peer Gynt* and *Around the World in Eighty Days*. In 1964, he joined the Royal Shakespeare Company and was made an Associate Director in 1965. Became the company's youngest ever Artistic Director in 1968 and was responsible for running the RSC until 1986. His productions for the RSC included: *The Revenger's Tragedy, The Relapse, The Alchemist, Henry V, The Taming of the Shrew, King Lear, Much Ado About Nothing, The Winter's Tale, Henry VIII, Hamlet, Macbeth, Antony and Cleopatra, Coriolanus, Julius Caesar, Titus Andronicus, Romeo and Juliet, The Comedy of Errors, As You Like It, All's Well That Ends Well, Once in a Lifetime, Three Sisters, Juno and the Paycock, Othello, The Blue Angel, Measure for Measure.* Co-directed with John Caird the award-winning *The Life and Adventures of Nicholas Nickleby* which transferred to Broadway and was shown on Channel 4. In 1982, he led the RSC into their new home in London at the Barbican, which opened with his production of *Henry IV Parts I and II.* 1986 saw the opening of the Swan Theatre in Stratford which he conceived and for which he directed one of the first productions, *The Fair Maid of the West.* He has directed several highly successful musicals: *Chess, Starlight Express, Aspects of Love, Sunset Boulevard, The Baker's Wife, Les Misérables* (which, with John Caird, his co-director, he also adapted from the Paris production). His Broadway production of *Cats* won a Tony award in 1983. Took over from Richard Eyre as Artistic Director of the Royal National Theatre in October 1997 where he has directed *Arcadia; An Enemy of the People* and *Mutabilitie.* Opera credits include: *Idomeneo, Cosi Fan Tutti* and *Peter Grimes* (Glyndebourne Festival Opera), *Porgy and Bess* and *Katya Kabanova* (Royal Opera House). TV credits: *Antony and Cleopatra* (BAFTA award), *The Comedy*

of Errors, Macbeth, Three Sisters, Word of Mouth, Othello, Porgy and Bess. Film credits: *Hedda, Lady Jane* and *Twelfth Night.*

Mike Ockrent

Theatre, film and TV director. From 1969 to 1973, was an ITV trainee director at the Perth Rep Theatre, where he later became an Associate Director. He was Artistic Director of the Traverse Theatre in Edinburgh (1973–76), where his productions included: *To Damascus, Dream Play* and *Kasper.* In 1974, his production of Stanley Eveling's *Union Jack* and *Bonzo* played at the Hampstead Theatre and *Schippel* (adapted by C. P. Taylor from Carl Sternheim's original) transferred to the Prince of Wales Theatre as *The Plumber's Progress* (with Harry Secombe). Other productions in the seventies included a No. 1 tour of *The Merchant of Venice, Knickers* by Carl Sternheim (Nottingham Playhouse, 1976), *Table Manners* (Oxford Playhouse, 1977), *Happy Returns* (Stigwood Group, 1978), *Hust and Hide* (Billingham/Newcastle/West End, 1978), *And a Nightingale Sang* (Queen's Theatre, London, 1979), *A Respectable Wedding* (Open Space Theatre, 1979). In 1980, he directed *Educating Rita* for the Royal Shakespeare Company at the Warehouse, the Piccadilly Theatre and on tour, and *Watch on the Rhine* at the National Theatre, with Peggy Ashcroft. Productions in 1982 were: *Ducking Out* by Eduardo di Filippo at Greenwich and the Duke of York's Theatre, *Good* for the National Theatre of Belgium, *Short List* by Michael Rudman at the Hampstead Theatre and *Inner Voices* by Eduardo di Filippo at the National Theatre (starring Ralph Richardson) in 1983. Other credits include: the Leicester Haymarket production of the musical *Me and My Girl* in London, on Broadway, in Los Angeles and in Australia, Sondheim's *Follies* (Shaftesbury Theatre), *The Nerd* (Aldwych Theatre, with Rowan Atkinson), *Look No Hans* (National Theatre tour with David Jason), *The Pajama Game* (tour), *Just So* (Cameron Mackintosh/Tricycle Theatre), Gershwin's *Crazy for You* in London, the US, Canada, Japan and South Africa, *A Christmas Carol* (Madison Square Gardens, New York), *Zenobia* (RSC, 1995), *King David* (by Tim Rice and Alan Mencken for Walt Disney, New Amsterdam Theatre, New York, 1997). Directed *Dancin' Thru the Dark*, a feature film, written by Willy Russell for Palace Pictures in 1989.

TV credits include: *Mrs Capper's Birthday* (BBC, 1984/5), *Money for Nothing* (BBC, 1993).

Richard Olivier

Theatre and TV director and writer. Son of Laurence Olivier and Joan Plowright. Trainee director, Royal Theatre, Northampton (1984–85). Co-founded the Actor's Gang Fringe in Los Angeles with Tim Robbins. Productions there included: *Habeas Corpus, Out of Sight Out of Mind, Wheels, Next Time I'll Sing to You, The Coarse Acting Show*. UK theatre credits include: *Infidelities* (Edinburgh/Donmar Warehouse; Perrier Pick of the Fringe), *Meetin's on the Porch* (Thorndike Theatre, Leatherhead/Canon Theatre, Los Angeles), *The Complaisant Lover* (Watford Palace Theatre), *M. Butterfly* (national tour with George Chakiris), *Present Laughter* (national tour), *Time and the Conways* (The Old Vic), *Shirley Valentine* (Duke of York's Theatre), *The Miracle Worker* (Wyndham's Theatre), *If We are Women* (Greenwich Theatre), *In Praise of Love* (Apollo Theatre), *Present Laughter* (Aldwych Theatre), *Henry V* (Shakespeare's Globe Theatre).

Anthony Page

Film, television and theatre director. Films include: *I Never Promised You a Rose Garden, The Lady Vanishes, Absolution, Alpha Beta, Inadmissible Evidence*. TV credits: *The Parachute* (with Jill Bennett and Alan Badel, 1967), *Pueblo Affair* (ABC/Titus Productions, 1973), *Missiles of October* (ABC/Titus Productions, 1974), *Scott Fitzgerald in Hollywood* (ABC, 1975), *The Patricia Neal Story* (NBC, 1980), *Bill* (CBS; Golden Globe award, 1981), *Johnny Belinda* (NBC, 1982), *FDR The Last Year* (NBC, 1982), *Bill on His Own* (CBS, 1983), *The Grace Kelly Story* (ABC, 1983), *Murder By Reason of Insanity* (CBS, 1984), *Forbidden* (HBO/Premier Films/CBS, 1985), *Second Serve* (CBS/Lorimar, 1986), *Monte Carlo* (CBS, 1986), *Heartbreak House* (Showtime, 1986), *Pack of Lies* (CBS/Robert Halmi, 1987), *Scandal in a Small Town* (NBC, 1988), *The Nightmare Years* (Consolidated, 1989), *Chernobyl, The Final Warning* (TNT, 1990), *Absolute Hell* (BBC, 1991), *Guests of the Emperor* (NBC/Yorkshire TV, 1992), *Middlemarch* (BBC, 1993), *The Human Bomb* (Showtime, 1996). Theatre includes the world première of *Inadmissible Evidence* with Nicol Williamson in 1964, *A Patriot for Me, Hotel in Amsterdam* and *Time Present*, all by John Osborne; *A Delicate Balance* (Theatre Royal, Haymarket).

Alan Parker

Film director. Credits include: *Bugsy Malone* (1977), *Midnight Express* (1978), *Fame* (1979), *Shoot the Moon* (1982), *Pink Floyd: The Wall* (1982), *Birdy* (1985),

Angel Heart (1987), *Mississippi Burning* (1988), *Come See the Paradise* (1990), *The Commitments* (1991), *The Road to Wellville* (1994), *Evita* (1996). Appointed Chairman Designate of the British Film Institute in 1997.

Brian Parker

TV director. Credits include: *Donal and Sally* (BBC, 1979), *Off-Peak* (STV, 1984), *Inspector Morse* (Zenith, 1986), *The Beiderbecke Tapes* (Yorkshire TV, 1987), *El CID* (Granada, 1989), *Sharp-End* (BBC, 1990), *The Bill* (Thames, 1991), *Strathblair* (BBC, 1992).

Lynne Parker

Born and educated in Dublin. Co-founded the Rough Magic Theatre Company in 1984. As Artistic Director, credits include: *Nightshade, Spokesong, The Country Wife, Top Girls, Serious Money, Aunt Dann and Lemon, The Dogs, Pentecost, Northern Star, Digging for Fire, New Morning, Love and a Bottle* (winner of a Time Out Award in 1992). Her production of *Lady Windermere's Fan* won a Bank of Ireland / RTE Arts Show award. Other companies she has worked for include: Druid, Tinderbox, Opera Theatre Co and 7:84 Scotland. An Associate Director of Charabanc for whom she adapted and directed Lorca's *The House of Bernarda Alba*. Other credits include: *The Trojan Women* (Peacock), *The Clearing* (Bush Theatre), *The Doctor's Dilemma* (Abbey Theatre), *The Playboy of the Western World, The Way of the World, Down on to Blue, Hidden Charges* and *Silver Tassie* (all at the Almeida Theatre), *The Shadow of a Gunman* (The Gate Theatre, Dublin), *Halloween Nights* (Donmar Warehouse); *Playhouse*

Creatures (The Peter Hall Company at The Old Vic).

Chris Petit

Film and TV director. Credits include: *Radio On* (film, 1979), *A Suitable Job for a Woman* (film, 1982), *Ear to the Ground* (Channel 4, 1982), *Actor and the Role* (Channel 4, 1983), *Flight to Berlin* (film, 1984), *Chinese Boxes* (film, 1984), *Destination Washington* (film, 1989), *Sixth Sense* (Anglia TV, 1991–93).

Nick Philippou

Artistic Director of the Actors Touring Company (ATC) since 1993, having formerly worked with the Education Departments of the Royal National Theatre and the Royal Shakespeare Theatre. For ATC, he has directed: *Celestina, The Maids, No Way Out, Ion, Venus and Adonis, The Modern Husband, Faust, Belle Vue*. Other credits include: *Arms and the Man* and *Lulu* for the Cambridge Theatre Company.

Harold Pinter

Writer, actor and director. Associate Director of the National Theatre from 1973 to 1983. For the stage, he has directed his own plays: *The Room*, (Hampstead Theatre), *The Lover* and *The Dwarfs* (Arts Theatre), *The Birthday Party* (RSC / Aldwych Theatre), *The Hothouse* (Hampstead Theatre / Ambassadors Theatre), *Mountain Language* (National Theatre / Almeida Theatre), *The Caretaker* (Comedy Theatre), *Party Time* (Almeida Theatre / Channel 4), *Landscape* (Gate Theatre, Dublin). Other theatre directing credits: James Joyce's *Exiles* (RSC / Aldwych Theatre). John Hopkin's *Next of Kin*, Coward's *Blithe Spirit* and Giraudoux's *The Trojan War*

Will Not Take Place for the National Theatre, William Archibald's *The Innocents*, Robert East's *Incident at Tulse Hill* (Hampstead Theatre), and seven plays by Simon Gray: *Butley* (also the film), *Otherwise Engaged, The Rear Column, Close of Play, Quartermaine's Terms, The Common Pursuit*, and most recently, *Life Support*. Also: *Sweet Bird of Youth* at the Theatre Royal Haymarket (starring Lauren Bacall), *Vanilla* (Lyric Theatre), *Circe and Bravo* (Hampstead Theatre/Wyndham's Theatre), *Oleanna* (Royal Court Theatre/Duke of Yorks), *Taking Sides* (Chichester Festival Theatre/Criterion Theatre), *Twelve Angry Men* (Comedy Theatre).

Stephen Poliakoff

Writer and TV and film director. Wrote his first play, *Day with My Sister*, while still at school; it was directed by David Halliwell at the Traverse Theatre, Edinburgh. Writer-in-residence at the National Theatre in 1976 and was awarded Most Promising Playwright for *City Sugar* (Bush Theatre/Comedy Theatre). Other stage plays include: *Hitting Town, Heroes, Shout Across the River, American Days, The Summer Party, Favourite Nights, Breaking the Silence, Coming in to Land, Playing with Trains, Sienna Red, Sweet Panic, Blinded by the Sun* (Critics Circle award). As a TV scriptwriter, credits include: *Stronger Than the Sun* (BBC Play for Today, 1977), *Caught on a Train* (BBC, 1979, with Peggy Ashcroft), *Soft Targets* (BBC, 1982, with Ian Holm and Helen Mirren), *She's Been Away* (1989, Venice Film Festival award), *Frontiers* (Carlton, 1996). Screenplay credits: *Hitting Town* (1976), *City Sugar* (1977), *Strawberry Fields* (1986) and the screenplays for *Bloody Kids* (1980) and *Runners* (1983). Has directed some of the later productions such as *Hidden City* (1988), *Close My Eyes* (1991), *Century* (Evening Standard award for Best British Film, *The Tribe* (Deep City Films/BBC, 1996) and *Food of Love* (Intrinsica Films/Channel 4, 1997).

Sue Pomeroy

Theatre director. Artistic Director of the Warehouse Theatre in Croydon from 1980 to 1984. Currently Artistic Director of the Good Company. Credits include: *Moll Flanders* (Bristol Old Vic), *Crowned with Fame* (Swan Theatre, Stratford and tour), *Ear, Nose and Throat* (Chichester Festival and tour), *The Pepys Show* (Cambridge Arts and tour), *I, Bertolt Brecht* (Schiffbauerdam Theatre, Berlin), *Educating Rita* (Wolverhampton Grand).

Lindsay Posner

Theatre, TV and opera director. Credits include: *Much Ado About Nothing* (Regent's Park Open Air Theatre), *The Doctor of Honour* (Cheek by Jowl), *Leonce and Lena* (Sheffield Crucible), *American Buffalo* and *The Misanthrope* (both for the Young Vic), *The Robbers* and *The Seagull* (both for The Gate Theatre, Dublin), *The Lady from the Sea* (Lyric Hammersmith/West Yorkshire Playhouse), *The Provok'd Wife* (The Peter Hall Company at The Old Vic). Made Associate Director of the Royal Court Theatre in 1987 and, from 1989 until 1992, was Deputy Director of the main house and Artistic Director of the Royal Court Theatre Upstairs. Productions for the Royal Court include: *American Bagpipes, Death and the Maiden, The Treatment, Colquhoun and McBryde, Ambulance, Downfall, Blood, Built on Sand, No One Sees the*

Video and *Ficky Stingers*. Opera credits include: *Julius Caesar* and *Giulio Cesare* for the Royal Opera House. TV credits include *The Maitlands* and *Two Oranges and a Mango* (both for the BBC).

Tristram Powell

TV director (drama and documentary). Credits include: *The Ghost Writer* by Philip Roth (BBC/PBS, 1983), *My Dinner with Louis* (1984), *From an Immigrant's Notebook – Karen Blixen in Africa* (1985), *The Journey Man: Norman Lewis, Travel Writer* (1986), *Alfred Hitchcock* (1986), *East of Ipswich* by Michael Palin (BAFTA nomination, 1987), *The Temptation of Eileen Hughes* by Brian Moore (1988), *Talking Heads* by Alan Bennett (BBC, 1988), *Number 27* by Michael Palin (1989), *The Kremlin Farewell* (BBC, 1990), *Count of Solar* (BBC, 1991), *The Old Devils* (BBC, 1992), *The Long Roads* by John McGrath (1992/3), *Selected Exits* (with Anthony Hopkins, 1993), *Tears Before Bedtime* (BBC, 1994/5), *Harvest Moon* (BBC, 1995/6), *Kavanagh QC* (Carlton). Film credits include: *American Friends* (co-wrote and starring Michael Palin, 1992).

Nicholas Prosser

Film and TV director. Credits include: *The Bill* (Thames, 1989), *The Hidden Lives of Thomas Hardy* (documentary, 1990), *House of Eliott* (BBC, 1991), *EastEnders* (BBC, 1991), *Eldorado* (Cinema Verity/BBC, 1992), *Emmerdale* (produced and directed, Yorkshire TV, 1993/4), *Brookside* (Mersey TV/Channel 4, 1994).

Philip Prowse

Theatre and opera director and designer. Co-director of the Glasgow Citizens' Theatre. Among the many productions directed and designed for the Citizens': *Troilus and Cressida, The Threepenny Opera, Summit Conference* (also Lyric Theatre, Shaftesbury Avenue), *The Country Wife, A Waste of Time, The Massacre at Paris, Philosophy of the Boudoir, The Blacks, French Knickers, The Spanish Bawd, The Vortex* (with Maria Aitken and Rupert Everett, also Garrick Theatre, London), *Phaedra* (also The Old Vic/ Aldwych), *Mother Courage* (with Glenda Jackson, also Greenwich Theatre), *Design for Living, Sweet Bird of Youth, The Second Mrs Tanqueray, Women Beware Women, In the Bar of a Tokyo Hotel, The Relapse*. Has also directed and designed *The White Devil, The Seagull* and *The Orphan* (Greenwich Theatre), *The Duchess of Malfi* and *The White Devil* (National Theatre); *The Milk Train Doesn't Stop Here Anymore* (Citizens' Theatre/Lyric Hammersmith). Opera – design and directing credits include: *Tamburlaine* (Welsh National Opera), *Aida, The Threepenny Opera, Orpheo ed Euridice, Daphne* and *La Gioconda* (all for Opera North), *Giovanna D'Arco* (Royal Opera House).

Michael Radford

Film director and writer. Credits as director include: *Another Time, Another Place* (1983), *1984* (1984), *White Mischief* (1987), *Il Postino* (1994).

Alvin Rakoff

Film, TV and theatre director. Credits include: *The Liberty Tree, Romeo and Juliet, Don Quixote, Requiem for a Heavy Weight, A Voyage Round My Father* (with Laurence Olivier, EMMY award), *The Best of Friends* (with John Gielgud, Wendy Hiller and Patrick McGoohan), *Sam Saturday, Molly* and the Antony

Powell novels, *A Dance to the Music of Time*.

Roger Redfarn

Artistic Director of the Theatre Royal, Plymouth. Credits include: *Annie Get Your Gun* (Prince of Wales Theatre), *Oliver!* (Theatre Gdynia, Poland), *Brigadoon* (Victoria Palace), *South Pacific* (Prince of Wales), *Ross* (The Old Vic), *Underneath the Arches* (Prince of Wales).

Karel Reisz

Czech film and theatre director. Credits include: *Saturday Night and Sunday Morning* (1960), *Morgan: A Suitable Case for Treatment* (1966), *Isadora* (1968), *The Gambler* (1974), *Dog Soldiers* (1978), *Who'll Stop the Rain?* (1978), *The French Lieutenant's Woman* (1981), *Sweet Dreams* (1986), *Everybody Wins* (1988), *Everybody Wins* (1990).

John Retallack

Founded the Actors Touring Company in 1978; awarded SWET award for *The Life and Death of Don Quixote* and *The Provok'd Wife*; four years as Artistic Director of Oldham Coliseum and became Artistic Director of the Oxford Stage Company in 1989.

David Richards

Initially employed as a researcher at Granada Television, he began directing for them in 1975. Over the next 14 years, he directed news, current affairs, documentaries, arts and music programmes. His first drama credits were a drama-documentary on the life of Thomas de Quincey with John McEnery, and Ian McKellen's one-man show. Credits include: *The Practice* (Granada), *Erasmus* and *Emmerdale* (Yorkshire TV), *Children's Ward*, *Coronation Street*, *September Song* (all for Granada), *The Bill* (Thames), *Crocodile Shoes* (Big Boy Productions/Red Rooster/BBC), *Moving Story* (ABTV/Carlton), *Out of the Blue* (BBC), *Kiss and Tell* (LWT, 1996), *Reckless* and *2020* (Granada).

Nicolas Roeg

Film director. Began as a clapper boy and worked as a cinematographer before becoming a director in the seventies. Credits include: *Performance* (co-directed with Donald Cammell, 1972), *Walkabout* (1972), *Don't Look Now* (1973), *The Man Who Fell to Earth* (1976), *Bad Timing* (1979), *Eureka* (1983), *Insignificance* (1985), *Castaway* (1987), *Track 29* (1987), *Aria* (1987), *The Witches* (1990), *Cold Heaven* (1992), *Two Deaths* (1995), *Hotel Paradise* (1996).

Michael Rudman

Theatre director. Has directed at many regional theatres, among them the Belgrade, Coventry; Newcastle Playhouse; Theatre Royal, Bath; The Palace, Watford; the Citizens', Glasgow and for the Royal Shakespeare Company, Stratford, and the Dublin Festival. Assistant Director at the Nottingham Playhouse (1964–69), Director of the Traverse Theatre, Edinburgh (1970–73), Artistic Director of Hampstead Theatre (1973–78) and Associate Director of the National (1979–88) and Director of the Lyttelton Theatre at the National from 1979 to 1982. West End productions have included: *Straight Up, Donkey's Years, Taking Steps, The Dragon's Tail, Camelot.* On Broadway, he has directed *The Changing Room* (1973), *Hamlet* (1975) and *Death of a Salesman* (with Dustin Hoffman, 1984). At the National Theatre, his productions have included: *For Services Rendered, Death of a Salesman, Thee and Me, The Browning Version, Harlequinade, Measure for Measure, The Second Mrs Tanqueray, Brighton Beach Memoirs* by Neil Simon, *Ting Tang Mine* by Nick Darke (at the Cottesloe), *Waiting for Godot* (with Alec McCowen and John Alderton), *Six Characters in Search of an Author, Fathers and Sons.* Director of Chichester Festival Theatre from 1989 to 1991. During the 1997 season at Chichester, he directed *The Admirable Crichton, Our Betters* and *Tallulah!.* Directed *The Heiress* at the Gate Theatre in Dublin.

Ken Russell

Film and TV director. Has worked as a ballet dancer and freelance photographer. Started working for BBC Television as a producer and director of arts programmes in the late fifties, and gained fame by a series of film biographies of leading composers. Once the enfant terrible of British cinema, his films are still often controversial. Credits include: *French Dressing* (1964), *Billion Dollar Brain* (1967), *Women in Love* (1969), *The Music Lovers* (1971), *The Devils* (1971), *The Boyfriend* (1971), *Savage Messiah* (1972), *Mahler* (1974), *Tommy* (1975), *Lisztomania* (1975), *Valentino* (1977), *Altered States* (1980), *Crimes of Passion* (1984), *Gothic* (1987), *Salome's Last Dance* (1988), *The Lair of the White Worm* (1988), *The Rainbow* (1989), *Whore* (1991), *Erotic Tales* (1994, co-directed).

Renny Rye

Film and TV director. Credits include: *The Box of Delights* (BBC, 1984), *Casualty* (BBC, 1986), *Poirot* (LWT/Carnival, 1988/90), *The Old Side of Paradise* (Central, 1991), *Lipstick on Your Collar* (Channel 4, 1992), *Midnight Movie* (Whistling Gypsy/BBC, 1993), *Chandler & Co.* (Skreba/BBC, 1994), *Kavanagh QC* (Central, 1994), *Big Women* (Bandung Productions, 1997).

Mark Rylance

Actor and Artistic Director of Phoebus Cart and Shakespeare's Globe Theatre. Also Associate Director of the Royal Shakespeare Company. His first job as an actor was with the Citizens' Theatre in Glasgow in 1980. Has since worked with the RSC, Royal National Theatre, Royal Opera House, Scottish Ballet, Shared Experience Theatre Company, Bush Theatre, Tricycle Theatre, London Theatre of Imagination, Contact Theatre, Oxford Playhouse, the Project Theatre in Dublin, Mermaid Theatre, Royal Court, American Repertory Theatre in Boston, Theatre for a New Audience in New York, the Pittsburgh Playhouse. Directing credits include: *Macbeth* (Phoebus Cart, also played title role),

Jeremy Sams

Theatre and opera director, composer, pianist, translator and writer. Directing credits include: *Schippel, the Plumber* (Greenwich Theatre), *Mozart in Milan* (Barbican Theatre), *The Card* (Watermill Theatre, Newbury), *Entertaining Mr Sloane* (Greenwich Theatre), *The Wind in the Willows* (Tokyo/The Old Vic), *Neville's Island* (Nottingham Playhouse/Apollo Theatre, London), *Le Roi Malgré Lui* (Opera North, co-wrote the libretto), *Forty Years On* (West

Yorkshire Playhouse), *Maria Friedman by Special Arrangement* (Donmar Warehouse/Whitehall Theatre), *Enjoy* (Nottingham Playhouse), *Wild Oats* and *Marat/Sade* (Royal National Theatre), *Passion* (Kenwright/West End).

Peter Sasdy

TV and film director. TV credits include: *Lytton's Diary* and *Callan* (Thames TV), *It Had to be You* (Warner Bros/ABC), *Minder* (Euston Films), *Making News* (Thames), *Luck of the Draw* (ITV), *The Caves of Steel, A Kiss Before Dying, The World That Summer, Spoils of Poynton, Wuthering Heights, If Winter Comes, Witchcraft* (all for BBC TV), *The Secret Diary of Adrian Mole, The Growing Pains of Adrian Mole, Imaginary Friends, Ending Up* (all for Thames TV), *Danube Blues* (Channel 4). Film credits: *Nothing but the Night* (Rank/Hammer), *Dracula* (Warner Bros/EMI/Hammer), *Lonely Lady* (Universal), *Countess Dracula* (Rank/Hammer), *Doomwatch* (Rank), *The Devil Within Her* (Rank), *Welcome to Blood City* (EMI), *Hands of the Ripper* (Rank/Hammer).

John Schlesinger, CBE

Film, TV, theatre and opera director. Acted in student plays at Oxford and played character parts in the fifties before joining the BBC as a director. In 1961, he won first prize at the Venice Film Festival for *Terminus*, a documentary about London's Waterloo Station. Credits include: *A Kind of Loving* (1962), *Billy Liar* (1963), *Darling* (1965), *Far from the Madding Crowd* (1967), *Midnight Cowboy* (1969, Academy awards for Best Picture and Best Director), *Sunday Bloody Sunday* (1972), *Visions of Eight* (1973), *The Day of the Locust* (1975), *Marathon Man* (1976), *Yanks* (1979),

Honky Tonk Freeway (1981), *The Falcon and the Snowman* (1985), *The Believers* (1987), *Madame Sousatzka* (1988), *Pacific Heights* (1990), *The Innocent* (1993), *Eye for an Eye* (1995). TV credits: *An Englishman Abroad* (1983), *A Question of Attribution* (1991), *The Lost Language of Cranes* (1991), *Cold Comfort Farm* (1995). Opera credits include: *Un Ballo in Maschera* (Salzburg Festival).

Ridley Scott

Film director. A highly successful director of commercials, where he learned his craft. Film credits (mostly American) include: *The Duellists* (1978), *Alien* (1979), *Blade Runner* (1981), *Legend* (1985), *Someone to Watch Over Me* (1987), *Black Rain* (1989), *Thelma and Louise* (1991), *1492: Conquest of Paradise* (1992), *White Squall* (1996).

Ian Sellar

Film and TV director and writer. Started as a runner on Bill Douglas's film *My Childhood* and then as Assistant Director on *My Ain Folk*. Graduate of the National Film and Television School. Film directing and screenplay credits include: *Over Germany* (Channel 4/ZDF), *Albert's Memorial* (1985), *Venus Peter* (1989, Official Selection, Cannes, Best Film, Atlantic Film Festival, Special Jury Prize, Belfort), *Prague* (Official Selection, Cannes and Tokyo, Writer's Prize, Atlantic Film Festival). TV credits: *Why East Grinstead?* (Zed Productions/Channel 4).

Caroline Smith

Theatre and radio director. Associate Director Wolsey Theatre, Ipswich 1994–97. Credits include: *An Enemy of the People* (Nottingham Playhouse), *Jim*

Davis (BBC Radio, Classic Serial), *Julius Caesar* (Regent's Park Open Air Theatre), *The Price* (Stephen Joseph Theatre, Scarborough), *Bedroom Farce* (tour), *Having a Ball* (tour), *Steel Magnolias* (Wolsey Theatre, Ipswich), *Indigo Mill* (Polka), *Watership Down* (Regent's Park).

Peter Smith

Film and TV director. TV credits include: *Writing on the Wall* (Littlebird Productions/BBC), *Touch of Frost* (Yorkshire TV), *A Perfect Spy* (BBC), *Bergerac* (BBC), *Shoestring* (BBC), *Resnick II* (Deco Films/BBC), *Children of the Dragon* (Xanadu Productions/ Zenith), *Testimony of a Child* (BBC), *Loving Hazel* (BBC), *The True Bride* (NBC), *A Perfect Spy* (BBC), *Between the Lines* (Island World/BBC), *Seaforth* (Initial Films/BBC), *The Price* (RTE/Channel 4), *The Intercessor* (Granada), *Mr Right – Love Story* (BBC), *Bread or Blood* (BBC). Film credits: *Murder East, Murder West, No Surrender* (Dumbarton Films; Critics Prize, Toronto Film Festival), *A Private Enterprise* (British Film Institute).

Max Stafford-Clark

Theatre director. Former Artistic Director of the English Stage Company at the Royal Court Theatre. Has worked at the Traverse Theatre in Edinburgh and was a founder member of the Joint Stock Theatre Group. Out of the Joint Stock adaptation of William Hinton's classic about the revolution in China, *Fanshen*, emerged the concept of a company that was run by all its constituents. Successful productions at the Royal Court included Caryl Churchill's *Top Girls* and *Serious Money*, *The Recruiting Officer* and Timberlake Wertenbaker's *Our Country's Good*. Stafford-Clark left the Court in 1993 and founded the Out of Joint Theatre Company in partnership with producer Sonia Friedman, with the aim of championing the work of contemporary writers. Out of Joint credits include: *Shopping and Fucking* by Mark Ravenhill and *Blue Heart* by Caryl Churchill.

Richard Standeven

TV director. Credits include: *Brookside* (Mersey TV/Channel 4), *Clem* (HTV/Channel 4), *Hard Cases* (Central), *Bergerac* (BBC), *The Bill* (Thames), *Paradise Club* (Zenith), *Spender* (BBC), *Minder* (Euston Films), *House of Eliott* (BBC), *Medics* (Granada), *Kinsey* (BBC), *Frank Stubbs Promotes* (Noel Gay/Carlton), *Between the Lines* (BBC/Island World Productions), *Band of Gold* (Granada), *Out of the Blue* (BBC), *Ballykissangel* (World Productions/ BBC), *Dalziel and Pascoe* (Portobello Productions/BBC), *Cracker: White Ghost* (Granada), *Bliss* (Abbey Films/Carlton), *Falling for a Dancer* (Channel 4).

Alan Strachan

First worked as an assistant stage manager at the Old Byre Theatre in St Andrews and then as Assistant Director to Jonathan Miller on *The Tempest* at the Mermaid Theatre in 1970. Remained at the Mermaid for five years, latterly as Associate Director. Productions included: *Old Boys, Misalliance, John Bull's Other Island, Cowardy Custard* (also co-devised). Has directed over 20 West End productions including *A Family and a Fortune* (with Alec Guinness), *Confusions* and *Just Between Ourselves* (both by Alan Ayckbourn). Artistic Director of the Greenwich Theatre

1979–88 where he directed over 25 productions including: *The Dining Room, The Perfect Party, Private Lives, A Streetcar Named Desire*. Other credits include: *Noel and Gertie* (with Patricia Hodge and Simon Cadell), *Re-Joyce* (Maureen Lipman), Alan Ayckbourn's *How the Other Half Loves, Taking Steps* and *Man of the Moment*, Rattigan's *The Deep Blue Sea* (with Penelope Keith). Artistic Director of the Theatre of Comedy 1991–97. London productions include: John Guare's *Six Degrees of Separation* (Royal Court/Comedy Theatre), *June Moon* (Hampstead Theatre/Vaudeville), *Hay Fever* (Albery Theatre, with Maria Aitken), *The Prime of Miss Jean Brodie* (Shaftesbury Theatre), *Loot* (Bromley/West Yorkshire Playhouse), *Hay Fever* (Copenhagen/Amsterdam), *Live and Kidding* (Duchess Theatre), *Mrs Warren's Profession* (tour), *All Things Considered* (Stephen Joseph Theatre, Scarborough/Hampstead Theatre).

Charles Sturridge

TV, film and theatre director. TV credits include: *Brideshead Revisited* (Granada, 1981), *Soft Targets* (BBC, 1982), *A Story Short – The Storyteller, A Foreign Field* (BBC, 1992), *Gulliver's Travels* (Henson/Hallmark/NBC, 1996), *Hard Times, The Seagull* (with Vanessa Redgrave, Jonathan Pryce, Natasha Richardson and John Lynch), *Buffalo Soldiers* (Channel 4). Film credits: *Runners* (1983), *Aria* (1987), *Handful of Dust* (1988), *Where Angels Fear to Tread* (1990). Directed *The Seagull* at the Queen's Theatre in London.

Jeremy Summers

Film and TV director. Credits include: *Tenko* (BBC), *Hannay* (Thames), *Strangers and Brothers* (BBC), *Big Deal*

(BBC), *All Creatures Great and Small* (BBC), *Howard's Way* (BBC), *The Bill* (Thames), *Truckers* (BBC), *Emmerdale* (Yorkshire TV), *Coronation Street* (Granada), *Brookside* (Mersey TV/Channel 4).

Janet Suzman

South African-born theatre and TV director and actress. In 1987, directed the first black *Othello* in South Africa (Market Theatre) and also directed the film for Channel 4. Other directing credits include: *A Dream of People* (Royal Shakespeare Company), *No Flies on Mr Hunter, Death of a Salesman, The Deep Blue Sea* (all for Theatr Clwyd), *The Good Woman of Sharpeville* (Market Theatre, Johannesburg/Hackney Empire, London), *The Cherry Orchard* (Birmingham Rep).

Polly Teale

Associate Director of Shared Experience Theatre Company. Credits for the company include: *Jane Eyre, Desire Under the Elms, War and Peace* and *Mill on the Floss* (both co-directed with Nancy Meckler). Other credits include: *Miss Julie* (Young Vic), *Babies* and *Uganda* (Royal Court), *A Taste of Honey* (English Touring Theatre), *Somewhere* (Cottesloe Theatre), *Waiting at the Water's Edge* (Bush Theatre), *What is Seized* (Drill Hall), *Ladies in the Lift* (Soho Poly), *Vows* and *On Air* (Scarlet Theatre), *Now You See Me* (Young Vic Studio). Writing credits: *Afters* (BBC Screen on Two) and *Fallen* (Traverse Theatre, Edinburgh/Drill Hall).

David Thacker

Theatre and television director. Began work as a stage manager at York Theatre Royal, where he became

Assistant Director in 1975. In 1976, he was awarded an Arts Council assistant director's bursary and went to the Chester Gateway Theatre. In 1978, he set up Rolling Stock Theatre Company in Crewe, which specialised in young people's and community theatre. In 1979, he became Arts Council Assistant Director at the Duke's, Lancaster, in 1980 becoming Director there. Appointed Director of the Young Vic in 1984 where, among many successful productions, he became Arthur Miller's chosen director for his plays, including world premières. Theatre credits include: *Othello; The Jail Diary of Albie Sachs; Stags and Hens; Macbeth; Hamlet; Measure for Measure; The Enemies Within; The Crucible; Romeo and Juliet; A Midsummer Night's Dream; Some Kind of Hero; Julius Caesar; Ghosts* (with Vanessa Redgrave); *A Touch of the Poet* (with Timothy Dalton and Vanessa Redgrave); *An Enemy of the People; Pericles* (RSC; Olivier Award 'Director of the Year' 1990); *Two Gentlemen of Verona; The Merchant of Venice; The Merry Wives of Windsor; The Last Yankee* (Young Vic/Duke of York's); *Ghosts* (Wyndham's Theatre/National Theatre of Norway). TV credits: *Death of a Salesman; A Doll's House; Measure for Measure*.

Bob Tomson

Theatre and television director, actor, stage and television writer. Was Artistic Director of the Theatr Powys touring company and the Queen's Theatre, Hornchurch. Was Resident Director at the Liverpool Everyman and Manchester Contact Theatre. Has directed for the Bristol Old Vic, Liverpool Playhouse, Windsor Theatre Royal, Churchill Theatre in Bromley. Productions include: *Having a Ball, Funny Peculiar, Jesus Christ Superstar,* *Oliver!, James and the Giant Peach, West Side Story, One Careful Owner, Hair, Grease,* the long-running West End musical, *Blood Brothers* (Phoenix; also Australia, New Zealand, Canada and USA; nominated for 6 Tony awards), *On the Piste* (Garrick Theatre), *One Fine Day* (Albery Theatre), *Scrooge* (Dominion Theatre; also Australia and Japan; Best Director awards), *A Christmas Carol* (Japan; Patrick Stewart's one-man version), and Karoline Leach's *The Mysterious Mr Love* (Comedy Theatre). TV credits: *Brookside* (Channel 4).

David Tucker

Film, theatre and TV director. Credits include: *Honeymoon* (BBC Play for Today), *The Holy Experiment* (BBC Play of the Month), *A Very Peculiar Practice* (BBC), *Behaving Badly* and *The Gravy Train* (both Channel 4), *Stanley and the Women* (Central), *A Very Polish Practice* (BBC), *Under the Hammer* (Meridian), *Bramwell* (Carlton).

Benjamin Twist

Artistic Director of the Contact Theatre, Manchester since 1995. Credits include: *Herringbone* (Traverse Theatre/King's Head), *Great Expectations* (Lyric Theatre, Belfast), *Noises Off* (Royal Lyceum, Edinburgh). Productions for Contact include: *Cinderella* and *Criminals in Love*.

Paul Unwin

Film, theatre and TV director and writer. Artistic Director of the Bristol Express Theatre Company (1980–81), Artistic Director of the Bristol Old Vic (1984–91). Credits for the latter company include: *Hamlet, Othello, The Man Who Had All the Luck* (also Young

Vic), *In the Ruins* (also Royal Court), *The Misanthrope* (also National Theatre). TV credits: *The Bill* (Thames), *EastEnders* (BBC), *Claire de Lune, Dirty Old Town* and *The Bare Necessities* (all for Granada), *Bramwell* (Carlton). Film credits include: *Crucible of Fools* (Storm/British Screen), *The Art of Success* (Sarah Radclyffe Productions). Oscar nomination for Best Live Action Short Film, and awarded Jury Prize at the Cannes Film Festival and Valladolid Film Festival for *Syrup*.

Charles Vance

Theatre director and producing manager, writer and publisher. With his wife, Charles Vance runs the weekly repertory theatre at the Manor Pavilion in Sidmouth; is Editor of *Amateur Stage* magazine and publisher of *The Amateur Theatre Yearbook*. Began his career as an actor at the Gaiety Theatre, Dublin, and subsequently played leading roles in numerous national tours of the UK. Directed his first production – *The Glass Menagerie* – at the Arts Theatre, Cambridge in 1960. His many producing and directing credits include: *Jane Eyre* (also adapted), *Lettice and Lovage* (with Hinge and Bracket), *Brideshead Revisited* (with Richard Todd), *My Cousin Rachel, Witness for the Prosecution, Time and Time Again, Gaslight, Spider's Web*.

Mike Vardy

Film and TV director. Credits include: *Let's Run Away to Africa* (Yorkshire TV), *Heart Attack Hotel, Time and the Conways, A Still Small Shout, Thunder Rock, Bon Voyage, Claws* (all BBC), *The One Game* (Central), *Capital City* and *Minder* (both for Euston Films), *London's Burning* (LWT), *Taggart: Ring of Deceit* and *Forbidden Fruit* (STV), *Stay Lucky* (Yorkshire TV), *House of Cards: The Final Cut* (BBC), *The Ruth Rendell Mysteries* (Blue Heaven Productions).

Jatinder Verma

Director of Tara Arts. Has written or adapted and directed many stage productions for Tara Arts, which he established in 1976. Productions range from those exploring contemporary Asian issues in Britain to European and Indian classics. Credits include: *A Midsummer Night's Dream* (Lyric Hammersmith/Tara Arts co-production; adapted and directed), *Cyrano de Bergerac* (Royal National Theatre and tour), *The Bourgeois Gentilhomme* (Tara Arts tour), *Troilus and Cressida* (Contact Theatre/Tara Arts tour), *Heer Ranjha* (Theatre Royal Stratford East and tour; adapted and directed), *The Little Clay Cart* (Royal National Theatre, adapted and directed), *Oedipus Rex* (Tara Arts, adapted and directed), *Tartuffe* (Royal National Theatre; adapted and directed), *The Government Inspector* (Tara Arts; adapted and directed). In 1990, won the *Time Out*/01 Special award 'For his outstanding contribution through both Tara Arts and the National Theatre to the London theatre scene and the bonding of British, European and Asian cultures'.

Glen Walford

Theatre director. Founding Artistic Director of the London Bubble Theatre Company (1972–79). Artistic Director of the Liverpool Everyman (1983–89). For that company, her credits included: *Tosca, Hamlet* and *The Winter's Tale*. Artistic Director of the Chung-Ying Company, Hong Kong (1979–82). Previous theatre work includes: *Return to the Forbidden Planet* (Tricycle Theatre,

London), *Archangels Don't Play Pinball* (Theatre Royal, Bristol), *Much Ado About Nothing* (Rhyming Theatre Company, Tokyo), *Animal Farm* (tour of Malaysia), *Prometheus* (Epidaurus Festival, Greece), *Comedy of Errors* (English Shakespeare Company), *Lettice and Lovage* (Bill Kenwright Productions tour).

Matthew Warchus

Theatre and opera director. On leaving Bristol University, he founded the New Classical Theatre Company, for which he directed *Sejanus: His Fall* at the Edinburgh Festival. As Associate Director of the West Yorkshire Playhouse, directed *Life is a Dream; Who's Afraid of Virginia Woolf, Fiddler on the Roof, The Plough and the Stars, Death of a Salesman, Betrayal, True West, Peter Pan*. Won the Shakespeare's Globe Most Promising Newcomer award for *Much Ado About Nothing* (Queen's Theatre), a TMA award for *Peter Pan* and the *Evening Standard* Best Director award for his Royal Shakespeare Company production of *Henry V* and Royal National Theatre production of *Volpone*. Other credits include: *Master Harold and the Boys* (Bristol Old Vic), *The Suicide* and *Coriolanus* (National Youth Theatre), *The Life of Stuff* and *True West* (Donmar Warehouse), *The Devil is an Ass* and *Hamlet* (Royal Shakespeare Company), *Art* (Wyndham's Theatre). Opera credits include: *Troilus and Cressida* (Opera North), *The Rake's Progress* and *The Magic Flute* (Welsh National Opera), *Falstaff* (Opera North/English National Opera).

Deborah Warner

Theatre and opera director. Trained as a stage manager at the Central School of Speech and Drama and worked at the Orange Tree and New End theatres and as an administrator for Steven Berkoff's London Theatre Group. In 1980, she decided to form her own theatre company to see if she could direct, and called it 'Kick' to symbolise energy. Kick Theatre quickly gained an international reputation for its highly innovative Shakespearean productions – *The Tempest, Measure for Measure, Hamlet, King Lear* and *Coriolanus* – many of which toured worldwide and three of which won Fringe Firsts at the Edinburgh Festival. Other productions with Kick were *The Good Person of Szechwan* and *Woyzeck*. In 1986, she received the *Time Out* award for Director of the Year and the next year was invited to Bangladesh to direct Bengali actors in a new version of *The Tempest*. Other theatre credits include: *Electra, King John* and *Titus Andronicus* for the Royal Shakespeare Company, *The Good Person of Szechwan, King Lear* and *Richard II* (with Fiona Shaw in the title role) for the Royal National Theatre, of which she is an Associate Director, *Hedda Gabler* (Abbey Theatre, Dublin/Playhouse, London), *Coriolanus* (Salzburg Festival), *Footfalls* (Garrick Theatre). Opera credits include: *Don Giovanni* (Glyndebourne Festival Opera), *Woyzeck* (Opera North), *The Turn of the Screw* (Royal Opera House). TV credits: *The Wasteland* (Illuminations/BBC), *Don Giovanni* (Channel 4), *Hedda Gabler* (BBC). She has been awarded the Chevalier de l'Ordre des Arts by the French government and the *Evening Standard* award for Best Director.

Stephen Whittaker

Started out as an actor, forming Kickshaw in 1979 to stage new plays and run workshops. Having made several training videos, his first television production was Anthony Minghella's *What If It's Raining* for Channel 4. Credits include: *Lovebirds* (BBC), *Eurocops – Hunting the Squirrel* (Channel 4), *Portrait of a Marriage* (BBC/WGBH; won Best Drama Serial and Best Overall Drama at the Banff TV Festival in 1972 and 4 BAFTA Craft awards); *Poirot – Death in the Clouds* (LWT), *Inspector Morse* (BBC/Zenith), *Closing Numbers* (Arden Films/Channel 4; Special Jury Prize at Monte Carlo TV Festival, 1995), Jimmy McGovern's *Hearts and Minds* (Witzend/Channel 4; Best Overall European Fiction Prize, Prix Europa and Royal Television Society's award for Best Drama Serial, 1996), *Killing Me Softly* (BBC, 1995), *Stone Cold* (BBC 1996), *Stone Scissors Paper* (BBC/Diverse Productions), *Tangier Cop* (Le Sabre Productions/Arte, 1997).

Clifford Williams

Theatre and opera director and writer. An Associate Director of the Royal Shakespeare Company since 1962; productions for the RSC include: *The Comedy of Errors, The Representative, The Jew of Malta, Dr Faustus, Wild Oats*. Has directed for the national theatres of Yugoslavia, Bulgaria, Mexico, Spain, as well as in Japan, France, Denmark, the USA, Sweden, Canada, Australia and Germany. Credits include: *As You Like It* and *Back to Methuselah* (both for the National Theatre), *Hochhuth's Soldiers* (in London and New York), *Sleuth* (London, Paris and New York), *Oh! Calcutta!* (London and Paris), Pirandello's *Henry IV* (London and New York), *The Importance of Being Earnest* (Royal Theatre, Copenhagen), *Breaking the Code* (with Derek Jacobi, London and New York), *Richard III* (with Derek Jacobi), *Legends* (with

Carol Channing and Mary Martin), *Arsenic and Old Lace* (Theatre Royal, Windsor), *Harvey* (Shaftesbury Theatre, London). Opera credits include: *The Flying Dutchman, Venus and Adonis, Dido and Aeneas*. Has made a film of Shaw's *Man and Superman* for Danish Television.

Richard Wilson, OBE

Theatre and TV director and actor. Directing credits include: *Simply Disconnected* (Chichester), *The Lodger* (Hampstead Theatre/Royal Exchange, Manchester), *Women Laughing* (Royal Exchange/Royal Court), *Imagine Drowning* (Hampstead), *Prin* (Lyric Hammersmith/Lyric, Shaftesbury Avenue), *A Wholly Healthy Glasgow* (Royal Exchange/Royal Court), *An Inspector Calls* (Royal Exchange), *God's Second in Command* (Royal Court Theatre Upstairs), *Staircase* (Westcliff), *President Wilson in Paris* and *Lenz* (both for Hampstead), *Other Worlds* and *Heaven and Hell* (both Royal Court), *Commitments* (Bush Theatre), *Teeth 'n' Smiles* (Oxford Playhouse), *Disabled* (Stables Theatre). TV directing credits: *Changing Step* (BBC Scotland), *A Wholly Healthy Glasgow, Under the Hammer, Remainder Man, Commitments* (all for BBC).

Michael Winner

Film director. Began making films for the BBC in the mid-fifties. Often works in Hollywood where he has been responsible for several Charles Bronson blockbusters. Credits include: *Play it Cool* (1962), *The Jokers* (1966), *I'll Never Forget What's 'is Name* (1967), *The Games* (1969), *Hannibal Brooks* (1969), *Lawman* (1970), *The Night Comers* (1971), *Chato's Land* (1972), *Scorpio* (1972), *The Mechanic* (1972), *Death Wish*

(1974), *The Sentinel* (1977), *The Big Sleep* (1978), *Firepower* (1979), *Death Wish II* (1981), *The Wicked Lady* (1983), *Scream for Help* (1984), *Death Wish III* (1985), *Appointment with Death* (1987), *A Chorus of Disapproval* (1989), *Bullseye* (1991), *Dirty Weekend* (1993), *Parting Shot* (1997).

Herbert Wise

Film, TV, theatre and opera director. Credits include: *I Claudius, Skokie, Reunion in Fairborough, Strange Interlude, The Woman in Black, The Speaker of Mandarin, Inspector Morse, The Strawberry Tree, Breaking the Code.*

Peter Wood

Theatre, opera, film and TV director. In the West End, he has directed *No Laughing Matter, The Wit to Woo, The Iceman Cometh, The Birthday Party, Who's Your Father?, Mary Stuart, Five Finger Exercise, The Private Ear* and *The Public Eye, Loot, Incident at Vichy, The Prime of Miss Jean Brodie, White Liars/Black Comedy, Dear Love, Night and Day, Windy City, The Real Thing, Wildfire.* For the Royal Shakespeare Company, he has directed *The Devils, Hamlet, The Beggar's Opera, Travesties.* Wood is an Associate Director of the National Theatre; productions there include: *The Master Builder, Love for Love, Jumpers, The Guardsman, The Double Dealer, Undiscovered Country, The Provok'd Wife, On the Razzle, The Rivals, Rough Crossing, Dalliance, Threepenny Opera, The America Clock.* Directed Tom Stoppard's *Hapgood* at the Aldwych. Opera credits include: *Don Giovanni* at the Royal Opera House, and *Macbeth* and *Otello* at the Vienna State Opera.

Peter Yates

Film and theatre director. Trained at RADA and worked as an actor and stage manager before directing his first plays – *An American Dream* and *The Death of Bessie Smith* at the Royal Court. In New York, he directed *Passing Games* at the American Place theatre and, in 1985, *Interpreters* at the Queen's Theatre, London. For TV, he directed episodes of *Danger Man, The Saint* and other series. Feature films include: *Summer Holiday* (1962), *One-Way Pendulum* (1965), *Bullitt* (1968), *The Friends of Eddie Coyle* (1972; Academy award nominations), *Krull* (1981/2), *Breaking Away* (1979), *The Dresser* (1983/4; Academy award nominations), *Eleni* (1984/5), *Suspect* (1987), *The Innocent Man* (1989), *The Year of the Comet* (1991), *Room Mates* (1993), *The Run of the Country* (1994).

Glossary

Actor/Actress
Person who performs a role.

Agent
Person who represents actors, setting up interviews, castings, auditions, negotiating fees and acting as a go-between to actors and managements.

Agitprop
Political theatre which originated in Russia at the time of the Revolution. From the words *agitation* and *propaganda*.

Angel
Person who provides financial backing for commercial theatre ventures. Can be exceedingly rich, can be exceedingly poor.

Apron
Front part of stage, projecting past the proscenium arch, covering the orchestra pit.

Assistant floor manager (AFM)
The television counterpart of the ASM (*see below*).

Assistant stage manager (ASM)
Third in the stage-management staff pecking order. Within any one production they could find themselves helping all backstage departments – from LX to Wardrobe. Usually respon-

sible for making and acquiring props. In some companies they are expected to understudy.

Audition
The opportunity for the actor to demonstrate his/her worth. Relax and try to enjoy it; those who are auditioning you want you to do well.

Auditorium
Where the audience sits.

Availability check (AV check)
Interest shown from a theatre, production company or casting director, checking to see if an actor might be free for a proposed production. Don't get too excited – this comes before the audition.

Backcloth
A cloth at the back of the stage which is hung from the flies. Mostly used in ballets, operas and pantomimes. (*See also* **Cyclorama**.)

Bars
Length of metal tube, suspended above the stage, from which lanterns are hung.

Beginners
The call given 5 minutes before curtain up.

Blacklight
Ultraviolet lighting, used for special effects, mainly in pantomimes. (*See* **Transformation**)

Blocking
The physical moves an actor and/or director decide upon in rehearsal, which are recorded in the prompt copy.

(The) Book
The text of the play. The prompt copy is sometimes referred to as the Book.

Box set
Representation on stage of a room, created by flats.

Breakdown
Brief description of characters in a film, television drama or advert. Is sometimes used for a new stage play.

Business
An unscripted physical action or routine within a play. Usually comic and much loved in pantomime and farce.

(To) Busk
To perform in a state of total or partial unreadiness.

Call
The time when the actor is required to be at rehearsals, the theatre, on set or at a television studio.

Cast
Collective term for actors in a production.

(To) Cast
To give an actor a part in a production.

Casting director
Person who suggests actors for plays, films, dramas and commercials. Although mainly involved with the mechanical media, theatre companies are using them more and more. Do not underestimate their importance. (*See* Casting Directors page 105)

Centre stage
The central point on stage. Most actors like to stand on this spot as this is the strongest point on stage – everyone can see you.

Check the gate
This is said at the end of every accepted take. The cameraman looks at the gate of the camera (an opening situated behind the lens through which the film runs) to make sure there's no debris, etc. that could ruin an otherwise perfect scene. No one can be cleared until the gate has been checked.

Chorus
A group of actors, most commonly used in Greek drama, who observe and comment (often in unison) on the action of the play.

Cleared
When you have been cleared by a floor manager or assistant director, you are free to leave the set and either get ready for your next scene or go home.

Close-up
A head and shoulders shot in film or television.

Cloths
The canvas backdrops used in theatres.

Commedia dell'arte
A style of theatre which originated in Italy and was most prominent in the sixteenth century. The play was improvised, from a storyline decided upon by the director of the company and incorporated acrobatics, music and stylised movements. Most of the male actors wore leather half-masks and the stock characters were Arlecchino, Columbina, Pulcinello, Pantaloni and young, starry-eyed lovers.

Company
Collective term for everyone working artistically and technically on a production.

Company stage manager (CSM)
See **Stage manager**.

Continuity
Usually kept in check by the PA. As films are shot out of sequence, it is vital that records are kept of costumes, hair, who was holding what and in what hand, etc., so that no join can be seen between one take and the next, even though they might have been shot days or weeks apart.

Cooperative management
An agency run by a group of actors.

Corporate theatre
This is fast becoming big business and involves using actors in the workplace; from livening up boring conferences, to educative training, to role-playing in a one-to-one interview situation.

(To) Corpse
An unrehearsed fit of giggles in performance which can spread to fellow actors and sometimes leads to mild hysteria.

Costume
The clothes an actor wears on stage or on set. For many actors, the costume can be the key to a character.

Crew
Collective term for the technical people who work on a production.

Critic
Reviewer. It is argued that they have the power to make or break a production.

Cue
A line or action on or after which the actor enters a scene or speaks a line.

Curtain (call)
Line-up of the cast at the end of a performance.

Cut
(a) Instruction from director to camera-

man during or at the end of recording a scene to stop filming.
(b) To unintentionally jump from one line to another and in doing so having to leave out one's own and fellow actors' lines.
(c) To remove speeches, scenes or parts of scenes from a script during rehearsals in the hope of making the play shorter, better or more understandable.

Cutaway
Close-up of actor recorded for a scene already in the can which can be put into the scene during editing.

Cyclorama (cyc.)
Curved wall or cloth at the rear of the stage, used for outside scenes. The curve, when lit, gives depth.

Deputy stage manager (DSM)
Second-in-command in the stage-management team. Sits next to the director in the rehearsal room noting the blocking and passing on the requirements that arise from rehearsals to the relevant theatre departments. Is responsible for running the show in the theatre.

Designer
Person responsible for designing sets and costumes.

Deus ex machina
Used in classical drama to wind up the action of the play. A character descends from the flies – literally, 'God from the machine'.

Director
Person in overall artistic and technical control of a production.

Downstage
The area of stage nearest the audience, the term resulting from the rake of proscenium theatre stages.

Dramatis personae
The characters in a play.

Dress
Costume. Also to adorn the set with objects relevant to the design – dress the set.

Dresser
Person who helps the actor get dressed, change costumes, quick-change. Less in theatre but still very much in film and television.

Dressing room
The actors' changing room.

Dress rehearsal
Final run(s) of the play in full costume, as per a public performance.

(To) Dry
The dreaded moment when the lines fail to come to mind.

Editor
Person who puts filmed or taped footage in sequence. Works closely with the director.

Entrance
The act of coming on to the stage.

Equity
The actors' union.

Equity deputy
Actor who represents Equity within each production. Voted in by all those in the production and acts as spokesperson on all union matters.

Exit/Exeunt
The act of leaving the stage.

Extra
Person employed in film and television to make up the crowd scenes. Has no lines and is only ever directed as part of a group.

Farce
High-speed comedy of a broad style. The plot often revolves around mistaken identity or people in the wrong place at the wrong time.

First night
The first time a play is performed before the public.

Fit-up
The building of the set and positioning of lights in readiness for the production.

Five-minute call
Given 10 minutes before curtain up.

Flat
A tall, narrow, rectangular frame over which canvas is stretched – nowadays plywood is often used instead of canvas – used to create a set.

Flies
The area above the stage from which scenery can be raised or lowered (flown).

Floats
A row of lights set at the downstage edge of the stage. More likely to be used in ballet or opera these days.

Floor manager
Person who is in charge of all the happenings on the television studio floor. Is the mouthpiece of the director who, during recording, is in the control gallery.

(To) Fluff
To stumble over your lines. (It can happen to the best of actors.)

Forestage
The area of stage which extends into the auditorium from the front of the proscenium arch. Also known as the apron.

Fringe theatre
Alternative to mainstream theatre (*see* Fringe and Alternative Theatre page 195).

Front of house
The areas available to the audience such as the foyer, auditorium, box office, bar, etc.

Get in/get out
The moving in and out of the set, props and costumes of a production.

Green room
A room backstage for theatre workers to relax in together.

Grid
The flying bars above the stage from which lights and scenery are hung.

Half-hour call (The half)
The time all the actors must be in the theatre for the performance – 35 minutes before curtain up.

Improvisation
To make up as one goes along. Successfully used by Mike Leigh in developing his theatre and film scripts. Also much employed in drama training.

Iron
The safety curtain.

ITC
Independent Theatre Council (*see entry under* Organisations, Associations and Societies, page 339).

Kitchen-sink drama
A term coined to describe John Osborne's *Look Back in Anger* in the fifties, a play which spawned a whole generation of writers of working-class drama – Arnold Wesker, Shelagh Delaney, John Arden, for example.

LX
Anything concerning the use of electricity within the theatre – e.g. lighting and sound.

Lanterns
Theatre lights.

Lighting designer
Person who designs the lighting states.

Lines
The words spoken by an actor – literally, the lines of scripts.

Low-budget
Euphemism for no wages. Low-budget films and television are made by all concerned giving their time and skills for free, on the promise of stardom and/or money should the production do well. Don't hold your breath.

Make-up
Stage make-up these days no longer relies on sticks of greasepaint, the old favourites being numbers 5 and 9, as modern lighting allows for use of subtler pancakes and powder. In films and television, a make-up artist is always used.

Masks
Originating in Greek drama and often used in drama training, there are still a few specialist companies that use masks.

Melodrama
A popular form of nineteenth-century moral drama consisting of extreme dramatic situations featuring heroes and villains.

The Method
A style of acting based on Stanislavski's work by which the actor discovers the truth of a role. As taught at the Actors' Studio in New York, with the emphasis on emotional recall, the Method came to resemble a form of therapy with introspection taking over.

Music hall
Variety entertainment which had its heyday in the mid- to late nineteenth century, continuing up to the Second World War. Famous names include

Marie Lloyd, Harry Lauder, Vesta Tilley, Dan Leno and George Robey.

Off
Anything that is, or happens, off-stage.

(To be) off
To be late for one's entrance.

Offer
If you receive an offer, congratulations – you've got a job!

Opposite prompt (OP)
Stage right – opposite side to the prompt corner.

PA
Production assistant on films and television. Theirs is a complicated and crucial job, looking after timings of scenes, continuity, noting which takes were the accepted ones, etc.

Pantomime
The term was originally used for a commedia dell'arte harlequinade. Once it was performed all year round, now it's a Christmas tradition. Although cross-dressing on stage goes back to the sixteenth century, panto was responsible for giving us the Dame – a man playing a woman, and the Principal Boy – a woman playing a man.

Pass door
Connecting door between the auditorium and backstage.

PCR
Professional Casting Report (*see* Publications and Services, page 371).

Pencil
A casting director thinks that they might like to use you for a film, television drama or commercial but they are not in a position to make you an offer (*see above*) as the director has yet to make up his mind. By pencilling you, they let you know their interest and

make you duty-bound to inform them if something else turns up that might clash with the dates for which you have been pencilled. Don't celebrate until the pencil has turned into an offer!

Pit
The orchestra pit, situated at the front of the stage but lower than the auditorium. When not in use, it can be covered over, thus creating the apron or forestage.

Post-production
The things that have to be done once a film or television production has been recorded, i.e. editing, post-synching, publicity, distribution, etc.

Post-synch
In some scenes in films it is not always possible to record sound while the action is being recorded. The actors concerned post-synch their dialogue in a sound studio at a later date by watching sections of the scenes being played over and over again and synchronising their lines to the movement of their lips upon the screen.

Press night
The performance which the critics are invited to. This used to be the first night but now directors let the play run for a week or two before inviting the press.

Pre-production
The things that have to be done before a film or television drama can be made, i.e. casting, set building, location finding, equipment hiring, etc.

Preview
Performing the play to the public before it is officially opened. Preview tickets are usually cheaper.

Principal Boy
See **Pantomime**.

Producer
Person who sets up productions, be they films, television dramas or commercial theatre. Responsible for finding the money.

Production
Play, film or television drama that has been, is being or will be made.

Prologue
An introduction to the play, first used in Greek drama. In Elizabethan drama, the character was sometimes referred to as Chorus.

Promenade production
Where the audience literally follows the action of the play by moving with the actors around the performance area. Used to great effect by director Bill Bryden with *The Passion* at the Cottesloe Theatre and, more recently, with *The Ship* in Glasgow.

Prompt book/Copy
Copy of the script in which all moves and direction, lighting and sound cues are noted. This copy is used to run the show.

Prompt corner/Side
Stage left, the prompt corner being located in the wings. This is the point from which the show is usually run.

Prompter
Person who follows the script during the performance and supplies the lines to actors who dry. Now usually part of the DSM's job though increasingly actors are left to their own devising – *see* **Improvisation**.

Properties (props)
All objects used by the actors in performance or placed on stage to dress the set.

Proscenium arch (pros)
Permanent or semi-permanent struc-

ture creating a picture-frame effect to the stage.

Quarter-hour call (The quarter)
Given 20 minutes before curtain up.

Rake
The slope of the stage, running from the front up to the back wall, from which the terms upstage and downstage originate.

Read-through
The first action of the rehearsal process. The company reads the play together for the first time. Sometimes happens with film and television dramas.

Recall
After you have auditioned, the director might want to see you again, and again. Recalls are liked more by the director than the actor.

Rehearsal
Where the play is explored and developed – usually about three weeks for rep productions but with companies that have more money, rehearsals can last from to six to eight weeks. Films and television tend to rehearse each scene immediately before recording it.

Rep
Repertory theatre, so called because the company would have a repertoire of plays. Since the last war, rep has come to mean regional theatre – now, sadly, becoming less and less.

Residuals
Repeat fees – monies paid on material recorded for television that is shown a second or third time. Especially commercials.

Resting
Euphemism for being out of work. This word is never used by actors themselves but usually by those who have no knowledge of the theatre. The

phrase 'Are you resting?' is most effective when said with a smirk.

Restoration comedy
Seventeenth-century comedies of manners which flourished following the bleak years of Puritanism.

Revolve
Revolving stage.

Rostrum
A movable, rigid raised platform used on-stage.

(The) run
The run of public performances of any one production.

Runner
Person on a film set who runs errands, ferries actors to the set and fetches and carries. Often the first stepping stone to directing or producing.

Run-through
Rehearsal of a play from beginning to end without stopping.

Rushes
The unedited developed takes of scenes – usually without sound.

SBS
Script Breakdown Service (*see entry under* Publications and Services, page 371).

Scenery
The flats, cloths and drops employed to create a setting on-stage.

Set
The picture created by scenery.

(On) set
The location or studio where a camera is filming a particular scene.

(A) shoot
The recording of a film or television production.

(To) shoot
To film or record.

SOLT
Society of London Theatres (*see entry under* Organisations, Associations and Societies, page 347). Formerly known as SWET – Society of West End Theatres.

Sound effects
Usually supplied electronically, although wind machines and thunder sheets can be found in some old theatres.

The Spotlight
See entry under Publications and Services, page 372.

Stage
Although the acting area is what is commonly meant by the stage, everything at stage level – wings, prompt corner and, if there is one, the scene dock – are all technically the stage.

Stage directions
Moves and actions given to the actors by the director or playwright.

Stage door
Entrance to backstage. In the West End or large regional theatres, these are presided over by a stage doorkeeper who acts as security and takes messages.

Stage machinery
The mechanical means of changing scenery or creating effects, such as revolves and traps.

Stage manager
Person in charge of everything that happens backstage. In touring companies, is known as Company Stage Manager (CSM) and is in charge of the company in the absence of the director or management.

Strike
To remove object(s) from the stage.

Sturm und Drang
German drama from the eighteenth century. Translates as 'Storm and Stress'.

(A) Take
A scene or part of a scene that is filmed.

Technical rehearsal (tech)
The rehearsal used to smooth out technical problems such as lighting and scene changes. Usually prolonged with much stopping and starting, requiring considerable patience from all involved.

Technical SM
A stage manager who is capable of running LX.

10 x 8
Actors' photographs used for publicity or to accompany cvs. So called because the preferred size is 10 inches by 8.

Theatre-in-the-round
Where the audience encircles the acting area. Purpose-built theatres-in-the-round include the Stephen Joseph at Scarborough and the New Victoria at Newcastle under Lyme.

Theatre of the Absurd
A term used to describe the work of playwrights such as Ionesco and Beckett.

Theatre of Cruelty
Created by Antonin Artaud and taken up by later writers such as Joe Orton, this style of theatre aims to shock the audience with extremes of behaviour.

Thrust stage
Where the audience sits on three sides of the acting area leaving the stage with a back wall – Sheffield's Crucible Theatre being a fine example.

TIE
Theatre-in-Education. Companies that go into schools using drama as a teaching method. Its heyday was in the seventies and is now disappearing due to lack of funding. (*See* Theatre-In-Education (TIE) Companies, page 223)

TMA
Theatrical Management Association (*see entry under* Organisations, Associations and Societies, page 349).

Tour
Where a play travels from one theatre to another. This can be weekly or nightly where smaller companies are concerned.

Tragedy
Originated in Greece – the plays of Euripides and Sophocles being classic examples.

Transformation
A 'magical' change of scenery in pantomime, achieved by the use of lighting and gauzes.

Traps
Stage mechanics by which a character can be lowered beneath the stage or raised up to appear on-stage – popular for Demon Kings in pantomime.

Traverse stage
Where the audience sits on two sides of the acting area.

Upstage
The area of the stage furthest away from the audience.

(To) Upstage
An unwelcome trick which can be employed by actors wishing to make themselves the focus of attention in a scene. Achieved by taking a step or two upstage, thus forcing fellow actors to turn away from the audience in order to communicate with the offender. Apocryphal stories tell of competing actors ending up near the back wall in their bid to upstage each other.

Understudy
Actor who 'covers' other actors' role(s). They learn the lines and rehearse but only go on if the main actor is indisposed.

Variety
See **Music hall**.

Vaudeville
The American equivalent of music hall.

Voiceover
Where an actor's voice is used over a film, video, commercial or television programme.

Walk-down
The long, extended curtain call of a pantomime, usually set to music, with the actors sporting gorgeous costumes.

Walk-on
Person in film or television drama with no lines but who is directed by the director.

Walk-up
Term given to paying public who buy their tickets on the night without having previously booked.

Wardrobe
The department in a theatre, television or film company that supplies, makes, repairs and cleans the costumes.

Wings
The off-stage spaces either side of the acting area in a proscenium theatre.

Wrap
To finish filming for the day.

Index

A & J Management 75
Aba Daba Productions 195–6
Academy Drama School 13–14
Academy of Live and Recorded Arts
   Ltd 14–15
ACID Publications 369
ACOD Cultuur (Belgium) 337
ACT Company (France) 234
Action Space Mobile 156
Action Transport Theatre Company
   Ltd 223
Actions & Words Theatre Company 155–6
Actors Alliance 76
Actors Centre, The 329–30
Actors Direct 76
Actors File 76
Actors Institute, The *see* TAI Artists
Actors List, The 76–7
Actors Network Agency *see* ANA
Actors Touring Company 156
Actors' Benevolent Fund 329
Actors' Centre (Manchester), The *see*
   Northern Actors Centre, The
Actors' Centre North-East, The 330
Actors' Charitable Trust, The 330
Actors' Church Union 330
Actors' Exchange Ltd 76
Actorum 77
Adelphi Theatre 237
Adrian King Associates 90
Advanced Residential Theatre and
   Television Skillcentre *see* ARTTS
   International
Advancement of Film Education
   Charitable Trust *see* AFECT
AFECT 53
Age Exchange Theatre Trust 156
Agents 75–102
Agents' Association (Great Britain),
   The 331
Agreement for Performers and Stage
   Managers (small-scale theatre
   companies) 328
Aitken, Maria 377

Alan Hydes Associates 297
Albany Empire 196
Albemarle of London 143
Albery Theatre 237
Aldwych Theatre 237–8
Alexander, Bill 377
Alexandra Theatre (Birmingham) 248–9
Alfreds, Mike 377–8
Alhambra Theatre (Bradford) 249–50
Almeida Theatre Company Ltd 143
Alomo Productions 288
Alpha Personal Management 77
ALRA *see* Academy of Live and Recorded
   Arts Ltd
Alternative theatre 195–210
Alternative Theatre Company Ltd 196
Alvarez Management 77
ALW Associates 78
Amateur Stage 369
Ambassadors Theatre 238
Amber Personal Management Ltd 78
American College in London, The 53
Amiel, Jon 378
ANA 78
Ancock, Jeremy 378
Anderson, Sarah Pia 378
Anglia Television 267
Ann Fielden Casting 110
Anna Scher Theatre Ltd 30–31
Anne Henderson Casting Ltd 112
Annexe Theatre Company 157
Antelope (UK) Ltd 288
Apex Television Production and Facilities
   Ltd 288
Apollo Theatre (London) 238
Apollo Theatre (Oxford) 258
Apollo Victoria Theatre 238
Applause 369
April Young Limited 102
APT (Association of Professional Theatre
   for Children and Young People –
   incorporating ASSITEJ GB) 331
Apted, Michael 378
Arc Theatre Ensemble 223

Arden School of Theatre at City College
  Manchester 15
Arena Personal Management Ltd 78–9
Arlington Productions Limited 288
Armada Theatre Productions 144
Armstrong, Moira 378
Artist Management Group Ltd 79
Arts (BBC)
  radio 276
  television 264
Arts associations, regional 353–8
Arts Club 331
Arts councils 353–8
Arts Educational Schools London, The
  15–16, 373
Artsline 331
ARTTS International 16–17, 53
Arundel Festival 361
Ash Productions 157
Ashcroft Theatre (Croydon) 252
Asianet 272
ASSITEJ GB see APT
Associated International Management 79
Association for Business Sponsorship of
  the Arts 332
Association of British Theatre Technicians
  332
Association of Professional Theatre for
  Children and Young People see APT
Associations see Organisations, associations
  and societies
Attenborough, Lord Richard 379
Attenborough, Michael 378–9
Attic Theatre Company (London)
  Ltd 196–7
Attwood, David 379
Audiobooks 309–11
Audiosport Limited see CYP Limited
Ayckbourn, Sir Alan, CBE 379–80

Babbacombe Theatre (Torquay) 260
BAC 197
BAC Young People's Theatre 197
BAFTA see British Academy of Film and
  Television Arts
Bamford, Roger 380
Banner Theatre 157–8
Bannerman, Celia 380
Barbara Speake Stage School 31
Barking College 35, 54
Barnes, Michael 105
Barry Burnett Organisation Ltd 80
Barry Palin Associates Ltd 299
Barton, John, CBE 380
Basic/J. D. Agency & Panto People 80
Battersea Arts Centre see BAC
Bayly, Stephen 380–81

BBC 3 Counties Radio 281
BBC Asian Network 279
BBC GLR 94.9 279
BBC Midlands and East 266
BBC North 266–7
BBC Northern Ireland
  radio 277
  television 265
BBC Radio 275–8
BBC Radio Berkshire see Thames Valley
  FM
BBC Radio Bristol 279
BBC Radio Cambridgeshire 279
BBC Radio Cleveland 279
BBC Radio Collection see BBC Worldwide
  Publishing
BBC Radio Cornwall 279
BBC Radio Lancashire 279
BBC Radio Merseyside 279–80
BBC Radio Newcastle 280
BBC Radio Norfolk 280
BBC Radio Northampton 280
BBC Radio Nottingham 280
BBC Radio Scotland 277–8
BBC Radio Stoke 280
BBC Radio Suffolk 280
BBC Scotland (television) 265–6
BBC South/BBC West/BBC South-
  West/BBC South-East 267
BBC Southern Counties Radio 280
BBC Television 263–5
  Equity agreement 320–21
BBC Thames Valley FM 280
BBC Wales
  television 266
  radio 278
BBC Wiltshire Sound 281
BBC World Service 277
BBC Worldwide Publishing Ltd (BBC
  Radio Collection) 309
BBC Young Writers' Festival see First Bite
Bean, Adrian 381
Beaver Arts 158
Beck Theatre, The (Hayes) 254–5
BECTU see Broadcasting Entertainment
  Cinematograph & Theatre Union
Belfast Civic Arts Youth Theatre see Civic
  Arts Theatre (Belfast)
Belfast Festival at Queen's 361
Belgrade Theatre (Coventry) 124
Bell, Alan 381
Bennett, Rodney 381
Beresford, Bruce 381
Berkoff, Steven 381
Besht Tellers 158
Beverley Keogh Casting 113
Bewick, Maureen 106

BFI Production 288–9
Big Bubble Theatre Company 158–9
Big Telly Theatre Co. 159
Bill Kenwright Ltd 149
Bill McLean Personal Management 92
Billboard Personal Management 79
Billington, Kevin 381–2
Bird, Sarah *see* Casting Company, The
Bird's Nest Theatre *see* Flying the Nest
Birkbeck College University of London 35
Birmingham Hippodrome 249
Birmingham Repertory Theatre 121
Birmingham School of Speech and
    Drama 17
Black Coral Productions 289
Black Mime Theatre Co. 159, 373
Black Theatre Cooperative 159
Blackpool Grand Theatre 249
Blair, Les 382
Blakemore, Michael 382
Bloomsbury Theatre 238
Blue Heaven Productions Ltd 289
Bogdanov, Michael 382–3
Bold & Saucy Theatre Company 160
Bond Clarkson Russell Ltd 289
Boorman, John 383
Booster Cushion Theatre 212
Booth, Stephanie 106
Bootleg Theatre Company 160
Border Television plc 267–8
Borderline Theatre Company 161
Boswell, Laurence 383
Bournemouth and Poole College of Art
    and Design 54
Box Hedge Theatre Company 161
Boxclever Productions 289
Boyd, Michael 383–4
Bracke, Siobhan 106
Bradford Festival 361
Braithwaite's School of Acrobatics 374
Branagh, Kenneth 384
Brayshaw, Michael 384
Brazington, Wendy 106
Breeze, The *see* Essex FM
Brewhouse Theatre and Arts Theatre, The
    (Taunton) 260
Brewster, Yvonne 384
Brian Taylor – Nina Quick Associates 100
Bridewell Theatre, The 197–8
Bridge Lane Theatre Company Ltd 198
Bridge Personal Management 80
Bright Ltd 161
Brighton, University of 36
Brighton Festival 362
Bristol Express Theatre Company 198
Bristol Hippodrome 250
Bristol Old Vic Company 122

Bristol Old Vic Theatre School 17–18
British Academy of Film and Television
    Arts (BAFTA) 332
British Actors' Equity Association
    (incorporating Variety Artistes'
    Federation) 315–16
British Alternative Theatre Directory see
    McGillivray's Theatre Guide
British American Arts Association 333
British Asian Theatre Company 161–2
British Council 333
British Film Commission 333
British Film Institute 333
British Library National Sound Archive
    334
British Lion Screen Entertainment Ltd 289
British Music Hall Society 334
British Screen Development 334
British Sky Broadcasting (BSkyB) 272–3
British Theatre Directory 369
Brix Theatre, The 198
Broadcast 370
Broadcasting Co. 106
Broadcasting Entertainment
    Cinematograph & Theatre Union
    (BECTU) 334–5
Brook, Peter, CBE 384–5
Broughton, Pip 385
Brown, Ian 385
Brown, Irena 385–6
Brunel University 36–7, 54–5
Brunskill Management Ltd 81
Brunton Theatre (Musselburgh) 133
Bruvvers Theatre Company
    162
Bryan Drew Ltd 84
Bryden, Bill 386
BSkyB *see* British Sky Broadcasting
Bullivant, Malcolm 106
Bunny Fildes Casting 10
Burge, Stuart, CBE 386–7
Bury St Edmunds Festival 362
Bush Theatre *see* Alternative Theatre
    Company Ltd
Butcher, Linda 107
Buxton Festival 362
Buxton Opera House 251
Byre Theatre (St Andrews) 137

C. V. Productions Ltd 144
Cable News Network International
    (CNNI) 273
Cable television 272–3
Caird, John 387
Caird Littlewood Casting 107
Cairns, Laura 107
Cambridge Arts Theatre 251

Cambridge Syllabus Players *see* Off The Shelf Theatre
Cambridge Theatre 238–9
Camden People's Theatre 199
Cameron Mackintosh 150
Campaign for Press and Broadcasting Freedom (CPBF) 335
Canal Café Theatre 199
Candid Casting 107
Cannon, Dudley & Associates 107
Canterbury Festival 362
Caravel Film Techniques Limited 289
Cardiff Casting 81
Carling, Di 107
Carlton Productions 290
Carlton Television 268
Carnival (Films & Theatre) Ltd 144, 290
Castcall Information Service 370
Casting Company, The 107
Casting Couch/Casting Couch Video File 370
Casting Directors, The 107–8
Castingdex 370
Castledine, Annie 387–8
Caton-Jones, Michael 388
Caught in the Act 223–4
CCC Wadlow 290
CCM 81
Celebration Theatre Company for the Young 212
Cellan-Jones, James 388
Central Broadcasting 268
Central Line, The 81
Central Office of Information Film and Video 290
Central Saint Martins College of Art and Design 55
Central School of Speech and Drama 18–19
Century Theatre (Keswick) 128
CFM 281
CGSP (Belgium) 337
Chancery Cooperative Management *see* CCM
Channel 4 268
Channel 5 268–9
Channel One Television Ltd 273
Channel Television 269
Channel Theatre Company/Channel Theatre Company TIE 162
Chard Helps Casting 108
Charkham Casting 108
Chatsworth Television 290
Cheek by Jowl 162
Cheltenham Radio 281
Cherub Company London, The 162–3
Chichester Festival Theatre 123–4
Children's and young people's theatre 211–21

Children's programmes (BBC) 264
Chivers Press Limited 309
Christ Church College Canterbury 37
Chuck Julian Associates 89–90
Churchill Theatre (Bromley) *see* Theatre of Comedy at the Churchill Theatre Ltd
Cinema Verity Productions Ltd 290–91
Ciniewicz, Penny 388
Circus artists *See under* Equity
Circus Films *see* Elstree (Production) C. Ltd
Citizen's Voice in Broadcasting *see* Voice of the Listener and Viewer
Citizens' Theatre (Glasgow) 127
City Actors Management Ltd 81–2
City Literary Institute, The 37–8
City of Liverpool Community College 38
City of London Festival 365
City University 38–9
Civic Arts Theatre (Belfast) 120
Civic Theatre (Chelmsford) *see* Newpalm Productions
Clark, Anthony 388
Clayton, Jack 388
Clean Break Theatre Company Ltd 163
Clive Corner Associates 82
Clyde 1 FM/Clyde 2 AM *see* Radio Clyde Ltd
CNNI *see* Cable News Network International
Coast FM *see* MFM
Cochrane Theatre 239
Cockpit Theatre 199
Comedy Theatre 239
Commercial Radio Companies Association 335
Communicado Theatre Company 163
Compass Theatre Company 163–4
Comsumer and leisure (BBC) 264
Comway, Van Gelder Ltd 82
Conference of Drama Schools 335
Conla Productions *see* Old Red Lion Theatre
Connaught Theatre (Worthing) 261
Constructive Teaching Centre 374
Contact Theatre Company 212
Contact Theatre Company (Manchester) 212
Contact Young Playwrights' Festival 362
Contacts see Spotlight, The
Cooney, Ray 388–9
Cotter, Tom 389
Courtyard, The (Hereford) 255
Coventry University 39
CPBF *see* Campaign for Press and Broadcasting Freedom
Craddock, Malcolm 389

Craig, Ted 389
Creative Casting International 108
Creative Film Makers Ltd 291
Crescent Management 82
Cricket Limited 291
Critics' Circle 335
Crocodile Casting 108
Croft Television & Graphics Ltd 291
Cromdale Films Limited 291
Crouch Associates 82
Crowded City 83
Crucible Theatre and Studio (Sheffield) 138
Crucible Theatre in Education 224
CSA Telltapes Ltd 309
Cumbernauld Theatre 124
Custard Factory Theatre Co. 164
Cwmni Theatr Gwynedd 164
Cygnet Training Theatre 19–20
CYP Limited/Audiosport Limited 309

Dacia Stevens Stage School 31–2
DAF (Denmark) 337
Daldry, Stephen 389–90
Dan Films Ltd 291
Daniels, Ron 390
Dareks Production House 291–2
Darlington Civic Theatre 252
Dartington College of Arts 39–40
David Daly Associates 83
Davies, Howard 390–1
De Freitas, Paul 109
De Montfort University Leicester 40
De Pettit, Lesley 109
Dead Earnest Theatre 164–5
Debbie Shepherd Casting 116
Denman Casting Agency 83
Denmark Street Management 83–4
Dennis Lyne Agency 91
Department for Culture, Media and
   Sport 336
Derby Playhouse 124–5
Desmond Jones School of Mime and
   Physical Theatre 24
Devonshire Park Theatre (Eastbourne) 253
DGM Productions Ltd 144–5
Diamond, Gillian 109
Direct Line Personal Management 84
Directors 377–429
Directors Guild of Great Britain 336
Documentaries and history (BBC) 264
Dome Complex (Brighton) 250
Dominion Theatre 239
Donmar Warehouse 145
Donnellan, Declan 391
Doran, Gregory 391
Dorothy Andrew see Mersey Television
   Company

Dossor, Alan 391–2
Douglas, Bill 392
Dove, John 392
Dover, Festival of 362–3
Dowd, Tim 392
Downes Agency 84
Drake AV Video Ltd 292
Drama (BBC)
   radio 275–6
   television 264
Drama Association of Wales 336
Drama Centre London 20–1
Drama House Ltd, The 292
Drama schools 13–33
Drama Studio London 21
Drill Hall, The 374
Drill Hall Arts Centre, The 199–200
Dromgoole, Dominic 392–3
Druid Theatre Company 165
DSF (Denmark) 337
Duchess Theatre 240
Duff, Julia 109–10
Duijvendak, Han 393
Duke of York's Theatre 240
Dukes, The (Lancaster) 128–9
Dunbar Agency 84
Duncan C. Weldon Productions 154
Dundee Repertory Theatre 125
Dunderdale, Sue 393
Dunlop, Frank 393

E & B Productions Ltd 145
Eagle & Eagle 292
East 15 Acting School 21, 374
East Anglia, University of 40–41
East Anglian Productions 292
East Midlands Arts Board 355–6
Eastern Angles Theatre Company 165–6
Eastern Arts Board 355
Eclipse Presentations Ltd 292
Eden Court Theatre (Inverness) 255
Edge Hill University College 41
Edinburgh Festival Fringe 363
Edinburgh Film & Video Productions
   292–3
Edinburgh International Festival 363
Edit 123 293
Education production (BBC) 264
Educational Television and Media
   Association see ETmA
Elaine Murphy Associates 94
ELAN – Wales 166
Elstree (Production) Co. Ltd 293
Emma Style Casting 116
Empire Theatre (Liverpool) 256
Empire Theatre (Sunderland) 259
Empty Space Theatre Company 166–7

England, Arts Council of 353
English Chamber Theatre 167
English Folk Dance and Song Society 336–7
English Pocket Theatre, Internationales
    Theatr Frankfurt (Main) 234
English Shakespeare Company
    International 145
English Stage Company Ltd see Royal
    Court Theatre
English Theater Frankfurt 235
English Theatre Company Ltd AB, The
    (Sweden) 236
English Theatre of Copenhagen, The see
    London Toast Theatre
English Theatre of Hamburg, The 235
English Touring Theatre Ltd 167
English-language, European theatre
    companies 233–6
Enigma Productions Ltd 293
Entertainment (BBC television) 264
    See also Light entertainment (BBC radio)
Enzyme Theatre Company 167
Equity 315–28
    guide to membership 316–17
    selected extracts from Equity agreements
        318–28
    student membership 317
Eric Glass Ltd 86
Essential Film & Television Productions
    Ltd 293
Essex, University of 41
Essex FM/The Breeze/Ten 17/Oasis
    FM/Vibe FM 282
Etcetera Theatre 200
ETmA (Educational Television and Media
    Association) 337
European Theatre Company Ltd 168
Events (BBC) 264
Everyman Theatre (Cheltenham) 123
Exeter, University of 41–2
Exeter Festival 363
Eyre, Sir Richard, CBE 393–4

Façade 145–6
Farnham Film Company Ltd, The 293
Farrant Partnership, The 294
Fecund Theatre 168
Federation of Entertainment Unions 337
FeS/UGT (Spain) 338
FESPACE (Spain) 338
Festival Film and Television Ltd 294
Festivals 361–7
FIA (International Federation of Actors)
    337
    Western European members 337–8
Figgis, Susie 110
FIL (Iceland) 338

Film courses 53–63
Film Log 370
Film production companies 287–307
Finborough Theatre see Steam Industry,
    The
First Bite – BBC Young Writers' Festival
    363
First Bite Theatre-in-Education Company
    224–5
Fitting Images Ltd 294
Flashback Communications Ltd 294
Flying the Nest 200
FM103 Horizon 282
Focus Films Ltd 294
Focus Management Ltd 85
Foenander, Allan 111
Forest Forge Theatre Company 168–9
Forsyth, Bill 394
Fortune Theatre 240
Forum Theatre, The (Billingham) 248
Foster, Giles 394–5
Fox, Celestia 111
FRACTALS see Institute for Creativity
Frances Phillips (Agency & Artists
    Management) 96
Frears, Stephen 395
Freeway Films 294
Friday Productions Ltd 294–5
Friend, Martyn 395
Fringe theatre 195–210
Frinton Summer Theatre 147
Frisby, Jane 111
Frontline Management 85–6
FSSkadelpelarforbund (Finland) Suomen
    Nayttelijalitto (Finland)338, 337–8SN
FUAEE (Spain) 338
Funnell, Caroline 111
Further education courses 35–52

Gaiety Theatre (Douglas) 252
Galaxy 101 282
Galleon Theatre Company Ltd 200
Gallie, Joyce 111
Galloways One 86
Gardner Centre Theatre (Brighton) 250
Garland, Patrick 395
Garrick Theatre 240
Gaskill, William 395–6
Gate Theatre, The 201
Gateway Theatre Trust Ltd (Chester) 123
GAU, Greek Actors' Union 338
Gay Sweatshop Theatre Company 169
GB Casting 111
GDBA (Germany) 338
Geese Theatre Company 169
Georgian Theatre Royal (Richmond, N.
    Yorks) 258

Gielgud Theatre 241
Giles, David 396
Gill, Peter 396–7
Gilmore, David 397
Glossary 431–40
GMTV 269
GNR 282
Godber, John 397
Gold, Jack 397
Gold, Nina 111
Goldcrest Films International Ltd 295
Goldsmiths' College, University of London 42, 55
Good Company 169
Gordon Craig Theatre (Stevenage) 259
Graeae Theatre Company 169–70
Grampian Television Ltd 269
Granada Film 295
Granada Television 269
Grand Opera House (Belfast) 248
Grand Opera House, The (York) 261
Grand Theatre (Wolverhampton) 261
Grant Naylor Productions see Noel Gay Television
Grays Management 87
Green Pavement Theatre Co. 170
Greenaway, Peter 397–8
Greenwich and Docklands International Festival 363–4
Greenwich and Lewisham's Young People's Theatre see GYPT
Greenwich Theatre (London) 147
Grieve, Andrew 398
GRiP Theatre 201
Guildford School of Acting 22
Guildhall School of Music and Drama 22–3
Guishe, Michelle see Casting Company, The
Gulbenkian Theatre (Canterbury) 251
Gwent Theatre 225
GYPT – Greenwich and Lewisham's Young People's Theatre 213

Hackney Empire 241
Haggard, Piers 398
Half Moon Young People's Theatre 213
Hall, Edward 398
Hall, Sir Peter, CBE 398–9
Hammer Film Productions Ltd 296
Hammerwood Film Productions Pan European Films 296
Hampstead Theatre 148
HandMade Films Ltd 296
Hands, Terry 399–400
Harbour & Coffey 87–8
Hare, David 400–1
Harlow Playhouse 254

HarperCollins Publishers Ltd 310
Harrogate International Festival 364
Harrogate Theatre 127
Harrogate Theatre-in-Education 225
Hartswood Films Ltd 296
Hat Trick Productions Ltd 296
Hauser, Frank, CBE 401
Hawth, The (Crawley) 252
Haymarket Theatre Company (Basingstoke) 120
Head to Head Communication 297
Heartbreak Productions 170
Heavy Pencil Management 88
Helen Stafford Management 99–100
Her Majesty's 241
Hijinx Theatre Cooperative Company Limited 170
His Majesty's Theatre (Aberdeen) 248
Hiss & Boo Company, The 148–9
Hodges, Mike 402
Holloway, Jonathan 402
Hourglass Pictures Ltd 297
Hourglass Productions Limited 297
Howard Hall 295
HTV Group Plc 270
Hubbard Casting 112
Huddersfield, University of 42–3, 55–6
Hudson, Hugh 402
Hull New Theatre 255
Hull Truck Theatre 171
Humberside Theatre-in-Education Company see Making Space Theatre Company
Huseyin, Metin 402
Hytner, Nicholas 402–3

ICA Theatre 241
Ideal Image Ltd 297
Ideal Theatre Company, The 201–2
IG Medien (Germany) 338
Illuminations Films 297
Independent managements 143–54
Independent production companies 287–307
    radio/Equity agreement 322
    television/Equity agreement 321
Independent radio 281–5
Independent television 267–72
Independent Television Commission 338–9
Independent Television News Ltd see ITN
Independent Theatre Council 339
Inspiration Management 88–9
Instant Classics 171
Institute for Creativity (in association with FRACTALS) 374
Inter-City Casting 88
International Association of Theatre

for Children and Young People
see APT
International Federation of Actors see FIA
International Playwriting Festival 364
International Theatre Institute (British
Centre) 339–40
International Visual Communication
Association see IVCA
Internationales Theatr Frankfurt (Main) see
English Pocket Theatre
Irene East Casting 110
Isis Publishing Limited 310
Italia Conti Academy of Theatre Arts 23–4
ITN (Independent Television News
Ltd) 270
ITV Network Centre 340
ITV/Equity agreement 318–19
Ivan Hale Ltd 147
IVCA (International Visual
Communication Association) 340
Ivory, James 403

J.D. Agency see Basic
Jack Watling Productions Ltd see Frinton
Summer Theatre
Jaclyn Agency 89
Jaffrey, Jennifer 112
James Sharkey Associates 99
James, Alby 403
James, Pedr 403
Jane Davies Casting 109
Jane Walker Casting 117
Janet Lynn Malone 92–3
Jeffrey & White Management 89
Jeremy Zimmerman Casting 118
Jermyn Street Theatre 202
JGM 89
Jill Freud & Company 146
Jill Pearce Casting 115
Jimmy Grafton Management 86
JLM see Janet Lynn Malone
Joan Gray Personal Management 87
Joan Reddin 97
Joffe, Roland 403
John, Priscilla 112
Johnny Dallas (Casting) 108–9
Johnson, Marilyn 113
Johnson, Sandy 404
Jonathan Altaras Associates 77
Jones, Doreen 113
Jones, Richard 404
Jones, Sue 113
Jones, Terry 404
Jordan, Neil 404
Joy Galloway Management see JGM
Joy Jameson Ltd 89
Judge, Ian 404–5

Julian Belfrage Associates 79
June Epstein Associates 84–5

Kaos Theatre UK 171–2
Kate Feast Management 85
Kaut-Howson, Helena 405
Kelly, Jude 405
Ken Desmond Agency & Management 84
Ken Sharp Productions see Old Red Lion
Theatre
Kenneth More Theatre (Ilford) 255
Kent, Jonathan 405–6
Kent, Nicolas 406
Kent and Canterbury, University of 43
Kerry Gardner Management 86
Key 103/Piccadilly 1152 283
Key Theatre 258
Kinetic Theatre Company 226
King Alfred's University College
Winchester 43–4, 56
King's Head Theatre 202
King's Theatre (Edinburgh) 253
King's Theatre (Glasgow) 253
Kirby, Alex 406
KMFB Artisten und Bühne (Austria) 337
Knights, Robert 406
Knox, Ian 406
Komedia 202
Korel, Suzy 113
Kubrick, Stanley 407
Kunstenbond FNV (Netherlands) 338
Kyle, Barry 407

L'Epine Smith, Jane 113
L'Epine Smith & Carney Associates 90–91
Labatt's Apollo Manchester 257
Lagan Pictures Ltd 298
Laird, Fiona 407
LAMDA 24–5
Lanb, Irene 113
Langford Associates 90
Langton, Simon 407
Larmour, Brigid 407–8
Larry Dalzell Associates Ltd 83
Lawrence Batley Theatre (Huddersfield)
128
LBC 1152 AM 283
LCPDT see London College of Printing and
Distributive Trades
Learning Through Action 226
Leeds, University of 44
Leeds Grand Theatre and Opera House
256
Leicester Haymarket Theatre 129–30
Leigh, Mike, OBE 408
Lesley Beastall see Broadcasting Co.

Lesley Grayburn Casting 111
Levinson, Sharon 113
Library Theatre Company (manchester) 132
Lichfield International Arts Festival 364
LIFT see London International Festival of Theatre
Light entertainment (BBC, radio) 276
Links Management 91
Lip Service Casting Ltd 91
Live Theatre Company 172
LIVE TV 273
Liverpool Playhouse 130
Liz England Casting 110
LJ's Theatre Bar see Enzyme Theatre Company
Lloyd, Phyllida 408
Loach, Ken 408–9
Loe, Judy 114
Logos Theatre Company 172
Loncraine, Richard 409
London Academy of Music and Dramatic Art see LAMDA
London Academy of Performing Arts, The 25–6
London and International School of Acting 26
London Arts Board 355
London Bubble Theatre Company 173
London Coliseum 241–2
London College of Printing and Distributive Trades (LCPDT) 374
London Institute (School of Media) 56
London Guildhall University 56
London International Festival of Theatre (LIFT) 364–5
London International Film School 57
London New Play Festival 365
London Palladium 242
London Screenwriters' Workshop 340
London Toast Theatre, The English Theatre of Copenhagen 233–4
London Weekend Television see LWT
Louder Than Words Productions 202–3
Loughborough University 44
Love, Robert 409
Ludlow Festival 365
LWA 91
LWT (London Weekend Television) 270
Lyceum Theatre (Crewe) 252
Lyceum Theatre (Sheffield) 259
Lyceum Theatre, The (London) 242
Lynn, Jonathan 409
Lyric Theatre (Belfast) 120–1
Lyric Theatre (London) 242
Lyric Theatre Hammersmith 149–50

M6 Theatre Company 227
MAC (Midlands Arts Centre) 249
McDiarmid, Ian 409
Macdonald, Robert David 409–10
MacFarlane Chard Associates 91–2
McGillivray's Theatre Guide (formerly The British Alternative Theatre Directory) 371
McIntosh Rae Management 92
Mackenzie, John 410
McMurray, Mary 410
McMurrich, Christine 114
MacRobert Arts Centre (Stirling) 259
Magic Carpet Theatre 213
Magic Mirror Theatre Company (UK) Ltd 214
Magnet Personal Management 92
Magnolia Management 92
Mahoney, Bob 410
Making Space Theatre Company 226–7
Malone & Knight Associates 93
Maltings Arts Theatre 259
Malvern Festival Theatre 257
Man in the Moon Theatre 203
Manchester Metropolitan University 44
Manley, Andrew 410
Marcher Gold see MFM
Marcia Gresham Casting 111–12
Marina Theatre, The (Lowestoft) 257
Marjorie Abel Ltd 75–6
Mark Summers Casting at Casting Unlimited 116
Marlowe Theatre, The (Cantebury) 251–2
Marmont Management Ltd 93
Mary Selway and Sarah Trevis 115
Mathias, Sean 410–11
Maverick Television 298
Maverick Theatre Company 173
Maya Vision Ltd 298
Mayflower Theatre (Southampton) 259
Meckler, Nancy 411
Medak, Peter 411
Media courses 53–63
Mendes, Sam 411–12
Mentorn Barraclough Carey 298
Merchant Ivory Productions 298–9
Mercury Theatre (Colchester) 124
Meridian Broadcasting 270
Merlin International Theatre (Hungary) 236
Mermaid Theatre 243
Mersey Television Company Ltd 299
Merseyside Young People's Theatre Company 214
Method & Madness 174
MFM/Marcher Gold/Coast FM 283
Michael Barrett Ltd 288
Michael Codron Plays Ltd 144

Michael Ladkin Personal Management 90
Michell, Roger 412
Michelle Braidman Associates 80
Middlesex University 45, 57
Midlands Arts Centre *see* MAC
Mikron Theatre Company 174
Mill at Sonning Theatre, The 139
Millar, Gavin 412
Miller, Jonathan 412
Millfield Theatre 203
Millstream Theatre Company 174
Minack Theatre Summer Festival 365
Minghella, Anthony 412–13
Mitchell, Katie 413
Montagu Associates 93
Morahan, Christopher 413
Moray Firth Radio 283
Morgan & Goodman 93–4
Morley Theatre School at Morley College 26
Morrison, Melika 114
Morrison Company, The 299
Mountview Theatre School 26–7
MTV Networks Europe Inc 273
Mugshots Ltd 114
Mull Theatre, The 150
Murray, Braham 413–14
Museum of the Moving Image: Actors' Company 150–51
Music (BBC) 264
Musicians' Union 341
MW Entertainments 151

National Campaign for the Arts 341
National Council for Drama Training 341–2
National Entertainment Agents Council 342
National Film and Television School 57–8
National Lottery 342
National Operatic and Dramatic Association (NODA) 342
National Student Drama Festival 365
National Youth Music Theatre 214
National Youth Theatre of Great Britain 214–15
Natural Theatre Company 175
Naxos Audiobooks 310
NBF (Norway) 338
Nemesis Agency Ltd 94
Nene College of Higher Education, Northampton 45, 58
Neptune Theatre, The (Liverpool) 256–7
Nettles, Joyce 114
NETWORKING for women in film, video and television 343
New End Theatre 203

New Era Academy of Drama amd Music (London) Ltd 27
New Everyman Ltd (Livrpool) 130
New London Theatre 243
New Playwrights Trust 343
New Shakespeare Company Ltd 151
New Victoria Theatre (Newcastle under Lyme) 134
New Victoria Theatre (Woking) 260
Newark and Sherwood College 45–6
Newgate Company 299
Newpalm Productions 151
News and current affairs (BBC) 264–5
News Direct 97.3 FM 283
Newton Wills Management 102
Noble, Adrian 414
NODA *see* National Operatic and Dramatic Association
Noel Davis Casting 109
Noel Gay Television 295
Non-producing theatres 237–61
North, Sophie *see* Broadcasting Co.
North London, University of 46, 58
North One Actors Management 94–5
North-West Art Board 356
North-West Playwrights *see* NWP
Northamton Repertory Players Ltd 135
Northcott Theatre (Exeter) 126
Northern Actors Centre, The 343–4
Northern Arts 356
Northern Broadsides 175
Northern Ireland, Arts Council of 353
Northern Lights Actors Management 94
Northern School of Film and Television 58–9
Northern Stage (Newcastle upon Tyne) 135
Northumbria, University of 46
Not the National Theatre Company 175
Nottingham Playhouse 135–6
NSF (Norway) 338
NTC Touring Theatre Company 176
Nuffield Theatre (Southampton) 139
Nunn, Trevor 414–15
NWP (North-West Playwrights) 344
Nyland Management 95

100.3 and 101.1 Scot FM 284
100.7 Heart FM 282
1984 Personal Management Ltd 95
O'Brien, Debbie 114
OAGL (Luxembourg) 338
Oasis FM *see* Essex FM
Ockrent, Mike 415–16
Octagon Theatre Company (Bolton) 121–2
Off The Shelf Theatre 227
Old Red Lion Theatre 203–4
Old Rep Theatre, The (Birmingham) 121

Oldham Coliseum Theatre 136
Olivier, Richard 416
Open Hand Theatre Company 176
Opera House, The (Manchester) 257
Orange Tree Theatre 204
Orchard FM 283
Orchard Theatre Company 176–7
Organisations, associations and societies 329–51
Otto Personal Management Ltd 95
Out of Joint Ltd 177
Oval House Theatre 204
Ovation Productions 299
Oxford School of Drama, The 28
Oxford Stage Company 177
Oxford Street Theatre 204
Oxfordshire Touring Theatre Company 178

PACT (Producers Alliance for Cinema and Television) 344
Page, Anthony 416
Paines Plough 178
Palace Theatre (London) 243–4
Palace Theatre Trust (Westcliff) 140
Palace Theatre Watford 139–40
Palace Theatre, The (Manchester) 257
Pan Artists Agency 95
Parallax Pictures Ltd 299–300
Parasol Theatre for Children 215
Park Personal Management Ltd 96
Parker, Alan 416–17
Parker, Brian 417
Parker, Lynne 417
Pascal Theatre Company 178
Pat Lovett Agency see PLA Scotland
Pavilion Theatre (Bournemouth) 249
PCR see Professional Casting Report
Peacock Theatre 244
Pearson Television Ltd 300
Penguin Audiobooks 310
Penny Barbour Casting 105
Pentameters Theatre 205
Penumbra Productions Ltd 300
People Show 179
Pepper Productions see Noel Gay Television
Performing Right Society Ltd (PRS), The 344
Perpetual Motion Theatre Ltd 179
Personal Managers' Association Limited, The 344–5
Perth Repertory Theatre 136
Peter Hall Company, The 147–8
See also Hall, Sir Peter
Petit, Chris 417
Philip Hindin Productions 148
Philip Shaw Casting 115

Philippa Howell Personal Management 88
Philippou, Nick 417
Phoenix Arts Centre (Leicester) 256
Phoenix Theatre (London) 244
PHPM see Philippa Howell Personal Management
Piccadilly 1152 see Key 103
Piccadilly Management 96
Piccadilly Theatre 244
Picture Palace Films Ltd 300
Pied Piper Theatre Company (in association with the Yvonne Arnaud Theatre) 216
Pilot Theatre Company 216
Pinter, Harold 417–18
Pitlochry Festival Theatre 136–7
PLA Scotland 96
Player-Playwrights 345
Playhouse Theatre (Edinburgh) 253
Plays and Players Applause 371
Plays International 371
Playtime Theatre Company 216
Pleasance London 205
Plymouth, University of 47, 59
Plymouth College of Art and Design 59
Pola Jones Associates Ltd 152
Poliakoff, Stephen 418
Polka Theatre for Children 217
Pollock, Patsy 115
Polly Hootkins Casting 112
PolyGram Spoken Word 311
Pomeroy, Sue 418
Poor School, The 28
Pop-up Theatre Ltd 217
Posner, Lindsay 418–19
Posser, Nicholas 419
Powell, Tristram 419
Pownsend, Moira 117
Praxis Theatre Company 179–80
Premier Radio 284
Prime Productions Ltd 180
Prince Edward Theatre 244
Prince of Wales 245
Prince Theatre, The see Galleon Theatre Company
Proctor, Carl 115
Producers Alliance for Cinema and Television see PACT
Producing theatres 143–54
Professional Casting Report (PCR) 371
Proteus Theatre Company 180
Provincial theatres/Equity agreement 326–7
Prowse, Philip 419
PRS see Performing Right Society Ltd, The
Publications and services 369–72

Queen Margaret College 47
Queen's Theatre (Hornchurch) 127
Queen's Theatre (London) 245
Quem Quaeritis Theatre Company 217–18
Quest Theatre Company 180–81
Quicksilver National Touring Theatre 218

Radford, Michael 419
Radio 275–85
    BBC/Equity agreement 322
Radio Authority 345
Radio Borders 281
Radio Clyde Ltd (Clyde 1 FM/Clyde 2
    AM) 281
Radio Forth Ltd 282
Radio Tay Ltd (Radio Tay AM/Tay
    FM) 284
Rakoff, Alvin 419–20
Random House Audiobooks 311
Ravensbourne College of Design and
    Communication 59
Raymond Mander and Joe Mitchenson
    Theatre Collection 340
RBM 97
Reading, University of 47, 60
Really Useful Theatre Company Ltd 152
Reardon Publishing 311
Red Ladder Theatre Company Ltd 181
Red Rooster Film & Television
    Entertainment Ltd 301
Red Shift Theatre Company 181–2
Redfarn, Roger 420
Redroofs Theatre School 28
Regional Arts Boards (RABs) 354–5
Regional radio stations 278–81
Regional theatres 119–41
Reich, Liora 115
Reisz, Karel 420
Rent-a-Role at the Barbican Theatre 228
Repertory REPORT 371
Repertory theatres 119–41
    subsidised repertory/Equity agreement
    327–8
Replay Theatre Company 228
Retallack, John 420
Reynolds, Simone 115
Rhubarb/Rhubarb Personal Management
    97
Richard Bucknall Management see RBM
Richard Evans Casting 110
Richards, David 420
Richmond Drama School 29
Richmond Films & Television Ltd 301
Richmond Theatre 258–9
Ridiculusmus 182
Riding Lights Theatre Company / Riding
    Lights Roughshod 182–3

Rigal Management 97
Ripon and York St John, University
    College of 50, 60
Riverside Studios 205
RNIB Talking Book Service 311
Robert Fox Ltd 146
Robert Smith Agency 99
Roeg, Nicolas 420
Roehampton Institute London 48, 60
Rogues & Vagabonds Management Ltd 98
Ronnie Marshall Agency 93
Rose Bay Film Productions see Noel Gay
    Television
Rose Bruford College 18
Rosemary Branch Theatre 205
Rossmore Personal Management 98
Roundabout Theatre-in-Education 228–9
Roxane Vacca Management 101
Royal Academy of Dramatic Art 29–30, 375
Royal College of Art 60–1
Royal Court Theatre/English Stage
    Company Ltd 152–3
Royal Court Young People's Theatre 218
Royal Court Young Writers' Festival 366
Royal Exchange Theatre (Manchester)
    132–3
Royal Hippodrome Theatre (Eastbourne)
    253
Royal Holloway, University of London 48
Royal Lyceum Theatre (Edinburgh) 125
Royal National Theatre 131
Royal Scottish Academy of Music and
    Drama 30
Royal Shakespeare Company 131–2
Royal Television Society 345
Royal Theatre-in-Education 229
Royal Theatrical Fund 345
Rudman, Michael 420–21
Russell, Ken 421
Rye, Renny 421
Rylance, Mark 421

6.15 Theatre Company 218
7:84 Theatre Company (Scotland) Ltd 183
S4C 271
SACV Cultuur (Belgium) 337
Sadler's Wells Theatre 245
SAI (Italy) 338
St Martin, University College of 50
St Martin's Theatre 245
St Mary's University College 48
Salamander Theatre Company 229
Salford, University of 49, 61
Salisbury Festival 366
Salisbury Playhouse 137–8
Sams, Jeremy 421–2
Sandpiper Productions Ltd 153

Sandra Griffin Management 87
Sands Films 301
Sara Crouch Management 82–3
Saraband Associates 98
Sarah Radclyffe Productions 301
Sasdy, Peter 422
Satellite television 272–3
Save London's Theatres Campaign 345–6
Savoy Theatre 245
SBKV (Switzerland) 338
SBS see Script Breakdown Service
SCA Management 98
Scala Productions 301
SCC (Belgium) 337
Schlesinger, John, CBE 422
School of the Science of Acting, The 31
Science (BBC) 265
Scott, Ridley 422
Scott Marshall Personal Management 93
Scottish Actors Studio 346
Scottish Arts Council 354
Scottish Television 271
Scottish Young Playwrights Festival 366
Screen International 371
Screenlite the Agency 98–9
Script Breakdown Service (SBS) 371
Sellar, Ian 422
Serio Ensemble 206
Services *see* Publications and Services
SFA (France) 338
Shaftesbury Theatre 245–6
Shakespeare's Globe Theatre 153
Shane Collins Associates 82
Shared Experience Theatre Company 183
Sharon Young Casting 118
Shaw, Rose Tobias 117
Sheridan Fitzgerald Management 85
Sherman Theatre (Cardiff) 122
Show of Strength Theatre Company 206
Sianco Cyf 301
Sight and Sound 372
Signal 105 284
Simon & Schuster Ltd 311
Simone Ireland and Vanessa Pereira Casting 112
Singer, Hazel 116
SIPTU (Ireland) 338
Sir John Mills Theatre (Ipswich) 256
Skills, aditional 373–5
Small-scale theatre companies/Equity agreement 328
Smith, Caroline 422–3
Smith, Peter 423
Smith & Watson 302
Snap People's Theatre Trust 218–19
Societies *see* Organisations, associations and societies
Society for Theatrical Research 347
Society of Authors 346–7
Society of London Theatre (SOLT) 347
Soho Theatre Company 206–7
Solent People's Theatre 184
Solo Plus Theatre Company 230
SOLT *see* Society of London Theatre
South-East Arts 356–7
South-West Arts 357
Southern Arts 357
Southwark Playhouse 205–6
Southwold Summer Theatre *see* Jill Freud & Company
Spare Tyre Theatre Company 184
Speak Limited 99
Spellbound Productions Limited 302
Sphinx Theatre Company, The 184
'Spoken' Image Ltd 302
Sport (BBC) 265
Spotlight, The 372
Springboard Theatre Company 185
SSRS (Switzerland) 338
Stafford-Clark, Max 423
Stage, The (incorporating *Television Today*) 372
Stage Centre Management 100
Stage Management Association 347
Stagescreen Productions 302
Standeven, Richard 423
STE (Portugal) 338
Steam Industry, The 207
Stella Richards Management 97
Stephen Hatton Management 88
Stephen Joseph Theatre (Scarborough) 138
STF (Sweden) 338
STL – Dance Artists (Finland) 337
Stoll, Liz 116
Strachan, Alan 423–4
Strand Theatre 246
Stratford-upon-Avon Poetry Festival 366
Strawberry Productions 302
Sturridge, Charles 424
Sue Hammer Personal Management 87
Summers, Jeremy 424
Sunday Times Hay Festival, The 367
Sunrise Radio (Yorkshire) 284
Surrey Institute of Art and Design 61–2
Susan Angel Associates Ltd 78
Susie Parriss Casting 114–15
Sussex Playwrights Club 347
Suzanne Smith Casting 116
Suzman, Janet 424
Swan Theatre (Worcester) 140
Swansea Sound Ltd 284

2CRFM 285

Tabard Theatre 207–8
Table Top Productions 302
TAG Theatre Company 219
TAI Artists 32
Talawa Theatre Company 185
Talisman Films Ltd 303
TalkBack Productions 303
Talking Heads – The Voice Agency 100
Tamasha 185
Tara Arts Group Ltd 185–6
Target Casting Ltd 100
Tay FM see Radio Tay Ltd
Teale, Polly 424
Teece, Shirley 116–17
Televideo Ltd 303
Television 263–73
    Equity agreements 318–21
Television commercials Equity agreement
    322–4
Television Today see Stage, The
Teliesyn 303
Ten 17 see Essex FM
Tern Television Productions Ltd 303–4
Tessa Le Bars Management 90
Thacker, David 424–5
Thames Television Ltd see Pearson
    Television Ltd
Thameside Theatre (Grays) 254
Theatr Clwyd (Mold) 133
Theatr Gorllewin Morgannwg see Theatre
    West Glamorgan
Theatr Iolo Ltd 230–31
Theatr Powys 189
Theatre 372
Theatre Absolute 186
Theatre Alibi 186–7
Theatre Centre Ltd 219
Theatre Company Blah Blah Blah! 230
Théâtre de Complicité 187
Theatre Investment Fund 348
Theatre Museum 348
Theatre of Comedy at the Churchill
    Theatre Ltd 153–4
Theatre of Comedy Company 153
Theatre Record 372
Theatre Rotto 187–8
Theatre Royal (Brighton) 250
Theatre Royal (Bury St Edmunds) 251
Theatre Royal (Glasgow) 253–4
Theatre Royal (Lincoln) 256
Theatre Royal (Newcastle upon Tyne) 258
Theatre Royal (Norwich) 258
Theatre Royal (Nottingham)
    258
Theatre Royal (Plymouth) 137
Theatre Royal (Windsor) 260
Theatre Royal (York) 140–41

Theatre Royal and Opera House
    (Wakefield) 260
Theatre Royal Bath 248
Theatre Royal Drury Lane 246
Theatre Royal Haymarket 246
Theatre Royal Stratford East 208
Theatre Venture 188
Theatre West Glamorgan/Theatr
    Gorllewin Morgannwg 188
Theatre Workshop 188–9
Theatre Writers' Union 348
Theatre-in-education (TIE) companies
    223–32
Theatregoers Club of Great Britain 348–9
Theatres see Provincial theatres; Repertory
    theatres; Small-scale theatre companies;
    West End theatres and specific names
Theatres Advisory Council 349
Theatres Trust 349
Theatrestorm 189
Theatrical Management Association
    (TMA) 349
Thompson, Jim 101
Thorndike Theatre (Leatherhead) 129
Ticklish Allsorts 219–20
Tiebreak Theatre Company Ltd 231
Tiger Aspect Productions 304
Tim Scott Personal Management 98
Titchmarsh, Gill 117
TMA see Theatrical Management
    Association
Toby Whale Casting 117
Tomson, Bob 425
Topical features (BBC)
    radio 276
    television 265
Torch Theatre Company Limited (Milford
    Haven) 133
Touring theatre companies 155–93
Tramway (Glasgow) 254
Travelling Light Theatre Company 231
Traverse Theatre (Edinburgh) 125–6
Trestle Theatre Company 189–90
Trevellick, Jill 117
Trevis, Sarah see Mary Selway
Tricycle Theatre 208
Trinity College Carmarthen 49
Tristan Bates Theatre 197
Tron Theatre Company 208–9
Tucker, David 425
Tudor Rose Theatre Company
    190
Turning Point Productions 304
Turnstyle Group Ltd 154
Twist, Benjamin 425
Two Four Productions Ltd 304
Tyne Tees Television 271

UGS, Union of Greek Singers 338
UK Living/UK Gold 273
Ulster, University of 51
Ulster Television *see* UTV
Unicorn Theatre for Children 220
United Film and Television Productions 304
United Media Ltd 304
University College Bretton Hall 36
University College Chester 49–50
University courses 35–52
University of Wales (Newport) 62
Unwin, Paul 425–6
UTV (Ulster Television) 272

Vance, Charles 426
Vanessa Ford Productions Ltd 146
Vardy, Mike 426
Variety & Allied Entertainments' Council of Great Britain 350
Variety Artistes' Federation *see* Equity
Vaudeville Theatre 247
Vera Media – Productions & Training 304–5
Verma, Jatinder 426
Vernon Conway Ltd *see* ALW Asociates
Vibe FM *see* Essex FM
Victoria Palace 247
Video Enterprises 305
Video Presentations 305
Video production companies 287–307
Vienna's English Theatre 233
Viking FM 285
Vincent Shaw Associates 99, 116
Visible Productions Limited 305
Voice Box, The 101
Voice of the Listener and Viewer (The Citizen's Voice in Broadcasting) 350
Voice Shop 101

Wales, Arts Council of 354
Wales, University of (Aberystwyth) 51
   See also University of Wales College
Walford, Glen 426–7
Wall to Wall Television 305
Walmsley Associates 101
Walnut Partnership, The 305
Warchus, Matthew 427
Warehouse Theatre Company 209
Waring & McKenna 101–2
Warner, Deborah 427
Warner Sisters Film & TV Ltd 306
Warwick and Leamington Festival 367
Watermill Theatre (Newbery) 134
Watershed Television 306
Webber Douglas Academy of Dramatic Art 32

Welsh College of Music and Drama 32–3
Wendy Wisbey Agency, The 102
West 28th Street 190–91
West End Festival (Glasgow) 363
West End theatres/Equity agreement 324–6
West Midlands Arts 357–8
West Sound/West FM 285
West Yorkshire Playhouse (Leeds) 129
West Yorkshire Playhouse Schools Company, The 232
Westcountry 272
Westminster, University of 62–3
Westminster Reference Library 350
Whirligig Theatre 220–21
White, Mela 118
White Bear Theatre Club 209–10
White Horse Theatre (Germany) 235–6
White Rock Theatre (Hastings) 254
Whitehall Theatre 247
Whittaker, Stephen 427–8
Who's Where see Professional Casting Report
Wigan Pier Theatre Company 191–2
Wildcat Stage Productions 192
William Morris Agency (UK) Ltd 94
Williams, Clifford 428
Wilson, Richard, OBE 428
Wimbledon Studio Theatre 210
Wimbledon Theatre 247
Winner, Michael 428–9
Wise, Herbert 429
Wolsey Theatre (Ipswich) 128
Wolverhampton, University of 52
Wood, Peter 429
Workhouse Television 306
Working Title Films 306
Wortman Productions UK 306
Wrestling School, The 191
Writers' Guild of Great Britain 351
Wycombe Swan Theatre and Town Hall 255
Wyndham's Theatre 247–8
Wyvern Theatre and Arts Centre (Swindon) 260

Y Touring Theatre Company 221
Yates, Peter 429
Yellow Earth Theatre 192
Yorick Internationalist Theatre Ensemble 192–3
York Citizens Theatre Trust Ltd *see* Theatre Royal (York)
Yorkshire and Humberside Arts 358
Yorkshire Television 272
Yorkshire Women Theatre 193
Young Casting Agency 102
Young National Trust Theatre, The 232

Young people's theatre *see* Children's and
  young people's theatre
Young Pleasance *see* Pleasance London
Young Vic Company 210
Yvonne Arnaud Theatre (Guildford) 126–7

See also Pied Piper Theatre Company

Zenith North 307
Zenith Productions Ltd 307
Zip Theatre 193